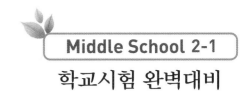

Middle School 2-1
학교시험 완벽대비

KB087180

1학기 전과정
적중100 plus

영어 기출문제집

중2
비상 | 김진완

Best Collection

구성과 특징

교과서의 주요 학습 내용을 중심으로 학습 영역별 특성에 맞춰 단계별로 다양한 학습 기회를 제공하여
단원별 학습능력 평가는 물론 중간 및 기말고사 시험 등에 완벽하게 대비할 수 있도록 내용을 구성

Words & Expressions

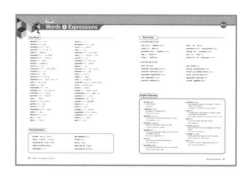

Step1 Key Words 단원별 핵심 단어 설명 및 풀이
Key Expression 단원별 핵심 숙어 및 관용어 설명
Word Power 반대 또는 비슷한 뜻 단어 배우기
English Dictionary 영어로 배우는 영어 단어

Step2 실력평가 단원별 수시평가 대비 주관식, 객관식 문제풀이

Step3 서술형 대비 학업성취도 및 수행능력평가 대비 서술형 문제풀이

Conversation

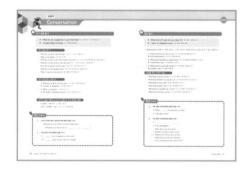

Step1 핵심 의사소통 소통에 필요한 주요 표현 방법 요약
핵심 Check 기본적인 표현 방법 및 활용능력 확인

Step2 대화문 익히기 교과서 대화문 심층 분석 및 확인

Step3 교과서 확인학습 빈칸 채우기를 통한 문장 완성 능력 확인

Step4 기본평가 시험대비 기초 학습 능력 평가

Step5 실력평가 단원별 수시평가 대비 주관식, 객관식 문제풀이

Step6 서술형 대비 학업성취도 및 수행능력평가 대비 서술형 문제풀이

Grammar

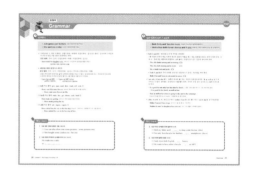

Step1 주요 문법 단원별 주요 문법 사항과 예문을 알기 쉽게 설명
핵심 Check 기본 문법사항에 대한 이해 여부 확인

Step2 기본평가 시험대비 기초 학습 능력 평가

Step3 실력평가 단원별 수시평가 대비 주관식, 객관식 문제풀이

Step4 서술형 대비 학업성취도 및 수행능력평가 대비 서술형 문제풀이

Reading

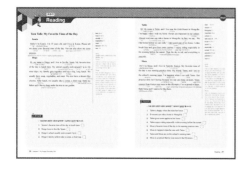

Step1 구문 분석 단원별로 제시된 문장에 대한 구문별 분석과 내용 설명
확인문제 문장에 대한 기본적인 이해와 인지능력 확인

Step2 확인학습A 빈칸 채우기를 통한 문장 완성 능력 확인

Step3 확인학습B 제시된 우리말을 영어로 완성하여 작문 능력 키우기

Step4 실력평가 단원별 수시평가 대비 주관식, 객관식 문제풀이

Step5 서술형 대비 학업성취도 및 수행능력평가 대비 서술형 문제풀이
교과서 구석구석 교과서에 나오는 기타 문장까지 완벽 학습

Composition

|영역별 핵심문제|

단어 및 어휘, 대화문, 문법, 독해 등 각 영역별 기출문제의 출제 유형을 분석하여 실전에 대비하고 연습할 수 있도록 문제를 배열

|단원별 예상문제|

기출문제를 분석한 후 새로운 시험 출제 경향을 더하여 새롭게 출제될 수 있는 문제를 포함하여 시험에 완벽하게 대비할 수 있도록 준비

|서술형 실전 및 창의사고력 문제|

학교 시험에서 점차 늘어나는 서술형 시험에 집중 대비하고 고득점을 취득하는데 만전을 기하기 위한 학습 코너

|단원별 모의고사|

영역별, 단계별 학습을 모두 마친 후 실전 연습을 위한 모의고사

교과서 파헤치기

- **단어Test1~3** 영어 단어 우리말 쓰기, 우리말을 영어 단어로 쓰기, 영영풀이에 해당하는 단어와 우리말 쓰기
- **대화문Test1~2** 대화문 빈칸 완성 및 전체 대화문 쓰기
- **본문Test1~5** 빈칸 완성, 우리말 쓰기, 문장 배열연습, 영어 작문하기 복습 등 단계별 반복 학습을 통해 교과서 지문에 대한 완벽한 습득
- **구석구석지문Test1~2** 지문 빈칸 완성 및 전문 영어로 쓰기

이책의 차례 Contents

Lesson 1

Suit Your Taste!

🎤 의사소통 기능

- 관심 있는 것 말하기
  A: What are you interested in?
  B: I'm interested in Spanish.

- 문제 해결 방법 알려 주기
  A: I baked this bread, but it came out too dry.
  B: I know how to bake bread without making it dry.

🎤 언어 형식

- 5형식 동사
  My pet **makes** me **happy.**

- 동명사
  Having a pet is great.

Words & Expressions

Key Words

- **actor** [ǽktər] 명 배우
- **after-school class** 방과 후 수업
- **artistic** [a:rtístik] 형 예술의, 예술적 감각이 있는
- **attractive** [ətrǽktiv] 형 매력적인
- **bake** [beik] 동 굽다
- **balance** [bǽləns] 명 균형
- **blog** [blɑg] 명 블로그
- **cage** [keidʒ] 명 새장, 우리
- **care** [kɛər] 명 주의, 보살핌
- **careful** [kɛ́ərfəl] 형 주의 깊은, 조심하는
- **comment** [kάment] 명 논평, 견해, 댓글
- **corner** [kɔ́:rnər] 명 구석, 골목
- **decorate** [dékərèit] 동 장식하다
- **fantastic** [fæntǽstik] 형 환상적인, 기막히게 좋은
- **handy** [hǽndi] 형 편리한, 유용한
- **hedgehog** [hedʒhɑg] 명 고슴도치
- **helpful** [hélpfəl] 형 도움이 되는, 유용한
- **hold** [hould] 동 쥐다, 잡다
- **hug** [hʌg] 동 껴안다
- **macaron** 명 마카롱
- **mainly** [méinli] 부 주로
- **normally** [nɔ́:rməli] 부 보통
- **note** [nout] 명 음, 음표
- **peace** [pi:s] 명 평화
- **pet** [pet] 명 애완동물
- **photographer** [fətάgrəfər] 명 사진사
- **photography** [fətάgrəfi] 명 사진술, 사진 찍기
- **place** [pleis] 동 두다, 놓다 명 장소
- **point** [pɔint] 동 가리키다, 지시하다
- **press** [pres] 동 누르다
- **raise** [reiz] 동 올리다, 세우다
- **rap** [ræp] 명 (음악) 랩
- **repeat** [ripí:t] 동 반복하다
- **romance** [roumǽns] 명 연애 이야기, 로맨스
- **romantic** [roumǽntik] 형 로맨틱한, 낭만적인
- **rule** [ru:l] 명 규칙 동 지배하다
- **scared** [skɛərd] 형 무서워하는, 겁먹은
- **seat** [si:t] 명 자리, 좌석
- **shower** [ʃáuər] 명 샤워, 소나기
- **skateboard** [skéitbɔ̀:rd] 명 스케이트보드
- **spike** [spaik] 명 가시, 뾰족한 것
- **suit** [su:t] 동 맞다, 어울리다
- **talent** [tǽlənt] 명 재능, 재주
- **taste** [teist] 명 맛, 미각, 취향
- **theater** [θí:ətər] 명 영화관
- **tip** [tip] 명 조언, 정보, 비법
- **view** [vju:] 명 시야
- **wipe** [waip] 동 닦다

Key Expressions

- **a few** 약간의, 조금의
- **be able to** ~할 수 있다
- **be interested in** ~에 관심을 갖다
- **be into** ~을 좋아하다, ~에 관심이 많다
- **clean up** ~을 치우다[청소하다]
- **come out** 나오다
- **from beginning to end** 처음부터 끝까지
- **get used to** ~에 익숙해지다
- **go get** ~을 가져오다
- **in person** 직접
- **look around** ~을 둘러보다
- **pick up** ~을 들어올리다[집다]
- **sign up (for)** ~에 등록하다
- **write down** ~을 적다

Word Power

※ 서로 반대되는 뜻을 가진 단어

- □ **careful** 주의 깊은 → **careless** 부주의한
- □ **actor** (남자) 배우 → **actress** 여자 배우
- □ **dry** 건조한 → **wet** 습한
- □ **normal** 정상적인 → **abnormal** 정상이 아닌
- □ **handy** 간편한, 다루기 쉬운 → **unhandy** 서투른, 다루기 어려운
- □ **famous** 유명한 → **unknown** 알려지지 않은
  cf. **notorious** (보통 나쁜 의미로) 소문난, 유명한

- □ **attractive** 매력적인 → **unattractive** 매력 없는
- □ **raise** 올리다 → **lower** 내리다
- □ **peace** 평화 → **war** 전쟁
- □ **interested** 관심 있어 하는 → **uninterested** 관심 없는
- □ **helpful** 도움이 되는 → **unhelpful** 도움이 되지 않는
- □ **interesting** 재미있는 → **boring** 지루한

English Dictionary

- □ **bake** 굽다
  → to cook food in an oven without extra fat or liquid
  여분의 지방이나 액체 없이 오븐으로 음식을 요리하다

- □ **cage** 우리, 새장
  → a structure made of metal bars or wire in which animals or birds are kept
  동물 또는 새를 가두는 금속이나 철사로 만들어진 구조물

- □ **decorate** 장식하다
  → to make something look more attractive by putting things on it
  무언가를 그 위에 놓음으로써 좀 더 매력적으로 만들다

- □ **dry** 마른, 건조한
  → having no or very little water or liquid
  물이나 액체가 없거나 극히 적은

- □ **hedgehog** 고슴도치
  → a small brown animal with stiff parts like needles covering its back
  등을 덮고 있는 바늘과 같은 뻣뻣한 부분을 가진 작은 갈색의 동물

- □ **hug** 껴안다
  → to have somebody/something in your hand, arms
  어떤 사람이나 사물을 당신의 손이나 팔 안에 있게 하다

- □ **peace** 평화
  → a situation or a period of time in which there is no war or violence in a country or an area
  국가나 지역에 전쟁이나 폭력이 없는 시기 또는 상황

- □ **photographer** 사진사
  → a person who takes photographs, especially as a job
  직업으로 사진을 찍는 사람

- □ **talent** 재능, 재주
  → a natural ability to do something well
  무언가를 잘하는 천부적 능력

- □ **raise** 세우다, 올리다
  → to lift or move something to a higher level
  더 높은 수준으로 무언가를 들어 올리거나 움직이다

- □ **rap** (음악) 랩
  → a type of popular music with a fast strong rhythm and words which are spoken fast, not sung
  노래를 부르는 것이 아니라 빠르고 강한 리듬과 빠르게 말해지는 가사를 가진 인기 있는 음악의 한 종류

- □ **repeat** 반복하다
  → to say or write something again or more than once
  무언가를 다시 또는 한 번 이상 말하거나 쓰다

- □ **seat** 좌석, 자리
  → a place where you can sit, for example a chair
  예를 들어 의자처럼 당신이 앉을 수 있는 자리

- □ **theater** 영화관
  → a building in which films/movies are shown
  영화를 보여주는 건물

- □ **tip** 조언, 정보
  → a small piece of advice about something practical
  실용적인 무언가에 대한 하나의 조언

서답형

01 다음 짝지어진 단어의 관계가 같도록 빈칸에 알맞은 말을 쓰시오.

> care : careful = romance : _____

서답형

[02~03] 다음 영영풀이에 해당하는 말을 쓰시오.

02

> a small brown animal with stiff parts like needles covering its back

➡ _____

03

> a natural ability to do something well

➡ _____

중요

04 다음 중 밑줄 친 부분의 뜻풀이가 바르지 않은 것은?

① If you want to open the door, press the red button twice. 누르다
② I felt that soccer is an attractive sport. 거친
③ It's a great honor to meet such a famous photographer. 사진작가
④ I'll decorate this room for my daughter's birthday. 장식하다
⑤ I was scared after watching the horror movie. 무서운

서답형

05 다음 문장의 빈칸에 들어갈 말을 〈보기〉에서 골라 쓰시오.

> ┤ 보기 ├
> in person / get used to / write down

(1) Did you _____ the answer on your book?
(2) I can't _____ this strange smell.
(3) I met a famous baseball star _____.

중요

06 다음 주어진 문장의 밑줄 친 의미와 다른 의미로 쓰인 것은?

> There are no rules for writing raps.

① There is no rule without some exceptions.
② You should follow the rules of our club.
③ We made several rules for the group project.
④ The president rules over the country.
⑤ Do you know the rules for basketball?

07 다음 문장의 빈칸에 공통으로 들어갈 말로 적절한 것은?

> • The parade came into _____.
> • Is there a room with a _____ of ocean?
> • Her _____ is always different from mine.

① view   ② help
③ theater   ④ rule
⑤ pet

01 다음 짝지어진 단어의 관계가 같도록 빈칸에 알맞은 말을 쓰시오.

law : lawyer = photograph : _____

[02~03] 다음 영영풀이에 해당하는 단어를 쓰시오.

02

a type of popular music with a fast strong rhythm and words which are spoken fast, not sung

➡ _____

03

a structure made of metal bars or wire in which animals or birds are kept

➡ _____

04 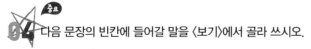 다음 문장의 빈칸에 들어갈 말을 〈보기〉에서 골라 쓰시오.

┌─ 보기 ─┐
normally / shower / point / repeat
└──────┘

(1) I usually take a _____ in the morning.
(2) _____ your finger at something far from you.
(3) Would you _____ what you said again?
(4) Where do you _____ sit in a theater?

05 다음 문장의 빈칸에 들어갈 말을 〈보기〉에서 골라 쓰시오.

┌─ 보기 ─┐
come out / clean up /
go get / look around
└──────┘

(1) When will you _____ your room?
(2) The bread is about to _____ of the oven.
(3) Feel free to _____ here.
(4) Would you _____ some tickets for me?

06 다음 우리말을 주어진 어구를 배열하여 문장을 완성하시오.

(1) 모든 것이 랩을 위한 이야기가 될 수 있다.
(a rap / can / for / everything / be / a story)
➡ _____

(2) 내 동생은 혼자 밖에 나가는 것을 무서워한다.
(alone / my / scared / out / sister / going / is / of)
➡ _____

(3) 이 정보는 당신이 자리를 고를 때 매우 유용하다.
(choose / this information / a seat / when / helpful / very / is / you)
➡ _____
_____

(4) 나는 보통 잠자리에 들기 전에 샤워를 한다.
(take / bed / to / I / a shower / before / going / usually)
➡ _____

교과서

Conversation

1 관심 있는 것 말하기

> **A** What are you interested in? 너는 무엇에 관심이 있니?
> **B** I'm interested in Spanish. 나는 스페인어에 관심이 있어.

■ What are you interested in? 또는 Are you interested in ~?을 통해 상대방의 관심사를 물어 볼 수 있다. 'be interested in'은 '~에 관심이 있다'는 의미로 have an interest in, be into, enjoy, like 등으로 바꾸어 쓸 수 있다.

관심 묻기

- What are you interested in? 너는 무엇에 관심이 있니?
- Which club do you have an interest in? 너는 무슨 동아리에 관심이 있니?
- Are you interested in sports? 너는 스포츠에 관심이 있니?
- Do you enjoy drawing pictures? 너는 그림 그리는 것을 즐기니?
- Do you like math? 너는 수학을 좋아하니?

관심 있는 것 말하기

- I'm interested in music. 나는 음악에 관심이 있다.
- I'm into sports. 나는 스포츠를 좋아한다.
- I enjoy taking pictures. 나는 사진 찍는 것을 즐긴다.
- I have an interest in Chinese. 나는 중국어에 관심이 있다.
- I'm fascinated by math. 나는 수학에 매료되었다.

관심 없다고 말하기

- I'm not interested in music. 나는 음악에 관심이 없다.
- I don't have any interest in computer games. 나는 컴퓨터 게임에 아무 관심이 없다.

핵심 Check

1. 다음 우리말과 일치하도록 빈칸에 알맞은 말을 쓰시오.

(1) **A:** _____ are you _____ in? (너는 무엇에 관심이 있니?)

  B: I'm _____ in the music club. (나는 음악 동아리에 관심이 있어.)

(2) **A:** _____ _____ _____ _____ the photography class?

  (너는 사진 수업에 관심이 있니?)

  B: Yes, I'm. I'm _____ taking pictures. (나는 사진 찍는 것을 좋아해.)

2 문제 해결 방법 알려 주기

A I baked this bread, but it came out too dry. 내가 이 빵을 구웠는데, 빵이 너무 마르게 나와 버렸어.

B I know how to bake bread without making it dry. 나 빵이 마르지 않도록 굽는 방법을 알고 있어.

■ 상대방이 문제점을 구체적으로 설명하거나 'I have some problems about ~'이라는 구문을 통해 문제점을 드러낼 수 있다. 이에 대해 해결책을 제시할 때 'Don't worry.' 'Take it easy.' 등의 표현을 사용하여 상대방을 진정시킬 수 있으며 'I know how to ~.'라는 구문을 사용하여 '~하는 법'을 알고 있음을 표현할 수 있다.

문제 해결 방법 알려 주기

- I know how to fix it. 나는 그것을 어떻게 고치는지 알고 있다.
- I heard that you need to put a glass of water in the oven.
  나는 네가 오븐에 물을 한 컵 넣을 필요가 있다고 들었다.
- I think you can clean up the glass pieces with bread. 나는 네가 빵으로 유리조각을 청소할 수 있다고 생각해.
- How[What] about using this program? 이 프로그램을 사용하는 것이 어때?
- The tip is you should start from the corner. 비법은 네가 구석에서부터 시작해야 한다는 것이다.
- I'll let you know how to make it. 내가 그것을 만드는 법을 알려 줄게.

핵심 Check

2. 다음 우리말과 일치하도록 빈칸에 알맞은 말을 쓰시오.

(1) **A:** There are so many pieces. It'll _____ a long time to finish.

(아주 많은 조각들이 있어. 끝내는 데 오랜 시간이 걸릴 거야.)

B: _____ _____ _____ _____ finish it quickly.

(나는 그것을 빨리 끝내는 법을 알고 있어.)

(2) **A:** I have some _____ of making my family album.

(나는 가족 앨범을 만드는 데 약간의 문제가 있어.)

B: _____ _____. _____ _____ asking Mike? He can help you.

(걱정하지 마. Mike에게 물어보는 게 어때? 그는 너를 도와줄 수 있어.)

(3) **A:** I _____ _____ _____ _____ make macarons.

(나는 마카롱을 어떻게 만드는지 몰라.)

B: I'll let you know _____ _____ make them. (내가 그것들을 어떻게 만드는지 알려 줄게.)

A. Listen & Talk ① A-1

Mike: Betty, what are you ❶looking at?

Betty: I'm reading the ❷comments on my blog.

Mike: What do you usually write ❸blog posts about?

Betty: I usually write about books. ❹I'm interested in reading.

Mike: Betty, 뭐 보고 있어?
Betty: 내 블로그에 달린 댓글을 읽어보는 중이야.
Mike: 넌 평소에 무엇에 관해 블로그 게시물을 쓰니?
Betty: 난 보통 책에 대해 써. 독서에 관심이 있거든.

❶ look at: ～을 보다, 바라보다
❷ comment: 댓글
❸ blog post: 블로그 게시물
❹ be interested in: ～에 관심이 있다

Check(√) True or False

(1) Betty has an interest in reading. T ☐ F ☐

(2) Mike is into reading the comments on his blog. T ☐ F ☐

B. Listen & Talk ① B

Jake: Hello, Elsa. Which ❶after-school class are you going to take?

Elsa: I'm going to take the drama class on Thursdays. ❷What about you, Jake?

Jake: I'm thinking of taking the Tuesday ❸photography class. I'm interested in ❹taking pictures.

Elsa: Oh, I heard that the teacher is a famous photographer.

Jake: Really? That's really ❺cool!

Jake: 안녕, Elsa. 너 어떤 방과 후 수업을 들을 거야?
Elsa: 나는 목요일마다 하는 드라마 수업을 들을 거야. Jake, 너는 어때?
Jake: 화요일에 하는 사진 수업을 들으려고 생각 중이야. 난 사진 찍는 거에 관심이 있거든.
Elsa: 오, 그 선생님 유명한 사진 작가라고 들었어.
Jake: 정말? 정말 멋지다!

❶ after-school class: 방과 후 수업
❷ What about you?: '너는 어때?' 상대방의 의견을 물을 때 사용한다.
❸ photography: 사진술, 사진 찍기
❹ take a picture[pictures]: 사진을 찍다
❺ cool: 멋진

Check(√) True or False

(3) Elsa is going to take the drama class on Thrusday. T ☐ F ☐

(4) Jake knows the teacher of photography class very well. T ☐ F ☐

Listen & Talk ① A-2

Jenny: Mike, who is the man on your SNS?

Mike: Oh, he is my ❶favorite baseball player, John Luke. I'm really interested in baseball.

Jenny: Wow, you met him ❷in person!

Mike: Yeah, that was the best day of my life.

❶ favorite: 가장 좋아하는 ❷ in person: 직접

Listen & Talk ② A-1

W: I ❶baked this bread, but it came out too ❷dry.

M: Oh, ❸I know how to bake bread without making it dry. Put a glass of water in the oven.

W: That's a great ❹tip. Where did you learn ❺that?

M: I saw it on a cooking show.

❶ bake: 굽다 ❷ dry: 건조한, 뻑뻑한 ❸ I know how to ~: 누군가에게 문제를 해결하는 방법을 가르쳐 주거나 정보를 제공할 때 사용된다. ❹ tip: 조언, 정보 ❺ 'Put a glass of water in the oven.'을 가리킨다.

Listen & Talk ② A-2

M: Is that a 1000-piece ❶puzzle?

W: Yeah, but there are so many ❷pieces. It'll take a long time to finish.

M: Oh, ❸I know how to do it quickly. Start from the corners, and then ❹group the pieces with the same colors.

W: I see. Thanks.

❶ puzzle: 퍼즐 ❷ piece: 조각 ❸ I know how to ~: 누군가에게 문제를 해결하는 방법을 가르쳐 주거나 정보를 제공할 때 사용된다. ❹ group: 동사로 쓰여 '모으다, 분류하다'를 뜻한다.

Listen & Talk ② B

Minsu: Oh, no. I broke a dish.

Tina: ❶Don't worry. I know how to clean up the glass pieces with bread. I read the tip in a magazine.

Minsu: With bread? How?

Tina: You can ❷wipe the area with it. It ❸picks up the small pieces.

Minsu: Great tip! Thanks, Tina. I'll ❹go get some bread in the kitchen.

❶ Don't worry.: '걱정하지 마.'라는 의미로 상대방을 안심시킬 때 쓰인다. ❷ wipe ... with ~: ~로 …을 닦다 ❸ pick up: ~을 집다 ❹ go get: ~을 가져오다

Communication

M: Welcome to *It's Your Stage*! We have a great show for you today. Let's meet the people with special ❶talents.

W: Hello. I'm Doremi. I'm interested in music.

M: Great! What are you going to show us today?

W: ❷I know how to sing high ❸notes easily. I can show you easy ❹steps.

M: Sounds interesting!

❶ talent: 재능 ❷ I know how to ~: ~하는 법을 알다 ❸ note: 음 ❹ step: 과정, 절차

Wrap Up 1

Aron: Emily, what ❶club are you going to ❷join?

Emily: I'm going to join the music club. ❸I'm into music. What about you, Aron?

Aron: I want to join ❹the gardening club. I'm interested in plants and flowers.

Emily: Oh, that sounds like an interesting club.

❶ club: 동아리 ❷ join: 가입하다 ❸ be into: ~을 좋아하다 ❹ the gardening club: 원예 동아리

Wrap Up 2

Mike: I'm ❶looking for a special gift for Clara. Do you have any idea, Lisa?

Lisa: Well, ❷why don't you make some macarons for her? She really loves them.

Mike: But I don't know how to make them.

Lisa: Don't worry. I know how to make them with easy steps. ❸I'll help you.

Mike: Great. Thanks, Lisa.

❶ look for: ~을 찾다 ❷ Why don't you ~?: ~하는 게 어때? ❸ I'll help you.: 도움을 제공할 때 쓰는 표현으로 'I'll give you a hand.'라고 표현할 수도 있다.

다음 우리말과 일치하도록 빈칸에 알맞은 말을 쓰시오.

Listen & Talk 1 A

1. Mike: Betty, what are you _____ _____?

   Betty: I'm reading the _____ on my blog.

   Mike: What do you usually write blog posts about?

   Betty: I usually write about books. _____ _____ _____ _____.

2. Jenny: Mike, who is the man on your SNS?

   Mike: Oh, he is my favorite baseball player, John Luke. _____ _____ _____ _____ baseball.

   Jenny: Wow, you met him _____ _____!

   Mike: Yeah, that was the best day of my life.

해석

1. Mike: Betty, 뭐 보고 있어?
   Betty: 내 블로그에 달린 댓글을 읽어보는 중이야.
   Mike: 넌 평소에 무엇에 관해 블로그 게시물을 쓰니?
   Betty: 난 보통 책에 대해 써. 독서에 관심이 있거든.

2. Jenny: Mike, 네 SNS에 있는 남자는 누구야?
   Mike: 오, 그는 John Luke라고 내가 제일 좋아하는 야구 선수야. 내가 야구에 정말 관심이 많거든.
   Jenny: 와, 그리고 너는 직접 그를 만났던 거고!
   Mike: 응, 그날이 내 인생 최고의 날이었지.

Listen & Talk 1 B

Jake: Hello, Elsa. _____ _____ _____ are you going to take?

Elsa: I'm going to _____ the drama class on Thursdays. What about you, Jake?

Jake: I'm thinking of taking the Tuesday _____ class. _____ _____ _____ _____.

Elsa: Oh, I heard that the teacher is a famous _____.

Jake: Really? That's really cool!

Jake: 안녕, Elsa. 너 어떤 방과 후 수업을 들을 거야?
Elsa: 나는 목요일마다 하는 드라마 수업을 들을 거야. Jake, 너는 어때?
Jake: 화요일에 하는 사진 수업을 들으려고 생각 중이야. 난 사진 찍는 거에 관심이 있거든.
Elsa: 오, 그 선생님 유명한 사진작가라고 들었어.
Jake: 정말? 정말 멋지다!

Listen & Talk 2 A-1

W: I baked this bread, but it came out too _____.

M: Oh, I _____ _____ _____ _____ _____ without making it dry. Put a glass of water in the oven.

W: That's a great _____. Where did you learn that?

M: I saw it on _____ _____.

W: 내가 이 빵을 구웠는데, 빵이 너무 마르게 나와 버렸어.
M: 오, 나 빵이 마르지 않도록 굽는 방법을 알고 있어. 오븐에 물 한 컵을 넣어봐.
W: 그거 정말 좋은 정보다. 너 그건 어디서 배웠어?
M: 요리 쇼에서 봤어.

Listen & Talk 2 A-2

M: Is that a 1000-piece puzzle?

W: Yeah, but there are so many pieces. It'll take a long time to finish.

M: Oh, _____ _____ _____ _____ _____

_____. Start from the corners, and then _____ the pieces with

the same colors.

W: I see. Thanks.

해석

M: 그거 조각이 1,000개짜리 퍼즐이야?
W: 응, 그런데 퍼즐 조각이 너무 많아. 다 맞추려면 한참 걸리겠어.
M: 아, 나 그 퍼즐 빨리 맞추는 방법 알아. 모서리들부터 맞추기 시작하고, 그런 다음에 같은 색깔로 조각들을 모아봐.
W: 알았어. 고마워.

Listen & Talk 2 B

Minsu: Oh, no. I broke a dish.

Tina: Don't worry. I _____ _____ _____ _____ _____

the glass pieces with bread. I read the tip in a magazine.

Minsu: With bread? _____?

Tina: You can _____ the area with it. It _____ _____ the small

pieces.

Minsu: Great tip! Thanks, Tina. I'll _____ _____ some bread in

the kitchen.

Minsu: 오, 안 돼. 접시를 깨 버렸어.
Tina: 걱정 마. 빵으로 유리 조각을 치우는 방법을 알아. 잡지에서 그 팁을 읽었거든.
Minsu: 빵으로? 어떻게?
Tina: 빵으로 그 부분을 닦으면 돼. 그게 작은 조각들을 주워 모으거든.
Minsu: 훌륭한 팁이다! 고마워, Tina. 내가 부엌에 가서 빵을 좀 가져올게.

Communication

M: Welcome to *It's Your Stage*! We have a great show for you today.
Let's meet the people with special talents.

W: Hello. I'm Doremi. _____ _____ _____ _____.

M: Great! What are you _____ _____ _____ _____ today?

W: I know _____ _____ _____ _____ _____ easily. I can
show you easy steps.

M: Sounds interesting!

M: '당신의 무대입니다!'에 오신 걸 환영합니다. 오늘 여러분을 위해 굉장한 볼거리를 마련했어요. 그럼 특별한 재능을 가진 사람들을 만나 볼게요.
W: 안녕하세요. 전 Doremi예요. 전 음악에 관심이 있어요.
M: 좋아요! 오늘 우리에게 무엇을 보여주실 건가요?
W: 전 높은 음을 쉽게 내는 방법을 알고 있어요. 제가 간단한 단계를 여러분께 보여 드릴게요.
M: 흥미롭네요!

Wrap Up 1

Aron: Emily, _____ _____ are you going to _____?

Emily: I'm going to join the music club. I'm _____ music. What
about you, Aron?

Aron: I want to join the gardening club. I'm _____ _____ _____

_____ _____.

Emily: Oh, that sounds like an _____ _____.

Aron: Emily, 너 어떤 동아리에 들 거야?
Emily: 음악 동아리에 들 거야. 나 음악에 빠져 있거든. Aron, 넌 어때?
Aron: 난 정원 가꾸기 동아리에 들고 싶어. 식물이랑 꽃에 관심이 있거든.
Emily: 오, 재미있는 동아리일 것 같은데.

01 다음 대화의 밑줄 친 우리말을 영어로 쓰시오.

> A: <u>당신은 무엇에 관심이 있나요?</u>
> B: I'm interested in Spanish.

➡ _____

02 다음 대화의 빈칸에 들어갈 말로 나머지와 의도가 <u>다른</u> 것은?

> A: I baked this bread, but it came out too dry.
> B: _____

① I'll let you know how to bake bread without making it dry.
② I heard about how to bake bread without making it dry.
③ I've been told how to bake bread without making it dry.
④ I don't have to bake bread without making it dry.
⑤ I know how to bake bread without making it dry.

[03~04] 다음 대화를 읽고, 물음에 답하시오.

> Jenny: Mike, who is the man on your SNS?
> Mike: Oh, he is my favorite baseball player, John Luke. I'm really interested in baseball.
> Jenny: Wow, you met him in person!
> Mike: Yeah, that was the best day of my life.

03 위 대화에서 나타난 Mike의 기분으로 적절한 것은?

① excited   ② depressed   ③ upset
④ disappointed   ⑤ nervous

04 위 대화의 내용과 일치하지 <u>않는</u> 것은?

① Mike와 Jenny는 함께 Mike의 SNS 사진을 보고 있다.
② Jenny는 야구에 많은 관심을 갖고 있다.
③ John Luke는 야구 선수이다.
④ Mike는 John Luke를 만난 날이 자기 인생 최고의 날이라고 생각한다.
⑤ Mike는 John Luke를 직접 만나 보았다.

01 다음 대화의 빈칸에 들어갈 말로 나머지와 의도가 <u>다른</u> 것은?

> **A:** _____
>
> **B:** I'm interested in Spanish.

① How can I get interests?
② What do you have an interest in?
③ What do you feel interested in?
④ Do you find Spanish interesting?
⑤ What are you interested in?

[02~03] 다음 대화를 읽고, 물음에 답하시오.

> **Minsu:** Oh, no. I broke a dish.
> **Tina:** Don't worry. I know how to clean up the glass pieces with bread. I read the tip in a magazine.
> **Minsu:** How?
> **Tina:** You can wipe the area with ⓐit. It picks up the small pieces.
> **Minsu:** Great tip! Thanks, Tina. I'll go get some bread in the kitchen.

서답형

02 위 대화의 ⓐit이 가리키는 것을 찾아 한 단어로 쓰시오.

➡ _____

03 위 대화를 읽고 대답할 수 <u>없는</u> 질문은?

① What's the matter with Minsu?
② Where did Tina get the tip about cleaning up the glass pieces?
③ How can Minsu clean up the glass pieces?
④ What is Minsu going to do next?
⑤ How can Minsu use a broken dish to wipe the area?

[04~05] 다음 대화를 읽고, 물음에 답하시오.

> **Jake:** Hello, Elsa. Which after-school class are you going to take? (A)
> **Elsa:** I'm going to take the drama class on Thursdays. What about you, Jake? (B)
> **Jake:** I'm thinking of taking the Tuesday photography class. (C)
> **Elsa:** Oh, I heard that the teacher is a famous photographer. (D)
> **Jake:** Really? I didn't know that. That's really cool! (E)

04 위 대화에서 주어진 문장이 들어가기에 적절한 곳은?

> I'm interested in taking pictures.

① (A) ② (B) ③ (C) ④ (D) ⑤ (E)

05 위 대화의 내용과 일치하지 <u>않는</u> 것은?

① Elsa is interested in the drama class as the after-school class.
② The dram class is planned on every Thursday.
③ Jake has an interest in taking the photography class on Tuesdays.
④ Jake already knows who the teacher of the photography class is.
⑤ Jake is looking forward to taking the photography class.

서답형

06 다음 대화가 자연스럽게 이어지도록 순서대로 배열하시오.

(A) What do you usually write blog posts about?

(B) I'm reading the comments on my blog.

(C) Betty, what are you looking at?

(D) I usually write about books. I'm interested in reading.

➡ _____

[07~08] 다음 대화를 읽고, 물음에 답하시오.

Sue: I baked this bread, but it came out too dry.

Mike: Oh, I know how (A)[to bake / bake] bread without making it dry. (B)[Put / Putting] a glass of water in the oven.

Sue: That's a great tip. Where did you learn that?

Mike: I saw it on a (C)[cook / cooking] show.

중요

07 위 대화의 괄호 (A)~(C)에 들어갈 말로 알맞은 것끼리 바르게 짝지어진 것은?

① to bake – Put – cook

② bake – Putting – cook

③ to bake – Putting – cook

④ bake – Put – cooking

⑤ to bake – Put – cooking

서답형

08 Sue가 Mike로부터 받은 조언을 우리말 15자 내외로 쓰시오.

➡ _____

[09~10] 다음 대화를 읽고, 물음에 답하시오.

Jake: Hello, Elsa. _____(A)_____

Elsa: I'm going to take the drama class on Thursdays. _____(B)_____

Jake: I'm thinking of taking the Tuesday photography class. I'm interested in taking pictures.

Elsa: Oh, I heard that the teacher is a famous photographer.

Jake: Really? That's really cool!

서답형

09 위 대화의 빈칸 (A)에 들어갈 말을 <보기>에 주어진 단어를 모두 배열하여 완성하시오.

┌ 보기 ┐

after-school / take / which / going / are / to / you / class

➡ _____

10 위 대화의 빈칸 (B)에 들어갈 말로 적절한 것은?

① What do you do?

② What about you?

③ How's it going?

④ How do you do?

⑤ What's going on?

서답형

11 다음 대화가 자연스럽게 이어지도록 순서대로 배열하시오.

(A) I see. Thanks.

(B) Is that a 1000-piece puzzle?

(C) Yeah, but there are so many pieces. It'll take a long time to finish.

(D) Oh, I know how to do it quickly. Start from the corners, and then group the pieces with the same colors.

➡ _____

 01 다음 대화의 빈칸에 주어진 표현을 사용하여 대답을 완성하시오.

> A: What are you interested in?
> B: _____ (Spanish)

➡ _____

 02 다음 대화의 빈칸에 주어진 표현을 사용하여 대답을 완성하시오.

> A: I baked this bread, but it came out too dry.
> B: _____

> ┤ 보기 ├
> how / it / dry / to / bread / bake / I / without / know / making

➡ _____

[03~04] 다음 대화를 읽고, 물음에 답하시오.

> Jenny: Mike, who is the man on your SNS?
> Mike: Oh, he is my favorite baseball player, John Luke. (A)내가 정말로 야구에 관심이 많거든.(really)
> Jenny: Wow, you met him ____(B)____!
> Mike: Yeah, that was the best day of my life.

03 위 대화의 밑줄 친 (A)의 우리말을 주어진 단어를 사용하여 영어로 쓰시오.

➡ _____

04 위 대화의 빈칸 (B)에 '직접'을 의미하는 숙어를 두 단어로 쓰시오.

➡ _____

05 다음 대화를 읽고 Emma가 퍼즐을 빨리 끝낼 수 있는 방법을 우리말 20자 내외로 설명하시오.

> John: Is that a 1000-piece puzzle?
> Emma: Yeah, but there are so many pieces. It'll take a long time to finish.
> John: Oh, I know how to do it quickly. Start from the corners, and then group the pieces with the same colors.
> Emma: I see. Thanks.

➡ _____

[06~07] 다음 대화를 읽고, 물음에 답하시오.

> M: Welcome to *It's Your Stage*! We have a great show for you today. Let's meet the people with special talents.
> W: Hello. I'm Doremi. I'm interested in music.
> M: Great! (A)오늘 우리에게 무엇을 보여 주실 건가요? (going, show)
> W: I know how to sing high notes easily. I can show you easy steps.
> M: Sounds interesting!

06 위 대화의 밑줄 친 (A)의 우리말을 주어진 단어를 사용하여 영작하시오.

➡ _____

07 What is Doremi's special talent?

➡ _____

Grammar

① 5형식 동사

- My pet **makes** me happy. 나의 애완동물은 나를 행복하게 해.
- I **consider** the movie a failure. 나는 그 영화를 실패작이라고 생각한다.

■ 5형식 동사는 목적어와 목적보어를 취하는 동사로, 이때 목적보어는 목적어와 동격을 이루거나 목적어를 보충 설명하는 역할을 한다. 명사나 형용사를 목적보어로 취하는 동사에는 make, call, keep, leave, appoint, elect, name 등이 있다.

- My dad **calls** me Princess. 우리 아빠는 나를 공주님이라고 부른다.
- We **elected** him chairman. 우리는 그를 의장으로 선출하였다.
- Please, don't **leave** me alone. 제발 나를 혼자 남겨두지 마.

■ 목적보어로 'to be+보어' 형태를 취하지만 'to be'를 생략할 수 있는 동사에는 consider, believe, find 등이 있다.

- They **found** the data useful. 그들은 그 자료가 유용하다는 것을 알았다.
- Brian **considers** himself a genius. Brian은 자신을 천재라고 여긴다.

■ 4형식 동사와 혼동하지 않도록 유의한다. 4형식 동사가 이끄는 간접목적어와 직접목적어는 동격의 관계가 성립하지 않지만, 5형식 동사가 이끄는 목적어와 목적보어는 동격을 이루거나 목적보어가 목적어를 보충 설명한다.

- Can you **find** me my book? 〈4형식〉 내 책 좀 찾아주겠니?
- I **found** the movie interesting. 〈5형식〉 나는 그 영화가 흥미롭다는 걸 알았어.

핵심 Check

1. 다음 우리말을 영어로 옮길 때 빈칸에 알맞은 말을 쓰시오.

(1) 그 문을 열린 채로 두어라.

➡ _____ the door _____.

(2) 그녀는 나를 운이 좋다고 여겼다.

➡ She considered _____ _____.

(3) 그의 이름은 Michael이지만, 우리는 그를 Mike라고 부른다.

➡ His name is Michael, but we _____ _____ _____.

② 동명사

> • Would you mind **closing** the door? 그 문 좀 닫아주시겠어요?
> • I am interested in **writing** songs. 나는 작곡하는 것에 관심이 있다.

■ '~하는 것'이라고 해석되는 동명사는 'V+ing' 형태로 명사 역할을 하여 주어, 목적어, 보어로 쓰인다. 동명사 주어는 단수 취급한다.

　• **Swimming** is the best exercise for you. 〈주어〉 수영하는 것은 너에게 최고의 운동이다.

　• Are you afraid of **walking** alone at night? 〈전치사의 목적어〉 밤에 혼자 걷는 것이 두렵니?

■ 동명사를 목적어로 취하는 동사에 유의하자. avoid, enjoy, finish, postpone, stop, deny, give up, practice, suggest, put off, mind, cannot help, imagine, consider, go on, feel like, quit 등은 동명사만을 목적어로 취하는 동사이다.

　• The man is considering **hiring** you. 그 남자가 널 고용하는 것을 고려하는 중이야.

　• I keep putting off **going** to the dentist. 나는 치과에 가는 것을 계속 미루고 있어.

■ 현재진행형을 만드는 현재분사와 혼동하지 않도록 유의한다. 'V+ing'로 형태가 같으나 현재분사는 '~하는 중'이라는 의미로, 동명사는 '~하는 것'이라는 의미로 쓰인다.

　• Sandra is **fixing** dinner. 〈현재분사〉 Sandra는 저녁을 차리는 중이다.

　• His hobby is **fixing** a machine. 〈동명사〉 그의 취미는 기계를 수리하는 것이다.

■ 동명사의 관용적 표현을 익혀두는 것이 좋다. go -ing(~하러 가다), be busy -ing(~하느라 바쁘다), look forward to -ing(~하는 것을 기대하다), be worth -ing(~할 가치가 있다), on -ing(~하자마자), by -ing(~함으로써) 등이 있다.

　• Jimmy goes **fishing** every Sunday. Jimmy는 일요일마다 낚시하러 간다.

　• I was busy **doing** the dishes. 나는 설거지하느라 바빴어.

핵심 Check

2. 다음 우리말을 영어로 옮길 때 빈칸에 알맞은 말을 쓰시오.

　(1) 웃는 것은 최고의 명약이다.

　➡ _____ is the best medicine.

　(2) 나는 열심히 공부하는 것에 집중했다.

　➡ I focused on _____ _____.

　(3) 그는 그것에 관하여 쓴 것을 부인했다.

　➡ He denied _____ about it.

01 다음 문장에서 어법상 어색한 부분을 바르게 고쳐 쓰시오.

(1) The news made me sadly.

_____ ➡ _____

(2) They gave up to climb the mountain.

_____ ➡ _____

(3) On see her, he ran away.

_____ ➡ _____

(4) We thought about to go to the beach.

_____ ➡ _____

02 주어진 어휘를 어법에 맞게 빈칸에 쓰시오.

(1) His behavior made me _____. (upset)

(2) _____ badminton is really fun. (play)

(3) I cannot help _____ at her. (smile)

(4) Jason was satisfied with _____ the job. (take)

(5) Did you think her _____? (smart)

03 주어진 단어를 이용하여 다음 우리말을 영어로 쓰시오. (필요하면 어형을 바꿀 것)

(1) 자전거를 타는 것은 신난다. (ride / a bike / be / exciting)

➡ _____

(2) Kelly는 그를 봐서 놀랐다. (be / surprise / at / see)

➡ _____

(3) 무엇이 널 그렇게 행복하게 만드니? (make / so / happy)

➡ _____

(4) 너는 이 책이 쉽다고 생각했어. (think / easy)

➡ _____

(5) 우리는 우리 강아지를 Tommy라고 이름 지었다. (name / puppy)

➡ _____

01 다음 중 빈칸에 들어갈 수 <u>없는</u> 것은?

> They _____ him honest.

① found
② thought
③ believed
④ considered
⑤ knew

02 다음 중 〈보기〉의 밑줄 친 부분과 쓰임이 <u>다른</u> 것은?

> ─┤ 보기 ├─
>
> His goal is <u>finishing</u> the project on time.

① Do you mind <u>looking</u> at this?
② I suggested <u>going</u> together.
③ Julia was tired of <u>doing</u> the same work.
④ Why did the baby keep <u>crying</u>?
⑤ The team was <u>making</u> a robot car then.

03 다음 빈칸에 공통으로 들어갈 말로 가장 적절한 것은?

> • My mom _____ us delicious cookies.
> • She _____ us really happy.

① took
② had
③ made
④ gave
⑤ cooked

04 다음 우리말을 영어로 바르게 옮긴 것은?

> 그들은 진수를 팀의 주장으로 임명하였다.

① They think Jinsu is captain of the team.
② They believed that Jinsu was captain of the team.
③ They appointed Jinsu captain of the team.
④ They found Jinsu captain of the team.
⑤ They elected Jinsu captain of the team.

서답형
05 다음 주어진 단어를 어법에 맞게 고쳐 쓰시오.

> He started to feel afraid of (speak) in front of many people.

➡ _____

06 다음 빈칸에 적합한 것을 <u>모두</u> 고르면?

> He _____ complaining about something.

① stopped
② made
③ wanted
④ kept
⑤ object

07 다음 중 어법상 바르지 <u>않은</u> 것은?

① We don't know much about playing tennis.
② I kept my room cleanly.
③ Did you find the computer cheap?
④ Jane was worried about waking up early in the morning.
⑤ Kyle felt like eating chicken soup.

서답형
08 주어진 어구를 활용하여 다음 우리말을 영어로 쓰시오.

> 너와 함께 걷는 것은 나를 행복하게 해.
> (walk with / make)

➡ _____

09 다음 중 어법상 옳은 것을 <u>모두</u> 고른 것은?

> ⓐ Kelly practiced playing the violin.
> ⓑ How did you make the room lovely?
> ⓒ Did you suggest to take the picture?
> ⓓ Jimmy kept the kitchen neatly.

① ⓐ, ⓑ
② ⓐ, ⓒ
③ ⓑ, ⓒ
④ ⓑ, ⓓ
⑤ ⓒ, ⓓ

10 다음 중 우리말을 영어로 바르게 옮기지 <u>않은</u> 것은?

① 나는 그녀와 춤추러 갈 거야.
  → I will go dancing with her.

② Katherine은 온라인에서 물건 사는 것을 그만 두었다.
  → Katherine stopped to buy things online.

③ 방을 계속 더럽게 하지 마.
  → Don't keep your room dirty.

④ 너는 항상 날 당황스럽게 해.
  → You always make me embarrassed.

⑤ 도와주셔서 감사합니다.
  → Thank you for helping me.

11 다음 빈칸에 들어갈 'help'의 형태가 <u>다른</u> 하나는?

① Jackson enjoys _____ poor children in Africa.

② He doesn't avoid _____ poor children in Africa.

③ I feel like _____ poor children in Africa.

④ Maria wants _____ poor children in Africa.

⑤ Don't put off _____ poor children in Africa.

서답형

12 같은 의미의 문장이 되도록 빈칸에 알맞은 말을 쓰시오.

> I am sorry that I am late for this meeting.
> = I am sorry for _____ _____ for this meeting.

➡ _____

13 다음 빈칸에 들어갈 말이 바르게 짝지어진 것은?

> • You don't mind _____ me Tony, do you?
> • Where are you thinking about _____ today?

① call – to go   ② to call – to go
③ calling – going   ④ to call – going
⑤ calling – to go

14 다음 중 어법상 옳은 것은?

① I imagined to fly high in the sky.
② Jason talked about skip a meal.
③ She postponed to run an errand.
④ These glasses make the view clearly.
⑤ We need to stop making a noise.

서답형

15 다음 중 밑줄 친 부분의 쓰임이 <u>다른</u> 하나는?

① <u>Riding</u> a bike is not easy.
② I am fond of <u>drawing</u> a picture.
③ His job is <u>delivering</u> lots of products.
④ They are <u>sleeping</u> in the bed.
⑤ My goal is <u>winning</u> the first prize.

16 다음 중 문장의 형식이 <u>다른</u> 하나는?

① Danny thought her a liar.
② Julia considers time more important than anything.
③ The man offered Jason a job the other day.
④ I have often wished myself a millionaire.
⑤ They called him Black Joe.

서답형

17 다음 문장에서 어법상 바르지 <u>않은</u> 것을 찾아 바르게 고치시오.

> This coat will keep you warmly.

➡ _____ ➡ _____

중요

18 다음 빈칸에 공통으로 들어갈 말은?

> • He _____ me lonely.
> • My grandfather _____ me a grand piano.

① gave 　② left 　③ bought
④ kept 　⑤ thought

19 주어진 문장과 같은 의미의 문장은?

> Could you turn the radio down, please?

① I feel like turning down the radio.
② Would you mind turning the radio down, please?
③ You cannot help turning down the radio.
④ Would you stop turning down the radio, please?
⑤ Would you keep turning the radio down, please?

서답형

20 주어진 단어를 활용하여 다음 물음에 답하시오.

> Q: Do you ever go to museums?
> A: Yes. (enjoy)

➡ _____

21 다음 빈칸에 들어갈 말로 가장 적절한 것은?

> 비오는 것이 멈출 때까지, 나는 나가지 않을 거야.
> = I'm not going out, _____.

① if it stops raining
② unless it doesn't stop raining
③ if it doesn't stop to rain
④ unless it stops raining
⑤ if the rain stops

서답형

22 주어진 어구를 활용하여 다음 우리말을 영어로 쓰시오.

> Larry는 매일 정장을 입는 것에 익숙하지 않다.
> (be used to / a suit)

➡ _____

중요

23 다음 중 빈칸에 들어갈 수 <u>없는</u> 것은?

> Kyle found the girl _____..

① friendly 　② lovely 　③ cheerful
④ diligently 　⑤ lively

24 다음 우리말을 영어로 바르게 옮긴 것은?

> 나는 그를 미워하지 않을 수 없다.

① I can't stop to hate him.
② It is no use hating him.
③ I cannot help hating him.
④ I feel like hating him.
⑤ I have difficulty hating him.

01 다음 두 문장의 의미가 같도록 빈칸에 알맞은 말을 쓰시오.

Kelly speaks English very well.
= Kelly is very good at _____ English.

➡ _____

02 주어진 단어를 바르게 배열하여 다음 우리말을 영어로 쓰시오.

당신은 그것을 단지 미국 문화의 일부분으로 여기면 된다.
(a / consider / part / culture / of / it / just / American / can / you)

➡ _____

03 주어진 단어를 활용하여 다음 우리말을 영어로 쓰시오.

나는 계속해서 뭔가를 잃어버려. (keep)

➡ _____

04 〈보기〉의 단어를 활용하여 어법과 내용에 맞도록 빈칸에 알맞은 말을 쓰시오.

┌─ 보기 ┤
stand   write   spend
└────────

(1) You cannot prevent him from _____ his own money.
(2) I have put off _____ the letter so many times. I really must do it today.
(3) I'm afraid there are no chairs. I hope you don't mind _____ .

05 다음 우리말과 같은 의미가 되도록 빈칸에 알맞은 말을 쓰시오.

나는 내 피부를 건강하게 지키길 원해.
= I want to keep _____ _____ _____ .

➡ _____

06 다음 대화를 읽고 아래 문장을 완성하시오.

Julia: What shall we do?
Molly: We could go to the zoo.

➡ Molly suggests _____ .

07 다음 상황을 읽고 빈칸에 알맞은 말을 쓰시오.

Sam thinks he needs to change his routine. He doesn't want to live like this any more. So he says to himself, "I can't go on _____ like this."   * routine 일상

➡ _____

08 주어진 문장과 같은 의미가 되도록 빈칸에 알맞은 말을 쓰시오.

It is not a good idea to drive during the rush hour.
= It's better to avoid _____ .

➡ _____

09 주어진 어구를 활용하여 다음 우리말을 영어로 쓰시오.

> 먼 거리를 걷는 것이 우리를 배고프게 한다.
> (walk a long distance)

➡ _____

10 다음 대화를 읽고 주어진 단어를 활용하여 Jackson에 관한 문장을 완성하시오.

> Adrian: Can you wait for a few minutes?
> Jackson: Sure, no problem.

> (mind)

➡ Jackson _____ for Adrian.

11 주어진 문장과 같은 의미가 되도록 빈칸에 알맞은 말을 쓰시오.

> Shall we paint the house next weekend instead of this weekend?
> = Shall we postpone _____ until _____?

➡ _____

12 다음 상황을 읽고 빈칸에 알맞은 말을 쓰시오.

> Kevin: You broke my smart phone.
> Emma: No, I didn't.

➡ Emma denied _____.

13 주어진 동사를 활용하여 다음 우리말을 영어로 쓰시오.

(1) 그의 아버지는 그를 유명한 축구선수로 만들었다. (make)

➡ _____

(2) 너는 그 경험이 중요하고 가치 있다고 알게 될 거야. (find / valuable)

➡ _____

(3) 그 신발이 널 계속 따뜻하게 해 줄 거야. (keep)

➡ _____

14 주어진 단어를 바르게 배열하여 다음 문장과 같은 의미의 문장을 쓰시오.

> Kathy used bad words and it made her friend upset.
> (Kathy / using / her friend / upset / by / made / words / bad)

➡ _____

15 주어진 어구를 바르게 배열하여 다음 우리말을 영어로 쓰시오. 필요하다면 어형을 바꾸시오.

> 불안감은 그녀를 밤새도록 깨어 있게 했다.
> (all night long / make / anxiety / awake / her)

➡ _____

16 주어진 동사와 동명사를 활용하여 다음 우리말을 영어로 쓰시오.

> 너를 만나는 것은 날 행복하게 해. (make)

➡ _____

Reading

STAY TUNED FOR MY STORY

Rap It Out

Open your mind, Open your heart

Look around and let's rap it out
~하자

Hey, I'm MC Joy. Do you want to write your own rap? You can rap
to부정사를 목적어로 취하는 동사(wish, hope, decide 등)

about anything because everything can be a story for a rap. I get ideas
이유를 나타내는 접속사

when I'm on the bus, in the shower, or in my bed. I write down my
때를 나타내는 접속사   또는

ideas and use them when I write my rap. There are no rules for writing
앞의 동사 write와 병렬   전치사의 목적어(동명사)

raps. You can start today!

Fantastic Pets

Welcome to *Fantastic Pets*! Having a pet is great. Today I'm going to
~에 온 것을 환영합니다   동명사 주어   동명사 주어는 단수 취급   ~할 예정이다

introduce my pet hedgehog, Polly.
동격 관계

When I first got Polly, she was very scared. I couldn't hold her
사람이 주어일 경우 감정을 나타내는 동사의 과거분사형을 사용

because she raised her spikes. So, I placed my T-shirt in her case and
결과를 나타내는 접속사

she got used to my smell. Finally, I was able to hold her in my hands.
~에 익숙해지다   마침내   be able to V: V할 수 있다

Now, Polly is my best friend and always makes me happy.
목적격보어로 형용사를 쓰는 동사(make, keep, find, think, leave, consider 등)

stay tuned 채널을 고정하다
look around 둘러보다
because 왜냐하면
get ~을 얻다
write down ~을 적다
there is/are ~ ~이 있다
rule 규칙
fantastic 환상적인
be going to V V할 예정이다
scared 겁먹은
hold 잡다
spike 가시, 뾰족한 것
place 두다
get used to N N에 익숙해지다
be able to V V할 수 있다

 확인문제

● 다음 문장이 본문의 내용과 일치하면 T, 일치하지 않으면 F를 쓰시오.

1 Joy is used to writing her own rap. ☐

2 Joy gets her ideas when she is taking a shower. ☐

3 There are some rules to keep in mind when we write our rap. ☐

4 Polly felt scared at first. ☐

5 Polly can't smell anything. ☐

Handy Tips

Welcome back to *Handy Tips*. Where do you normally sit in a movie theater? Here is a tip. You will find it easy and helpful.
여기 ~이 있다 　　　5형식 문장으로 목적격 보어로 형용사 easy와 helpful을 씀

Step 1 Point your finger at something far from you.
far something (X)

Step 2 Close one eye and open it.
두 개 중에 첫 번째 것은 one. 나머지 하나는 the other로 나타냄.

Step 3 Repeat it with the other eye.
앞 문장 'Close one eye and open it'을 가리킴

When does your finger move? Is it when you close your right eye?
의문부사(언제)　　　　　　　　　앞 문장 'When does your finger move?'를 가리킴

Then you mainly use your right eye. This means you should sit on
그러면, 그렇다면　　　　　　　　　　　　　　　의무를 나타내는 조동사 '~해야 한다'
the left side in the theater. That way, you can enjoy a full view of the
그런 방식으로
screen better. This information is also helpful when you choose a seat
well의 비교급 '더 잘'　　　　　　　help+-ful(형용사 어미)
in a classroom, too.

handy 유용한, 편리한
normally 보통
sit 앉다
helpful 유용한
point ~을 가리키다
far from ~로부터 먼
repeat 반복하다
mainly 주로
mean 의미하다
enjoy 즐기다
information 정보
choose 선택하다

 확인문제

● 다음 문장이 본문의 내용과 일치하면 T, 일치하지 않으면 F를 쓰시오.

1 Here is a useful tip about how to choose a seat. ☐

2 The writer thinks we will find the tip useless. ☐

3 The first thing we should do is to point our finger at something just in front of us. ☐

4 The second step is to close one eye and open it. ☐

5 If we mainly use our right eye, we'd better sit on the right side in the theater. ☐

6 We can use the tip when we pick a seat in a classroom. ☐

● 우리말을 참고하여 빈칸에 알맞은 말을 쓰시오.

1 Rap It _____

2 _____ your mind, _____ your heart

3 Look _____ and let's rap it _____

4 Hey, I'm MC Joy. Do you _____ _____ _____ your own rap?

5 You can rap _____ _____ because everything _____ _____ a story for a rap.

6 I get ideas _____ I'm _____ the bus, _____ the shower, or _____ my bed.

7 I _____ _____ my ideas and _____ _____ when I write my rap.

8 There _____ _____ _____ for _____ raps. You can start today!

9 _____ Pets

10 Welcome to _____ *Pets*! _____ a pet is great.

11 Today I'm going to _____ my _____ hedgehog, Polly.

12 _____ I first _____ Polly, she was very _____.

13 I couldn't _____ her _____ she _____ her spikes.

14 So, I _____ my T-shirt _____ _____ _____ and she _____ _____ _____ my smell.

15 Finally, I _____ _____ _____ _____ _____ her in my hands.

16 Now, Polly is my best friend and always _____ _____ _____.

1 랩으로 표현해 봐

2 너의 생각을 열어 봐. 너의 마음을 열어 봐

3 주변을 둘러보고 랩으로 표현해 봐

4 안녕. 난 MC Joy야. 너만의 랩을 쓰고 싶니?

5 세상 모든 것들이 랩의 이야깃거리가 될 수 있기 때문에 넌 어떤 것에 대해서든 랩을 할 수 있어.

6 난 버스에서, 샤워 중에 또는 침대에서 아이디어들을 얻어.

7 내 아이디어들을 적어 두고 내가 랩을 쓸 때 그것들을 활용하지.

8 랩을 쓰는 데에는 어떤 규칙도 없어. 넌 오늘 당장 시작할 수 있어!

9 환상의 애완동물

10 '환상의 애완동물'에 온 걸 환영해! 애완동물을 기른다는 건 멋진 일이야.

11 오늘 난 나의 애완 고슴도치인 Polly를 소개할 거야.

12 내가 Polly를 처음 만났을 때, 그 애는 너무 겁을 먹었어.

13 그 애가 가시를 세워서 난 그 애를 손에 쥘 수가 없었어.

14 그래서 내가 그 애의 우리 안에 내 티셔츠를 두었더니 그 애가 내 냄새에 적응했어.

15 마침내, 난 손으로 그 애를 쥘 수 있게 되었지.

16 이제 Polly는 나의 가장 친한 친구이고 항상 나를 행복하게 해 줘.

17 _____ Tips

18 _____ _____ to *Handy Tips*.

19 _____ do you _____ _____ _____ a movie theater?

20 _____ _____ a tip.

21 You will _____ _____ _____ _____ _____ .

22 Step 1 _____ your finger _____ something _____ _____ you.

23 Step 2 _____ one eye and _____ _____ .

24 Step 3 Repeat _____ with _____ _____ eye.

25 When _____ your finger _____ ?

26 Is it _____ you _____ your right eye?

27 Then you _____ _____ your right eye.

28 This _____ you should _____ _____ the left side in the theater.

29 _____ _____ , you can _____ a _____ _____ of the screen better.

30 _____ _____ is also _____ when you _____ _____ in a classroom, _____ .

17 쓸모 있는 팁

18 '쓸모 있는 팁'에 돌아온 걸 환영해.

19 넌 보통 영화관에서 어디에 앉니?

20 여기 팁이 하나 있어.

21 넌 이것이 쉽고 유용하다는 걸 알게 될 거야.

22 1단계: 멀리 떨어져 있는 물체를 손가락으로 가리켜 봐.

23 2단계: 한쪽 눈을 감았다가 떠 봐.

24 3단계: 반대쪽 눈으로 반복해 봐.

25 언제 네 손가락이 움직이니?

26 오른쪽 눈을 감았을 때니?

27 그렇다면 너는 주로 오른쪽 눈을 사용하는 거야.

28 그 말은 너는 영화관에서 왼편에 앉아야 한다는 걸 뜻해.

29 그렇게 하면, 너는 스크린의 꽉 찬 화면을 더 잘 즐길 수 있어.

30 이 정보는 네가 교실에서 자리를 고를 때도 도움이 될 거야.

● 우리말을 참고하여 본문을 영작하시오.

1 랩으로 표현해 봐

➡ _____

2 너의 생각을 열어 봐, 너의 마음을 열어 봐

➡ _____

3 주변을 둘러보고 랩으로 표현해 봐

➡ _____

4 안녕. 난 MC Joy야. 너만의 랩을 쓰고 싶니?

➡ _____

5 세상 모든 것들이 랩의 이야깃거리가 될 수 있기 때문에 넌 어떤 것에 대해서든 랩을 할 수 있어.

➡ _____

6 난 버스에서, 샤워 중에 또는 침대에서 아이디어들을 얻어.

➡ _____

7 내 아이디어들을 적어 두고 내가 랩을 쓸 때 그것들을 활용하지.

➡ _____

8 랩을 쓰는 데에는 어떤 규칙도 없어. 넌 오늘 당장 시작할 수 있어!

➡ _____

9 환상의 애완동물

➡ _____

10 '환상의 애완동물'에 온 걸 환영해! 애완동물을 기른다는 건 멋진 일이야.

➡ _____

11 오늘 난 나의 애완 고슴도치인 Polly를 소개할 거야.

➡ _____

12 내가 Polly를 처음 만났을 때, 그 애는 너무 겁을 먹었어.

➡ _____

13 그 애가 가시를 세워서 난 그 애를 손에 쥘 수가 없었어.

➡ _____

14 그래서 내가 그 애의 우리 안에 내 티셔츠를 두었더니 그 애가 내 냄새에 적응했어.

➡ _____

15 마침내, 난 손으로 그 애를 쥘 수 있게 되었지.

➡ _____

16 이제 Polly는 나의 가장 친한 친구이고 항상 나를 행복하게 해 줘.

➡ _____

17 쓸모 있는 팁

➡ _____

18 '쓸모 있는 팁'에 돌아온 걸 환영 해.

➡ _____

19 넌 보통 영화관에서 어디에 앉니?

➡ _____

20 여기 팁이 하나 있어.

➡ _____

21 넌 이것이 쉽고 유용하다는 걸 알게 될 거야.

➡ _____

22 1단계: 멀리 떨어져 있는 물체를 손가락으로 가리켜 봐.

➡ _____

23 2단계: 한쪽 눈을 감았다가 떠 봐.

➡ _____

24 3단계: 반대쪽 눈으로 반복해 봐.

➡ _____

25 언제 네 손가락이 움직이니?

➡ _____

26 오른쪽 눈을 감았을 때니?

➡ _____

27 그렇다면 너는 주로 오른쪽 눈을 사용하는 거야.

➡ _____

28 그 말은 너는 영화관에서 왼편에 앉아야 한다는 걸 뜻해.

➡ _____

29 그렇게 하면, 너는 스크린의 꽉 찬 화면을 더 잘 즐길 수 있어.

➡ _____

30 이 정보는 네가 교실에서 자리를 고를 때도 도움이 될 거야.

➡ _____

[01~04] 다음 글을 읽고, 물음에 답하시오.

Rap It Out

Open your mind, Open your heart
Look around and let's rap it out

　Hey, I'm MC Joy. Do you want ____ⓐ____ your own rap? You can rap about (A)[something / anything] because everything can be a story for a rap. I get ideas when I'm ____ⓑ____ the bus, in the shower, or in my bed. I write down my ideas and use (B)[it / them] when I write my rap. There (C)[is / are] no rules for ____ⓒ____ raps. You can start today!

서답형

01 주어진 어휘를 어법에 맞게 빈칸 ⓐ와 ⓒ에 쓰시오.

(write)

ⓐ_____ ⓒ_____

02 위 글을 읽고 답할 수 있는 질문은?

① Where is MC Joy now?
② How does MC Joy start her rap?
③ When Does MC Joy get her idea?
④ How does MC Joy go to school?
⑤ What is rap?

03 위 글의 빈칸 ⓑ에 들어갈 말로 가장 적절한 것은?

① at 　　　② by 　　　③ about
④ under 　　⑤ on

중요

04 위 글의 (A)~(C)에서 어법상 옳은 것끼리 바르게 짝지은 것은?

① something – it – is
② something – them – are
③ anything – it – are
④ anything – them – is
⑤ anything – them – are

[05~09] 다음 글을 읽고, 물음에 답하시오.

Fantastic Pets

　Welcome to *Fantastic Pets*! ____(A)____ a pet is great. (①) Today I'm going to introduce my pet hedgehog, Polly. (②) When I first got Polly, she was very scared. I couldn't hold her because she raised her spikes. (③) So, I placed my T-shirt ____ⓐ____ her cage and she got used ____ⓑ____ my smell. (④) Now, Polly is my best friend and always makes me happy. (⑤)

서답형

05 주어진 동사를 어법에 맞게 빈칸 (A)에 쓰시오.

(have)

➡ _____

서답형

06 위 글의 ①~⑤ 중 주어진 문장이 들어가기에 가장 적합한 곳은?

Finally, I was able to hold her in my hands.

① 　　② 　　③ 　　④ 　　⑤

07 위 글의 내용과 일치하지 <u>않는</u> 것은?

① The writer thinks that it is great to have a pet.
② Polly is a hedgehog.
③ Polly is the first pet the writer has ever had.
④ Polly felt scared at first.
⑤ Polly is the best friend of the writer.

08 위 글의 빈칸 ⓐ와 ⓑ에 들어갈 말이 바르게 짝지어진 것은?

① at – by
② in – to
③ on – into
④ to – to
⑤ in – by

서답형

09 Write the reason the writer couldn't hold Polly when he first got it.

➡ It was because _____ .

[10~15] 다음 글을 읽고, 물음에 답하시오.

ⓐ**Handy Tips**

Welcome back to *Handy Tips*. Where do you normally (A)[sit / seat] in a movie theater? Here is a tip. You will find ⓑit easy and helpful.
Step 1 Point your finger at something far from you.
Step 2 Close one eye and open (B)[it / them].
Step 3 Repeat it with (C)[another / the other] eye.

When does your finger move? Is it when you close your right eye? Then you mainly use your right eye. This means you should sit on the left side in the theater. That way, you can enjoy a full view of the screen better. ⓒ<u>This information is also helpful when you choose a seat in a classroom, too.</u>

10 위 글의 (A)~(C)에서 어법상 옳은 것끼리 바르게 짝지은 것은?

① sit – it – another
② sit – it – the other
③ sit – them – another
④ seat – it – the other
⑤ seat – them – another

11 위 글의 내용과 일치하는 것의 개수는?

- The passage is about how to choose a movie.
- There are three steps to find out which eye you normally use.
- You should close both eyes.
- The tip is helpful only in a movie theater.
- You should point your finger at something in front of you.

① 1개   ② 2개   ③ 3개
④ 4개   ⑤ 5개

12 위 글의 밑줄 친 ⓐ를 대신하여 쓸 수 있는 것은?

① Thankful ② Mindful ③ Careful
④ Useful ⑤ Peaceful

서답형

13 위 글의 밑줄 친 ⓑ가 가리키는 것을 쓰시오.

➡ _____

서답형

14 위 글의 밑줄 친 문장 ⓒ와 같은 의미가 되도록 빈칸에 알맞은 말을 쓰시오.

This information is _____ not only _____ but also _____ when you choose _____ .

➡ _____

서답형
15 위 글의 내용에 맞도록 다음 빈칸에 들어갈 말을 위 글에서 찾아 쓰시오.

> **Kelly:** What do you think about the tip?
> **Jimmy:** I thought it _____ .

➡ _____

[16~20] 다음 글을 읽고, 물음에 답하시오.

Rap It Out

Open your mind, Open your heart
Look around and let's rap it out

Hey, I'm MC Joy. Do you want to write your own rap? You can rap about anything ⓐunderline because everything ⓑ___ be a story for a rap. I get ideas when I'm on the bus, in the shower, or in my bed. I write down my ideas and use them when I write my rap. There are no rules for writing raps. You ___ⓒ___ start today!

16 위 글의 내용과 일치하지 않는 것은?

① MC Joy is a rapper.
② MC Joy sees everything as a story for a rap.
③ MC Joy gets ideas when she's in her bed.
④ It takes long to start rapping.
⑤ Anyone can become a rapper.

17 위 글의 밑줄 친 ⓐ를 대신하여 쓸 수 있는 것은?

① since   ② if   ③ that
④ when   ⑤ unless

중요
18 위 글의 빈칸 ⓑ와 ⓒ에 공통으로 들어갈 말로 가장 적절한 것은?

① must   ② should   ③ can
④ will   ⑤ might

서답형
19 주어진 단어를 이용하여 다음 질문에 답하시오.

> **Q:** What does Joy do when she is on the bus?

> (for)

➡ _____

서답형
20 위 글의 내용에 맞도록 빈칸에 알맞은 말을 쓰시오.

> **Kelly:** What do you use when you write your rap?
> **Joy:** I use _____ _____ that I wrote down before.

➡ _____

[21~26] 다음 글을 읽고, 물음에 답하시오.

Fantastic Pets

Welcome to *Fantastic Pets*! ⓐHaving a pet is great. Today I'm going to introduce my pet hedgehog, Polly. When I first got Polly, she was very (A)[scaring / scared]. I couldn't hold her because she (B)[rose / raised] her spikes. So, I placed my T-shirt in her cage and she ___ⓑ___ used to my smell. ⓒFinally, I was able to hold her in my hands. Now, Polly is my best friend and always makes me (C)[happy / happily].

21 위 글의 밑줄 친 ⓐ와 쓰임이 다른 하나는?

① His hobby is going fishing at night.
② Kelly enjoys taking a nap.
③ Jason is reading a magazine.
④ My mom doesn't mind writing poems.
⑤ I finally finished making a doll.

22 위 글의 빈칸 ⓑ에 적절한 것을 <u>모두</u> 고르면?

① got   ② made   ③ had

④ became   ⑤ put

23 위 글의 (A)~(C)에서 어법상 옳은 것끼리 바르게 짝지은 것은?

① scaring – rose – happy

② scaring – raised – happy

③ scared – raised – happy

④ scared – rose – happy

⑤ scared – rose – happily

24 위 글의 밑줄 친 ⓒ를 대신하여 쓸 수 있는 것을 <u>모두</u> 고르면?

① In the end   ② Unfortunately

③ In fact   ④ At last

⑤ Indeed

서답형

25 위 글의 내용에 맞게 빈칸에 알맞은 말을 쓰시오.

> There _____ _____ on Polly's back.
> She uses them when she feels afraid.

➡ _____

서답형

26 다음 빈칸에 알맞은 말을 위 글에서 찾아 어법에 맞게 쓰시오.

> The passage is focused on _____ the writer's pet, Polly.

➡ _____

[27~29] 다음 글을 읽고, 물음에 답하시오.

Handy Tips

Welcome back to *Handy Tips*. Where do you normally sit in a movie theater? Here is a tip. You will find it easy and helpful.

Step 1 Point your finger at something far _____ⓐ you.

Step 2 Close one eye and open it.

Step 3 Repeat it with the other eye.

When does your finger move? (①) Is it when you close your right eye? (②) This means you should sit on the left side in the theater. (③) That way, you can enjoy a full view of the screen better. (④) This information is also helpful when you choose a seat in a classroom, too. (⑤)

27 다음 문장이 들어가기에 가장 적합한 곳은?

> Then you mainly use your right eye.

①   ②   ③   ④   ⑤

28 다음 중 빈칸 ⓐ에 들어갈 말과 같은 것은?

① He is the man I can depend _____.

② Could you turn _____ the radio?

③ Cheese is made _____ milk.

④ I'm looking _____ my sister.

⑤ Ms. Kim put _____ the test.

서답형

29 위 글의 내용에 맞게 빈칸에 알맞은 말을 쓰시오.

> Step 2 is closing one eye and opening it.
> Step 3 is _____.

➡ _____

[01~05] 다음 글을 읽고 물음에 답하시오.

Rap It Out

Open your mind, Open your heart
(A)*Look around and let's rap it out*

Hey, I'm MC Joy. (B)너만의 랩을 쓰고 싶니? You can rap about anything because everything can be a story for a rap. (C)I get ideas when I'm on the bus, in the shower, or in my bed. I write down my ideas and use them when I write my rap. There are no rules for writing raps. (D)You can start today!

01 다음은 랩을 쓰기를 원하는 친구들에게 밑줄 친 (A)와 같이 말한 이유이다. 빈칸에 알맞은 말을 위 글에서 찾아 쓰시오.

> It's because _____.

➡ _____

02 주어진 단어를 이용하여 밑줄 친 우리말 (B)를 영어로 쓰시오.

> (want / own)

➡ _____

03 주어진 단어를 이용하여 밑줄 친 (C)를 답으로 할 수 있는 질문을 쓰시오.

> (when / usually / your)

➡ _____

04 다음 질문의 답을 위 글에서 찾아 쓰시오.

> Q: In writing raps, are there any rules to keep in mind?

➡ _____

05 다음은 밑줄 친 (D)를 구체적으로 쓴 것이다. 빈칸에 알맞은 말을 쓰시오.

> You can start _____ today!

➡ _____

[06~11] 다음 글을 읽고, 물음에 답하시오.

Fantastic Pets

Welcome to *Fantastic Pets*! _____(A)_____. Today I'm going ___ⓐ___ my pet hedgehog, Polly. When I first got Polly, she was very scared. I couldn't hold her because she raised her spikes. So, I placed my T-shirt in her cage and she got used to my smell. Finally, I was able ___ⓑ___ her in my hands. Now, Polly is my best friend and (B)항상 나를 행복하게 해 줘.

*I = Sam

06 빈칸 (A)에 들어갈 다음 문장과 같은 의미의 문장을 쓰시오.

> It is great to have a pet.
> = ___ ___ ___ ___ .

07 다음 주어진 동사를 어법에 맞게 빈칸 ⓐ~ⓑ에 쓰시오.

> (introduce / hold)

ⓐ_____ ⓑ_____

08 위 글의 내용에 맞게 빈칸에 알맞은 말을 쓰시오.

> _____ made it hard for Sam to hold Polly.

➡ _____

09 How did Polly look when the writer first got her? Answer in English.

➡ _____

⭐ 🔵중요
10 위 글의 내용에 맞게 조언을 완성하시오.

> Jane: I have a hedgehog. But I think she doesn't like me. I want to be friends with her. What should I do?
>
> Joy: _____ _____ _____ _____
> _____ _____ will make her familiar with your smell. Try it.

11 주어진 단어를 어법에 맞게 활용하여 우리말 (B)를 영어로 쓰시오.

> (make)

➡ _____

[12~17] 다음 글을 읽고, 물음에 답하시오.

Handy Tips

Welcome back to *Handy Tips*. Where do you normally sit in a movie theater? ⓐHere is a tip. You will find it easy and helpful.
Step 1 Point your finger at something far from you.
Step 2 Close one eye and open it.
Step 3 Repeat ⓑit with the other eye.

When does your finger move? Is it when you close your right eye? Then you mainly use your right eye. This means you should sit on the left side in the theater. That way, you can enjoy a full view of the screen better. This information is also helpful when you choose a seat in a classroom, too.

12 주어진 단어를 바르게 배열하여 밑줄 친 ⓐ의 구체적인 의미를 쓰시오.

> (is / a / a / here / tip / choose / better / to / seat)

➡ _____

13 위 글의 밑줄 친 ⓑ가 가리키는 것을 우리말로 쓰시오.

➡ _____

14 If your finger moves when you close your left eye, where do you have to sit in a movie theater?

➡ _____

15 위 글의 내용에 맞도록 빈칸에 알맞은 말을 쓰시오.

> If you mainly use your right eye, _____ enables you to enjoy a full view of the screen better.

➡ _____

16 다음 글을 읽고 완전한 문장의 영어로 답하시오.

> After reading the tip, you sat on the right side in the theater. That made your view of the screen better than before. In this case, which eye do you mostly use?

➡ _____

⭐ 🔵중요
17 동명사와 위 글의 표현을 이용하여 다음 우리말을 영어로 쓰시오.

> 교실에서 자리를 선택하는 것은 쉽다.

➡ _____

구석구석

Communication Step B

A: Welcome to *It's Your Stage!* Can you introduce <u>yourself</u>?
동사의 목적어가 되는 재귀대명사

B: Hello. I'm Bob. I'm <u>interested in</u> painting.
~에 관심이 있다

A: What are you going to show us today?

B: I know <u>how to</u> draw a face quickly. I can show you easy steps.
의문사 + to부정사

A: Sounds interesting!

구문해설 • introduce: 소개하다 • painting: 그림 • draw: 그리다 • step 단계, 절차

해석
A: '당신의 무대입니다!'에 오신 걸 환영합니다. 자기소개를 해주겠어요?
B: 안녕하세요. 전 Bob예요. 전 그림 그리기에 관심이 있어요.
A: 오늘 우리에게 무엇을 보여 주실 건가요?
B: 전 얼굴을 빠르게 그리는 방법을 알고 있어요. 제가 간단한 단계를 여러분께 보여 드릴게요.
A: 흥미롭네요!

Look and Write

MOVIE REVIEW – SPY COUPLE

Thomas: Great action scenes <u>kept me excited</u> from beginning to end.
5형식 동사 + 목적어 + 목적보어

Kelly: I <u>found the main actor attractive</u>. He is a great actor, too!
5형식 동사 + 목적어 + 목적보어

Ria: I enjoyed the music in the movie. It <u>made everything romantic</u>.
5형식 동사 + 목적어 + 목적보어

구문해설 • great: 훌륭한 • scene: 장면 • excited: 흥분한
• from beginning to end: 처음부터 끝까지 • attractive: 매력적인 • romantic: 낭만적인

영화 리뷰 – SPY COUPLE
Thomas: 멋진 액션 장면이 시종일관 나를 흥분되게 만들었다.
Kelly: 나는 주연 남배우가 매력적이라는 것을 알았다. 그는 훌륭한 배우이기도 하다.
Ria: 나는 영화 속 음악을 즐겼다. 그 음악이 모든 것을 낭만적으로 만들었다.

Think and Write

Welcome to Cooking Class!

Are you interested in <u>baking</u> cookies? I can <u>give you some helpful tips</u>! In this
전치사의 목적어(동명사)   4형식동사 +간접목적어 + 직접목적어

class, you will learn basic cooking skills. <u>Anyone</u> can bake cookies <u>in only</u>
누구든지   단 하루 만에

<u>one day</u>. This class is free and everything is ready for you. Sign up today!

구문해설 • be interested in: ~에 흥미가 있다 • basic: 기본적인 • free: 무료의 • ready: 준비된
• sign up: 등록하다

요리 수업에 오신 것을 환영합니다!
쿠키를 굽는 것에 흥미가 있나요? 내가 몇 가지 유용한 팁을 줄게요. 이 수업에서, 당신은 기본적인 요리 기술을 배울 겁니다. 누구든지 단 하루 만에 쿠키를 구울 수 있어요. 이 수업은 무료이고 당신을 위해 모든 것이 준비되어 있습니다. 오늘 등록하세요!

Words & Expressions

01 다음 주어진 영영풀이가 나타내는 말을 쓰시오.

> a person who takes photographs, especially as a job

➡ _____

02 다음 짝지어진 단어의 관계가 같도록 빈칸에 알맞은 말을 쓰시오.

> polite : impolite = _____ : abnormally

03 다음 우리말에 맞게 빈칸에 알맞은 말을 쓰시오.

(1) 나는 바쁜 일정에 익숙해지고 있다.
   ➡ I'm _____ _____ _____ busy schedule.
(2) 제가 부엌에 있는 빵을 가져올게요.
   ➡ I'll _____ _____ some bread in the kitchen.
(3) 나는 오늘 드라마 수업을 신청할 거야.
   ➡ I'll _____ _____ for the drama class today.

04 다음 중 밑줄 친 부분의 뜻풀이가 바르지 <u>않은</u> 것은?

① I'll place this note on the table. (장소)
② If you want to take part in the event, raise your hand first. (들어올리다)
③ I'll let you know handy tips for you. (편리한)
④ You should wipe the floor before going out. (닦다)
⑤ Emily has a talent for drawing pictures. (재능)

05 다음 문장의 빈칸에 공통으로 들어갈 말로 적절한 것은?

> • Tom, _____ one eye and open it.
> • The restaurant is _____ to my office.
> • Would you _____ the window for me?

① close
② near
③ far
④ shut
⑤ clear

Conversation

[06~07] 다음 대화를 읽고, 물음에 답하시오.

Mike: (A) I'm looking for a special gift for Clara. Do you have any idea, Lisa?
Lisa: (B) Well, why don't you make some macarons for her? ⓐShe really loves them. (into)
Mike: (C) But I don't know how to make them.
Lisa: (D) I know how to make them with easy steps. I'll help you.
Mike: (E) Great. Thanks, Lisa.

06 위 대화의 (A)~(E) 중 주어진 문장이 들어가기에 적절한 곳은?

> Don't worry.

① (A)   ② (B)   ③ (C)   ④ (D)   ⑤ (E)

07 위 대화의 밑줄 친 ⓐ와 의미가 같도록 주어진 단어를 이용하여 다시 쓰시오.

➡ _____

[08~10] 다음 대화를 읽고, 물음에 답하시오.

M: Welcome to *It's Your Stage*! We have a great show for you today. Let's meet the people with special talents.

W: Hello. I'm Doremi. I'm interested in music.

M: Great! What are you going to show us today?

W: I know how to sing high (A)notes easily. I can show you easy steps.

M: Sounds interesting!

08 위 대화의 밑줄 친 (A)와 같은 의미로 쓰인 것은?

① You should not forget to bring your notes.

② To play the piano, you should know how to read notes.

③ You'd better take notes in the class.

④ What did you draw on your notes?

⑤ The guest wrote the note and left it on the table.

09 위 대화에서 다음의 영영풀이에 해당하는 단어를 찾아 쓰시오.

a natural ability to do something well

➡ _____

10 위 대화의 남자와 여자의 관계로 적절한 것은?

① guide – traveler　② host – guest

③ doctor – patient　④ waiter – guest

⑤ flight attendant – passenger

[11~13] 다음 대화를 읽고, 물음에 답하시오.

Minsu: Oh, no. I broke a dish.

Tina: Don't worry. _____(A)_____ I read the tip in a magazine.

Minsu: With bread? How?

Tina: You can wipe the area with it. It picks up the small pieces.

Minsu: Great tip! Thanks, Tina. I'll go get some bread in the kitchen.

11 위 대화의 빈칸 (A)에 들어갈 말을 주어진 어구를 모두 배열하여 완성하시오.

┤ 보기 ├
how / bread / with / glass / clean up / pieces / know / I / to / the

➡ _____

12 위 대화에서 Minsu의 심경 변화로 적절한 것은?

① upset → surprised

② happy → nervous

③ worried → relieved

④ depressed → angry

⑤ satisfied → nervous

13 위 대화의 내용과 일치하지 <u>않는</u> 것은?

① Minsu는 그릇을 깼다.

② Tina는 빵으로 유리 조각을 청소하는 법을 알고 있다.

③ Tina에 따르면 작은 유리 조각을 손으로 집어야 한다.

④ Tina는 깨진 유리 조각을 청소하는 법에 대한 정보를 잡지에서 읽었다.

⑤ Minsu는 부엌에 가서 빵을 가져올 것이다.

[14~16] 다음 대화를 읽고, 물음에 답하시오.

Jake: Hello, Elsa. Which after-school class are you going to take?

Elsa: I'm going to take the drama class on Thursdays. What about you, Jake?

Jake: I'm thinking of taking the Tuesday photography class. (A)<u>나는 사진 찍기에 관심이 있어.</u>

Elsa: Oh, I heard that the teacher is a (B) <u>famous</u> photographer.

Jake: Really? That's really cool!

14 위 대화의 밑줄 친 (A)의 우리말을 영어로 쓰시오.

➡ _____

15 위 대화의 밑줄 친 (B)와 바꾸어 쓸 수 있는 것은?

① familiar ② well-known
③ popular ④ strict
⑤ humorous

16 What does Elsa know about the photography class?

➡ _____

[17~18] 다음 대화를 읽고, 물음에 답하시오.

W: I baked this bread, but it came out too dry.

M: Oh, _____ Put a glass of water in the oven.

W: That's (A)<u>a great tip.</u> Where did you learn that?

M: I saw it on a cooking show.

17 위 대화의 빈칸에 들어갈 말로 <u>어색한</u> 것은?

① I know how to bake bread without making it dry.
② I'll tell you how to bake bread without making it dry.
③ I learned how to bake bread without making it dry.
④ I have information about how to bake bread without making it dry.
⑤ I forgot how to bake bread without making it dry.

18 위 대화의 밑줄 친 (A)와 바꾸어 쓸 수 <u>없는</u> 것은?

① a good idea
② a good piece of advice
③ a good piece of information
④ a great rap
⑤ a nice guidance

Grammar

19 다음 빈칸에 공통으로 들어갈 말로 가장 적절한 것은?

- Thank you for _____ for me.
- He kept me _____ for an hour.

① waiting ② to wait ③ waits
④ to waiting ⑤ waited

20 다음 빈칸에 들어갈 말이 바르게 짝지어진 것은?

- My sister is busy _____ her luggage.
- My dad quit _____.

① to pack – to smoke
② pack – smoking
③ packing – to smoke
④ to pack – smoke
⑤ packing – smoking

21 주어진 단어를 활용하여 다음 우리말을 영어로 쓰시오.

> 스마트 시계를 사용하는 것은 너의 삶을 편리하게 해 줄 거야.
>
> (use / make / convenient)

➡ _____

_____

22 다음 중 빈칸에 적절한 것을 <u>모두</u> 고르면?

> A refrigerator _____ foods cool.

① finds   ② makes   ③ considers
④ keeps   ⑤ gives

23 주어진 문장을 같은 의미를 지닌 다른 표현으로 바꾸어 쓸 때 <u>잘못된</u> 것은?

① Tom tried to avoid answering my question.
   = Tom tried not to answer my question.
② She wants to go on working.
   = She wants to continue working.
③ Please wake me up at 8 o'clock.
   = Would you mind waking me up at 8 o'clock?
④ Kelly cannot help laughing at him.
   = Kelly can't help him laugh.
⑤ Could you pick me up at the airport?
   = Would you mind picking me up at the airport?

24 다음 〈보기〉의 밑줄 친 부분과 쓰임이 <u>다른</u> 것은?

> ┌─ 보기 ─┐
> It isn't <u>raining</u> now.

① The water is <u>boiling</u>.
② You are always <u>watching</u> television.
③ I am <u>living</u> with some friends.
④ His job is <u>helping</u> the poor.
⑤ Jinsu is <u>listening</u> to his favorite music.

25 주어진 어구를 바르게 배열하여 다음 우리말을 영어로 쓰시오. 필요하다면 어형을 바꾸시오.

> Jimmy는 컴퓨터 게임을 너무 많이 하는 것을 부인했다.
>
> (Jimmy / play / deny / computer games / too much)

➡ _____

26 다음 빈칸에 공통으로 쓰일 수 있는 동사는?

> • We _____ reading the newspaper.
> • I _____ to talk with him.

① made   ② found
③ stopped   ④ imagined
⑤ thought

27 우리말과 같은 의미가 되도록 다음 빈칸에 알맞은 말을 쓰시오.

> 네가 예상하는 것보다 그 일이 더 쉽다는 걸 알게 될 거야.
>
> = You will find _____ than you expect.

➡ _____

28 다음 중 어법상 옳은 것은?

① Mom keeps the refrigerator cleanly.
② I'm sorry for use your pen.
③ Did you finish to do the laundry?
④ Jenny considered going alone by taxi.
⑤ Kyle suggested to have dinner with us.

[29~31] 다음 글을 읽고, 물음에 답하시오.

Rap It Out

Open your mind, Open your heart
①*Look around and let's rap it out*

Hey, I'm MC Joy. Do you want ②to write your own rap? You can rap about anything because ③nothing can be a story for a rap. I get ideas ⓐ I'm on the bus, in the shower, or in my bed. I ④write down my ideas and use ⓑthem ⓒ I write my rap. There are ⑤no rules for writing raps. You can start today!

29 위 글의 빈칸 ⓐ와 ⓒ에 공통으로 들어갈 말은?

① because   ② when   ③ if
④ as soon as   ⑤ but

30 위 글의 ①~⑤ 중 글의 흐름상 어색한 것은?

①   ②   ③   ④   ⑤

31 위 글의 밑줄 친 ⓑ가 가리키는 것을 위 글에서 찾아 쓰시오.

➡ _____

[32~34] 다음 글을 읽고, 물음에 답하시오.

Fantastic Pets

Welcome to *Fantastic Pets*! Having a pet is great. Today I'm going to introduce my pet hedgehog, Polly. When I first got Polly, she was very scared. I couldn't hold her because she raised her spikes. So, I placed my T-shirt in her cage and she got used to my smell. Finally, I was able to hold her in my hands. Now, Polly is my best friend and always ⓐ makes me happy.   *I = Sam

32 위 글을 읽고 답할 수 <u>없는</u> 질문은?

① How does Sam feel about having a pet?
② What is Sam mainly talking about?
③ What kind of animal is Polly?
④ What kind of T-shirt does Polly like?
⑤ How does Polly make Sam feel now?

33 위 글의 밑줄 친 ⓐ와 쓰임이 같은 것은?

① Kelly <u>made</u> pizza for us all.
② Julia <u>made</u> her opinion clear.
③ The grapes are <u>made</u> into wine.
④ He <u>made</u> several movies.
⑤ My dad <u>made</u> me a doll.

34 What did Sam place in Polly's cage? Answer in English.

➡ _____

출제율 90%

01 다음 문장의 빈칸에 알맞은 말을 쓰시오.

> • Put a glass of water (A)_____ the oven.
> • Which class did you sign (B)_____ for?
> • I'm looking (C)_____ a special gift for Clara.

출제율 95%

02 다음 대화의 빈칸 (A)와 (B)에 interest를 알맞은 형태로 채워 넣으시오.

> A: What club are you going to join?
> B: I want to join the gardening club. I'm (A)_____ in plants and flowers.
> A: Oh, that sounds like an (B)_____ club.

출제율 90%

03 다음 대화의 ⓐ~ⓓ 중 어법상 어색한 것을 찾아 바르게 고치시오.

> Mike: Betty, what are you looking ⓐat?
> Betty: I'm reading the comments ⓑon my blog.
> Mike: What do you usually write blog posts ⓒabout?
> Betty: I usually write about books. I'm ⓓinteresting in reading.

➡ _____

출제율 85%

04 다음 대화가 자연스럽게 이어지도록 순서대로 배열하시오.

> (A) Really? That's really cool!
> (B) Which after-school class are you going to take?
> (C) Oh, I heard that the teacher is a famous photographer.
> (D) I'm going to take the drama class on Thursdays. What about you?
> (E) I'm thinking of taking the Tuesday photography class. I'm interested in taking pictures.

➡ _____

[05~06] 다음 대화를 읽고, 물음에 답하시오.

> M: Welcome to *It's Your Stage*! We have a great show for you today. (A)
> W: Hello. I'm Doremi. I'm interested in music. (B)
> M: Great! What are you going to show us today? (C)
> W: I know how to sing high notes easily. I can show you easy steps. (D)
> M: Sounds interesting! (E)

출제율 95%

05 위 대화의 (A)~(E) 중 주어진 대화가 들어가기에 가장 적절한 곳은?

> Let's meet the people with special talents.

① (A) ② (B) ③ (C) ④ (D) ⑤ (E)

출제율 95%

06 위 대화의 내용과 일치하지 <u>않는</u> 것은?

① People with special talents are on *It's Your Stage*.
② Doremi has an interest in music.
③ Doremi is going to show how to play high notes easily.
④ Doremi is going to introduce easy steps to sing high notes.
⑤ The man shows an interest in Doremi's talent.

[07~09] 다음 대화를 읽고, 물음에 답하시오.

G: I baked this bread, but it came out too dry.
B: Oh, I know how to bake bread without making it dry. Put a glass of water in the oven.
G: That's a great tip. Where did you learn that?
B: I saw it on a cooking show.

출제율 95%

07 What's the matter with the girl?

➡ _____

출제율 90%

08 According to the boy's advice, how can the girl solve her problem?

➡ _____

_____

출제율 95%

09 How did the boy get the useful tip about baking?

➡ _____

출제율 90%

10 주어진 단어를 이용하여 다음 우리말을 영어로 쓰시오.

장갑은 우리의 손을 따뜻하게 한다. (keep)

➡ _____

출제율 95%

11 다음 우리말을 영어로 바르게 옮긴 것은?

책을 읽음으로써, 너는 더 나은 사람이 될 수 있어.

① On reading books, you are a better person.
② In reading books, you can be a better person.
③ By reading books, you have to be a better person.
④ On reading books, you had better be a better person.
⑤ By reading books, you can be a better person.

출제율 100%

12 다음 괄호 안의 단어를 어법에 맞게 고친 것을 바르게 짝지은 것은?

- (dance) on the stage made Amy excited yesterday.
- Jimmy was excited about (sing) in front of many people.

① Dancing – to sing
② To dance – to sing
③ Dancing – sing
④ To dance – singing
⑤ To dance – sing

13 다음 중 어법상 바르지 않은 것은?

① Jason found the house easily.
② She made me a lawyer.
③ Making fun of your friend is not a good thing to do.
④ The situation kept me anxiously.
⑤ Rinda went canoeing with her cousins.

14 다음 우리말을 영어로 옮길 때 6번째 오는 단어는?

나는 다음 달에 집에 갈 것을 기대하고 있어.

① forward   ② looking
③ going   ④ to
⑤ home

15 다음 〈보기〉의 단어를 어법과 문맥에 맞게 빈칸에 쓰시오.

┌── 보기 ──┐
listen to   spend   have

(1) I am used to _____ a big breakfast.
(2) Brad was upset. The teacher was listening to the girl instead of _____ _____ his version of the story.
(3) Karl avoids _____ hours at a computer.

16 다음 우리말 의미에 맞도록 빈칸에 알맞은 말을 쓰시오.

나는 기다리는 것에 싫증났어.
➡ I am tired of _____.

17 다음 빈칸에 공통으로 들어갈 말을 어법에 맞게 쓰시오.

• Are you interested in _____ pictures?
너 사진 찍는 것에 관심이 있니?
• _____ too much salt is not good for our health.
소금을 너무 많이 섭취하는 것은 우리 건강에 좋지 않다.

[18~20] 다음 글을 읽고, 물음에 답하시오.

Rap It Out

Open your mind, Open your heart
Look around and let's rap it out

Hey, I'm MC Joy. Do you want to write your own rap? You can rap about anything because everything can be a story for a rap. I get ideas when I'm on the bus, in the shower, or in my bed. I write down my ideas and use them when I write my rap. There are no rules for writing raps. You can start today!

18 위 글의 주제로 가장 적절한 것은?

① how to see the world
② how to get ideas for everything
③ how to write your own rap
④ how to start writing some rules
⑤ how to get a story for a rap

19 위 글의 내용에 맞도록 빈칸에 알맞은 말을 쓰시오.

Julian: Is it difficult to write raps?
Joy: _____ _____ is easy. Just look around and rap it out.

20 다음 중 Joy에 관한 설명 중 옳은 것은?

① She wants to write her own rap.

② She will write some stories for a rap.

③ She doesn't know how to write raps.

④ She writes down her ideas to use them later.

⑤ She knows many rules for writing raps.

[21~22] 다음 글을 읽고, 물음에 답하시오.

Fantastic Pets

Welcome to *Fantastic Pets*! Having a pet is ①great. Today I'm going to introduce my pet hedgehog, Polly. When I first got Polly, she was very ②scared. I couldn't hold her because she ③raised her spikes. So, I placed my T-shirt in her cage and she got used to ④ my smell. Finally, I ⑤could not hold her in my hands. Now, Polly is my best friend and always makes me happy. *I = Sam

21 위 글의 ①~⑤ 중 흐름상 어색한 것은?

①   ②   ③   ④   ⑤

22 위 글의 내용에 맞게 빈칸에 알맞은 말을 쓰시오.

Sam has _____ _____ . It is a hedgehog named _____. When Sam first got her, he thought she needed time to _____ _____ _____ Sam's smell. Some time later, they became best friends.

[23~25] 다음 글을 읽고, 물음에 답하시오.

MC Joy: How to __(A)__ Your Own Rap

There are no rules for writing raps!

Everything can be a story for your rap. You can get ideas anytime and use them for your rap.

Sam: How to __(B)__ a Hedgehog

Do you want to hold her in your hands?

Place your T-shirt in her cage. She will get used to your smell and won't raise her spikes.

Sally: How to __(C)__ a Better Seat

Which eye do you mainly use?

Point your finger at something. Close one eye and open it. Repeat it with the other eye. When does your finger move?

23 주어진 단어를 문맥에 맞게 빈칸 (A)~(C)에 쓰시오.

(choose / write / care for)

(A)_____   (B)_____   (C)_____

24 위 글을 읽고 답할 수 <u>없는</u> 질문은?

① Are there any guidelines for writing raps?

② When can we get our ideas for raps?

③ Why do we have to place our T-shirt in the cage?

④ How can we make our hedgehog get used to our smell?

⑤ Why does a hedgehog raise its spikes?

25 위 글의 내용에 맞게 빈칸에 알맞은 말을 쓰시오.

If you want to know which eye you usually use, the first thing you should do is _____ and then closing one eye.

서술형 실전문제

 01 다음 대화의 (A)~(C)에 들어갈 알맞은 말을 쓰시오.

> Mike: Betty, what are you looking (A)_____?
> Betty: I'm reading the comments on my blog.
> Mike: What do you usually write blog posts (B)_____?
> Betty: I usually write about books. I'm interested (C)_____ reading.

[02~03] 다음 대화를 읽고, 물음에 답하시오.

> Jenny: Mike, who is the man on your SNS?
> Mike: Oh, he is my favorite baseball player, John Luke. I'm really interested in baseball.
> Jenny: Wow, you met him in person!
> Mike: Yeah, that was the best day of my life.

02 Which baseball player does Mike like best?

➡ _____

03 What is Mike interested in?

➡ _____

04 주어진 동사를 활용하여 다음 우리말을 영어로 쓰시오.

> 과식은 그를 아프게 한다. (overeat, ill)

➡ _____

05 주어진 단어를 활용하여 빈칸에 알맞은 말을 쓰시오.

> 너는 왜 내게 계속 질문하는 거야? 나를 혼자 내 버려둘 수는 없어?
> = Why do you _____ _____ me questions? Can't you _____ me alone? (keep / ask / leave)

06 주어진 단어를 활용하여 다음 속담을 영어로 쓰시오.

> 백문이 불여일견이다. (see / believe)

➡ _____

07 주어진 어구를 바르게 배열하여 다음 우리말을 영어로 쓰시오. 필요하다면 어형을 바꾸시오.

> 물을 많이 마시는 것은 우리를 건강하게 만든다. (healthy / drinking / us / water / make / lots of)

➡ _____

08 주어진 단어를 이용하여 다음 우리말을 영어로 쓰시오. 필요하다면 어형을 바꾸시오.

> 그는 그 영화가 교육적이라는 것을 알았다. (find / educational)

➡ _____

Rap It Out

Open your mind, Open your heart
Look around and let's rap it out

Hey, I'm MC Joy. Do you want to write your own rap? You can rap about anything because everything can be a story for a rap. I get ideas when I'm on the bus, in the shower, or in my bed. I write down my ideas and use them when I write my rap. There are no rules for writing raps. You can start today!

09 다음 대화에서 Jimmy에게 해줄 조언을 명령문으로 쓰시오.

> Jimmy: When I grow up, I want to be a rapper. But writing my own rap is so difficult. I think I have to give up.
>
> Joy: Don't give up _____!
> You can rap about anything.

➡ _____

10 주어진 단어를 활용하여 다음 대화를 완성하시오.

> Kelly: Joy, _____? (enjoy)
> Joy: Yes, I do. I enjoy it very much.

➡ _____

Handy Tips

Welcome back to *Handy Tips*. (A)너는 보통 영화관에서 어디에 앉니? Here is a tip. You will find it easy and helpful.

Step 1 Point your finger at something far from you.
Step 2 Close one eye and open it.
Step 3 Repeat it with the other eye.

When does your finger move? Is it when you close your right eye? Then you mainly use your right eye. This means you should sit on the left side in the theater. That way, you can enjoy a full view of the screen better. (B) This information is also helpful when you choose a seat in a classroom, too.

11 다음 주어진 단어를 활용하여 밑줄 친 우리말 (A)를 영어로 쓰시오.

> (usually)

➡ _____

12 주어진 단어를 바르게 배열하여 밑줄 친 (B)와 같은 의미의 문장을 쓰시오. 필요하다면 어형을 바꾸시오.

> This information is also helpful _____
> _____, too.
> (in / in / choose / a classroom / a seat)

13 위 글의 내용에 맞게 빈칸을 채우시오.

> Kelly: How can I know which eye I normally use?
> Jimmy: Let me tell you. It's simple. The first step is _____ at something. The next step is _____ and opening it. The last step is _____ the second step with _____.

➡ _____
_____

01 다음 대화를 읽고 대화의 내용과 일치하도록 빈칸을 완성하시오.

> Jake: Hello, Elsa. Which after-school class are you going to take?
>
> Elsa: I'm going to take the drama class on Thursdays. What about you, Jake?
>
> Jake: I'm thinking of taking the Tuesday photography class. I'm interested in taking pictures.
>
> Elsa: Oh, I heard that the teacher is a famous photographer.
>
> Jake: Really? That's really cool!

> Today, I talked about the after-school class with Jake. I'm planning to (A)_____
> _____. Jake told me that he was considering (B)_____
> because (C)_____. I thought that it was a good chance for
> him because I heard that (D)_____. I hope that he'll enjoy the
> photography class.

02 주어진 동사와 형용사를 활용하여 여러 가지 문장을 쓰시오.

> 동 find make keep
>
> 형 peaceful attractive comfortable awake valuable

(1) _____
(2) _____
(3) _____
(4) _____
(5) _____

03 〈보기〉와 같이 동명사를 목적어로 취하는 동사를 이용하여 자신에 관한 여러 가지 문장을 쓰시오.

> ┤ 보기 ├
> • I don't <u>mind</u> getting up early in the morning.
> • Tom <u>suggested</u> going to the cinema.
> • She has just <u>finished</u> bathing the cat.

(1) _____
(2) _____
(3) _____
(4) _____
(5) _____

단원별 모의고사

01 다음 문장의 빈칸에 들어갈 말을 〈보기〉에서 골라 쓰시오.

> ┌── 보기 ──┐
> artistic / careful / peaceful / romantic

(1) Please be _____ not to catch a cold.
(2) His painting shows his _____ talent.
(3) I'd like to see a _____ movie.
(4) My parents enjoy a quiet and _____ time in the country.

02 다음 우리말에 맞게 빈칸에 알맞은 말을 쓰시오.

(1) 나는 빵 굽기에 관심을 갖고 있다.
➡ I'm _____ _____ baking bread.
(2) 나는 스포츠를 매우 좋아한다.
➡ I'm _____ sports.
(3) 제가 이 건물의 네 개의 방을 둘러보겠습니다.
➡ I'll _____ _____ four rooms in this building.

03 다음 대화의 우리말을 주어진 단어를 사용하여 영작하시오.

> A: I'm looking for a special gift for Clara. Do you have any idea, Lisa?
> B: Well, 그녀에게 마카롱을 만들어 주는 게 어때? (don't, macarons, for, why)

➡ _____

04 다음 대화의 빈칸에 들어갈 말을 주어진 단어를 모두 배열하여 완성하시오.

> ┌── 보기 ──┐
> don't / cut / know / this / I / to / image / how

> A: What are you doing on the computer?
> B: I'm making a family photo album. But,
> _____
> A: Don't worry. I'll let you know.

➡ _____

05 다음 우리말을 주어진 단어를 이용하여 영작하시오.

(1) 다른 문화들에 익숙해지려면 시간이 걸립니다. (used, get)
➡ _____
(2) 제가 당신을 직접 만날 때 이야기할게요. (person, tell, when)
(부사절을 주절의 뒤에 오도록 할 것)
➡ _____
(3) 제가 이 프로그램을 어떻게 신청할 수 있나요? (up, sign)
➡ _____

[06~07] 다음 대화를 읽고, 물음에 답하시오.

> Mike: Betty, what are you looking at?
> Betty: I'm reading the comments on my blog.
> Mike: What do you usually write blog posts about?
> Betty: I usually write about books. I'm interested in reading.

06 What is usually Betty's blog about?

➡ _____

07 What does Betty have an interest in?

➡ _____

[08~09] 다음 대화를 읽고, 물음에 답하시오.

Sue: I baked this bread, but it came out too ⓐ <u>dry</u>.

Mike: Oh, I know ⓑ<u>what</u> to bake bread without making it dry. ⓒ<u>Put</u> a glass of water in the oven.

Sue: That's a great tip. ⓓ<u>Where</u> did you learn that?

Mike: I saw it ⓔ<u>on</u> a cooking show.

08 위 대화의 밑줄 친 ⓐ~ⓔ 중 어색한 것을 찾아 바르게 고치시오.

➡ _____

09 위 대화의 내용과 일치하는 것은?

① Sue was very good at baking the bread
② Mike has baked the bread on a cooking show.
③ Mike is worried about his dry bread.
④ Mike advised Sue to put a glass of water in the oven.
⑤ Sue got lots of great tips about baking from the cooking show.

[10~11] 다음 대화를 읽고, 물음에 답하시오.

Aron: Emily, _____(A)_____ ?

Emily: I'm going to join the music club. (B)<u>I'm into music.</u> What about you, Aron?

Aron: I want to join the gardening club. I'm interested in plants and flowers.

Emily: Oh, that sounds like an interesting club.

10 위 대화의 빈칸 (A)에 들어갈 말을 <보기>에 주어진 단어를 모두 배열하여 완성하시오.

┌─ 보기 ─
join / going / what / to / are / club / you
└─

➡ _____

11 위 대화의 밑줄 친 (B)와 바꾸어 쓸 수 <u>없는</u> 것은?

① I have an interest in music.
② I love music.
③ I really like music.
④ I'm fond of music.
⑤ I don't care for music.

[12~13] 다음 대화를 읽고, 물음에 답하시오.

Mike: I'm looking for a special gift for Clara. Do you have any idea, Lisa?

Lisa: Well, why don't you make some macarons for her? She really loves them.

Mike: (A)그렇지만 난 그걸 어떻게 만드는지 몰라. (them, know)

Lisa: Don't worry. I know how to make them with easy steps. I'll help you.

Mike: Great. Thanks, Lisa.

12 What will Mike make as a special gift for Clara?

➡ _____

13 위 대화의 (A)의 우리말을 주어진 단어를 이용하여 영작하시오.

➡ _____

[14~15] 다음 대화를 읽고, 물음에 답하시오.

John: ⓐIs that a 1000-piece puzzle?

Emma: Yeah, but there ⓑare so many pieces. It'll take a long time ⓒto finish.

John: Oh, I know how ⓓto do it quickly. Start from the corners, and then ⓔgrouping the pieces with the same colors.

Emma: I see. Thanks.

14 위 대화의 ⓐ~ⓔ 중 어법상 어색한 것을 찾아 바르게 고치시오.

➡ _____

15 How can Emma finish a 1000-piece puzzle quickly?

➡ _____
_____
_____

16 주어진 단어를 활용하여 다음 우리말을 영어로 쓰시오.

그는 나를 미치게 만들어. (make)

➡ _____

17 다음 중 어법상 바르지 <u>않은</u> 것은?

①Are you ②satisfied ③with ④making me ⑤nervously?

① ② ③ ④ ⑤

18 다음 우리말을 영어로 바르게 옮긴 것은?

베이킹 소다는 우리 신발을 깨끗하게 만들 수 있다.

① Baking soda must make our shoes cleanly.
② Baking soda can make our shoes cleanly.
③ Baking soda can keep our shoes cleanly.
④ Baking soda can make our shoes clean.
⑤ Baking soda must keep our shoes clean.

19 다음 우리말 의미에 맞도록 빈칸에 알맞은 말을 쓰시오.

창문이 열린 채로 둬. 나는 창문을 열어둔 채로 자고 싶어.

➡ _____ the window _____. I feel like _____ with the window open.

20 다음 밑줄 친 부분 중 쓰임이 <u>다른</u> 하나는?

① What are you <u>doing</u> now?
② The children are excited about <u>taking</u> their first flight.
③ Karen is interested in <u>learning</u> a foreign language.
④ My job is <u>protecting</u> you.
⑤ I'm thinking about <u>going</u> to church.

[21~24] 다음 글을 읽고, 물음에 답하시오.

Fantastic Pets

Welcome ⓐto *Fantastic Pets*! Having a pet ⓑis great. Today I'm going to introduce my pet hedgehog, Polly. When I first got Polly, she was very scared. I couldn't hold her ⓒbecause she raised her spikes. So, I placed my T-shirt in her cage and she got ___(A)___ to my smell. Finally, I was able to hold her ⓓin my hands. Now, Polly is my best friend and always ⓔ<u>make me happy.</u>

*I = Sam

21 위 글의 ⓐ~ⓔ 중 어법상 바르지 않은 것은?

① ⓐ   ② ⓑ   ③ ⓒ   ④ ⓓ   ⑤ ⓔ

22 주어진 동사를 빈칸 (A)에 어법에 맞게 쓰시오.

> (use)

➡ _____

23 다음과 같이 풀이되는 단어를 위 글에서 찾아 쓰시오.

> an animal that you keep in your home to give you company and pleasure

➡ _____

24 위 글의 내용과 일치하지 않는 것은?

① Sam thinks having a pet is fine.
② Polly is Sam's hedgehog.
③ Polly got along well with Sam from the first.
④ Polly doesn't raise her spikes to Sam now.
⑤ Polly makes Sam happy.

[25~28] 다음 글을 읽고, 물음에 답하시오.

Handy Tips

Welcome back to ⓐ*Handy Tips*. Where do you ⓑnormally sit in a movie theater? Here is a tip. You will find it easy and helpful.
Step 1 Point your finger at something far from you.
Step 2 Close one eye and open it.

Step 3 ⓒRepeat it with the other eye.
When does your finger move? Is it when you close your right eye? Then you ⓓmainly use your right eye. This means ___(A)___ you should sit on the left side in the theater. That way, you can enjoy a full view of the screen better. This information is also ___(B)___ when you ⓔchoose a seat in a classroom, too.

25 위 글의 빈칸 (A)에 들어갈 말로 가장 적절한 것은?

① what   ② that
③ where   ④ when
⑤ if

26 주어진 단어를 어법에 맞게 빈칸 (B)에 쓰시오.

> (use)

➡ _____

27 다음 중 밑줄 친 ⓐ~ⓔ를 대신하여 쓸 수 없는 것은?

① ⓐ: Helpful   ② ⓑ: usually
③ ⓒ: Do it again   ④ ⓓ: hardly
⑤ ⓔ: select

28 위 글의 제목으로 가장 적절한 것은?

① Handy Information for Your Health
② How to Protect Your Eyes
③ How to Choose a Better Seat
④ The Importance of Where You Sit
⑤ How to Get Helpful Tips

Lesson 2

Half a World Away

의사소통 기능

- 바라거나 기대하는 일 표현하기
  A: What are you going to do this Sunday?
  B: I'm going to go to the Food Fair. I'm looking forward to trying traditional foods.
- 어떤 일을 해야 한다고 알려 주기
  A: Don't forget to look to the right in London.
  B: Okay, I see.

언어 형식

- 조건을 나타내는 접속사 if
  If you see me, it is your lucky day.
- to부정사를 목적격보어로 취하는 동사
  We **want** our sombreros **to look** fancy.

교과서
Words & Expressions

Key Words

- **band**[bænd] 몡 악단, 밴드
- **bead**[biːd] 몡 구슬
- **chimney**[tʃímni] 몡 굴뚝
- **chimney sweep** 굴뚝 청소부
- **cross**[krɔːs] 동 건너다, 가로지르다 몡 십자가
- **decorate**[dékərèit] 동 장식하다, 꾸미다
- **dependent**[dipéndənt] 혱 의지하는, 의존하는
- **different**[dífərənt] 혱 다양한, 다른
- **doll**[dal] 몡 인형
- **drum**[drʌm] 몡 북, 드럼
- **excel**[iksél] 동 뛰어나다, 탁월하다
- **excellent**[éksələnt] 혱 훌륭한, 우수한
- **express**[iksprés] 동 나타내다, 표현하다
- **fair**[fɛər] 몡 장, 박람회
- **fancy**[fǽnsi] 혱 장식이 많은, 화려한
- **fireplace**[faiərpleis] 몡 벽난로, 난로
- **folk music** 민속 음악
- **following**[fάlouiŋ] 혱 다음에 나오는
- **foreign**[fɔ́ːrən] 혱 외국의
- **introduce**[intrədjúːs] 동 소개하다
- **lucky**[lʌki] 혱 운 좋은, 행운의
- **mask**[mæsk] 몡 가면

- **material**[mətíəriəl] 몡 재료
- **Mongolia**[mɑŋgóuliə] 몡 몽골
- **monster**[mάnstər] 몡 괴물, 요괴
- **palace**[pǽlis] 몡 궁전, 왕궁
- **performance**[pərfɔ́ːrməns] 몡 공연
- **present**[préznt] 몡 선물 혱 현재의, 출석하는
- **rope**[roup] 몡 (밧)줄, 끈
- **sombrero**[sɑmbréərou] 몡 솜브레로 (챙이 넓은 멕시코 모자)
- **stay**[stei] 동 머무르다
- **stranger**[stréindʒər] 몡 모르는[낯선] 사람
- **sunlight**[sənlait] 몡 햇빛
- **system**[sístəm] 몡 체계
- **tent**[tent] 몡 텐트, 천막
- **traditional**[trədíʃənl] 혱 전통적인
- **treasure**[tréʒər] 몡 보물
- **tribe**[traib] 몡 부족
- **various**[vɛ́əriəs] 혱 다양한
- **warm-up exercise** 준비 운동
- **wealth**[welθ] 혱 부, 재산
- **wedding**[wédiŋ] 몡 결혼식, 결혼
- **wrap**[ræp] 동 싸다, 포장하다

Key Expressions

- **a lot of** 많은
- **by the way** 그런데
- **check out** 확인하다, 살펴보다
- **communicate with** ~와 의사소통하다
- **first of all** 우선, 가장 먼저
- **from country to country** 나라마다
- **for free** 무료로
- **get into** ~에 들어가다

- **look forward to ~ing** ~을 고대하다
- **put away** ~을 치우다
- **put on** ~을 입다, ~을 바르다
- **sign up for** ~에 등록하다
- **stand for** ~을 상징하다, ~을 나타내다
- **thanks to** ~ 덕분에
- **try on** ~을 입어 보다
- **turn off** ~을 끄다

Word Power

※ 서로 반대되는 뜻을 가진 단어

- traditional 전통적인 → modern 현대적인
- turn on 켜다 → turn off 끄다
- lucky 운 좋은 → unlucky 불운한
- put on 입다 → take off 벗다
- different 다른 → same 같은
- get into ~에 들어가다 → get out of ~에서 나가다

- following 그 다음의 → preceding 선행의
- wealth 부 → poverty 가난
- dependent 의존하는 → independent 독립적인
- forget 잊다 → remember 기억하다
- strong 강한 → weak 약한

English Dictionary

- **cross** 건너다
  → to go across; to pass from one side to the other
  가로지르다. 한쪽에서 다른 쪽으로 지나가다

- **decorate** 장식하다
  → to make something look more attractive by putting things on it
  어떤 것에 무언가를 더함으로써 더 매력적으로 보이게 만들다

- **dependent** 의지하는
  → needing somebody/something in order to survive or be successful
  생존하거나 성공하기 위해 누군가 또는 무언가를 필요로 하는

- **doll** 인형
  → a child's toy in the shape of a person, especially a baby or a child
  특히 아기나 어린 아이같은 사람의 모양을 한 어린이 장난감

- **express** 표현하다
  → to show or make known a feeling, an opinion, etc. by words, looks or actions
  감정, 의견 등을 말이나 모습 또는 행동으로 보여주거나 알게 하다

- **fireplace** 벽난로
  → an open space for a fire in the wall of a room
  방의 벽에 있는 난로를 위해 트인 공간

- **folk** 민속의
  → traditional and typical of the ordinary people of a country or community
  국가나 공동체의 평범한 사람들의 전통적이거나 전형적인

- **following** 다음에 나오는
  → that is/are going to be mentioned next
  다음에 언급될

- **lucky** 운이 좋은
  → having good luck
  좋은 운을 가진

- **mask** 가면
  → a covering for part or all of the face, worn to hide or protect it
  얼굴을 가리거나 보호하기 위해 쓰는 얼굴 전체나 부분을 위한 덮개

- **stranger** 낯선 사람
  → a person that you do not know
  당신이 모르는 사람

- **traditional** 전통적인
  → being part of the beliefs, customs or way of life of a particular group of people, that have not changed for a long time
  오랜 시간 동안 변하지 않은 특정 그룹의 사람들의 믿음, 관습 또는 생활 방식의 부분인

- **treasure** 보물
  → a collection of valuable things such as gold, silver and jewellery
  금, 은, 귀금속 같이 귀중한 것들의 모음

- **visit** 방문하다
  → to go to see someone and spend time with them
  어떤 사람을 보러 가서 그들과 시간을 보내다

- **wrap** 싸다, 포장하다
  → to cover something completely in paper or other material, for example when you are giving it as a present
  예를 들어 당신이 선물을 줄 때 종이나 다른 재료로 무언가를 완전히 감싸다

서답형

01 다음 짝지어진 단어의 관계가 같도록 빈칸에 알맞은 말을 쓰시오.

> luck : lucky = noise : _____

서답형

02 다음 영영풀이에 해당하는 말을 쓰시오.

> a person that you do not know

➡ _____

03 다음 문장의 빈칸에 공통으로 들어갈 말로 적절한 것은?

> • Kathy saw the _____, passing by the church.
> • Be careful when you _____ the river.

① excel
② follow
③ perform
④ cross
⑤ wrap

중요

04 다음 중 밑줄 친 부분의 뜻풀이가 바르지 <u>않은</u> 것은?

① She is making a necklace with beads.
　　　　　　　　　　　　　　　　구슬
② I want to express my feelings freely.
　　　표현하다
③ Each tribe has its own tradition and custom. 부족
④ Smoke is rising from the chimney of that factory.　　　　　배수관
⑤ Do you know the driver of this fancy car?
　　　　　　　　　　　　　　　　　멋진

05 다음 주어진 문장의 밑줄 친 의미와 같은 의미로 쓰인 것은?

> I bought some tea as Brian's birthday present.

① I was present at the meeting to discuss our issue.
② You have to present your ID to borrow the books.
③ Why don't you wrap this present with red paper?
④ Minsu was happy to present his research in front of many people.
⑤ I expect over 100 students to be present.

서답형

06 다음 문장의 빈칸에 들어갈 말을 〈보기〉에서 골라 쓰시오.

> ┤ 보기 ├
> stand for / try on / put on / check out

(1) I don't have enough time to _____ all the documents.
(2) You'd better _____ your hat to stay cool under the strong sunlight.
(3) What does this symbol _____?
(4) Can I _____ this jacket?

서답형

07 다음 대화의 우리말을 주어진 단어를 사용하여 영작하시오.

> A: Take care, my friend. I'll miss you.
> B: 편지 쓰는 거 잊지 마. (forget)

➡ _____

01 다음 짝지어진 단어의 관계가 같도록 빈칸에 알맞은 말을 쓰시오.

> differ : different = excel : _____

02 다음 영영풀이에 해당하는 말을 쓰시오.

> to cover something completely in paper or other material, for example when you are giving it as a present

➡ _____

03 다음 문장의 빈칸에 들어갈 말을 보기에서 골라 쓰시오.

> ┌─ 보기 ─┐
> wedding / fair / cross / performance

(1) When you _____ the road, you should always be careful.

(2) I was so nervous before the _____.

(3) I'll attend Bill's _____ ceremony.

(4) The world food _____ is being held at the city hall.

04 다음 대화의 밑줄 친 (A)와 의미가 같도록 주어진 단어를 사용하여 다시 쓰시오.

> A: What are you going to do this Sunday?
> B: I'm going to visit the World Food Fair. (A)I'm looking forward to trying various foods. (wait to)

➡ _____

05 다음 우리말에 맞게 빈칸에 알맞은 말을 쓰시오.

(1) 그들은 서로 영어로 의사소통을 합니다.

➡ They _____ _____ each other in English.

(2) 너는 도서관에서 책을 무료로 빌릴 수 있다.

➡ You can borrow books _____ _____ in the library.

(3) 이 장난감들을 치우는 것을 잊지 마세요.

➡ Don't forget to _____ _____ these toys.

06 다음 우리말을 주어진 단어를 모두 배열하여 문장을 완성하시오.

(1) 우리는 서로 의사소통하기 위해 영어를 사용하였다.

(used / communicate / we / each / to / other / English / with)

➡ _____

(2) 사람들이 민속 음악에 맞추어 춤을 추고 있다.

(dancing / people / to / are / music / folk)

➡ _____

(3) 아빠는 멋있어 보이기 위해 모자를 쓰셨다.

(fancy / a / my / hat / father / look / wore / to)

➡ _____

1 바라거나 기대하는 일 표현하기

A What are you going to do this Sunday? 이번 주 일요일에 뭐 할 거야?

B I'm going to go to the Food Fair. I'm looking forward to trying traditional foods.
나는 음식 박람회에 갈 거야. 나는 전통 음식을 먹어 보는 것이 기대가 돼.

■ 'look forward to+(동)명사'는 '~하기를 기대하다[고대하다]'라는 의미로 바라거나 기대하는 일을 표현하기 위해 쓸 수 있으며 'can't wait to+동사 원형' 또는 'can't wait for+명사'로 바꾸어 쓸 수 있다.

바라거나 기대하는 일 표현하기

• I'm looking forward to meeting my friend. 나는 내 친구를 만나기를 기대하고 있다.
• I can't wait for the cooking class. 나는 요리 수업이 몹시 기다려진다.
• I can't wait to go on a picnic. 나는 소풍가는 것이 몹시 기다려진다.
• I really want to visit the museum. 나는 정말로 박물관에 가고 싶다.

핵심 Check

1. 다음 우리말과 일치하도록 빈칸에 알맞은 말을 쓰시오.

(1) **A:** What are you going to do this Sunday? (이번 주 일요일에 뭐 할 거야?)

   B: I'm going to visit my grandparents. I'm _____ _____ _____ _____ them. (나는 그분들을 만나기를 기대하고 있어.)

(2) **A:** I heard that you're going to visit Jeju-do during the vacation.
   (나는 네가 방학 동안에 제주도를 방문할 거라고 들었어.)

   B: Yeah, I _____ _____ _____ visit there. (나는 그곳을 방문하는 것이 몹시 기다려져.)

(3) **A:** I bought it for Emma's birthday. (Emma의 생일을 위해 그것을 샀어.)

   B: I'm sure she'll like it. I _____ _____ _____ her birthday.
   (나는 그녀가 그것을 좋아할 것이라고 확신해. 나는 그녀의 생일이 몹시 기다려져.)

② 어떤 일을 해야 한다고 알려 주기

    A Don't forget to look to the right in London. 런던에서는 오른쪽을 보는 것을 잊지 마.

    B Okay, I see. 응. 알았어.

■ 'Don't forget to ~'는 상대방에게 어떤 일을 해야 한다고 알려 주거나 해야 할 일을 상기시켜 주기 위해 사용하는 표현으로 'Remember to+동사원형 ~' 또는 'Make sure that 주어+동사 ~' 또는 'Make sure to+ 동사원형 ~'으로 바꾸어 쓸 수 있다.

어떤 일을 해야 한다고 알려 주기

- Don't forget to wrap it in red. 그것을 빨간색으로 포장해야 한다는 것을 잊지 마라.
- Remember to wrap it in red. 그것을 빨간색으로 포장해야 한다는 것을 기억해라.
- Make sure that you should wrap it in red. 그것을 빨간 색으로 포장해야 함을 명심해라.
- Make sure to wrap it in red. 그것을 빨간색으로 포장해야 함을 명심해라.
- Keep in mind that you should wrap it in red. 그것을 빨간색으로 포장해야 한다는 것을 명심해라.

■ forget이나 remember 뒤에 -ing를 쓰면 '(과거에) ~했던 것을 잊다[기억하다]'라는 의미가 되고 'to+동 사원형'을 쓰면 '(미래에) ~해야 할 것을 잊다[기억하다]'라는 의미를 나타낸다.

- forget + -ing: (과거에) ~한 것을 잊다
- forget + to 동사원형: (미래에) ~해야 할 것을 잊다
- remember + -ing: (과거에) ~한 것을 기억하다
- remember + to 동사원형: (미래에) ~해야 할 것을 기억하다

핵심 Check

  2. 다음 우리말과 일치하도록 빈칸에 알맞은 말을 쓰시오.

    (1) **A:** _____ _____ _____ bring your umbrella. (너의 우산을 가져올 것을 잊지 마라.)

        B: Okay, I see. (네. 알겠어요.)

    (2) **A:** It looks like it's going to rain soon. _____ _____ close the windows.

        (창문을 닫아야 한다는 것을 기억해라.)

        B: Okay, I will. (네. 그럴게요.)

    (3) **A:** I'm going skating. (나는 스케이트를 타러 갈 거야.)

        B: _____ _____ _____ put your gloves on. (장갑 끼는 것을 명심해라.)

A. Listen and Talk 2 B

Amy: Look, Brandon. A horse is crossing the street over there.

Brandon: Yes, there is ❶a crossing light for horses here in London.

Amy: Oh, I didn't know ❷that. That's interesting. Now ❸let's cross the street.

Brandon: Wait! Cars come from the right side in London.

Amy: Right, I forgot about ❹that.

Brandon: Yeah, it's different ❺from country to country. Don't forget to look to the right before you cross in London.

Amy: 봐, Brandon. 저기 말이 길을 건너고 있어.

Brandon: 맞아, 여기 런던에는 말을 위한 교통 신호등이 있어.

Amy: 오, 난 몰랐는걸. 흥미롭다. 이제 우리도 길을 건너자.

Brandon: 기다려! 런던에는 차가 오른쪽에서 와.

Amy: 맞다, 깜박했어.

Brandon: 응. 나라마다 다르잖아. 런던에서는 길을 건너기 전에 오른쪽을 보는 것을 잊지 마.

❶ a crossing light: 신호등
❷ 런던에 말을 위한 교통 신호등이 있다는 것을 가리킨다.
❸ Let's + 동사 원형: '~하자.'라고 제안하는 표현이다.
❹ 런던에서는 차가 오른쪽에서 온다는 내용을 가리킨다.
❺ from country to country: 나라마다

Check(√) True or False

(1) Amy didn't know that there is a crossing light for horses in London.　　T ☐ F ☐

(2) Amy should look to the right before she crosses in London because of horses.　　T ☐ F ☐

B. Communication

Sue: How was your first day here in Mongolia?

Jake: It was great. ❶By the way, where am I going to stay tonight?

Sue: You're going to sleep in a *ger*, a Mongolian tent.

Jake: Oh, ❷I'm looking forward to it.

Sue: You'll like it. There is a ❸fireplace in the *ger*. So, don't forget to ❹ put your things away from the fireplace.

Jake: I see. Thank you.

Sue: 여기 몽골에서의 첫날은 어떠셨나요?

Jake: 아주 좋았어요. 그런데 오늘 밤 어디에서 머무르게 되나요?

Sue: 몽골 천막인 '게르'에서 주무시게 될 거예요.

Jake: 오, 정말 기대가 되네요.

Sue: 마음에 드실 거예요. 게르에는 난로가 있어요. 그러니 물건을 난로에서 치워두는 것을 잊지 마세요.

Jake: 알겠습니다. 감사합니다.

❶ by the way: 그런데
❷ 'I'm looking forward to ~'는 무언가에 대해 기대감을 표현할 때 사용된다.
❸ fireplace: 난로
❹ put ~ away: ~을 치우다

Check(√) True or False

(3) Jake is going to sleep in a *ger*, a Mongolian tent.　　T ☐ F ☐

(4) Jake should remember to put his things around the fireplace.　　T ☐ F ☐

Listen and Talk 1 A-1

Mike: Elsa, how is your Hula dance class going?

Elsa: Oh, it's great. We are going to ❶perform at the ACB Hall this weekend.

Mike: Wow, that sounds like ❷a big day for you!

Elsa: Yeah, ❸I'm looking forward to the performance.

❶ perform: 공연하다 ❷ a big day: 중요한 날 ❸ I'm looking forward to ~: ~을 고대하다

Listen and Talk 1 A-2

Sora: Chris, what are you going to do this Sunday?

Chris: I'm going to go to ❶the World Food Fair.

Sora: Oh, I was ❷there last weekend. There were lots of ❸traditional foods from all over the world.

Chris: Great! I'm looking forward to ❹trying ❺ them.

❶ the World Food Fair: 세계 음식 박람회 ❷ there = at the World Food Fair ❸ traditional foods: 전통 음식 ❹ to는 전치사로 동명사 형태가 이어져야 한다. ❺ them = traditional foods

Listen and Talk 1 B

Tom: Jane, what are you doing?

Jane: I'm ❶signing up for a program at the African Museum.

Tom: Is there an interesting ❷one?

Jane: Yeah, I'm going to make an African drum and a traditional mask.

Tom: Oh, ❸how fun!

Jane: Yeah, I'm looking forward to visiting the museum.

❶ sign up for: ~에 등록하다, 신청하다 ❷ one = program ❸ 'how fun it is.' 를 줄여 쓴 말로 '재미있겠다!'라는 감탄문이다.

Listen and Talk 2 A-1

W: I bought this tea for Wang's birthday. Will he like ❶it?

M: Sure, ❷he will. Wang ❸enjoys drinking tea.

W: Great. Then I'll wrap the present.

M: Don't forget to wrap ❹it in red. Red ❺stands for wealth in China.

❶ it = the tea ❷ 'he will like it.'을 줄인 형태이다. ❸ enjoy는 동명사를 목적어로 취한다. ❹ it = the present ❺ stand for: ~을 나타내다, 상징하다

Listen and Talk 2 A-2

Elsa: Our visit to Gyengbokgung is this Friday. Let's meet at two.

Jake: Okay, I'll see you at the bus stop.

Elsa: Oh, and ❶don't forget to wear a *hanbok*. We can ❷get into the palace ❸for free in our *hanboks*.

Jake: Right. I almost forgot.

❶ don't forget to ~ = remember to ~: 어떤 것을 잊지 말라는 의미를 나타낸다. ❷ get into: ~에 들어가다 ❸ for free: 무료로

Wrap Up 1

Harry: Jina, is it you? You're wearing a *kimono* in this photo.

Jina: Yeah, it's me. I tried ❶it on at the World Culture Festival.

Harry: That sounds fun. I should go ❷there. How long does the festival go on for?

Jina: Until this weekend. When you visit, don't forget to try on traditional clothes from other countries.

Harry: Okay. I'll try ❸them.

❶ *kimono*를 가리킨다. ❷ there = to the World Culture Festival ❸ traditional clothes를 가리킨다.

Wrap Up 2

Sue: What are we going to cook in the next cooking class, Mr. Jones?

Mr. Jones: We'll make *Ratatouille*.

Sue: *Ratatouille*? What is ❶it?

Mr. Jones: ❶It's vegetable dish. People in France enjoy eating ❶it.

Sue: Oh, I'm looking forward to the class.

Mr. Jones: ❷Glad to hear that. I'm sure you'll like ❸it.

❶ 모두 Ratatouille를 가리킨다. ❷ I'm glad(= happy, pleased) to hear that. ❸ Ratatouille를 가리킨다.

● 다음 우리말과 일치하도록 빈칸에 알맞은 말을 쓰시오.

Listen and Talk 1 A-1

Mike: Elsa, _____ _____ your Hula dance class _____?

Elsa: Oh, it's great. We are going to _____ at the ACB Hall this weekend.

Mike: Wow, that sounds _____ a big day for you!

Elsa: Yeah, I'm _____ _____ _____ the performance.

Listen and Talk 1 A-2

Sora: Chris, what _____ _____ _____ _____ _____ this Sunday?

Chris: _____ _____ _____ _____ _____ the World Food Fair.

Sora: Oh, I was there last weekend. There were lots of _____ _____ from all over the world.

Chris: Great! I'm looking forward to _____ them.

Listen and Talk 1 B

Tom: Jane, what are you doing?

Jane: I'm _____ _____ for a program at the African Museum.

Tom: Is there an _____ one?

Jane: Yeah, I'm going to make an _____ _____ and a _____ _____.

Tom: Oh, _____ _____!

Jane: Yeah, I'm looking forward to _____ _____ _____.

Listen and Talk 2 A-1

W: I bought this tea _____ Wang's birthday. Will he like it?

M: Sure, he _____. Wang enjoys _____ _____.

W: Great. Then I'll _____ _____ _____.

M: _____ _____ _____ _____ _____ _____ _____ _____.
Red _____ _____ wealth in China.

해석

Mike: Elsa, 너희 훌라댄스 수업은 어때?
Elsa: 오, 아주 좋아. 우리 이번 주말에 ACB 홀에서 공연을 할 거야.
Mike: 와, 너에게 정말 중요한 날로 들리는 걸!
Elsa: 맞아, 나는 공연이 정말 기대가 돼.

Sora: Chris, 이번 주 일요일에 뭐 할 거야?
Chris: 세계 음식 박람회에 갈 거야.
Sora: 오, 나 지난 주말에 거기 갔었어. 전 세계의 전통 음식이 많이 있었어.
Chris: 멋지다! 그 음식을 먹어 보는 것이 기대돼.

Tom: Jane, 뭐 하고 있니?
Jane: 아프리카 박물관에서 하는 프로그램을 신청하고 있어.
Tom: 흥미로운 것이 있니?
Jane: 응, 나는 아프리카의 북과 전통 가면을 만들 거야.
Tom: 오, 재미있겠다!
Jane: 맞아, 난 박물관에 가는 것이 기대가 돼.

W: Wang의 생일을 위해 이 차를 샀어. 그 애가 좋아할까?
M: 물론, 좋아할 거야. Wang은 차를 즐겨 마시잖아.
W: 잘됐다. 그러면 선물을 포장할게.
M: 빨간색으로 포장하는 것을 잊지 마. 빨간색은 중국에서 부를 상징하거든.

Listen and Talk 2 A-2

Elsa: Our visit to Gyengbokgung is this Friday. _____ _____ at two.

Jake: Okay, I'll _____ _____ at the bus stop.

Elsa: Oh, and _____ _____ _____ _____ a *hanbok*. we can _____ _____ _____ _____ for free in our *hanboks*.

Jake: Right. I almost forgot.

해석

Elsa: 우리 경복궁 방문이 이번 주 금요일이지. 두 시에 만나자.
Jake: 알겠어, 버스 정류장에서 보자.
Elsa: 오, 한복 입는 것을 잊지 마. 한복을 입으면 궁에 무료로 들어갈 수 있어.
Jake: 맞다, 하마터면 잊을 뻔했네.

Listen and Talk 2 B

Amy: Look, Brandon. A horse is crossing the street over there.

Brandon: Yes, there is _____ _____ _____ for horses here in London.

Amy: Oh, I didn't know that. That's interesting. Now _____ _____ _____ _____.

Brandon: Wait! Cars come from the _____ _____ in London.

Amy: Right, I forgot about that.

Brandon: Yeah, it's different _____ _____ _____ _____.

_____ _____ _____ _____ _____ _____ _____ before you cross in London.

Amy: 봐, Brandon. 저기 말이 길을 건너고 있어.
Brandon: 맞아, 여기 런던에는 말을 위한 교통 신호등이 있어.
Amy: 오, 난 몰랐는걸. 흥미롭다. 이제 우리도 길을 건너자.
Brandon: 기다려! 런던에는 차가 오른쪽에서 와.
Amy: 맞다, 깜박했어.
Brandon: 응, 나라마다 다르잖아. 런던에서는 길을 건너기 전에 오른쪽을 보는 것을 잊지 마.

Communication

Sue: How was your first day here in Mongolia?

Jake: It was great. _____ _____ _____, where am I going to stay tonight?

Sue: You're going to sleep in a *ger*, a Mongolian tent.

Jake: Oh, _____ _____ _____ _____ _____.

Sue: You'll like it. There is a _____ in the *ger*. So, don't forget to _____ your things _____ from the fireplace.

Jake: I see. Thank you.

Sue: 여기 몽골에서의 첫날은 어떠셨나요?
Jake: 아주 좋았어요. 그런데 오늘 밤 어디에서 머무르게 되나요?
Sue: 몽골 천막인 '게르'에서 주무시게 될 거예요.
Jake: 오, 정말 기대가 되네요.
Sue: 마음에 드실 거예요. 게르에는 난로가 있어요. 그러니 물건을 난로에서 치워 두는 것을 잊지 마세요.
Jake: 알겠습니다. 감사합니다.

Conversation 시험대비 기본평가

01 다음 대화의 밑줄 친 부분과 의미가 같도록 한 단어로 바꾸어 쓰시오.

> A: Don't <u>forget</u> to look to the right before you cross in London.
> B: Okay, I see.

➡ _____

02 다음 대화의 우리말을 주어진 단어를 모두 배열하여 영작하시오.

> A: Time flies. The new year is coming.
> B: 나는 새해를 기대하고 있어.
> (looking / I'm / the / to / new / forward / year)

➡ _____

[03~04] 다음 대화를 읽고, 물음에 답하시오.

Mike: Elsa, (A)[how / what] is your Hula dance class going?
Elsa: Oh, it's great. We are going to perform at the ACB Hall this weekend.
Mike: Wow, that (B)[sounds / sounding] like a big day for you!
Elsa: Yeah, I'm looking (C)[for / forward] to the performance.

03 위 대화의 (A)~(C)에 들어갈 말로 알맞은 것끼리 짝지어진 것은?

① how – sounds – for
② how – sounding – forward
③ how – sounds – forward
④ what – sounding – forward
⑤ what – sounds – for

04 위 대화에서 나타난 Elsa의 심경으로 적절한 것은?

① nervous   ② depressed
③ upset   ④ excited
⑤ disappointed

중요

01 다음 대화의 빈칸에 들어갈 말로 나머지와 의미가 <u>다른</u> 것은?

> A: What are you going to do this Sunday?
> B: I'm going to go to the Food Fair.
> _____(A)_____

① I want to try traditional foods.
② I would like to try traditional foods.
③ I'm looking forward to trying traditional foods.
④ I can't wait for trying traditional foods.
⑤ I'm afraid of trying traditional foods.

서답형

02 다음 대화의 우리말을 주어진 단어를 사용하여 영작하시오.

> A: Mike, I'm going to visit Seoul next month. Let's see in Seoul.
> B: Really? 나는 너를 서울에서 다시 만나기를 기대해. (forward, Seoul)

➡ _____

[03~04] 다음 대화를 읽고, 물음에 답하시오.

Elsa: Our visit to Gyengbokgung is this Friday. Let's meet at two.
Jake: Okay, I'll see you at the bus stop.
Elsa: Oh, and don't forget to wear a *hanbok*. we can get into the palace for free in our *hanboks*.
Jake: Right. I almost forgot.

서답형

03 When and where are Elsa and Jake going to meet?

➡ _____

서답형

04 Why should Elsa and Jake wear a *hanbok*?

➡ _____
_____

[05~07] 다음 대화를 읽고, 물음에 답하시오.

Sora: I bought this tea for Wang's birthday. Will he like it?
Jake: Sure, he will. Wang enjoys drinking tea.
Sora: Great. Then I'll wrap the present.
Jake: (A)Don't forget to wrap it in red. Red ___(B)___ wealth in China.

중요

05 위 대화의 밑줄 친 (A)와 바꾸어 쓸 수 있는 것을 <u>모두</u> 고르시오.

① Remember to wrap it in red.
② I'm afraid if I can't wrap it in red.
③ Remind me to wrap it in red.
④ Don't wrap it in red.
⑤ Keep in mind that you should wrap it in red.

서답형

06 위 대화의 빈칸 (B)에 '상징하다'를 뜻하는 숙어를 알맞은 형태로 쓰시오.

➡ _____

07 위 대화의 내용과 일치하지 <u>않는</u> 것은?

① Sora는 Wang의 생일 선물로 차를 샀다.
② Wang은 차 마시는 것을 즐긴다.
③ Sora는 직접 선물을 포장할 것이다.
④ Jake는 선물을 빨간색으로 포장해야 한다는 것을 잊어버렸다.
⑤ 중국에서 빨간색은 부를 상징한다.

[08~10] 다음 대화를 읽고, 물음에 답하시오.

> Sue: What are we going ⓐ(cook) in the next cooking class, Mr. Jones?
> Mr. Jones: We'll make *Ratatouille*.
> Sue: *Ratatouille*? What is it?
> Mr. Jones: It's vegetable dish. People in France enjoy ⓑ(eat) it.
> Sue: Oh, _____ (A)
> Mr. Jones: Glad to hear that. I'm sure you'll like it.

08 위 대화의 빈칸 (A)에 들어갈 말로 적절한 것을 <u>모두</u> 고르시오.

① I'm looking forward to the class.
② I don't know how to make it.
③ I can't wait for the class.
④ I'm not sure if I can make it.
⑤ I'm not good at cooking.

서답형

09 위 대화의 ⓐ, ⓑ에 주어진 어휘를 어법에 맞게 쓰시오.

ⓐ _____ ⓑ _____

10 위 대화의 내용과 일치하지 <u>않는</u> 것은?

① Mr. Jones와 Sue는 다음 요리 시간에 *Ratatouille*를 요리할 것이다.
② *Ratatouille*는 프랑스 사람들이 즐겨 먹는다.
③ Sue는 다음 요리 수업을 기대하고 있다.
④ Mr. Jones는 Sue가 *Ratatouille*를 좋아할 것이라고 확신한다.
⑤ Sue는 *Ratatouille*를 만들어 본 적이 있다.

서답형

11 다음 대화의 내용과 일치하도록 Amy의 일기를 완성하시오.

> Amy: Look, Brandon. A horse is crossing the street over there.
> Brandon: Yes, there is a crossing light for horses here in London.
> Amy: Oh, I didn't know that. That's interesting. Now let's cross the street.
> Brandon: Wait! Cars come from the right side in London.
> Amy: Right, I forgot about that.
> Brandon: Yeah, it's different from country to country. Don't forget to look to the right before you cross in London.

> Wed. April. 17th 2019.
> It was the first day of my life in London and I was so excited. When I was walking down the street with Brandon, I saw (A)_____. Surprisingly, there is (B)_____ in London. When I crossed the street, I almost forgot that I should (C)_____ _____ in London. Brandon reminded me of it. Tomorrow, I'll be more careful when crossing the street in London.

서답형

12 다음 대화가 자연스럽게 이어지도록 순서대로 배열하시오.

> (A) Wow, that sounds like a big day for you!
> (B) How is your Hula dance class going?
> (C) Yeah, I'm looking forward to the performance.
> (D) Oh, it's great. We are going to perform at the ACB Hall this weekend.

➡ _____

01 다음 대화의 빈칸에 들어갈 말을 주어진 단어를 모두 배열하여 완성하시오.

> A: What are you going to do this Sunday?
> B: I'm going to go to the Food Fair.
> _____

┤ 보기 ├
> traditional / trying / forward / I'm /
> foods / looking / to

➡ _____

[02~04] 다음 대화를 읽고, 물음에 답하시오.

> Mina: Chris, what are you going to do this Sunday?
> Chris: I'm going to go to the World Food Fair.
> Mina: Oh, I was there last weekend. There were (A)lots of traditional foods from all over the world.
> Chris: Great! (B)I'm looking forward to trying them.

02 위 대화의 밑줄 친 (A)를 한 단어로 바꿔 쓰시오.

➡ _____

03 ^{중요} 위 대화의 밑줄 친 (B)와 문장의 의미가 같도록 주어진 빈칸을 완성하시오.

➡ I can't _____.

04 What is Chris going to do this Sunday?

➡ _____

[05~06] 다음 대화를 읽고, 물음에 답하시오.

> Amy: Look, Brandon. A horse is crossing the street over there.
> Brandon: Yes, there is a crossing light for horses here in London.
> Amy: Oh, I didn't know (A)that. That's interesting. Now let's cross the street.
> Brandon: Wait! Cars come from the right side in London.
> Amy: Right, I forgot about (B)that.
> Brandon: Yeah, it's different from country to country. Don't forget to look to the right before you cross in London.

05 ^{중요} 위 대화에서 (A)that과 (B)that이 가리키는 내용을 우리말 20자 이내로 각각 쓰시오.

(A) _____
(B) _____

06 What should Amy remember when crossing the street in London?

➡ _____
     _____

07 주어진 글에 이어 대화가 자연스럽게 이어지도록 순서대로 배열하시오.

> What are we going to cook in the next cooking class, Mr. Jones?

> (A) *Ratatouille*? What is it?
> (B) We'll make *Ratatouille*.
> (C) Glad to hear that. I'm sure you'll like it.
> (D) Oh, I'm looking forward to the class.
> (E) It's vegetable dish. People in France enjoy eating it.

➡ _____

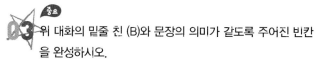

교과서

Grammar

1 조건절을 나타내는 접속사 if

- **If** you watch this movie, you will love it. 네가 만약 이 영화를 본다면, 너는 그것을 아주 좋아할 거야.
- **If** I have time to do this, I will let you know. 내가 이걸 할 시간이 있다면, 너에게 말할게.

■ 시간·조건의 부사절에서는 현재시제를 사용하여 미래를 나타내며 '만약 ~라면'이라고 해석한다.

- **If** we go by bus, it will be comfortable. 우리가 버스를 타고 간다면, 편할 거야.
- We will go on a picnic **after** we finish cleaning our house. 집 청소를 끝낸 후에 우리는 소풍을 갈 거야.
- **If** you are hungry, you may eat the sandwich on the table.
  네가 배고프다면, 식탁 위에 있는 샌드위치를 먹어도 좋아.

■ If가 이끄는 절이 명사 역할을 하는 경우도 있다. 명사절을 이끄는 접속사 If와 부사절을 이끄는 접속사 If의 쓰임을 구별하자. 명사절 접속사 If의 경우 '~인지 아닌지'로 해석하며 미래를 나타낼 때에는 미래시제를 써야 한다.

- **If** he has some rest, he will be much better. 그가 좀 쉰다면, 훨씬 더 좋아질 거야.
- I wonder **if** you **will** come or not. 나는 당신이 올지 안 올지가 궁금합니다.

■ If ~ not은 '만약 ~하지 않으면'의 의미인 Unless로 쓸 수 있다. Unless 역시 조건을 이끄므로 현재시제로 미래를 나타낸다.

- **If** you **don't** hurry, you will be late for class.
  = **Unless** you hurry, you will be late for class. 서두르지 않으면, 수업에 늦을 거야.

✏️ 핵심 Check

1. 다음 우리말과 같도록 빈칸에 알맞은 말을 쓰시오.

(1) 목이 마르면, 이 물을 마셔라.

➡ _____ you _____ thirsty, drink this water.

(2) 내일 비가 오면 우리는 집에 머물 것이다.

➡ _____ it _____ tomorrow, we _____ _____ home.

(3) 피곤하지 않으면, 내 파티에 올 거야?

➡ _____ you are tired, _____ _____ _____ to my party?

2 to부정사를 목적격보어로 취하는 동사

> • I **want** you **to come** back. 나는 네가 돌아오길 원해.
>
> • Karen **asked** us **to work** harder. Karen은 우리에게 일을 더 열심히 해달라고 요청했다.

■ '동사+목적어+to V' 형태로 목적어가 to부정사의 주체가 되도록 해석한다.

  • I don't **want** you **to go** yet. 나는 아직 네가 가길 원하지 않아.

  • Mom **persuaded** me **to join** the club. 엄마는 내가 그 클럽에 가입하도록 설득하셨다.

■ to부정사를 목적격보어로 취하는 동사에는 allow, ask, tell, advise, get, force, require, order, persuade, encourage, enable, cause, need, want, help, would like, teach, expect 등이 있다.

  • Our teacher **encourages** us **to cheer** up. 우리 선생님은 우리에게 힘을 내라고 격려하신다.

  • We **would like** you **to introduce** yourself. 우리는 당신이 자신을 소개하길 원해요.

■ to부정사 목적격보어의 부정형은 'not to V'로 표현한다.

  • My lawyer **advised** me **not to tell** anything. 나의 변호사는 내게 아무 말도 하지 말라고 충고했다.

  • Ted **ordered** her **not to make** any noise. Ted는 그녀에게 어떠한 소음도 내지 말라고 명령했다.

핵심 Check

2. 다음 우리말과 같도록 빈칸에 알맞은 말을 쓰시오.

(1) Jason은 나에게 극장에 가도록 설득했다.

➡ Jason _____ me _____ _____ to the cinema.

(2) 그녀는 그가 훨씬 더 늦게 도착하리라고 예상한다.

➡ She _____ him _____ _____ much later.

(3) 그 여자는 자기 딸에게 뛰지 말라고 말했다.

➡ The woman _____ her daughter _____ _____ _____ .

01 다음 문장에서 어법상 <u>어색한</u> 부분을 바르게 고쳐 쓰시오.

(1) Helen wants Jim leaving now.

_____ ➡ _____

(2) If you will want this magazine, I will lend it to you.

_____ ➡ _____

(3) Dad advised me to not stay awake late at night.

_____ ➡ _____

(4) If you hurry, you will miss the train.

_____ ➡ _____

02 주어진 어휘를 어법에 맞게 빈칸에 쓰시오.

(1) Mike asked us _____ quiet. (be)
(2) If you leave a message, I _____ it to Kelly. (give)
(3) He advised me _____ water more often. (drink)
(4) My friend allowed me _____ his laptop computer. (use)

03 다음 우리말에 맞게 주어진 단어를 바르게 배열하시오. (필요하면 단어를 추가하거나 어형을 바꿀 것)

(1) 나의 부모님은 내가 건축가가 되기를 원하신다.

(my parents / be / an architect / want / me)

➡ _____

(2) 네가 숙제를 끝내면, 나가도 좋아.

(can / homework / finish / you / you / go out / your / if)

➡ _____

(3) 이 신발은 내가 편안하게 걷는 것을 가능하게 해.

(enable / comfortably / me / these shoes / walk)

➡ _____

(4) 그들은 우리에게 돌아와 달라고 간청했다.

(beg / come / they / us / back)

➡ _____

01 다음 빈칸에 알맞은 것은?

> She asked her friend _____ her some money.

① lend   ② have lent   ③ to lend
④ lending   ⑤ lent

중요
02 다음 중 밑줄 친 if의 쓰임이 다른 하나는?

① If anyone calls, I will tell you.
② He will be sad if you leave.
③ I wonder if she liked it or not.
④ He will stay longer if she wants him to.
⑤ If it rains tomorrow, we won't go out.

03 다음 중 어법상 바르지 않은 것은?

> ①Will you call ②me ③if I ④will give you ⑤my phone number?

①   ②   ③   ④   ⑤

서답형
04 다음 괄호 안의 동사를 어법에 맞게 고쳐 쓰시오.

> She (allow) me (go) to the party yesterday.

➡ _____

05 다음 빈칸에 적절하지 않은 것은?

> We _____ him to go there.

① wanted   ② expected   ③ persuaded
④ told   ⑤ felt

중요
06 다음 우리말을 영어로 바르게 옮긴 것은?

> 나는 모든 손님들이 일찍 자기를 원해.

① I sleep all the guests with me.
② I would sleep all the guests early.
③ I would like all the guests to sleep early.
④ I would like to sleep early with all the guests.
⑤ I would like you to sleep all the guests early.

서답형
07 다음 두 문장의 의미가 같도록 빈칸에 알맞은 말을 쓰시오.

> If you don't do your best, you will fail the test.
> = _____ you do your best, you will fail the test.

➡ _____

08 다음 빈칸에 공통으로 들어갈 말은? (대·소문자 무시)

> • Can you tell me _____ Dominic will attend the orientation?
> • _____ you heat water, it will boil.

① unless   ② because   ③ if
④ as soon as   ⑤ that

서답형
09 주어진 단어를 바르게 배열하여 다음 우리말을 영어로 쓰시오.

> 내가 설거지하는 것을 네가 도와줘야겠어.
> (need / with the dishes / help / I / you / me / to)

➡ _____

10 다음 빈칸에 들어갈 동사 do의 형태가 <u>다른</u> 하나는?

① Dan asked me _____ the dishes.
② She hopes _____ the project.
③ Can you _____ me a favor?
④ Do you want her _____ it?
⑤ Our teacher expects us _____ our best.

11 다음 빈칸에 알맞은 것이 바르게 짝지어진 것은?

| The teacher encourages students _____ together and wants them _____ well. |

① working – get along
② work – to get along
③ to work – get along
④ to work – to get along
⑤ working – getting along

12 다음 빈칸에 들어갈 말로 알맞지 <u>않은</u> 것은?

| If it rains, _____. |

① we will stay home
② I might decide to stay home
③ we can't go bike riding
④ he won't go anywhere
⑤ you were allowed to use my umbrella

서답형

13 주어진 단어를 활용하여 다음 빈칸에 알맞은 말을 쓰시오.

| Don't be upset. I don't _____. (want / be) |

➡ _____

14 다음 빈칸에 들어갈 동사 talk의 형태가 <u>다른</u> 하나는?

① Helen wants you _____ about it.
② She has many friends _____ with.
③ Don't persuade her _____ to him.
④ He has trouble _____ to someone.
⑤ They helped him _____ about himself.

15 다음 빈칸에 적절하지 <u>않은</u> 것은?

| _____ you arrive here, we will start to eat the food. |

① If　　　　　　② After
③ As soon as　　④ When
⑤ Though

16 다음 중 어법상 바르지 <u>않은</u> 것은?

① If it is sunny tomorrow, we don't need to cancel the picnic.
② My aunt forced me to help her son.
③ Her laziness caused her to fail.
④ Harry invited the boys to come to his party.
⑤ I warned you not driving too fast.

서답형

17 괄호 안의 동사를 어법에 맞게 고쳐 쓰시오.

| • The students stopped (talk) when the teacher entered the room.
• I asked Jimmy (talk) with Emily. |

➡ _____

18 다음 중 if의 쓰임이 같은 것끼리 바르게 묶여진 것은?

> ⓐ He will come here <u>if</u> he gets up early tomorrow.
> ⓑ <u>If</u> songs are chosen, we can practice together.
> ⓒ I wonder <u>if</u> there is some food to eat.
> ⓓ <u>If</u> you need money, I will lend you some.
> ⓔ She couldn't tell <u>if</u> he said the truth.

① ⓐⓑⓒ, ⓓⓔ   ② ⓐⓒ, ⓓⓔ
③ ⓐⓑⓓ, ⓒⓔ   ④ ⓐⓒⓓ, ⓑⓔ
⑤ ⓑⓒ, ⓐⓓⓔ

19 다음 중 빈칸에 들어갈 말이 바르게 짝지어진 것은?

> • I will consider _____ with you.
> • June persuaded him _____ for a visit.
> • If you _____ me tomorrow, you will get to know me better.

① going – coming – meet
② to go – to come – meet
③ going – to come – will meet
④ to go – coming – will meet
⑤ going – to come – meet

서답형

20 주어진 어구를 바르게 배열하여 다음 우리말을 영어로 쓰시오.

> Molly는 그녀의 아이들이 한동안 수영장에서 첨벙거리며 놀게 두었다.
> (for a while / Molly / her children / around / splash / let / in the pool)

➡ _____

_____

21 다음 중 어법상 옳은 문장의 개수는?

> ⓐ Mary kept avoiding to answer my question.
> ⓑ I forbid you to tell him my secret.
> ⓒ Are you thinking of watching the movie with Jane?
> ⓓ Would you like me to cut your hair?
> ⓔ Who taught you driving?

① 1개   ② 2개   ③ 3개
④ 4개   ⑤ 5개

22 다음 중 어법상 바르지 <u>않은</u> 것은?

> If you ①<u>wear</u> a cap, ②<u>it</u> ③<u>will protect</u> your skin. So I ④<u>want</u> you ⑤<u>wear</u> a cap.

①   ②   ③   ④   ⑤

서답형

23 다음 상황을 읽고 빈칸에 알맞은 말을 쓰시오.

> Ann: Why don't you come and stay with us?
> Linda: That would be nice. Thank you.

➡ Ann invites _____.

서답형

24 주어진 단어를 활용하여 다음 우리말을 영어로 쓰시오.

> 내가 당신을 직접 만나게 된다면, 나는 당신에게 많은 질문을 할 거예요.
> (meet / in person / ask)

➡ _____

_____

01 주어진 어구를 바르게 배열하여 다음 우리말을 영어로 쓰시오.

> 우리가 그 길을 못 찾으면 무엇을 해야 할지 모르겠어.
> (don't know / will / we / I / what / we / don't find / the way / do / if)

➡ _____

_____

02 두 개의 문장을 연결하여 자연스러운 하나의 문장으로 만드시오.

> • You need money.
> • You want those pictures.
> • You are busy now.

> • You can have them.
> • I will call you later.
> • I will lend you some.

➡ _____
➡ _____
➡ _____

03 주어진 동사를 어법에 맞게 빈칸에 쓰시오.

(1) If you _____ _____ early, please wake me up. (get up)

(2) I'm not sure if Maggie _____ _____ a tree tomorrow. (plant)

(3) I _____ _____ a new computer next month if I _____ some extra money. (buy, have)

04 다음 우리말에 맞도록 빈칸에 알맞은 말을 쓰시오.

> • _____ you hurry, you _____ _____ the bus.
> 서두르지 않는다면 너는 버스를 놓칠 거야.
> • If you win the prize, I _____ _____ _____ _____.
> 네가 그 상을 탄다면, 나는 매우 놀랄 거야.
> • If the museum is crowded with many people tomorrow, I _____ _____ to another museum.
> 내일 그 박물관이 많은 사람들로 붐빈다면, 나는 다른 박물관으로 갈 거야.
> • Our teacher required us _____ _____ on time.
> 우리 선생님은 우리에게 정각에 오라고 요구하셨다.

05 주어진 어구를 활용하여 다음 우리말을 영어로 쓰시오.

> 그녀는 내가 그녀의 집에 들러주길 요청했다.
> (me / ask / drop by)

➡ _____

06 다음 문장을 읽고 주어진 단어를 활용하여 빈칸에 알맞은 말을 쓰시오.

> Jason: I don't feel well.
> Linda: You should see a doctor.

➡ Linda advises _____.

07 주어진 단어를 활용하여 다음 우리말을 영어로 쓰시오.

- 불이 난다면, 화재경보기가 울릴 거야.
  (there / a fire / the alarm)
- 내가 너를 도와주길 원한다면, 도와줄게.
  (want / to / help)
- 내일 몸이 좋지 않으면, 집에 머물 거야.
  (feel well / stay at)

➡ _____

➡ _____

➡ _____

08 다음 문장을 읽고 빈칸에 알맞은 말을 쓰시오.

> Sarah: I heard you had a big fight with Kelly. She wants to apologize to you. I think you must accept her apology.

➡ Sarah advises _____ .

09 다음 두 문장이 같은 의미가 되도록 빈칸에 알맞은 말을 쓰시오.

> If you have a car, you are able to go to any place you want to go.
> = Having a car enables _____ .

➡ _____

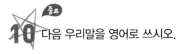
10 다음 우리말을 영어로 쓰시오.

> 내일 일찍 일어난다면, 뭘 할 거니?

➡ _____

11 주어진 어구를 바르게 배열하여 우리말을 영어로 쓰시오. 필요하다면 단어를 추가하시오.

> 그들은 사람들이 건물 앞에 주차하는 것을 허락하지 않습니다.
> (the building / they / park / in front of / allow / people)

➡ _____

_____

12 다음 각 문장에서 어법상 틀린 것을 찾아 바르게 고치시오.

> (1) They practiced to throw the ball.
> (2) The doctor told me taking these pills.
> (3) Unless you are not busy, can you do me a favor?
> (4) I couldn't move the desk by myself. I got one of my friends help me.

(1) _____ ➡ _____

(2) _____ ➡ _____

(3) _____ ➡ _____

(4) _____ ➡ _____

13 다음 상황을 읽고 빈칸에 알맞은 말을 쓰시오.

> You feel a little cold. You look around and find that a window is wide open. Jason is sitting near the window. You want Jason to close the window. In this situation, you can say like this, "Jason, _____"

➡ do you mind _____ ?

➡ I would like you _____ .

Dolls around the World

I'm Sweepy. I'm from Germany and my job is to clean chimneys.
자신을 소개하는 표현(= My name is ~)　　　　　　　　　　　　주어 my job의 보어

During winter, chimney sweeps help people to keep warm and safe. So
특정 기간을 나타내는 명사 앞에서 쓰임　　　　　　help+목적어+to V: 목적어가 V하는 것을 돕다

people think chimney sweeps bring them good luck. People even want
　　　think (that) 접속사 that 생략　　수여동사+간접목적어+직접목적어 (= bring good luck to them)　　want+목적어+to부정사

chimney sweeps to be at their weddings! If you see me, it is your lucky
　　　　　　　　　　　　　　　　　　　　(목적어가 to부정사의 의미상 주체)
　　　　　　　　　　　　　　조건절을 이끄는 접속사

day.

My name is José and these are my mariachi band members. We play
　　　　　　　　　　this의 복수형

folk music and always wear our sombreros, or big hats. In Mexico,
　　　　　　　　빈도부사　　　　　　　　즉(동격을 나타내는 접속사)

people wear these hats to stay cool under the hot and strong sunlight.
　　　　　　　　목적을 나타내는 to부정사 '시원하게 지내기 위해서'

We mariachi players want our sombreros to look fancy. So we often
　　　　　　　　　want+목적어+to부정사　　　　　　'그래서'라는 의미의 접속사

decorate them with a lot of different materials. Which of our sombreros
= sombreros　　= many　　　　'어느 것, 어떤 것'이라는 의미로 선택을 나타낼 때 씀

do you like best?

---

from ~ 출신인
chimney sweep 굴뚝 청소부
chimney 굴뚝
during ~ 동안에
keep (특정 상태를) 유지하다
bring ~을 가져다주다
wedding 결혼식
lucky 행운의
mariachi (멕시코의) 거리의 악대(의 일원, 마리아치 음악
member 구성원, 멤버
folk 민속의, 전통적인
sombrero 솜브레로(챙이 넓은 미국 남서부·멕시코의 중절모)
stay (특정 상태를) 유지하다
strong 강렬한
fancy 장식이 많은, 화려한
decorate ~을 꾸미다
different 각각 다른
material 재료

 확인문제

● 다음 문장이 본문의 내용과 일치하면 T, 일치하지 <u>않으면</u> F를 쓰시오.

1 What Sweepy does is to clean chimneys. ☐

2 Chimney sweeps are helpful especially during winter. ☐

3 People don't want to see chimney sweeps at their wedding. ☐

4 Mariachi band members wear big hats. ☐

5 Mariachi players want their sombreros to look fancy because of strong sunlight. ☐

My name is Ayanda and I'm a Zulu. We are a tribe in South Africa.

What do you think of my beads? Zulu people enjoy making clothes
~에 대해 어떻게 생각하니?   동명사를 목적어로 취하는 동사

with beads. They are beautiful and each color has a special meaning.
~으로(수단)   '각각의'라는 의미의 한정사. 뒤에 단수명사가 오며 현재일 경우 3인칭 단수형을 씀

When we did not have our own writing system, we used beads to
'~할 때'라는 의미의 접속사로 부사절을 이끎   자신의

communicate with each other. If you want to know the meaning of the
목적을 나타내는 to부정사의 부사적 용법   부정대명사로 전치사 with의 목적어

colors, check out the following box.

Color	Good Meaning	Bad Meaning
Black	marriage	death
Yellow	wealth	badness
Red	love	anger
White	love	—

If you want to send someone a special message, you can express
                    = send a special message to someone

yourself with these beads. What message do you want to make?
재귀대명사 (문장의 주어와 목적어가 같을 때 재귀대명사를 씀)   의문문에서 쓰이는 what은 '어떤'이란 의미로 선택의 범위가 한정되어 있지 않을 때 씀

tribe: 부족

bead: 구슬

clothes: 옷, 의복

special: 특별한

writing system: 문자 체계

communicate: 의사소통을 하다

each other: 서로서로

meaning: 의미

check out: ~을 확인하다

following: 다음에 나오는

express: 표현하다

message: 메시지

📎 **확인문제**

● 다음 문장이 본문의 내용과 일치하면 T, 일치하지 않으면 F를 쓰시오.

1 Zulu people live in South Africa. ☐

2 Zulu people like making clothes with beads. ☐

3 The colors of beads have the same meaning. ☐

4 Zulu people communicated with each other with body language. ☐

5 Every color has both good and bad meanings. ☐

6 You can send a special message to someone with beads. ☐

• 우리말을 참고하여 빈칸에 알맞은 말을 쓰시오.

1 I'm Sweepy.

2 I'm _____ _____ and my job _____ _____ _____ chimneys.

3 _____ winter, chimney sweeps _____ people _____ _____ warm and safe.

4 So people think chimney sweeps _____ _____ _____ _____.

5 People even _____ chimney sweeps _____ _____ at their weddings!

6 If you _____ _____, it is your _____ _____.

7 My name is José and _____ _____ my mariachi band members.

8 We play _____ _____ and _____ _____ our sombreros, or big hats.

9 In Mexico, people _____ these hats _____ _____ _____ under the _____ and _____ _____.

10 We mariachi players _____ our sombreros _____ _____ _____.

11 So we _____ _____ them _____ a lot of different _____.

12 _____ of our sombreros do you like _____?

1	나는 Sweepy야.
2	나는 독일에서 왔고, 내 직업은 굴뚝을 청소하는 거야.
3	겨울에 굴뚝 청소부들은 사람들이 따뜻하고 안전하게 지낼 수 있도록 도와주지.
4	그래서 사람들은 굴뚝 청소부들이 자신들에게 행운을 가져다준다고 생각해.
5	사람들은 심지어 굴뚝 청소부들이 자신의 결혼식에 있기를 바란단다!
6	네가 만일 나를 본다면, 그날은 너의 행운의 날인 거야.
7	내 이름은 José이고, 이 사람들은 마리아치 악단 단원들이야.
8	우리는 민속 음악을 연주하고 항상 솜브레로라는 큰 모자를 쓰지.
9	멕시코에서 사람들은 뜨겁고 강한 햇볕 아래서 시원하게 지내기 위해 이 모자들을 써.
10	우리 마리아치 연주자들은 우리의 솜브레로가 화려하게 보이길 원해.
11	그래서 우리는 종종 여러 가지 재료들을 많이 이용해서 그것들을 장식하지.
12	우리 솜브레로 중 어느 것이 가장 마음에 드니?

13 My name is Ayanda and I'm _____ _____.

14 We are _____ _____ _____ South Africa.

15 _____ _____ _____ _____ of my beads?

16 Zulu people enjoy _____ _____ _____ beads.

17 _____ _____ beautiful and _____ _____ _____ a special meaning.

18 _____ we did not have _____ _____ _____ _____, we used beads _____ _____ with each other.

19 If you want _____ _____ _____ _____ _____ _____ _____, check out the following box.

Color	_____ _____	_____ _____
Black	_____	_____
_____	_____	badness
Red	love	_____
_____	_____	—

20 If you want to send someone a special message, you can _____ _____ _____ these beads.

21 _____ _____ do you want _____ _____?

13 내 이름은 Ayanda이고 나는 줄루 사람이야.

14 우리는 남아프리카의 부족이지.

15 내 구슬들에 대해 어떻게 생각하니?

16 줄루족 사람들은 구슬로 옷 만드는 것을 즐겨.

17 그것들은 아름답고 각각의 색깔에는 특별한 의미가 있어.

18 우리 자신의 문자 체계가 없었을 때, 우리는 서로 의소통하기 위해서 구슬들을 이용했어.

색	좋은 의미	나쁜 의미
검은색	결혼	죽음
노란색	부	나쁨
빨간색	사랑	분노
흰색	사랑	-

19 만약 네가 그 색깔들의 의미를 알고 싶다면, 다음에 나오는 네모를 확인해 봐.

20 만약 네가 누군가에게 특별한 메시지를 보내고 싶다면, 이 구슬들로 네 자신을 표현할 수 있어.

21 너는 어떤 메시지를 만들고 싶니?

● 우리말을 참고하여 본문을 영작하시오.

1 나는 Sweepy야.

➡ _____

2 나는 독일에서 왔고, 내 직업은 굴뚝을 청소하는 거야.

➡ _____

3 겨울에 굴뚝 청소부들은 사람들이 따뜻하고 안전하게 지낼 수 있도록 도와주지.

➡ _____

4 그래서 사람들은 굴뚝 청소부들이 자신들에게 행운을 가져다준다고 생각해.

➡ _____

5 사람들은 심지어 굴뚝 청소부들이 자신의 결혼식에 있기를 바란단다!

➡ _____

6 네가 만일 나를 본다면, 그날은 너의 행운의 날인 거야.

➡ _____

7 내 이름은 José이고, 이 사람들은 마리아치 악단 단원들이야.

➡ _____

8 우리는 민속 음악을 연주하고 항상 솜브레로라는 큰 모자를 쓰지.

➡ _____

9 멕시코에서 사람들은 뜨겁고 강한 햇볕 아래서 시원하게 지내기 위해 이 모자들을 써.

➡ _____

10 우리 마리아치 연주자들은 우리의 솜브레로가 화려하게 보이길 원해.

➡ _____

11 그래서 우리는 종종 여러 가지 재료들을 많이 이용해서 그것들을 장식하지.

➡ _____

12 우리 솜브레로 중 어느 것이 가장 마음에 드니?

➡ _____

13 내 이름은 Ayanda이고 나는 줄루 사람이야.

➡ _____

14 우리는 남아프리카의 부족이지.

➡ _____

15 내 구슬들에 대해 어떻게 생각하니?

➡ _____

16 줄루족 사람들은 구슬로 옷 만드는 것을 즐겨.

➡ _____

17 그것들은 아름답고 각각의 색깔에는 특별한 의미가 있어.

➡ _____

18 우리 자신의 문자 체계가 없었을 때, 우리는 서로 의소소통하기 위해서 구슬들을 이용했어.

➡ _____

19 만약 네가 그 색깔들의 의미를 알고 싶다면, 다음에 나오는 네모를 확인해 봐.

➡ _____

색	_____	좋은 의미	_____ _____	나쁜 의미	_____ _____
검은색	_____	결혼	_____	죽음	_____
노란색	_____	부	_____	나쁨	_____
빨간색	_____	사랑	_____	분노	_____
흰색	_____	사랑	_____		—

20 만약 네가 누군가에게 특별한 메시지를 보내고 싶다면, 이 구슬들로 네 자신을 표현할 수 있어.

➡ _____

21 너는 어떤 메시지를 만들고 싶니?

➡ _____

[01~04] 다음 글을 읽고, 물음에 답하시오.

I'm Sweepy. I'm from Germany and my job is ⓐ_____ chimneys. During winter, chimney sweeps help people to ⓑkeep warm and safe. So people think chimney sweeps bring them good luck. People even want chimney sweeps to be at their weddings! If you see me, it is your lucky day.

01 위 글의 빈칸 ⓐ에 어법상 적절한 것을 모두 고르면?

① cleaning   ② cleans

③ cleaned   ④ to clean

⑤ cleaning

02 위 글에 관한 내용 중 바르지 않은 것은?

① Sweepy comes from Germany.
② People want to see Sweepy at their weddings.
③ Chimney sweeps make people busy during summer.
④ People think chimney sweeps bring people good luck.
⑤ Seeing chimney sweeps is considered to be lucky.

03 다음 중 밑줄 친 ⓑ를 대신하여 쓸 수 있는 것은?

① make   ② stay
③ take   ④ have
⑤ leave

서답형

04 위 글의 내용에 맞게 빈칸에 알맞은 말을 쓰시오.

> A: Our wedding is coming. Do you want anything else?
> B: I want to invite chimney sweeps to our wedding. I believe that they will bring us _____.

➡ _____

[05~08] 다음 글을 읽고, 물음에 답하시오.

My name is José and these are my mariachi band members. ① We play folk music and always wear our sombreros, or big hats. ② In Mexico, people wear these hats to stay cool under the hot and strong sunlight. ③ We mariachi players want our sombreros _____ⓐ_____ ④ Which of our sombreros do you like best? ⑤

서답형

05 다음 주어진 어구를 어법에 맞게 빈칸 ⓐ에 쓰시오.

> look fancy

➡ _____

06 위 글의 ①~⑤ 중 다음 문장이 들어가기에 가장 적절한 곳은?

> So we often decorate them with a lot of different materials.

①   ②   ③   ④   ⑤

07 위 글에 관한 내용으로 옳지 <u>않은</u> 것은?

① José is one of the members of the mariachi band.

② José always wears his sombrero.

③ The mariachi band plays folk music.

④ A sombrero is a long coat to keep people cool.

⑤ People in Mexico usually wear sombreros.

서답형

08 Write the reason why Mexican people wear sombreros. Answer in English with seven words.

➡ _____

[09~11] 다음 글을 읽고, 물음에 답하시오.

My name is Ayanda and I'm a Zulu. We are a tribe in South Africa. What do you think of _____ⓐ_____? Zulu people enjoy making clothes with beads. They are beautiful and each color has a special meaning. When we did not have our own writing system, we used beads to communicate with each other. If you want to know the meaning of the colors, check out the following box.

Color	Good Meaning	Bad Meaning
Black	marriage	death
Yellow	wealth	badness
Red	love	anger
White	love	–

If you want to send someone a special message, you can express yourself with these beads. What message do you want to make?

중요

09 위 글의 흐름상 빈칸 ⓐ에 들어갈 말로 가장 적절한 것은?

① my neckless ② my tribe

③ my beads ④ my hair color

⑤ my writing

서답형

10 다음 설명에 해당하는 단어를 위 글에서 찾아 쓰시오.

> This word is used to refer to a group of people of the same race, language, and customs.

➡ _____

11 다음 중 글의 내용과 일치하지 <u>않는</u> 것은?

① Ayanda is from South Africa.

② Zulu is a tribe in South Africa.

③ Zulu people don't have their own writing system.

④ There are many beads with various colors.

⑤ Zulu people express themselves with beads.

[12~16] 다음 글을 읽고, 물음에 답하시오.

I'm Sweepy. I'm ①from Germany and my job is ②to clean chimneys. ③During winter, chimney sweeps help people to keep ④warm and safe. So people think chimney sweeps bring ⓐthem good luck. People even want chimney sweeps ⑤are at their weddings! ⓑ If you see me, it is your lucky day.

12 위 글을 읽고 답할 수 <u>없는</u> 질문은?

① What does Sweepy do?

② Where does Sweepy come from?

③ How do chimney sweeps help people?

④ Why do people think chimney sweeps bring them good luck?

⑤ How old is Sweepy?

13 위 글의 ①~⑤ 중 어법상 바르지 <u>않은</u> 것은?

①   ②   ③   ④   ⑤

서답형

14 위 글의 밑줄 친 ⓐ가 가리키는 것을 영어로 쓰시오.

➡ _____

15 위 글의 Sweepy가 밑줄 친 ⓑ와 같이 말한 이유를 고르시오.

① It's because people like to sweep a chimney.
② It's because Sweepy makes people warm.
③ It's because people believe that Sweepy brings good luck to them.
④ It's because Sweepy likes to attend the wedding.
⑤ It's because Sweepy helps people well.

서답형

16 위 글의 내용에 맞게 빈칸에 알맞은 말을 쓰시오.

> People in _____ stay _____ and safe in winter thanks to _____ _____.

[17~21] 다음 글을 읽고, 물음에 답하시오.

My name is José and these are my mariachi band members. We play folk music and always (A)[wears / wear] our sombreros, or big hats. In Mexico, people wear these hats ⓐto stay cool (B)[under / over] the hot and strong sunlight. We mariachi players want our sombreros to look fancy. So ⓑwe often decorate (C)[it / them] with a lot of different materials. Which of our sombreros do you like best?

17 위 글을 읽고 답할 수 있는 질문을 <u>모두</u> 고르시오.

① How was the mariachi band made?
② What does the mariachi band do?
③ What does José do in the band?
④ How do the band members decorate their sombreros?
⑤ What kind of sombrero does José like most?

18 위 글의 (A)~(C) 중 어법상 옳은 것끼리 바르게 짝지은 것은?

① wears – under – it
② wears – over – it
③ wear – under – it
④ wear – over – them
⑤ wear – under – them

19 다음 중 밑줄 친 ⓐ와 쓰임이 같은 것은?

① I want to meet him in person.
② It was great pleasure to listen to the music.
③ He went to church to pray for his friend.
④ Jimmy encouraged his friends to take part in the campaign.
⑤ Is there a chair to sit on?

서답형

20 위 글의 내용에 맞게 빈칸에 알맞은 말을 쓰시오.

> Jason: Hey, Helen. I decorated my sombrero. How does it look?
> Helen: _____

➡ _____

서답형

21 위 글의 밑줄 친 ⓑ가 가리키는 것을 위 글에서 찾아 쓰시오.

➡ _____

서답형

23 밑줄 친 ⓑ가 가리키는 것을 위 글에서 찾아 쓰시오.

➡ _____

24 위 글의 빈칸 ⓒ와 ⓓ에 공통으로 들어갈 말은?

① about   ② on   ③ by
④ with   ⑤ to

[22~24] 다음 글을 읽고, 물음에 답하시오.

My name is Ayanda and I'm a Zulu. We are a tribe in South Africa. What do you think of my beads? Zulu people enjoy ___ⓐ___ clothes with beads. ⓑThey are beautiful and each color has a special meaning. When we did not have our own writing system, we used beads to communicate ___ⓒ___ each other. If you want to know the meaning of the colors, check out the following box.

Color	Good Meaning	Bad Meaning
Black	marriage	death
Yellow	wealth	badness
Red	love	anger
White	love	–

If you want to send someone a special message, you can express yourself ___ⓓ___ these beads. What message do you want to make?

중요

22 다음 중 빈칸 ⓐ에 들어갈 단어의 형태와 같은 것은?

① I would like _____ some pasta for you.
② Are you interested in _____ your own clothes?
③ Jane decided _____ him happy.
④ She planned _____ $100,000 a year.
⑤ Jason hoped _____ me his assistant.

25 자연스러운 의미가 되도록 다음 글을 바르게 나열하시오.

My name is José and these are my mariachi band members.

(A) In Mexico, people wear these hats to stay cool under the hot and strong sunlight. We mariachi players want our sombreros to look fancy.

(B) So we often decorate them with a lot of different materials. Which of our sombreros do you like best?

(C) We play folk music and always wear our sombreros, or big hats.

① (A) – (C) – (B)   ② (B) – (A) – (C)
③ (B) – (C) – (A)   ④ (C) – (A) – (B)
⑤ (C) – (B) – (A)

[01~05] 다음 글을 읽고 물음에 답하시오.

Dolls around the World

I'm Sweepy. I'm from Germany and my job is to clean chimneys. ⓐDuring winter, chimney sweeps help people keeping warm and safe. So people think chimney sweeps bring them good luck. People even want chimney sweeps to be at their weddings! If you see me, it is your ____ⓑ____ day.

01 동명사를 이용하여 위 글의 내용에 맞게 빈칸을 채우시오.

Sweepy's job is _____.

➡ _____

02 위 글의 밑줄 친 문장 ⓐ에서 어법상 틀린 것을 바르게 고쳐 올바른 문장으로 다시 쓰시오.

➡ _____
_____

03 What do people think chimney sweeps bring them? Answer in English with a full sentence.

➡ _____

04 위 글에 나오는 명사를 적절히 변형하여 빈칸 ⓑ에 알맞은 형용사를 쓰시오.

➡ _____

05 위 글의 내용에 맞게 빈칸에 알맞은 말을 쓰시오.

Sweepy is a _____ doll whose job is to clean chimneys. If you want to spend a _____ and _____ winter, Sweepy will help you.

➡ _____

[06~10] 다음 글을 읽고, 물음에 답하시오.

My name is José and these are my mariachi band members. We play folk music and always wear our sombreros, or big hats. In Mexico, people wear these hats to stay cool under the hot and strong sunlight. We mariachi players want our sombreros to look fancy. So we often decorate them with a lot of different materials. (A)우리의 솜브레로 중 어느 것이 가장 마음에 드니?

06 다음 물음에 5단어로 이루어진 완전한 문장의 영어로 답하시오.

Q: What do the mariachi band members wear?

➡ _____

07 위 글의 내용에 맞게 빈칸에 알맞은 말을 쓰시오.

A: What are you doing with your sombrero?
B: I am _____ it.
A: Why?
B: I want it _____.

➡ _____

08 다음은 멕시코에 체류 중인 한국인 학생이 쓴 글이다. 글의 내용에 맞게 빈칸에 알맞은 말을 쓰시오.

> The sunlight in Mexico is _____.
> So when I first came here, my Mexican
> friend advised me _____ a sombrero.

➡ _____

09 다음 주어진 단어를 이용하여 빈칸에 알맞은 말을 쓰시오.

> Wearing sombreros _____.
> (enable / people)

➡ _____

10 다음 주어진 단어를 이용하여 밑줄 친 우리말 (A)를 영어로 쓰시오.

> like, best

➡ _____

[11~15] 다음 글을 읽고, 물음에 답하시오.

My name is Ayanda and I'm a Zulu. We are a tribe in South Africa. What do you think of my beads? Zulu people enjoy ___ⓐ___ clothes with beads. They are beautiful and (A)each color has a special meaning. When we did not have our own writing system, we used beads to communicate with each other. If you want to know the meaning of the colors, check out the following box.

Color	Good Meaning	Bad Meaning
Black	marriage	death
Yellow	wealth	badness
Red	love	anger
White	love	–

If you want to send someone a special message, you can express yourself with these beads. What message do you want ___ⓑ___?

11 주어진 동사를 어법에 맞게 빈칸 ⓐ와 ⓑ에 각각 쓰시오.

> make

ⓐ _____ ⓑ _____

12 주어진 단어를 바르게 배열하여 밑줄 친 (A)와 같은 의미의 문장을 쓰시오.

> own / each / meaning / has / its / color

➡ _____

13 위 글의 내용에 맞게 빈칸에 알맞은 말을 쓰시오.

> Beads enabled Zulu people _____
> _____.

➡ _____

14 위 글의 내용에 맞도록 대화의 빈칸을 채우시오.

> Jimmy: I fell in love with Jane. I want to
> _____ my feeling with something.
> What should I use?
> Helen: I advise you _____ _____
> _____. _____ color beads
> have the meaning of love. And it
> doesn't have any bad meaning.

➡ _____

15 If you want to express your anger, which color bead will you use? Answer in English with five words.

➡ _____

Grammar in Real Life

Mom: Mike, I'm going to be late. Can you make dinner for Sam?
요청의 표현　　　　= make Sam dinner

Mike: Okay, don't worry. Sam, come home early.
부 집으로

Sam: Okay.

Mom: Mike and Sam, be sure to do your homework.
반드시 ~해라

Sam: I will, Mom. Can you get us some ice cream?
4형식 동사+간접목적어+직접목적어

Mom: Sure.

구문해설 · make dinner: 저녁식사를 준비하다　· worry: 걱정하다　· early: 일찍

· do one's homework: 숙제하다 · get: 가져다주다

Think & Write

A: Which festival do you want to introduce to your foreign friends?
어느(의문형용사)　　　　　　　　　　　　　　　　　외국인 친구들

B: I want to introduce the Haenyeo festival.
to부정사를 목적어로 취하는 동사

A: Where and when can your foreign friends enjoy the festival?
가능

B: They can enjoy the festival in Jeju in September.
비교적 넓은 시간, 장소를 나타낼 때 쓰는 전치사

A: What can your foreign friends do if they visit the festival?
조건을 나타내는 접속사

B: They can catch fish with their hands and learn old *haenyeo* songs.
단수와 복수가 동형

구문해설 · festival: 축제　· introduce: 소개하다　· foreign: 외국의　· catch: ~을 잡다

Wrap Up 3

A: What are you going to do this Saturday?

B: I'm going to meet my friend, Lashi. He's staying in Korea during the
~할 예정이다　　　　　　　　　　　　　현재진행형　　　　　~ 동안(전치사)

vacation.

A: Oh, he's from India, isn't he?
부가의문문

B: Yeah, he is. I'm looking forward to showing him around Seoul.
look forward to ~ing: ~하기를 기대하다

A: Great. Have a good time with your friend.
좋은 시간을 보내다

구문해설 · stay: 머물다　· vacation: 휴가

해석

엄마: Mike, 나 오늘 늦을 거야. Sam에게 저녁식사를 차려 주겠니?

Mike: 알았어요, 걱정 마세요. Sam, 집에 일찍 와.

Sam: 알았어.

엄마: Mike, Same. 반드시 숙제를 하렴.

Sam: 할게요, 엄마. 우리에게 아이스크림을 사 오실 수 있어요?

엄마: 물론이지.

A: 너의 외국인 친구들에게 어느 축제를 소개하고 싶니?

B: 나는 해녀 축제를 소개하고 싶어.

A: 너의 외국인 친구들이 언제 어디서 그 축제를 즐길 수 있어?

B: 그들은 9월에 제주에서 그 축제를 즐길 수 있지.

A: 외국인 친구들이 축제에 방문한다면, 무엇을 할 수 있을까?

B: 그들은 손으로 물고기를 잡고 해녀 노래를 배울 수 있지.

A: 이번 주 토요일에 뭐 할 거야?

B: 나는 내 친구인 Lashi를 만날 거야. 그는 방학 동안에 한국에 머물고 있어.

A: 오, 인도에서 온 친구 맞지?

B: 맞아. 나는 그에게 서울을 구경시켜 주고 싶어.

A: 멋지다. 친구와 좋은 시간 보내.

Words & Expressions

01 다음 짝지어진 단어의 관계가 같도록 빈칸에 알맞은 말을 쓰시오.

same : different = strong: _____

02 다음 영영풀이에 해당하는 말을 쓰시오.

a child's toy in the shape of a person, especially a baby or a child

➡ _____

03 다음 중 밑줄 친 부분의 뜻풀이가 바르지 <u>않은</u> 것은?

① You should protect your skin from the strong <u>sunlight</u>. 햇빛
② She would like to <u>decorate</u> her daughter's room for her birthday party. 장식하다
③ You're very <u>lucky</u> to find such a rare item. 운이 좋은
④ My team always <u>excels</u> others in basketball games. 뛰어난
⑤ His voice is a <u>treasure</u> of our country. 보물

04 다음 문장의 빈칸에 들어갈 말을 〈보기〉에서 골라 알맞은 형태로 쓰시오.

┤ 보기 ├
stay / introduce / material / fireplace

(1) A lot of different _____ are needed to build the house.
(2) How long will you _____ in Mongolia?
(3) Which festival do you want to _____ to your friend?
(4) My family is gathering in front of the _____.

05 다음 문장의 빈칸에 들어갈 말을 〈보기〉에서 골라 쓰시오.

┤ 보기 ├
turn off / put on / get in / try on

(1) A: I'm going to swim in the pool.
   B: Don't forget to take a shower before _____ _____ the pool and do warm-up exercise.
(2) A: I'm going to see a musical.
   B: Remember to _____ _____ your phone.
(3) A: I'm going to the beach.
   B: It's too hot outside. Don't forget to _____ _____ some sun cream.

Conversation

[06~08] 다음 대화를 읽고, 물음에 답하시오.

Sora: I bought this tea for Wang's birthday. Will he like it?
Jack: Sure, he will. Wang enjoys drinking tea.
Sora: Great. Then I'll wrap the present.
Jack: _____(A)_____ Red (B)<u>stands for</u> wealth in China.

06 위 대화의 빈칸 (A)에 들어갈 말을 〈보기〉에 주어진 단어를 모두 배열하여 완성하시오.

┤ 보기 ├
forget / it / to / don't / red / wrap / in

➡ _____

07 Why is Jack sure that Wang will like Sora's birthday present?

➡ _____

08 위 대화의 밑줄 친 (B)와 바꾸어 쓸 수 있는 것은?

① symbolizes   ② sets
③ decorates   ④ sweeps
⑤ ranks

[09~11] 다음 대화를 읽고, 물음에 답하시오.

Tom: Jane, what are you doing?
Jane: I'm signing up for a program at the African Museum.
Tom: Is there an interesting one?
Jane: Yeah, I'm going to make an African drum and a traditional mask.
Tom: Oh, _____(A)_____
Jane: Yeah, (B)난 박물관에 가는 것이 기대돼. (forward, look)

09 위 대화의 빈칸 (A)에 들어갈 말로 <u>어색한</u> 것은?

① how fun!
② that'll be nice.
③ what a nice program!
④ it doesn't matter.
⑤ that sounds interesting.

10 위 대화의 우리말 (B)를 주어진 단어를 사용하여 영작하시오.

➡ _____

11 What can Jane make in the program held at the African Museum?

➡ She can _____
_____ .

12 다음 대화가 자연스럽게 이어지도록 순서대로 배열하시오.

(A) What are you going to do this Sunday?
(B) Great! I'm looking forward to trying them.
(C) I'm going to go to the World Food Fair.
(D) Oh, I was there last weekend. There were lots of traditional foods from all over the world.

➡ _____

[13~14] 다음 대화를 읽고, 물음에 답하시오.

Sue: How was your first day here in Mongolia?
Jake: It was great. _____(A)_____, where am I going to stay tonight?
Sue: You're going to sleep in a *ger*, a Mongolian tent.
Jake: Oh, I'm looking forward to it.
Sue: You'll like it. There is a fireplace in the *ger*. So, don't forget to put your thing away from the fireplace.
Jake: I see. Thank you.

13 위 대화의 빈칸 (A)에 '그런데'를 의미하는 표현을 3 단어를 사용하여 쓰시오.

➡ _____

14 위 대화의 내용과 일치하지 <u>않는</u> 것은?

① Jake와 Sue는 몽골에 머물고 있다.
② Jake는 오늘밤 게르에서 잠을 잘 것이다.
③ 게르는 몽골의 텐트를 가리킨다.
④ 게르에는 난로가 있다.
⑤ Sue는 Jake에게 게르에 있는 난로를 치우도록 조언하였다.

[15~16] 다음 대화를 읽고, 물음에 답하시오.

Harry: (A) Jina, is it you? You're wearing a *kimono* in this photo.
Jina: (B) Yeah, it's me. I tried it on at the World Culture Festival.
Harry: (C) That sounds fun. I should go there. How long does the festival go on for?
Jina: (D) When you visit, don't forget to try on traditional clothes from other countries.
Harry: (E) Okay. I'll try them.

15 위 대화의 (A)~(E) 중 주어진 문장이 들어가기에 가장 적절한 곳은?

> Until this weekend.

① (A) ② (B) ③ (C) ④ (D) ⑤ (E)

16 위 대화의 내용과 일치하지 <u>않는</u> 것은?

① Jina tried wearing a *kimono* at the World Culture Festival.
② Harry wanted to visit the World Culture Festival.
③ Harry took a photo with Jina, wearing a *kimono*.
④ The World Culture Festival is going to be held until this weekend.
⑤ Jina recommended that Harry should try on traditional clothes from other countries.

Grammar

17 다음 빈칸에 들어갈 말로 알맞은 것은?

> _____ you speak too fast, your classmates will not understand you.

① Unless ② If ③ That
④ Until ⑤ Whether

18 다음 상황을 영어로 바르게 옮긴 것은?

> Angela had lots of luggage. She needed a help to carry the luggage. So she said to Jason, "Can you help me?"

① Jason can help Angela with the luggage.
② Angela asked Jason to help her.
③ Jason asked Angela to help him.
④ Angela asked Jason to help himself.
⑤ Angela told Jason to move away.

19 다음 문장의 빈칸에 들어갈 말로 가장 적절한 것은?

> _____ late again tonight, I won't wait for you.

① Because you were ② If you are
③ If you will be ④ When you will be
⑤ Though you were

20 다음 빈칸에 들어갈 말로 가장 적절한 것은?

> Jim said to me, "Don't use my phone."
> = Jim forbade me _____ his phone.
> = Jim told me _____ his phone.

① use – to use ② to use – not to use
③ to use – to use ④ use – to not use
⑤ not to use – to use

21 다음 중 쓰임이 <u>다른</u> 하나는?

① <u>If</u> it is sunny tomorrow, will you go out with me?
② I will be there <u>if</u> you want me to be there.
③ I wonder <u>if</u> he is going to go with us.
④ You will look good <u>if</u> you wear the jacket.
⑤ <u>If</u> you solve this problem, I will admit that you are a genius.

22 다음 우리말의 의미에 맞도록 빈칸에 알맞은 말을 쓰시오.

> If you _____ _____ _____ the computer game right now, I _____ _____ _____ _____ play it again.
>
> 지금 당장 게임하는 것을 멈추지 않으면, 나는 네가 그것을 가지고 노는 것을 다시는 허락하지 않을 거야.

➡ _____

23 다음 빈칸에 들어갈 말로 가장 적절한 것은?

> Do you want _____ with you or do you want to go alone?

① to go ② me going
③ that I go ④ that I will go
⑤ me to go

24 다음 빈칸에 알맞은 것이 바르게 짝지어진 것은?

> • You must encourage him _____ again.
> • The doctor advised me _____ more exercise.

① trying – get ② try – to get
③ to try – get ④ to try – to get
⑤ trying – getting

25 주어진 어구를 활용하여 다음 우리말을 영어로 쓰시오.

> 그 언덕을 뛰어오르면, 너의 심장이 빠르게 뛸 거야.
> (run up / beat)

➡ _____

26 다음 중 어법상 바르지 <u>않은</u> 것은?

① If you are finished, may I use it?
② Do you want me to give you a hand?
③ If you don't use soap, your clothes will not get clean.
④ This machine enables you living a comfortable life.
⑤ If you see him tomorrow, give him this note.

27 주어진 어구를 이용하여 빈칸에 알맞은 말을 쓰시오.

> A: Do you have time to go surfing?
> B: I don't know yet if there will be homework to do. If I _____ (not / have / any homework / do), I _____ (go) with you.

➡ _____

Reading

[28~29] 다음 글을 읽고, 물음에 답하시오.

> I'm Sweepy. I'm ___ⓐ___ Germany and my job is ①to clean chimneys. During winter, chimney sweeps help people to keep ②cold and safe. So people think chimney sweeps bring them ③good luck. People even want chimney sweeps ④to be at their weddings! If you see me, it is ⑤your lucky day.

28 위 글의 ①~⑤ 중 글의 흐름상 <u>어색한</u> 것은?

① ② ③ ④ ⑤

29 다음 중 빈칸 ⓐ에 들어갈 말과 같은 것은?

① Mary is good _____ speaking English.
② I am interested _____ acting in front of many people.
③ The first class was full _____ students.
④ He looked forward _____ riding a bike with you again.
⑤ Cream cheese is made _____ milk and cream.

[30~33] 다음 글을 읽고, 물음에 답하시오.

My name is José and these are my mariachi band members. We play folk music and always wear our sombreros, or big hats. In Mexico, people wear these hats to stay cool under the hot and strong sunlight. We mariachi players want our sombreros to look ⓐfancy. So we often decorate ⓑthem with a lot of different materials. Which of our sombreros do you like best?

30 다음 중 위 글을 읽고 답할 수 있는 질문은?

① What is José's last name?
② What is José's role in the mariachi band?
③ What kind of music does the mariachi band play?
④ How big is the sombrero?
⑤ How many hats does José have?

31 다음 중 밑줄 친 ⓐ와 반대되는 말은?

① serious   ② simple
③ decorative   ④ expensive
⑤ lonely

32 위 글의 밑줄 친 ⓑ가 가리키는 것을 위 글에서 찾아 쓰시오.

➡ _____

33 위 글의 내용에 맞게 빈칸에 알맞은 말을 쓰시오.

> Sombreros help people in Mexico _____ _____ _____ under the strong sunlight.

[34~35] 다음 글을 읽고, 물음에 답하시오.

My name is Ayanda and I'm a Zulu. We are a tribe in South Africa. (A)[How / What] do you think of my beads? Zulu people enjoy making clothes with beads. They are beautiful and each color has a special meaning. When we did not have our own writing system, we used beads (B)[communicating / to communicate] with each other. If you want to know the meaning of the colors, check out the following box.

Color	Good Meaning	Bad Meaning
Black	marriage	death
Yellow	wealth	badness
Red	love	anger
White	love	–

If you want to send someone a special message, you can express (C)[you / yourself] with these beads. What message do you want to make?

34 위 글을 읽고 답할 수 없는 질문은?

① Where do Zulu people live?
② What do Zulu people enjoy doing?
③ What is the bad meaning of the black beads?
④ When did Zulu people use beads as a way of communication?
⑤ When did Zulu people start to have their own writing system?

35 위 글의 (A)~(C) 중 어법상 알맞은 것을 바르게 쓰시오.

(A) _____ (B) _____ (C) _____

01 출제율 95%

다음 문장의 빈칸에 공통으로 들어갈 말로 적절한 것은?

> • I don't think it is a _____ game.
> • Many people are gathered at the international IT _____.
> • The judge always tries to make a _____ decision.

① tent　　　　② proper
③ square　　　④ display
⑤ fair

02 출제율 90%

다음 주어진 문장의 밑줄 친 의미와 다른 의미로 쓰인 것은?

> You can express yourself with colors freely.

① I can't find appropriate words to express my feelings.
② There are many ways to express your love.
③ How much is it for the express to Busan?
④ He wrote this poem to express his anger.
⑤ Their faces express how happy they are.

03 출제율 90%

다음 우리말을 주어진 단어를 이용하여 영작하시오.

(1) 나는 학교 축제를 기대하고 있다. (look, to)
➡ _____

(2) 너는 저녁 먹기 전에 장난감을 치워야 한다. (put, toys)
➡ _____

(3) 제가 이 앱을 무료로 다운받을 수 있나요? (free, app)
➡ _____

04 출제율 90%

다음 주어진 문장에 이어지는 대화가 자연스럽게 이어지도록 순서대로 배열하시오.

> Jane, what are you doing?
> (A) Oh, how fun!
> (B) Is there an interesting one?
> (C) Yeah, I'm looking forward to visiting the museum.
> (D) I'm signing up for a program at the African Museum.
> (E) Yeah, I'm going to make an African drum and a traditional mask.

➡ _____

[05~06] 다음 대화를 읽고, 물음에 답하시오.

> Mike: Elsa, how is your Hula dance class going?
> Elsa: Oh, it's great. We are going to perform at the ACB Hall this weekend.
> Mike: Wow, that sounds like a big day for you!
> Elsa: Yeah, (A)나는 공연이 정말 기대가 돼. (forward)

05 출제율 100%

위 대화의 밑줄 친 (A)의 우리말을 주어진 표현을 사용하여 영작하시오.

➡ _____

06 출제율 85%

What is Elsa going to do this weekend?

➡ _____

[07~08] 다음 대화를 읽고, 물음에 답하시오.

Sora: I bought this tea (A)[for / of] Wang's birthday. Will he like it?

Jack: Sure, he will. Wang enjoys (B)[to drink / drinking] tea.

Sora: Great. Then I'll wrap the present.

Jack: Don't forget (C)[wrapping / to wrap] it in red. Red stands for wealth in China.

07 Why did Jack want Sora to wrap the present in red?

➡ _____

08 위 대화의 (A)~(C)에 들어갈 말로 적절할 것끼리 짝지어진 것은?

① for – to drink – wrapping

② for – drinking – to wrap

③ for – drinking – wrapping

④ of – drinking – to wrap

⑤ of – to drink – wrapping

[09~10] 다음 대화를 읽고, 물음에 답하시오.

Elsa: Our visit to Gyengbokgung is this Friday. Let's meet at two.

Jake: Okay, I'll see you at the bus stop.

Elsa: Oh, and ____(A)____. We can get into the palace for free in our *hanboks*.

Jake: Right. I almost forgot.

09 위 대화의 빈칸 (A)에 들어갈 말울 〈보기〉의 주어진 단어를 모두 배열하여 완성하시오.

┌─── 보기 ───┐
wear / don't / a *hanbok* / forget / to
└─────────────┘

➡ _____

10 위 대화의 내용과 일치하지 않는 것은?

① Elsa와 Jake는 이번 주 금요일에 경복궁을 방문할 예정이다.

② Elsa와 Jake는 버스 정류장에서 두 시에 만날 예정이다.

③ Elsa와 Jake는 금요일에 한복을 입을 것이다.

④ 한복을 입으면 무료로 경복궁에 입장할 수 있다.

⑤ Jake는 한복을 무료로 대여할 수 있다.

11 다음 중 어법상 바르지 않은 것은?

> We ①are scheduled ②to go on ③a field trip. But if it ④will rain on the day, we ⑤will change the plan.

①　　②　　③　　④　　⑤

12 다음 중 어법상 바른 문장의 개수는?

> ⓐ Would you like me running the restaurant by myself?
> ⓑ We needed Christopher to help us to figure out the solution.
> ⓒ I will fix your bike if I have a screwdriver.
> ⓓ If you order me wait in the car, I'll do as you say.
> ⓔ My parents expect me to do my best all the time.

① 1개　　② 2개　　③ 3개

④ 4개　　⑤ 5개

13 다음 빈칸에 들어갈 동사 'have'의 형태가 <u>다른</u> 하나는?

① Kelly wanted Jane _____ a great time with her.

② The net enabled us _____ the fish.

③ My sister encouraged me _____ a lot of courage.

④ I am excited about _____ the car.

⑤ Jimmy allowed me _____ another cup of tea.

14 다음 대화를 읽고 주어진 단어를 활용하여 Julia에 관하여 영어로 쓰시오.

> Jane: Do you play the violin?
> Julia: Yes, my mother taught me.

> (teach / Julia)

➡ _____

15 다음 우리말의 의미에 맞도록 빈칸에 알맞은 말을 쓰시오.

> 내게 선택권이 있다면, 나는 그 방을 선택할 거야.
> If I _____ the choice, I _____ the room.

➡ _____

16 다음 우리말을 영어로 바르게 옮긴 것을 <u>모두</u> 고르시오.

> 그는 아이들이 늦게까지 자지 않고 있도록 허락하였다.

① He allowed the children to stay up late.

② He made the children stay up late.

③ He permitted the children to stay up late.

④ He enjoyed the children staying up late.

⑤ He forced the children to stay up late.

[17~19] 다음 인형에 관한 글을 읽고, 물음에 답하시오.

Dolls around the World

I'm Sweepy. I'm from Germany and my job is to clean chimneys. During winter, chimney sweeps help people to keep warm and safe. So people think chimney sweeps bring good luck ____(A)____ them. People even want chimney sweeps to be at their weddings! If you see me, it is your lucky day.

17 위 글에 관한 내용 중 바르지 <u>않은</u> 문장의 개수는?

> ⓐ The doll's name is Sweepy.
> ⓑ Sweepy is a German doll.
> ⓒ Cleaning chimneys is Sweepy's job.
> ⓓ Sweepy helps people to get home safely.
> ⓔ Sweepy is popular during spring and summer.

① 1개   ② 2개   ③ 3개

④ 4개   ⑤ 5개

18 위 글의 빈칸 (A)에 들어갈 말로 가장 적절한 것은?

① for   ② at   ③ by

④ to   ⑤ into

19 다음 질문을 읽고 빈칸에 알맞은 말을 쓰시오.

> Q: Why are chimney sweeps good for people during winter?
> A: Because _____
> _____ during winter.

[20~22] 다음 글을 읽고, 물음에 답하시오.

My name is José and these ①are my mariachi band members. We play folk music and always wear our ②sombreros, or big hats. In Mexico, people wear these hats to stay ③coolly under the hot and strong sunlight. We mariachi players want our sombreros ④to look fancy. So we often decorate them with ⓐa lot of different materials. Which of our sombreros do you like ⑤best?

출제율 95%

20 위 글의 ①~⑤ 중 어법상 바르지 <u>않은</u> 것은?

①   ②   ③   ④   ⑤

출제율 90%

21 위 글의 밑줄 친 ⓐ를 대신하여 사용할 수 <u>없는</u> 것은?

① lots of   ② a large number of

③ many   ④ a great deal of

⑤ plenty of

출제율 100%

22 다음 주어진 어구를 활용하여 위 글에 관한 내용을 쓰시오. 필요하다면 단어를 추가 및 변형하시오.

(the hot sunlight / wear / people / force / sombreros)

➡ _____

[23~25] 다음 글을 읽고, 물음에 답하시오.

My name is Ayanda and I'm a Zulu. We are a tribe in South Africa. What do you think of my beads? Zulu people enjoy making clothes with beads. They are beautiful and each color has a special meaning.   ⓐ   we did not have our own writing system, we used beads to communicate with each other. If you want to know the meaning of the colors, check out the following box.

Color	Good Meaning	Bad Meaning
Black	marriage	death
Yellow	wealth	badness
Red	love	anger
White	love	—

If you want to send someone a special message, you can express yourself with these beads. What message do you want to make?

출제율 90%

23 다음 중 빈칸 ⓐ에 들어갈 말과 같은 것은? (대·소문자 무시)

① _____ I went to bed late last night, I am not tired at all.

② What were you doing _____ I called you yesterday?

③ _____ you want to know her name, why don't you ask her yourself?

④ _____ I'm busy, I will attend your party.

⑤ _____ it was late, we decided to visit him.

출제율 85%

24 다음 주어진 단어를 활용하여 글의 빈칸에 알맞은 말을 쓰시오.

Like Zulu people, Jason wanted to express his wealth with beads. Emily _____ _____ because the color means wealth.

(tell / color)

➡ _____

출제율 90%

25 위 글의 제목으로 알맞은 질문은?

① The Beads in Zulu People

② How to Make Beads

③ Beads Bring Fortune

④ Various Colors of Beads

⑤ Making Clothes with Beads

[01~03] 다음 대화를 읽고, 물음에 답하시오.

> Mina: Chris, ⓐwhat are you going to do this Sunday?
>
> Chris: I'm going to go ⓑto the World Food Fair.
>
> Mina: Oh, I was ⓒthere last weekend. There ⓓwere lots of traditional foods from all over the world.
>
> Chris: Great! I'm looking forward to ⓔtry them.

01 위 대화의 ⓐ~ⓔ 중 어법상 바르지 않은 것을 찾아 올바르게 고치시오.

➡ _____

02 When did Mina go to the World Food Fair?

➡ _____

03 What can Chris enjoy at the World Food Fair?

➡ _____

_____

04 다음 대화의 괄호 안에 주어진 동사를 어법에 맞게 쓰시오.

> A: I think I left my jacket and my watch at your house. Have you seen them?
> B: No, but if I (find) them, I (tell) you.

➡ _____

05 주어진 단어를 활용하여 다음 우리말을 영어로 쓰시오.

> 몇몇 사람이 그 소문이 퍼지도록 하였다. (cause, rumor)
> Some people _____.

➡ _____

06 다음 우리말 뜻에 맞도록 주어진 빈칸을 채우시오. (한 칸에 한 단어씩 쓸 것)

> If _____ _____ _____ _____, _____ _____ _____ a pineapple pie this afternoon.
> (내가 충분한 파인애플을 가지고 있다면, 나는 오늘 오후에 파인애플 파이를 구을 거야.)

➡ _____

07 주어진 단어를 바르게 배열하여 다음 우리말의 의미에 맞도록 빈칸을 채우시오. 필요하다면 단어를 추가하시오.

> 이 새로운 프로그램은 나이든 사람들이 대학에서 공부하는 것을 가능하게 합니다.
> This new program _____.
> (study / college / enables / people / at / older)

➡ _____

[08~09] 다음 글을 읽고, 물음에 답하시오.

> My name is José and these are my mariachi band members. We play folk music and always wear our sombreros, or big hats. In Mexico, people wear these hats to stay cool under the hot and strong sunlight. We mariachi players want our sombreros to look fancy. So we often decorate them with a lot of different materials. Which of our sombreros do you like best?

08 위 글의 내용에 맞게 빈칸에 알맞은 말을 쓰시오.

> A: It's so hot. I can't help _____ a sombrero.
> B: You should. It helps you _____.

➡ _____

09 위 글의 내용에 맞게 빈칸에 알맞은 말을 쓰시오.

> With lots of different materials, you can _____ your sombrero. They help your sombrero _____.

➡ _____

[10~12] 다음 글을 읽고, 물음에 답하시오.

My name is Ayanda and I'm a Zulu. We are a tribe in South Africa. What do you think of my beads? Zulu people enjoy making clothes with beads. They are beautiful and each color has a special meaning. When we did not have our own writing system, ⓐwe used beads to communicate with each other. If you want to know the meaning of the colors, check out the following box.

Color	Good Meaning	Bad Meaning
Black	marriage	death
Yellow	wealth	badness
Red	love	anger
White	love	—

If you want to send someone a special message, you can express yourself with these beads. What message do you want to make?

10 주어진 표현을 이용하여 밑줄 친 ⓐ와 같은 의미의 문장을 쓰시오.

> by V+-ing: V함으로써

➡ _____

11 다음 빈칸에 알맞은 말을 위 글에서 찾아 한 칸에 한 단어씩 쓰시오.

> If you _____ _____ show your love to your friend, I would like you _____ _____ _____ beads. But be careful. It also has a bad meaning. It can be _____ when you want to _____ your anger.

➡ _____

12 Write the reason why Zulu people used beads to communicate with each other. Answer in English with the word 'because.'

➡ _____

13 주어진 글 다음에 (A)~(C)를 적절하게 나열하시오.

> My name is José and these are my mariachi band members.

> (A) So we often decorate them with a lot of different materials. Which of our sombreros do you like best?
> (B) We play folk music and always wear our sombreros, or big hats.
> (C) In Mexico, people wear these hats to stay cool under the hot and strong sunlight. We mariachi players want our sombreros to look fancy.

➡ _____

01 다음 대화와 일치하도록 빈칸을 완성하시오.

> Sora: I bought this tea for Wang's birthday. Will he like it?
>
> Jack: Sure, he will. Wang enjoys drinking tea.
>
> Sora: Great. Then I'll wrap the present.
>
> Jack: Don't forget to wrap it in red. Red stands for wealth in China.

> Sora bought the (A)_____ for Wang's birthday present. Jack was sure that Wang would like it because (B)_____. When Sora was about to wrap it, Jack told her that she should remember to (C)_____ because red symbolizes (D)_____.

02 접속사 If와 주어진 동사를 사용하여 〈보기〉와 같이 다양한 문장을 써 보시오.

> ┌─ 보기 ────────────────────────────────
> (cancel / go / wear / use / travel / make)
> If it is cloudy tomorrow, I will cancel my appointment.

(1) _____

(2) _____

(3) _____

(4) _____

(5) _____

03 다음 〈보기〉의 동사와 to부정사를 이용하여 여러 가지 문장을 써 보시오.

> ┌─ 보기 ────────────────────────────────
> encourage   allow   cause   persuade   advise   enable

(1) _____

(2) _____

(3) _____

(4) _____

(5) _____

(6) _____

단원별 모의고사

01 다음 문장의 빈칸에 들어갈 말을 쓰시오.

> • Remember to put (A)_____ your stuffs from the fireplace.
> • Wow, there are lots of fancy dresses. Can I try (B)_____ one of them?
> • What does this mark stand (C)_____?

02 다음 우리말에 맞게 빈칸에 알맞은 말을 쓰시오.

(1) 흰색은 평화를 상징한다.
➡ White _____ _____ peace.
(2) 제가 이 드레스를 입어 봐도 될까요?
➡ Can I _____ _____ this dress?
(3) 나는 Mike와의 만남을 기대하고 있다.
➡ I'm_____ _____ _____ meeting Mike.

[03~04] 다음 대화를 읽고, 물음에 답하시오.

> Sora: I bought this tea for Wang's birthday. Will he like it?
> Jack: Sure, he will. Wang enjoys drinking tea.
> Sora: Great. Then I'll wrap the present.
> Jack: Don't forget to wrap it in red. Red stands for wealth in China.

03 위 대화에서 다음의 영영풀이가 나타내는 것을 찾아 쓰시오.

> the state of being rich

➡ _____

04 위 대화를 읽고 대답할 수 없는 질문은?

① What did Sora buy for Wang's birthday?
② Who is going to wrap the present?
③ What did Jack advise to Sora?
④ What does red symbolize in China?
⑤ What kind of tea does Wang usually enjoy?

[05~06] 다음 대화를 읽고, 물음에 답하시오.

> Tom: Jane, what are you doing?
> Jane: I'm _____(A)_____ a program at the African Museum.
> Tom: Is there an ____(B)____ (interest) one?
> Jane: Yeah, I'm going to make an African drum and a traditional mask.
> Tom: Oh, how fun!
> Jane: Yeah, I'm looking forward to ____(C)____ (visit) the museum.

05 위 대화의 (A)에 '신청하다'라는 의미의 숙어를 적절한 형태로 쓰시오.

➡ _____

06 위 대화의 빈칸 (B)와 (C)에 주어진 단어를 적절한 형태로 쓰시오.

(B) _____ (C) _____

[07~08] 다음 대화를 읽고, 물음에 답하시오.

> Elsa: (A) Our visit to Gyengbokgung is this Friday. (B) Let's meet at two.
> Jake: (C) Okay, I'll see you at the bus stop.
> Elsa: (D) We can get into the palace for free in our *hanboks*.
> Jake: (E) Right. I almost forgot.

07 위 대화에서 주어진 영영풀이에 해당하는 단어를 찾아 쓰시오.

> the official home of a king, queen, president, etc.

➡ _____

08 위 대화의 (A)~(E) 중 주어진 문장이 들어가기에 적절한 곳은?

> Oh, and don't forget to wear a *hanbok*.

① (A)   ② (B)   ③ (C)   ④ (D)   ⑤ (E)

[09~10] 다음 대화를 읽고, 물음에 답하시오.

Mina: Chris, what are you going to do this Sunday?
Chris: I'm going to go to the World Food Fair.
Mina: Oh, I was there last weekend. There were lots of traditional foods from all over the world.
Chris: Great! _____ (A)

09 위 대화의 빈칸 (A)에 들어갈 말을 주어진 단어를 알맞게 배열하여 완성하시오.

┌── 보기 ──┐
forward / I'm / to / them / trying / looking
└──────────┘

➡ _____

10 위 대화의 내용과 일치하지 <u>않는</u> 것은?

① Chris는 이번 주 일요일에 세계 음식 박람회에 갈 것이다.
② Mina는 지난 주말에 세계 음식 박람회에 다녀왔다.
③ 세계 음식 박람회에는 전 세계에서 온 많은 전통적인 음식들이 있다.
④ Chris는 전통 음식들을 먹어 보기를 기대하고 있다.
⑤ Chris는 많은 전통 음식들을 살펴보고 있다.

[11~12] 다음 대화를 읽고, 물음에 답하시오.

Sue: How was your first day here in Mongolia?
Jake: It was great. By the way, where am I going to stay tonight?
Sue: You're going to sleep in a *ger*, a Mongolian tent.
Jake: Oh, I'm looking forward to it.
Sue: You'll like it. There is a fireplace in the *ger*. So, don't forget to put your things away from the fireplace.
Jake: I see. Thank you.

11 What is Jake looking forward to?

➡ _____
_____

12 What should Jake remember when he sleeps in a *ger*?

➡ _____
_____

13 주어진 단어를 이용하여 다음 대화를 문맥에 맞게 완성하시오.

┌── 보기 ──┐
back / pay
└──────────┘

A: I don't have enough money to buy the ear phone. If _____ _____ _____ ten dollars, _____ _____ you _____ tomorrow.
B: Sure. I can lend you more than that.

14 다음 빈칸에 공통으로 들어갈 수 있는 것을 <u>모두</u> 고르시오.

> • I _____ you to come to my birthday party.
>
> • We _____ to have dinner with you.

① would like　　② cause
③ tell　　　　　④ want
⑤ take

15 다음 중 어법상 올바른 것은?

① I wonder if he accepts our offer tomorrow.
② My brother taught me swim in the river.
③ Jackson didn't ask me to pay for the tickets.
④ Does she really want him to not sing the song?
⑤ My uncle advises me to learning a foreign language.

16 다음 빈칸에 알맞지 <u>않은</u> 것은?

> He _____ me to do the job.

① wants　　② allows　　③ encourages
④ persuades　　⑤ keeps

17 다음 우리말 뜻에 맞도록 빈칸에 알맞은 말을 쓰시오.

> 우리가 택시를 탄다면, 그곳에 곧 도착할 거야.
> ➡ If we _____ a taxi, we _____
> _____ there soon.

[18~19] 다음 글을 읽고, 물음에 답하시오.

My name is José and these are my mariachi band members. ⓐWe play folk music and wear always our sombreros, or big hats. In Mexico, people wear these hats to stay cool under the hot and strong sunlight. We mariachi players want our sombreros to look fancy. So we often decorate them with a lot of different materials. Which of our sombreros do you like best?

18 위 글의 밑줄 친 ⓐ에서 어법상 바르지 <u>않은</u> 것을 바르게 고쳐 올바른 문장으로 다시 쓰시오.

➡ _____

_____

19 다음 중 위 글의 내용과 일치하지 <u>않는</u> 것은?

① José belongs to the mariachi band.
② People in Mexico wear sombreros.
③ A sombrero is a big hat.
④ People in Mexico look fancy.
⑤ By using lots of different materials, Mexican people decorate their sombreros.

[20~24] 다음 글을 읽고, 물음에 답하시오.

My name is Ayanda and I'm a Zulu. We are a tribe ①in South Africa. _____(A)_____ Zulu people enjoy ②making clothes with beads. They are beautiful and each ③colors has a special meaning. When we did not have our own ④writing system, we used beads to communicate with each other. If you want ⓐ _____ the meaning of the colors, check out the ⑤following box.

Color	Good Meaning	Bad Meaning
Black	marriage	death
Yellow	wealth	badness
Red	love	anger
White	love	—

If you want _____ⓑ_____ a special message to someone, you can express yourself with these beads. What message do you want _____ⓒ_____?

20 주어진 단어를 활용하여 자신의 구슬을 어떻게 생각하는지를 묻는 말을 빈칸 (A)에 쓰시오.

what / of

➡ _____

21 위 글의 ①~⑤ 중 어법상 바르지 <u>않은</u> 것은?

①   ②   ③   ④   ⑤

22 What is the bad meaning of yellow? Answer in English.

➡ _____

23 다음 중 위 글의 내용과 일치하지 <u>않는</u> 것은?

① Ayanda is a Zulu.
② Zulu people love to make clothes with beads.
③ There are four colors with eight meanings.
④ The bad meaning of black is death.
⑤ Both red and white beads mean love.

24 주어진 동사를 의미와 어법에 맞게 빈칸 ⓐ~ⓒ에 각각 쓰시오.

know   make   send

ⓐ _____   ⓑ _____   ⓒ _____

25 자연스러운 글이 되도록 (A)~(C)를 바르게 나열한 것은?

I'm Sweepy. I'm from Germany and my job is to clean chimneys.

(A) So people think chimney sweeps bring them good luck.
(B) During winter, chimney sweeps help people to keep warm and safe.
(C) People even want chimney sweeps to be at their weddings! If you see me, it is your lucky day.

① (A) – (C) – (B)   ② (B) – (A) – (C)
③ (B) – (C) – (A)   ④ (C) – (A) – (B)
⑤ (C) – (B) – (A)

I Wonder Why, I Wonder How

🎤 의사소통 기능

- 들어 본 적이 있는지 묻기

  A: Have you heard about the Sci-Magic show?
  B: No, I haven't.

- 설명 요청하기

  A: I made a potato clock yesterday!

  B: A potato clock? What do you mean?

  A: My clock works with potatoes, not with batteries.

🎤 언어 형식

- 수동태

  The city **is powered by** the screams.

- to 부정사의 형용사적 용법

  Rapunzel has the ability **to hold** up a person.

교과서
Words & Expressions

Key Words

- **ability** [əbíləti] 명 능력
- **activity** [æktívəti] 명 활동
- **actually** [ǽktʃuəli] 부 실제로, 정말로
- **add** [æd] 동 더하다
- **advice** [ædváis] 명 충고, 조언
- **amazingly** [əméiziŋli] 부 놀랍게도
- **amount** [əmáunt] 명 양
- **amusement** [əmjú:zmənt] 명 재미, 놀이, 오락
- **appear** [əpíər] 동 나타나다
- **application** [æpləkéiʃən] 명 응용 프로그램, 적용
- **average** [ǽvəridʒ] 명 평균
- **balloon** [bəlú:n] 명 풍선
- **battery** [bǽtəri] 명 건전지, 배터리
- **bean** [bi:n] 명 콩
- **car horn** 자동차 경적
- **challenge** [tʃǽlindʒ] 명 도전, 난제 동 도전하다
- **collector** [kəléktər] 명 수집가
- **drone** [droun] 명 무인 비행기, 무인 항공기
- **electricity** [ilektrísəti] 명 전기, 전류
- **entire** [intáiər] 형 전체의
- **experiment** [ikspérəmənt] 명 실험
- **explain** [ikspléin] 동 설명하다
- **fair** [fɛər] 명 박람회, 장 형 공정한
- **fold** [fould] 동 접다

- **hide** [haid] 동 숨기다, 숨다
- **however** [hauévər] 부 그러나
- **impossible** [impásəbl] 형 불가능한
- **lift** [ift] 동 들어 올리다
- **lower** [lóuər] 동 내리다, 낮추다
- **miss** [mis] 동 놓치다, 그리워하다
- **monster** [mánstər] 명 괴물, 요괴
- **normal** [nɔ́:rməl] 형 보통의, 평범한
- **pick** [pik] 동 따다, 뜯다, 집다
- **possible** [pásəbl] 형 가능한, 있을 수 있는
- **produce** [prədjú:s] 동 생산하다, 제작하다
- **record** [rikɔ́:rd] 동 기록하다, 녹음하다
- **ring** [riŋ] 명 반지 동 울리다
- **scare** [skɛər] 동 겁주다, 겁먹게 하다
- **scream** [skri:m] 명 비명, 외침(소리)
- **single** [síŋgl] 형 단 하나의
- **sore** [sɔ:r] 형 아픈
- **string** [striŋ] 명 실
- **unbelievable** [ənbəlivəbəl] 형 믿을 수 없는
- **unlock** [ənlak] 동 자물쇠를 열다
- **useful** [jú:sfəl] 형 유용한
- **vinegar** [vínəgər] 명 식초
- **weigh** [wei] 동 무게가 ~이다
- **youth** [ju:θ] 동 젊은, 청춘

Key Expressions

- **a couple of** 둘의, 몇 개의
- **for example** 예를 들어
- **hold up** ~을 떠받치다
- **in front of** ~의 앞에
- **let's say that** ~라고 하자
- **light up** ~을 환하게 하다, 점등하다
- **paint over** 덧칠하다
- **pick one's brain** ~의 지혜를 빌리다

- **pump up** 주입하다, 채워 넣다
- **turn into** ~가 되다
- **take care of** ~을 돌보다
- **take away** ~을 제거하다, ~을 치우다
- **turn off** ~을 끄다
- **turn on** ~을 켜다
- **what's more** 게다가, 더구나
- **wrap ~ around** ~을 두르다, ~을 감다

Word Power

서로 반대되는 뜻을 가진 단어

- □ **possible** 가능한 → **impossible** 불가능한
- □ **lift** 들어 올리다 → **lower** 낮추다
- □ **lock** 잠그다 → **unlock** 자물쇠를 풀다
- □ **hide** 숨기다 → **reveal** 드러내다
- □ **entire** 전체의 → **partial** 부분의
- □ **turn on** ~을 켜다 → **turn off** ~을 끄다

- □ **useful** 유용한 → **useless** 쓸모없는
- □ **fair** 공정한, 공평한 → **unfair** 불공정한
- □ **believable** 믿을 수 있는 → **unbelievable** 믿을 수 없는
- □ **real** 현실의 → **imaginary** 상상의, 가상의
- □ **normal** 보통의, 정상적인 → **abnormal** 비정상적인
- □ **active** 활동적인 → **inactive** 활동하지 않은, 활발하지 않은

English Dictionary

□ **add** 더하다
→ to put something together with something else so as to increase the size, number, amount, etc.
무언가를 크기, 수, 양 등을 증가시키기 위해 다른 무언가와 함께 놓다

□ **amusement** 재미, 즐거움
→ the feeling that you have when you think that something is funny
어떤 것이 재미있다고 생각할 때 가지는 느낌

□ **average** 평균
→ calculated by adding several amounts together, finding a total, and dividing the total by the number of amounts
몇몇 합을 더해 총합을 찾은 후 합의 수로 전체를 나누어 계산한 것

□ **battery** 건전지
→ a device that is placed inside a car engine, clock, radio, etc. and that produces the electricity that makes it work
자동차 엔진, 시계, 라디오 등 안에 위치하여 그것이 작동할 수 있게 하는 전기를 만들어 내는 장치

□ **challenge** 도전
→ a new or difficult task that tests somebody's ability and skill
누군가의 능력과 기술을 시험해 보기 위한 새롭거나 어려운 과제

□ **collector** 수집가
→ a person who collects things, either as a hobby or as a job
취미나 직업으로 물건들을 모으는 사람

□ **drone** 무인 비행기
→ an aircraft without a pilot, controlled from the ground
조종사 없이 땅에서 조작되는 항공기

□ **experiment** 실험
→ a scientific test that is done in order to study what happens and to gain new knowledge
무슨 일이 일어나는지 연구해서 새로운 과학적 지식을 얻기 위해 행해지는 과학적 검사

□ **hide** 숨기다
→ to put or keep something/somebody in a place where it cannot be seen or found
어떤 물건이나 사람을 보이지 않거나 찾을 수 없는 장소에 놓거나 보관하다

□ **lift** 들어 올리다
→ to raise somebody/something or be raised to a higher position or level
누군가나 무언가를 더 높은 곳이나 수준으로 들어 올리거나 올려지다

□ **lower** 내리다, 낮추다
→ to let or make something/somebody go down
무언가나 누군가를 내려가게 만들다

□ **possible** 가능한
→ that can be done or achieved
할 수 있거나 성취될 수 있는

□ **record** 기록하다
→ to write something down so that it can be used or seen again in the future
어떤 것을 글로 적어서 나중에 다시 사용하거나 볼 수 있게 하다

□ **scare** 무서워하다
→ to become frightened
겁에 질리다

□ **scream** 비명
→ a loud high cry made by somebody who is hurt, frightened, excited, etc.
다치거나 놀라거나 흥분한 누군가에 의한 크고 높은 고함소리

□ **weigh** 무게를 재다
→ to measure how heavy somebody/something is, usually by using scales
보통 저울을 사용해서 어떤 사람이나 사물이 얼마나 무거운지 측정하다

서답형

01 다음 짝지어진 단어의 관계가 같도록 빈칸에 알맞은 말을 쓰시오.

active : inactive = possible : _____

서답형

02 다음 영영풀이에 해당하는 말을 쓰시오.

to measure how heavy somebody/ something is, usually by using scales

➡ _____

03 다음 중 밑줄 친 부분의 뜻풀이가 바르지 <u>않은</u> 것은?

① Let's find out what happens in the <u>experiment</u>. 경험
② How much <u>vinegar</u> is used to make salad? 식초
③ My grandmother used to <u>hide</u> money in a cupboard. 숨기다
④ Minho is blowing up a <u>balloon</u>. 풍선
⑤ Many artists do their best to <u>produce</u> great works of art. 제작하다

04 다음 문장에 공통으로 들어갈 말을 고르시오.

• Be sure to _____ the door before you leave.
• Sue is using a _____ to protect the important document in her drawer.
• When Ann saw me, she _____(e)d me in her arms.

① move   ② lock   ③ record
④ check   ⑤ challenge

서답형

05 다음 문장의 빈칸에 들어갈 말을 〈보기〉에서 골라 쓰시오.

┌─ 보기 ┐
amusement / amount / challenge / add
└─────┘

(1) His big _____ is to win in an election.
(2) One day, my father took me to the _____ park.
(3) Would you _____ my name to the list?
(4) He gave an equal _____ of pocket money to each child.

06 다음 주어진 문장의 밑줄 친 의미와 같은 의미로 쓰인 것은?

Have you heard about the science <u>fair</u>?

① The referee didn't make a <u>fair</u> decision.
② It's important to play the <u>fair</u> game.
③ We are planning to visit the international IT <u>fair</u>.
④ That sounds like a <u>fair</u> deal.
⑤ It's not <u>fair</u> to blame others for your mistakes.

07 다음 문장의 빈칸에 들어갈 말을 순서대로 쓰시오.

(1) The app tells you how to take care (A)_____ your pet.
(2) Pick (B)_____ the purse.
(3) We need candles to light (C)_____ the room.

(A)_____ (B)_____ (C)_____

01 다음 짝지어진 단어의 관계가 같도록 빈칸에 알맞은 말을 쓰시오.

> fair : unfair = lock : _____

[02~03] 다음 영영풀이에 해당하는 말을 쓰시오.

02

> a person who collects things, either as a hobby or as a job

➡ _____

03

> to put or keep something in a place where it cannot be seen or found

➡ _____

04 다음 우리말에 맞게 빈칸에 알맞은 말을 쓰시오.

(1) 당신이 부유하다고 가정해 보자.
➡ _____ _____ _____ you are rich.

(2) 너는 멀리 떠나기 전에 타이어에 바람을 넣어야 한다.
➡ You should _____ _____ the tires before going far away.

(3) 촛불을 켜 주시겠어요?
➡ Would you _____ _____ the candle?

05 다음 주어진 우리말과 일치하도록 빈칸을 완성하시오.

(1) 자동차 경적 소리가 나를 놀라게 했다.
➡ The sounds from a _____ _____ made me surprised.

(2) 그는 믿기 어려울 만큼의 많은 돈을 벌었다.
➡ He made an _____ amount of money.

(3) 야수는 미녀에게 겁을 주고 싶지 않았다.
➡ The beast didn't want to _____ the beauty.

06 다음 빈칸에 주어진 단어를 적절한 형태로 채우시오.

> (1) There is a strong _____ (possible) of snow tomorrow.
> (2) It is _____(amazing) easy to make 'Dancing Beans'.
> (3) My teacher praised my _____ (able) to speak Chinese well.

(A)_____ (B)_____ (C)_____

07 다음 우리말과 일치하도록 주어진 단어를 모두 배열하여 완성하시오.

(1) 벽을 노란색으로 고르게 칠해 보자.
(paint / let's / with / the / wall / yellow / over / evenly)
➡ _____

(2) 과학 박물관의 특별 행사에 대해 들어봤니?
(the special / have / about / you / event / at / the science / heard / museum)
➡ _____

(3) 감자가 전기를 생산한다고 가정해 봅시다.
(electricity / say / produce / potatoes / that / let's)
➡ _____

Conartion

교과서

Conversation

① 들어 본 적이 있는지 묻기

> **A** Have you heard about the Sci-Magic show? 과학 마술 쇼에 대해 들어 본 적 있어?
>
> **B** No, I haven't. 아니, 없어.

- 'Have you ever+과거분사 ~?'는 경험을 묻는 표현으로 'Have you ever heard ~?'는 들어 본 적이 있는지 묻는다. 이에 대한 대답으로 긍정일 때는 'Yes, I have.', 부정일 때는 'No, I haven't.'로 대답한다. Have you?는 상대방에게서 받은 질문을 다시 상대방에게 묻는 표현으로 반복된 부분은 생략한다.

- **경험 말하기**

  1. 현재까지의 경험을 물을 때 현재완료 시제를 사용하므로 'Have you ever+과거 분사 ~?' 형태에 유의한다.

  2. 경험하지 못한 것으로 '전혀 ~해 본 적이 없다.'라고 강조하기 위해 'No, I've never ~.'로 대답할 수 있다.

  3. 과거의 경험은 과거시제를 이용한다.

  • Did you hear the news? 과거에 뉴스를 들었는지 묻는 표현

  • Have you heard about the news? 과거부터 현재까지 뉴스를 들어 본 적이 있는지 묻는 표현

핵심 Check

1. 다음 우리말과 일치하도록 빈칸에 알맞은 말을 쓰시오.

   (1) **A:** _____ _____ _____ _____ the pop song contest?

   (팝송 대회에 대해 들어 본 적이 있나요?)

   B: No, I haven't. (아니요, 들어 본 적 없어요.)

   (2) **A:** Have you heard about Beethoven? (베토벤에 대해 들어 본 적이 있나요?)

   B: _____, _____ _____. _____ _____? (예, 들어 보았어요. 당신은요?)

   (3) **A:** Have you heard about a paper soap? (종이비누에 대해 들어 본 적이 있나요?)

   B: _____, _____ _____. (아니요, 들어 본 적 없어요.)

② 설명 요청하기

> **A** I made a potato clock yesterday! 나 어제 감자시계를 만들었어!
>
> **B** A potato clock? What do you mean? 감자시계? 무슨 말이야?
>
> **A** My clock works with potatoes, not with batteries. 내 시계는 건전지가 아니라 감자로 작동을 해.

■ 'What do you mean?'은 상대방이 언급한 것에 대해 명확한 설명을 요청하는 표현으로 What is it? 또는 Can you explain it specifically? 또는 Can you tell me more about it? 등으로 바꾸어 쓸 수 있다.

설명 요청하기

• What is it? 그게 무엇이니?

• Can you explain it specifically? 그것을 명확하게 설명해 줄 수 있니?

• Can you tell me more about it? 너는 내게 그것에 대해 더 이야기해 줄 수 있니?

• What do you mean? 무슨 뜻이니?

• Would you give me more information? 내게 더 정보를 주겠니?

핵심 Check

2. 다음 우리말과 일치하도록 빈칸에 알맞은 말을 쓰시오.

(1) **A:** We can make the 'Dancing Beans.' (우리는 '춤추는 콩'을 만들 수 있어.)

 B: Dancing Beans? _____ _____ _____ _____? (춤추는 콩? 무슨 뜻이야?)

(2) **A:** I made an egg ball with my brother. (남동생이랑 달걀 공을 만들었어.)

 B: An egg ball? _____ _____ _____? (달걀 공? 그게 무엇이니?)

(3) **A:** Let's make a "Mystery Card" for the science experiment.

 (과학 실험으로 '미스터리 카드'를 만들자.)

 B: "Mystery Card"? Can you _____ me _____ about it?

 (미스터리 카드? 내게 그것에 대해 더 이야기해 줄 수 있니?)

A. Listen & Talk 2-B

Minho: Anna, ❶let's make a "Mystery Card" for the science experiment.

Anna: A "Mystery Card?" ❷What do you mean?

Minho: It's a special card. It can hide your message.

Anna: How do you make ❸it?

Minho: Mix baking soda and water. Then, write a message on the card with ❹it.

Anna: How can you read the card?

Minho: ❺Paint over the card with grape juice, and then the message appears.

Minho: Anna, 우리 과학 실험으로 '미스터리 카드'를 만들자.

Anna: 미스터리 카드? 무슨 말이야?

Minho: 그건 특별한 카드야. 그 카드는 너의 메시지를 숨길 수 있어.

Anna: 어떻게 만드는데?

Minho: 베이킹 소다랑 물을 섞어. 그러고 나서 그걸로 카드 위에 메시지를 써.

Anna: 카드를 어떻게 읽을 수 있어?

Minho: 카드를 포도 주스로 칠하면 메시지가 나타나.

❶ 'let's ~'는 '~하자'라고 제안하는 표현이다.
❷ 'What do you mean?'은 상대방이 한 말을 잘 알아듣지 못했거나 자신이 제대로 이해했는지 다시 확인하기 위해서 사용하는 표현이다.
❸ it은 '미스터리 카드'를 가리킨다.
❹ it은 베이킹 소다와 물을 섞은 것을 가리킨다.
❺ 명령문+and ~: ~해라, 그러면 ~

Check(√) True or False

(1) A "Mystery Card" can hide the message.　　　　　　　　　T ☐ F ☐

(2) Minho needs baking soda and water to read the card.　　　T ☐ F ☐

B. Communication

Jane: ❶Have you heard about the Smart App Contest?

Minho: Yes, I have. Are you going to enter ❷it?

Jane: Yeah, I'm going to send my idea about a Pic Gardener App.

Minho: A Pic Gardener App? ❸What do you mean?

Jane: When you take a picture of a plant, the app tells you how to ❹take care of it.

Minho: It sounds like a very useful app.

Jane: 너 스마트 앱 대회에 대해 들어 본 적 있어?

Minho: 응, 들어 봤어. 너 거기 나갈 거야?

Jane: 응, Pic Gardener 앱에 관한 내 아이디어를 보내 보려고.

Minho: Pic Gardener 앱? 무슨 말이야?

Jane: 식물의 사진을 찍으면, 그 앱이 그 식물을 가꾸는 법을 알려 주는 거야.

Minho: 그거 매우 유용한 앱 같구나.

❶ 'Have you heard about ~?'은 상대방에게 어떤 것에 대해서 들어 본 적이 있는지 혹은 알고 있는지 여부를 묻기 위해서 사용된다.
❷ it은 스마트 앱 대회를 가리킨다.
❸ 설명을 요청하는 표현이다.
❹ take care of: ~을 돌보다, 가꾸다

Check(√) True or False

(3) Jane is going to take part in the Smart App Contest.　　　　T ☐ F ☐

(4) Jane is taking a picture to take care of her plant.　　　　　　T ☐ F ☐

Listen & Talk 1 A-1

Mike: What show are you watching, Sally?

Sally: I'm watching the Sci-Magic show. It's a new program. Have you heard about ❶it?

Mike: No, I haven't. ❷What's it about?

Sally: The program uses science to explain magic tricks.

Mike: Oh, it sounds interesting.

❶ the Sci-Magic show를 가리킨다.
❷ the Sci-Magic show에 대한 설명을 요청하는 표현이다.

Listen & Talk A-2

Tom: Mom, ❶have you heard about the Chat Robot?

Mom: No, I haven't. What is ❷it?

Tom: It's a phone application. You can ask any questions and it will answer. ❸Let me show you. "Emily, what's the weather like today?"

Emily: "It's going to rain, so you'll need an umbrella."

Mom: Wow, ❹what a great application!

❶ Chat Robot에 관해 들어 본 적이 있는지 묻는 표현이다.
❷ Chat Robot을 가리킨다.
❸ 시범으로 보여주기 위해 쓰는 표현이다.
❹ 감탄문으로 'What+a(n)+형용사+명사!' 순서로 나타낸다.

Listen & Talk B

W: Hello, students. Have you heard about the DIY Drone Class? You can make your own drone in the class. The Youth Community Center ❶offers the class at 3 p.m. every Wednesday in May. Make your special drone and learn how to control it. Don't ❷miss this great ❸chance!

❶ offer: 제공하다, 주다
❷ miss: 놓치다
❸ chance: 기회(= opportunity)

Listen & Talk 2 A-1

Mina: ❶You know what? I made a potato clock yesterday!

Jack: A potato clock? What do you mean?

Mina: My clock works with potatoes, not with batteries. Potatoes can produce ❷electricity.

Jack: That's interesting!

❶ 상대방의 주의를 끌 때 사용하는 표현이다. ❷ electricity: 전기

Listen & Talk 2 A-2

Jimmy: Lisa, what did you do last weekend?

Lisa: I made an egg ball with my brother.

Jimmy: An egg ball? ❶What do you mean?

Lisa: We put an egg in ❷vinegar for two days. Then, the egg ❸turns into a ball.

Jimmy: Wow, I want to make ❹one, too!

❶ 달걀 공에 대한 설명을 요청하는 표현이다. ❷ vinegar: 식초 ❸ turn into ~: ~이 되다 ❹ 달걀 공을 가리킨다.

Wrap Up 1

Hojin: Hey, Katy. Have you heard about ❶the science fair?

Katy: Yeah, I'm going to go ❷there.

Hojin: ❸Me, too! I'm excited about doing different kinds of experiments.

Katy: Yeah, I'm also ❹looking forward to it!

❶ the science fair: 과학 박람회 ❷ there = to the science fair ❸ '나도 그래!'라는 의미로 'So am I.'로 바꾸어 쓸 수 있다. ❹ look forward to: ~을 기대하다

Wrap Up 2

Emma: ❶How about making "Dancing Beans" for the science project?

David: "Dancing Beans?" What do you mean?

Emma: ❷They are beans that move in the water ❸like they're dancing.

David: Sounds interesting! What do we need?

Emma: We just need some water, vinegar, baking soda, and beans.

❶ 'How about ~?'은 '~하는 게 어때?'라고 제안하는 표현이다. 'What about ~?'으로 바꾸어 쓸 수 있다. ❷ They는 Dancing Beans를 가리킨다. ❸ like: ~ 하는 것처럼

다음 우리말과 일치하도록 빈칸에 알맞은 말을 쓰시오.

Listen & Talk 1 A-1

Mike: _____ _____ are you watching, Sally?

Sally: I'm watching the Sci-Magic show. It's a new program. _____ _____ _____ _____ _____?

Mike: No, I haven't. What's it about?

Sally: The program uses _____ to explain magic tricks.

Mike: Oh, it sounds _____.

해석

Mike: Sally, 무슨 쇼 프로그램을 보고 있니?
Sally: '과학 마술 쇼'를 보고 있어. 새로 하는 프로그램이야. 너 그것에 대해 들어 본 적 있어?
Mike: 아니, 없어. 무엇에 관한 거야?
Sally: 그 프로그램에서는 마술 묘기를 설명하기 위해 과학을 이용해.
Mike: 오, 흥미로울 것 같아.

Listen & Talk 1 A-2

Tom: Mom, have you heard about the Chat Robot?

Mom: _____, _____ _____. What is it?

Tom: It's a phone application. You can ask any questions and it will answer. _____ _____ _____ _____. "Emily, what's the weather like today?"

Emily: "It's going to rain, so you'll need an umbrella."

Mom: Wow, _____ _____ _____ _____!

Tom: 엄마, Chat Robot에 관해 들어 본 적 있으세요?
Mom: 아니, 없어. 그게 뭐니?
Tom: 그건 휴대폰 앱이에요. 어떤 질문이든 물으면 그것을 대답해 줘요. 보여 드릴게요. "Emily, 오늘 날씨는 어때?"
Emily: "비가 올 예정이니까, 당신은 우산이 필요할 것입니다."
Mom: 와, 정말 멋진 앱이구나!

Listen & Talk 1 B

W: Hello, students. _____ _____ _____ _____ the DIY Drone Class? You can make your own drone in the class. The Youth Community Center _____ the class at 3 p.m. every Wednesday in May. Make your special drone and learn _____ _____ _____ _____. Don't miss this great chance!

W: 학생 여러분, 안녕하세요. DIY 무인기(드론) 수업에 관해 들어 본 적이 있나요? 그 수업에서 여러분은 자신만의 무인기를 만들 수 있어요. 청소년 지역 문화 회관에서 5월에 수요일마다 오후 3시에 수업이 있어요. 여러분의 특별한 무인기를 만들고, 조종하는 방법을 배워 보세요. 이 좋은 기회를 놓치지 마세요.

Listen & Talk 2 A-1

Mina: You know what? I made a potato clock yesterday!

Jack: A potato clock? _____ _____ _____ _____ _____?

Mina: My clock works with potatoes, not with batteries. Potatoes can produce _____.

Jack: That's interesting!

Mina: 그거 알아? 나 어제 감자 시계를 만들었어!
Jack: 감자 시계? 무슨 말이야?
Mina: 내 시계는 건전지가 아니라 감자로 작동을 해. 감자로 전기를 만들 수 있거든.
Jack: 그거 흥미롭다!

Listen & Talk 2 A-2

Jimmy: Lisa, _____ _____ _____ _____ _____ _____ _____?

Lisa: I made an egg ball with my brother.

Jimmy: An egg ball? What do you mean?

Lisa: We _____ an egg _____ _____ for two days. Then, the egg _____ _____ a ball.

Jimmy: Wow, I want to make one, too!

Jimmy: Lisa, 지난 주말에 뭐 했어?
Lisa: 남동생이랑 달걀 공을 만들었어.
Jimmy: 달걀 공? 무슨 말이야?
Lisa: 우리는 달걀을 이틀 동안 식초에 담가놨어. 그러면 달걀이 공으로 변해.
Jimmy: 와, 나도 하나 만들고 싶어!

Listen & Talk 2 B

Minho: Anna, let's make a "Mystery Card" for the science experiment.

Anna: A "Mystery Card?" _____ _____ _____ _____?

Minho: It's a special card. It can _____ your message.

Anna: How do you make it?

Minho: _____ baking soda and water. Then, write a message on the card with it.

Anna: _____ _____ _____ _____ _____ _____?

Minho: Paint over the card with grape juice, and then the message _____.

Minho: Anna, 우리 과학 실험으로 '미스터리 카드'를 만들자.
Anna: 미스터리 카드? 무슨 말이야?
Minho: 그건 특별한 카드야. 그 카드는 너의 메시지를 숨길 수 있어.
Anna: 어떻게 만드는데?
Minho: 베이킹 소다랑 물을 섞어. 그러고 나서 그걸로 카드 위에 메시지를 써.
Anna: 카드를 어떻게 읽을 수 있어?
Minho: 카드를 포도 주스로 칠하면 메시지가 나타나.

Communication

Jane: _____ _____ _____ _____ the Smart App Contest?

Minho: _____, _____ _____. Are you going to enter it?

Jane: Yeah, I'm going to send my idea about a Pic Gardener App.

Minho: A Pic Gardener App? _____ _____ _____ _____?

Jane: When you take a picture of a plant, the app tells you _____ _____ _____ _____ _____ _____.

Minho: It sounds like a very _____ app.

Jane: 너 스마트 앱 대회에 대해 들어 본 적 있어?
Minho: 응, 들어 봤어. 너 거기 나갈 거야?
Jane: 응, Pic Gardener 앱에 관한 내 아이디어를 보내 보려고.
Minho: Pic Gardener 앱? 무슨 말이야?
Jane: 식물의 사진을 찍으면, 그 앱이 그 식물을 가꾸는 법을 알려 주는 거야.
Minho: 매우 유용한 앱 같아.

Wrap Up 1

Hojin: Hey, Katy. Have you heard about the science fair?

Katy: Yeah, I'm going to go there.

Hojin: Me, too! I'm _____ about doing different kinds of _____.

Katy: Yeah, I'm also _____ _____ _____ it!

Hojin: 저기, Katy. 너 과학 박람회에 대해 들어 본 적 있어?
Katy: 응, 나 거기에 갈 거야.
Hojin: 나도! 난 다양한 종류의 실험들을 할 생각을 하니 신나.
Katy: 맞아, 나도 그게 정말 기대돼!

01 다음 대화의 밑줄 친 (A)의 우리말을 영어로 쓰시오.

> A: I made a potato clock yesterday!
> B: A potato clock? (A)무슨 말이야?
> A: My clock works with potatoes, not with batteries.

➡ _____

02 다음 대화의 빈칸에 들어갈 말로 적절한 것은?

> A: Have you heard about the Chat Robot?
> B: _____

① Yes, I haven't   ② Yes, I did.
③ No, I didn't.   ④ No, I have.
⑤ No, I haven't.

[03~04] 다음 대화를 읽고, 물음에 답하시오.

Mike: What show are you watching, Sally? (A)
Sally: I'm watching the Sci-Magic show. It's a new program. (B)
Mike: No, I haven't. What's it about? (C)
Sally: The program uses science to explain magic tricks. (D)
Mike: Oh, it sounds interesting. (E)

03 위 대화의 (A)~(E) 중 주어진 문장이 들어가기에 적절한 곳은?

> Have you heard about it?

① (A)   ② (B)   ③ (C)   ④ (D)   ⑤ (E)

04 위 대화의 내용과 일치하지 <u>않는</u> 것은?

① Sally는 과학 마술 쇼를 보고 있다.
② 과학 마술 쇼는 새로운 프로그램이다.
③ Mike는 마술과 과학에 관심이 많다.
④ Mike는 과학 마술 쇼에 대해 들어 본 적이 없다.
⑤ 과학 마술 쇼는 마술 묘기를 설명하기 위해 과학을 사용한다.

서답형
01 다음 대화가 자연스럽게 이어지도록 순서대로 배열하시오.

> (A) No, I haven't. What is it?
> (B) Mom, have you heard about the Chat Robot?
> (C) Wow, what a great application!
> (D) "It's going to rain, so you'll need an umbrella."
> (E) It's a phone application. You can ask any questions and it will answer. Let me show you. "Emily, what's the weather like today?"

➡ _____

[02~04] 다음 담화문을 읽고, 물음에 답하시오.

> W: Hello, students. _____(A)_____?
> You can make your own drone in the class. The Youth Community Center offers the class at 3 p.m. every Wednesday in May. Make your special drone and learn how to control it. Don't miss this great chance!

서답형
02 위 담화문의 빈칸 (A)에 들어갈 말을 〈보기〉에 주어진 어구를 모두 배열하여 완성하시오.

> ┤ 보기 ├
> you / the / about / DIY Drone Class / have / heard

➡ _____

중요
03 위 담화문의 목적으로 적절한 것은?

① to advertise   ② to apologize
③ to appreciate   ④ to celebrate
⑤ to protest

서답형
04 What can you do in the DIY Drone Class?

➡ _____
_____

[05~06] 다음 대화를 읽고, 물음에 답하시오.

> Mike: What show are you watching, Sally?
> Sally: I'm watching the Sci-Magic show. It's a new program. Have you heard about it?
> Mike: (A)아니, 없어. What's it about?
> Sally: The program uses science to ___(B)___ magic tricks.
> Mike: Oh, it sounds interesting.

서답형
05 위 대화의 (A)의 우리말을 영어로 쓰시오.

➡ _____

중요
06 위 대화의 빈칸 (B)에 알맞은 것은?

① explain   ② produce
③ challenge   ④ pump
⑤ decorate

[07~08] 다음 대화를 읽고, 물음에 답하시오.

> Mina: You know what? I made a potato clock yesterday!
> Jack: A potato clock? What do you mean?
> Mina: My clock works with potatoes, not with batteries. Potatoes can produce electricity.
> Jack: _____(A)_____

07 위 대화의 빈칸 (A)에 들어갈 말로 나머지와 의도가 <u>다른</u> 것은?

① That's interesting!

② It sounds interesting.

③ How interesting!

④ What an interesting invention!

⑤ I'm not interested in it.

08 위 대화의 내용과 일치하지 <u>않는</u> 것은?

① Mina는 어제 감자 시계를 만들었다.

② Jack은 감자 시계에 대해 잘 알지 못했다.

③ 감자 시계는 배터리가 필요하지 않다.

④ 감자 시계는 전기를 만들어 내는 데 감자를 사용한다.

⑤ Jack은 감자 시계를 만드는 데 참여했다.

[09~10] 다음 대화를 읽고, 물음에 답하시오.

Jimmy: Lisa, what did you do last weekend? (A)

Lisa: I made an egg ball with my brother. (B)

Jimmy: An egg ball? (C)

Lisa: We put an egg in vinegar for two days. Then, the egg turns into a ball. (D)

Jimmy: Wow, I want to make one, too! (E)

09 위 대화의 (A)~(E) 중 주어진 문장이 들어가기에 적절한 곳은?

> What do you mean?

① (A) ② (B) ③ (C) ④ (D) ⑤ (E)

서답형

10 Egg ball을 만드는 법을 우리말 15자 내외로 서술하시오.

➡ _____

[11~12] 다음 대화를 읽고, 물음에 답하시오.

Minho: Anna, let's make a "Mystery Card" for the science experiment.

Anna: A "Mystery Card?" What do you mean?

Minho: It's a special card. It can (A)[hide / reveal] your message.

Anna: How do you make it?

Minho: (B)[Separate / Mix] baking soda and water. Then, write a message on the card with it.

Anna: How can you read the card?

Minho: Paint over the card with grape juice, and then the message (C)[appears / disappears].

11 위 대화의 (A)~(C)에 들어갈 말이 바르게 짝지어진 것은?

① hide – Separate – appears

② hide – Mix – appears

③ hide – Separate – disappears

④ reveal – Mix – disappears

⑤ reveal – Separate – appears

12 위 대화의 내용과 일치하지 <u>않는</u> 것은?

① Minho는 과학 실험을 위해 미스터리 카드를 만들 것을 제안하였다.

② 미스터리 카드는 메시지를 숨길 수 있다.

③ 미스터리 카드를 만들기 위해 카드, 베이킹 소다, 물이 필요하다.

④ 펜으로 미스터리 카드를 쓴 후 베이킹 소다와 물을 붓는다.

⑤ 포도 주스로 미스터리 카드를 칠하면 메시지를 볼 수 있다.

01 다음 대화의 빈칸에 들어갈 말을 주어진 어구를 모두 배열하여 완성하시오.

> A: _____
>
> B: No, I haven't.

┌─ 보기 ─┐
about / heard / the / you /
Sci-Magic show / have

➡ _____

02 다음 대화의 빈칸에 들어갈 말을 주어진 단어를 사용하여 쓰시오.

> A: You are my BFF.
> B: BFF? _____ (mean)
> C: It means "Best Friends Forever."

➡ _____

[03~04] 다음 대화를 읽고, 물음에 답하시오.

> Mike: ⓐWhat show are you watching, Sally?
> Sally: I'm watching the Sci-Magic show. It's a new program. Have you ⓑheard about it?
> Mike: No, I ⓒhaven't. What's it about?
> Sally: The program uses science ⓓexplain magic tricks.
> Mike: Oh, it sounds ⓔinteresting.

03 위 대화의 ⓐ~ⓔ 중 어법상 어색한 것을 골라 바르게 고치시오.

➡ _____

04 What is the Sci-Magic show about?

➡ _____

05 다음 대화의 빈칸에 알맞은 말을 쓰시오.

> A: I made a potato clock yesterday!
> B: A potato clock? What do you _____?
> A: My clock works with potatoes, not with batteries.

➡ _____

06 다음 대화의 내용과 일치하도록 빈칸을 완성하시오.

> Tom: Mom, have you heard about the Chat Robot?
> Mom: No, I haven't. What is it?
> Tom: It's a phone application. You can ask any questions and it will answer. Let me show you. "Emily, what's the weather like today?"
> Emily: "It's going to rain, so you'll need an umbrella."
> Mom: Wow, what a great application!

> Today, my lovely son, Tom, introduced a new (A)_____, the Chat Robot. It could answer (B)_____. Tom showed me how it worked, asking about (C)_____. Surprisingly, it let us know about the weather and what we would need. I was so surprised at this application.

Grammar

① 수동태

- Jack **built** this bridge. Jack은 이 다리를 건설했다. 〈능동태〉
- This bridge **was built** by Jack. 이 다리는 Jack에 의해 건설되었다. 〈수동태〉

■ 수동태는 능동태의 목적어를 주어로 만들고 동사를 'be+p.p.' 형태로 만든 후, 능동태의 주어를 'by+목적격' 형태로 하여 '주어가 ~되다'라고 해석한다. 능동태 문장의 시제에 따라 수동태 시제를 결정한다. 주체가 불분명할 경우 'by+행위자'는 생략되기도 한다.

- Sophie **cleans** the window every day. Sophie는 매일 창문을 청소한다.
- The window **is cleaned** by Sophie every day. 창문은 Sophie에 의해 매일 청소된다.

■ 4형식 문장의 수동태는 두 가지 형태를 갖는다. 직접목적어를 주어로 한 수동태에서는 간접목적어에 특정 전치사를 붙인다. 전치사 to를 쓰는 동사는 'give, tell, teach, show, bring' 등이고, 전치사 for를 쓰는 동사는 'buy, make, cook, get' 등이며, 전치사 of를 쓰는 동사는 'ask'가 있다.

- Math **is taught to** us by Mr. Kim. 수학은 김 선생님에 의해서 우리에게 가르쳐진다.
- Pizza **was cooked for** her by me. 피자는 그녀를 위해 나에 의해 만들어졌다.

■ 5형식 문장의 목적격보어가 원형부정사인 경우, 수동태 문장에서는 to부정사로 바꾼다. 그 외에는 모든 목적격보어를 그대로 쓸 수 있다.

- He **is called** Zuzu by us. 그는 우리에 의해 Zuzu라고 불린다.
- I **was made to finish** the job by him. 나는 그에 의해 그 일을 끝내도록 시켜졌다.

■ 조동사의 수동태는 '조동사+be+p.p.' 형태를 취한다.

- A new school **will be built** next year. 새로운 학교가 내년에 지어질 것이다.
- The desks **can be replaced** with other ones. 그 책상들은 다른 것들로 교체될 수 있다.

■ by 이외의 전치사를 사용하는 수동태에 유의한다.

- I **am interested in** English. 나는 영어에 흥미가 있다.
- Cake **is made from** flour, milk and eggs. 케이크는 밀가루, 우유, 달걀로 만들어진다.
- John **was surprised at** seeing him. John은 그를 보고 놀랐다.

핵심 Check

1. 다음 우리말과 일치하도록 빈칸에 알맞은 말을 쓰시오.

    (1) 그의 코트는 먼지로 덮여 있다.

      ➡ His coat _____ _____ _____ dirt.

    (2) 그 식당은 우리 이모가 운영하신다.

      ➡ The restaurant _____ _____ _____ my aunt.

② to부정사의 형용사적 용법

- Give the boys a chance to **introduce** themselves. 그 소년들에게 자신을 소개할 기회를 주어라.
- I have a project **to finish** today. 나는 오늘 끝낼 프로젝트가 있다.

■ to부정사는 'to+동사원형'의 형태로 명사, 형용사, 부사로 사용될 수 있다.
- **To write** a song is his favorite hobby. 작곡하는 것은 그가 가장 좋아하는 취미이다.
- Do you have anything **to drink**? 마실 것을 가지고 있니?
- I went to the market **to buy** some eggs. 나는 달걀을 사기 위해 시장으로 갔다.

■ to부정사가 형용사로 사용될 때는 바로 앞에 위치한 명사를 꾸며준다.
- Click the title of the message **to read**. 읽을 메시지의 제목을 누르세요.
- The game was something **to remember**. 그 경기는 기억할 만한 것이었다.

■ to부정사가 형용사로 사용될 때 전치사로 끝나는 경우를 주의하자. 수식하는 명사가 본래 전치사의 목적어로 사용됐으므로, 이때는 수식하는 명사를 to부정사 뒤로 넣어 전치사가 필요한지 유무를 확인하는 것이 좋다.
- I have many friends **to rely on**. (rely on friends (○)) 나는 의지할 많은 친구들이 있다.
- There is an issue **to deal with**. (deal with an issue (○)) 다룰 문제가 있습니다.

■ 형용사와 to부정사가 -thing, -body, -one으로 끝나는 부정대명사를 동시에 수식할 때는 '부정대명사+형용사+to부정사'의 어순을 따른다.
- Can you give me anything **warm to drink**? 따뜻한 마실 것 좀 주시겠어요?
- Jina has something **interesting to see**. Jina에게는 흥미로운 볼거리가 있다.

핵심 Check

2. 다음 우리말과 같도록 빈칸에 알맞은 말을 쓰시오.
(1) Jason은 읽을 책을 가지고 있다.
➡ Jason has a book _____ _____.
(2) 그녀는 노벨상을 탄 최초의 여성이었다.
➡ She was the first woman _____ _____ the Nobel Prize.
(3) 쓸 종이를 좀 가지고 있나요?
➡ Do you have some paper _____ _____ _____?

01 다음 문장에서 어법상 <u>어색한</u> 부분을 바르게 고쳐 쓰시오.

(1) Can I have a book to read about?

_____ ➡ _____

(2) Kelly born in Canada in 2005.

_____ ➡ _____

(3) There are many options choose.

_____ ➡ _____

(4) A gift was given for her yesterday.

_____ ➡ _____

02 주어진 어휘를 어법에 맞게 빈칸에 쓰시오.

(1) I _____ _____ to the meeting, but I didn't go. (invite)
(2) Keep in mind the goal _____ _____. (achieve)
(3) Many accidents _____ _____ by careless driving. (cause)
(4) I don't want to do anything _____ _____ her feelings. (hurt)
(5) My keys _____ _____ in the parking lot two days ago. (find)

03 다음 우리말에 맞게 주어진 어구를 바르게 배열하시오. (필요하면 어형을 바꾸고 단어를 추가할 것)

(1) 나는 먹을 것을 원해요. (want / eat / I / something)

➡ _____

(2) 우리에게는 계획할 여행이 있어. (We / a trip / have / plan)

➡ _____

(3) 새로운 고속도로가 지난달에 완공되었다.

(the new highway / complete / last month)

➡ _____

(4) 그 잉크는 물로 쉽게 지워진다.

(the ink / wash off / water / with / easily)

➡ _____

01 다음 빈칸에 알맞은 말이 바르게 짝지어진 것은?

> • He has twin sisters _____.
> • Actually, they have many questions _____.

① to take care – to ask about
② to take care – to ask
③ to take care of – to ask to
④ to take care of – to ask
⑤ taking care of – to ask

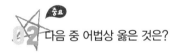

02 다음 중 어법상 옳은 것은?

① The glass is filled by milk.
② June is satisfied with the test result.
③ I want something to wear warm.
④ He was made do the homework first.
⑤ Some cookies were made to me by Julia.

03 다음 중 용법이 <u>다른</u> 하나는?

① She will buy a house to live in.
② I have a number of letters to write.
③ We need some food to buy.
④ He went out to see the scenery.
⑤ They have a problem to solve.

서답형

04 다음 빈칸에 들어갈 알맞은 말을 주어진 단어를 이용하여 쓰시오. 필요한 단어가 있으면 추가할 것.

> Her child is bored. He needs _____.
> (something / play)

➡ _____

05 다음 중 수동태로의 전환이 바르지 <u>않은</u> 것은?

① Did somebody clean my room?
 → Was my room cleaned by somebody?
② Someone stole my backpack.
 → My backpack was stolen by someone.
③ Jane made the dolls.
 → The dolls were made by Jane.
④ She looked after the injured bird.
 → The injured bird was looked after her.
⑤ Julian gave me some flowers.
 → I was given some flowers by Julian.

06 다음 문장과 같은 의미의 문장을 <u>모두</u> 고르시오.

> A note was given to me by Amelia.

① Amelia gave a note me.
② I was given a note by Amelia.
③ A note was given for me by Amelia.
④ Amelia gave to me a note.
⑤ Amelia gave me a note.

07 다음 중 빈칸에 들어갈 동사 'make'의 형태가 <u>다른</u> 하나는?

① The fuel is _____ from corn.
② Some comments were _____ to the event.
③ These games were _____ by creative young men.
④ This floor is _____ of wood.
⑤ The girl is _____ a box now.

서답형

08 주어진 단어를 이용하여 다음 우리말을 영어로 쓰시오. 필요한 단어가 있으면 추가할 것.

> 여기에는 볼만한 것이 없다.
> (there / nothing / see / here)

➡ _____

서답형

09 다음 우리말에 맞도록 빈칸을 채우시오.

> 여행하면서 읽을 책 한 권을 빌릴 수 있을까요?
> = May I _____ a book _____
>   _____ on my journey?

➡ _____

중요

10 다음 빈칸에 공통으로 들어갈 말로 가장 적절한 것은?

> • The bucket is filled _____ sand.
> • He was pleased _____ the news.

① by　　　② at　　　③ with
④ in　　　⑤ from

11 다음 두 문장이 같은 의미가 되도록 빈칸에 알맞은 것은?

> Jane saw the child playing football with his friends.
> = The child _____ football with his friends by Jane.

① was seen play　　② is seen to play
③ was seen playing　④ saw playing
⑤ is seen playing

12 다음 중 어법상 바르지 <u>않은</u> 것은?

> Kelly ①has to ②prepare ③lunch ④for serve a hundred ⑤guests.

①　　　②　　　③　　　④　　　⑤

13 다음 중 어법상 바르지 <u>않은</u> 것은?

① Jason was employed by his uncle.
② Tom was made to fix the bike by his dad.
③ Did the building designed by the brothers?
④ The pill was taken by the patient regularly.
⑤ The sweet potato was given to her by her grandmother.

서답형

14 다음 괄호 안의 단어를 어법에 맞게 고쳐 쓰시오.

> A: Is the plane going to be late?
> B: No. It (expect) to be on time.

➡ _____

중요

15 다음 빈칸에 들어갈 말이 <u>다른</u> 하나는?

① These shoes were given _____ me by John.
② Korean history is taught _____ us by Mr. Kim.
③ A package was sent _____ Kelly by someone.
④ A scarf was bought _____ my mother by us.
⑤ Paper dolls were sold _____ a lot of children at the amusement park.

16 다음 빈칸에 알맞은 것은?

> I am looking for _____ to my best friend.

① something giving
② something to give
③ something give
④ something to giving
⑤ giving something

17 다음 중 주어진 문장의 to부정사와 쓰임이 같은 것은?

> They didn't have much time to spend with my children.

① We will be glad to meet you again.
② Briana wanted to become the greatest pianist in the world.
③ It is important to be honest with your parents.
④ Do you have a friend to trust?
⑤ Ms. Greene encouraged us to do our best.

`서답형`
18 주어진 단어를 이용하여 다음 문장을 수동태로 쓰시오.

> Nobody saw me singing a song with my friends. (wasn't / anybody)

➡ _____
_____

`서답형`
19 다음 물음에 주어진 단어를 주어로 하여 답하시오.

> A: Do you know who discovered the treasure?
> B: Yes, I do. It _____ Captain Jackson.

➡ _____

20 다음 중 빈칸에 가장 적절한 것은?

> High blood pressure is a serious health problem _____ .

① to deal
② to deal about
③ to deal with
④ to look
⑤ to look into

21 다음 빈칸에 들어갈 말로 적절하지 <u>않은</u> 것은?

> Marin has a few friends _____ .

① to help her
② to play
③ to talk to
④ to trust
⑤ to meet

22 다음 밑줄 친 문장을 수동태로 바르게 전환한 것은?

> The CEO offered Robert the job, but he refused to accept it.

① The job offered to Robert by the CEO.
② The job was offered to Robert by the CEO.
③ Robert was offered the job by the CEO.
④ The job was offered for Robert by the CEO.
⑤ Robert was offered the CEO to the job.

`서답형`
23 다음 우리말을 괄호 안의 어구들을 이용하여 영작하시오.

> 들려줄 이야기가 있나요?
> (you / a story / tell)

➡ _____

`서답형`
24 다음 문장을 수동태로 전환하시오.

> Mom told me to taste the food.

➡ _____

01 다음 대화의 빈칸에 알맞은 말을 쓰시오.

> A: Who wrote *Hamlet*?
> B: *Hamlet* _____ Shakespeare.

➡ _____

02 다음 빈칸에 괄호 안에 주어진 단어의 올바른 형태를 쓰시오.

(1) Give her a magazine _____ _____. (read)
(2) There are many difficult subjects _____ _____ for this exam. (study)
(3) You have nothing _____ _____ _____. (worry about)

03 다음 문장을 두 가지 형태의 수동태로 쓰시오.

> My father gave me the watch a few years ago.

➡ _____
  _____
➡ _____
  _____

04 다음 문장을 주어진 단어로 시작하는 문장으로 다시 쓰시오.

> Helen's brother made me laugh a lot.

➡ I _____ .

05 주어진 단어를 어법에 맞도록 빈칸에 쓰시오.

> invent / surround / divide / surprise / build

> • As construction cost wasn't high, a new dormitory _____ by the Hans.
> • The game of baseball _____ by Americans.
> • Our country _____ into two halves.
> • Korea _____ by water on three sides.
> • We didn't expect them to come to the meeting, but they were there. We _____ to see them.

06 주어진 단어를 이용하여 다음 우리말에 맞게 빈칸을 채우시오.

> I heard Jenny had _____.
> (something / say)
> Jenny가 네게 할 말이 있다고 들었어.

07 주어진 어구를 바르게 배열하여 다음 우리말을 영어로 쓰시오. 필요하다면 단어를 추가하시오.

> 나는 요즈음 운동할 충분한 시간이 없어.
> (these days / enough / I / work out / don't / time / have)

➡ _____

08 다음 괄호 안에 주어진 단어를 이용하여 빈칸 ⓐ, ⓑ에 알맞은 말을 쓰시오.

> A: I have so many things ⓐ_____
> _____(do).
> B: What makes you so busy?
> A: Actually, my birthday party ⓑ
> _____ _____ (throw) yesterday.
> So I put off what I had to do yesterday.

09 다음 괄호 안에 주어진 단어를 어법에 맞게 각각 쓰시오.

> Neil Armstrong was the first man ⓐ
> _____ _____(walk) on the moon.
> No one can imagine how he felt when
> Neil ⓑ_____(set) his foot on the
> moon. Some pictures of the moon ©
> _____ _____(take) and they ⓓ
> _____ _____(bring) to the earth by
> him.

10 주어진 단어를 활용하여 다음 우리말을 8 단어로 이루어진 영어 문장으로 쓰시오.

> 나는 그의 부탁을 거절할 이유가 없어.
> (have / refuse / request)

➡ _____

11 다음 각 문장을 수동태는 능동태로, 능동태는 수동태로 전환하시오.

(1) The Emperor planted a tree himself.

➡ _____

(2) This car was made for us by a French company.

➡ _____

(3) The man is looked up to by the young girls.

➡ _____

(4) Worker bees make honey.

➡ _____

12 어법상 틀린 것을 바르게 고쳐 다음 문장을 다시 쓰시오.

> Do you have any samples giving out?

➡ _____

13 다음 우리말과 뜻이 같도록 빈칸에 알맞은 말을 쓰시오.

(1) 해야 할 지겨운 일들이 많이 있어.
➡ There are many boring things
_____ _____.

(2) 먹을 것을 가지고 있나요?
➡ Do you have something _____
_____?

(3) 그녀는 그것에 대해 할 말이 많이 있다.
➡ She has many things _____
_____ _____ it.

(4) 나는 탈 자전거를 샀어.
➡ I bought a bicycle _____ _____.

(5) 우리는 그것을 읽을 시간이 없어.
➡ We don't have time _____ _____
it.

14 주어진 단어를 활용하여 다음 우리말을 능동태와 수동태로 쓰시오.

> 그 도둑은 그 용감한 젊은 남자에 의해 붙잡혔다.
> (catch)

➡ _____

➡ _____

Reading

In animation movies, amazing things are possible. But are they actually possible in real life?

Let Down Your Hair, Rapunzel!

In the animation, Rapunzel must lower her long hair to let people in her tower. But could human hair really hold up a person?

Surprisingly, yes! A single hair can hold up 100g and an average head has about 120,000 hairs. All those hairs could hold up a couple of elephants! With her hair, Rapunzel has the ability to hold up a person. But she should wrap her hair around something strong and heavy. If she doesn't, she will get a very sore neck.

We Scare for Energy

In the animation, monsters scare children to get energy from their screams. Amazingly, their city is powered by this sound! But could we actually produce electricity to light up a city from sound?

---

animation 애니메이션
amazing 놀라운
possible 가능한
actually 실제로
let down ~을 내리다
lower ~을 내리다
let ~ in ~를 … 안으로 들이다
hold up ~을 들어 올리다
surprisingly 놀랍게도
average 평균의
about 대략, ~쯤
a couple of 둘의, 몇 개의
ability 능력
wrap ~ around ~을 …에 감다
sore 아픈
scare ~을 겁주다
get ~을 얻다
scream 비명
be powered by ~에 의하여 전기를 공급받다
produce 생산하다
light up ~을 환하게 밝히다, 환하게 하다

 확인문제

● 다음 문장이 본문의 내용과 일치하면 T, 일치하지 않으면 F를 쓰시오.

1 When she wants people to enter her tower, Rapunzel has to drop her long hair. ☐

2 It is possible to hold up a person with human hair. ☐

3 There are about 12,000 hairs on an average head. ☐

4 Rapunzel is able to hold up a person with her hair. ☐

5 Monsters' city is not powered by children's screams. ☐

Yes, sound can be changed into electricity. But it would not be
_{조동사가 있는 수동태} _{= sound}

helpful in our everyday activities because the amount is too small. For
_{이유를 나타내는 접속사: ~이기 때문에}

example, the sound from a car horn only produces 50mv. That is only
_{주어 the sound가 단수이므로 단수 동사}

1/4400 of the average 220v of electricity in our homes. So, we would

need an unbelievable amount of screams to light up an entire city.
_{믿기 힘든 양의} _{목적을 나타내는 to부정사의 부사적 용법: 밝히기 위하여}

Up, Up and Away!

The house is lifted and flown by thousands of balloons in the animation.
_{= Thousands of balloons lift and fly the house in the animation.}
Could that actually work?
_{앞 문장의 내용을 받는 지시대명사}

Let's say that a house weighs about 50,000kg. A normal balloon at
_{Let's say that+주어+동사: ~라고 가정해 보자} _{약, ~쯤}

an amusement park can lift about 14g. So we need about 3,570,000
_{그래서}

balloons to lift up the house. We also have to think about the weight
_{목적을 나타내는 to부정사의 부사적 용법: 들어 올리기 위해} _{= must}

of the balloons themselves and the strings. Then, we need to add a few
_{재귀대명사로 balloons를 강조} _{need to+동사원형: ~할 필요가 있다}

more thousand balloons. Now, the biggest challenge is pumping up all
_{형용사의 최상급 앞에 the}

those balloons!

be changed into ~으로 바뀌다
helpful 유용한
activity 활동
amount 양
for example 예를 들어
horn (차량의) 경적
unbelievable 믿을 수 없는
entire 전체의
lift ~을 들어 올리다
fly(-flew-flown) ~을 날리다
work 작동하다
weigh 무게가 ~이다
normal 보통의
amusement park 놀이공원
have to ~해야만 하다
weight 무게
string 줄
add 더하다
a few 조금, 약간의
challenge 도전,
pump up (공기 등을) 주입하다

확인문제

● 다음 문장이 본문의 내용과 일치하면 T, 일치하지 않으면 F를 쓰시오.

1 Electricity changed from sound is useful in our everyday activities. ☐

2 The sound produced by a car horn is 50mv. ☐

3 We use 220v of electricity in our homes. ☐

4 Thousands of balloons are lifted by the house in the animation. ☐

5 When we plan to lift a house with balloons, the only thing that has to be considered is the number of the balloons. ☐

6 Pumping up millions of balloons is difficult thing to do. ☐

● 우리말을 참고하여 빈칸에 알맞은 말을 쓰시오.

1 In animation movies, _____ _____ _____ _____.

2 But _____ _____ _____ _____ in real life?

3 _____ _____ Your Hair, Rapunzel!

4 In the animation, Rapunzel _____ _____ her long hair _____ _____ _____ _____ her tower.

5 But _____ human hair really _____ _____ _____ _____?

6 Surprisingly, yes! A single hair can _____ _____ 100g and an average head _____ _____ 120,000 hairs.

7 _____ _____ _____ could _____ _____ a couple of elephants!

8 With her hair, Rapunzel has _____ _____ _____ _____ _____ a person.

9 But she should _____ _____ _____ _____ something strong and heavy.

10 If she _____, she _____ _____ a very _____ neck.

11 We _____ _____ Energy

12 In the animation, monsters _____ _____ _____ _____ energy _____ their screams.

13 Amazingly, their city _____ _____ _____ this sound!

14 But could we actually _____ _____ _____ _____ _____ a city _____ sound?

---

1 만화 영화에서는 놀라운 일들이 가능하다.

2 하지만 그런 일들이 실생활에서 정말 가능할까?

3 라푼젤, 네 머리카락을 내려!

4 만화 영화에서 라푼젤은 사람들이 탑에 들어오게 하기 위해서 그녀의 긴 머리카락을 내려야 한다.

5 하지만 인간의 머리카락이 정말로 사람을 들어 올릴 수 있을까?

6 놀랍게도 그렇다! 머리카락 한 가닥은 100그램의 무게를 들어 올릴 수 있고 보통 머리에는 12만 개 정도의 머리카락이 있다.

7 그 모든 머리카락은 코끼리 두 마리를 들어 올릴 수 있다!

8 라푼젤에게는 머리카락으로 사람을 들어 올릴 수 있는 능력이 있다.

9 하지만 그녀는 머리카락을 어떤 강하고 무거운 것에 감아야 한다.

10 만약 그렇게 하지 않으면 그녀는 목이 많이 아플 것이다.

11 우리는 에너지를 얻기 위해 겁을 준다

12 만화 영화에서 괴물들은 아이들의 비명에서 에너지를 얻기 위해 아이들을 겁준다.

13 놀랍게도 그들의 도시는 이 소리로 동력을 공급받는다!

14 하지만 정말 소리로부터 도시를 밝히는 전기를 만들 수 있을까?

15 Yes, sound can _____ _____ _____ electricity.

16 But it would not be _____ _____ our everyday activities _____ _____ _____ _____ too _____.

17 _____ _____, the sound _____ a car horn only _____ 50mv.

18 That is only 1/4400 _____ _____ _____ 220v of _____ in our homes.

19 So, we would need _____ _____ _____ _____ _____ to light up an _____ city.

20 Up, Up and _____!

21 The house _____ _____ _____ _____ thousands of balloons in the animation.

22 Could that _____ _____?

23 Let's say that a house _____ _____ 50,000kg.

24 A _____ balloon at _____ _____ _____ _____ can lift about 14g.

25 So we need _____ 3,570,000 balloons _____ _____ _____ the house.

26 We also _____ _____ _____ _____ _____ the weight of the balloons _____ and the strings.

27 Then, we need to _____ _____ _____ _____ balloons.

28 Now, the biggest _____ is _____ _____ _____ balloons!

15 그렇다, 소리는 전기로 바뀔 수 있다.

16 그렇지만 그 양이 너무 적기 때문에 그것은 우리의 일상 활동에서는 도움이 되지 않을 것이다.

17 예를 들어, 자동차 경적 소리는 겨우 50밀리볼트를 만들어 낸다.

18 그것은 우리 가정에서 사용하는 일반적인 220볼트 전기의 1/4400밖에 되지 않는다.

19 그래서 도시 전체를 밝히기 위해서는 믿기 어려운 정도로 많은 양의 비명이 필요할 것이다.

20 높이, 높이 그리고 멀리!

21 만화 영화에서 집은 수천 개의 풍선에 의해 들려 올라가고 날아간다.

22 이게 실제로 가능할까?

23 집 한 채의 무게가 5만 킬로그램 정도라고 가정해 보자.

24 놀이공원에 있는 보통의 풍선은 대략 14그램을 들어 올릴 수 있다.

25 그래서 집을 들어 올리기 위해 우리는 약 3.570.000개의 풍선이 필요하다.

26 우리는 또한 풍선 자체와 줄의 무게에 대해서도 생각해야 한다.

27 그렇게 되면, 수천 개의 풍선을 더 추가할 필요가 있다.

28 이제 가장 큰 어려움은 그 모든 풍선에 바람을 넣는 일이다!

● 우리말을 참고하여 본문을 영작하시오.

1 만화 영화에서는 놀라운 일들이 가능하다.

➡ _____

2 하지만 그런 일들이 실생활에서 정말 가능할까?

➡ _____

3 라푼젤, 네 머리카락을 내려!

➡ _____

4 만화 영화에서 라푼젤은 사람들이 탑에 들어오게 하기 위해서 그녀의 긴 머리카락을 내려야 한다.

➡ _____

5 하지만 인간의 머리카락이 정말로 사람을 들어 올릴 수 있을까?

➡ _____

6 놀랍게도 그렇다! 머리카락 한 가닥은 100그램의 무게를 들어 올릴 수 있고 보통 머리에는 12만 개 정도의 머리카락이 있다.

➡ _____

7 그 모든 머리카락은 코끼리 두 마리를 들어 올릴 수 있다!

➡ _____

8 라푼젤에게는 머리카락으로 사람을 들어 올릴 수 있는 능력이 있다.

➡ _____

9 하지만 그녀는 머리카락을 어떤 강하고 무거운 것에 감아야 한다.

➡ _____

10 만약 그렇게 하지 않으면 그녀는 목이 많이 아플 것이다.

➡ _____

11 우리는 에너지를 얻기 위해 겁을 준다

➡ _____

12 만화 영화에서 괴물들은 아이들의 비명에서 에너지를 얻기 위해 아이들을 겁준다.

➡ _____

13 놀랍게도 그들의 도시는 이 소리로 동력을 공급받는다!

➡ _____

14 하지만 정말 소리로부터 도시를 밝히는 전기를 만들 수 있을까?

➡ _____

15 그렇다. 소리는 전기로 바뀔 수 있다.

➡ _____

16 그렇지만 그 양이 너무 적기 때문에 그것은 우리의 일상 활동에서는 도움이 되지 않을 것이다.

➡ _____

17 예를 들어, 자동차 경적 소리는 겨우 50밀리볼트를 만들어 낸다.

➡ _____

18 그것은 우리 가정에서 사용하는 일반적인 220볼트 전기의 1/4400밖에 되지 않는다.

➡ _____

19 그래서 도시 전체를 밝히기 위해서는 믿기 어려운 정도로 많은 양의 비명이 필요할 것이다.

➡ _____

20 높이, 높이 그리고 멀리!

➡ _____

21 만화 영화에서 집은 수천 개의 풍선에 의해 들려 올라가고 날아간다.

➡ _____

22 이게 실제로 가능할까?

➡ _____

23 집 한 채의 무게가 5만 킬로그램 정도라고 가정해 보자.

➡ _____

24 놀이공원에 있는 보통의 풍선은 대략 14그램을 들어 올릴 수 있다.

➡ _____

25 그래서 집을 들어 올리기 위해 우리는 약 3,570,000개의 풍선이 필요하다.

➡ _____

26 우리는 또한 풍선 자체와 줄의 무게에 대해서도 생각해야 한다.

➡ _____

27 그렇게 되면, 수천 개의 풍선을 더 추가할 필요가 있다.

➡ _____

28 이제 가장 큰 어려움은 그 모든 풍선에 바람을 넣는 일이다!

➡ _____

[01~04] 다음 글을 읽고, 물음에 답하시오.

In animation movies, amazing things are possible. But are ⓐthey actually possible in real life?

Let Down Your Hair, Rapunzel!

In the animation, Rapunzel must ①lower her long hair to let people ②in her tower. But could human hair really hold up a person?

Surprisingly, yes! A single hair can hold up 100g and an average head has about 120,000 hairs. All those hairs could hold up a couple of elephants! ③Without her hair, Rapunzel has the ability to hold up a person. But she should ④wrap her hair around something ⑤ strong and heavy. If she doesn't, she will get a very ⓑsore neck.

서답형

01 위 글의 밑줄 친 ⓐ가 가리키는 것을 위 글에서 찾아 쓰시오.

➡ _____

02 위 글의 내용과 일치하지 <u>않는</u> 것은?

① Amazing things happen in animation movies.
② Rapunzel has long hair.
③ Rapunzel has to use her hair to let people in her tower.
④ Holding up a person with human hair is not possible in real life.
⑤ Rapunzel needs to wrap her hair around something strong when she wants to hold up someone.

중요

03 위 글의 ①~⑤ 중 글의 흐름상 <u>어색한</u> 것은?

①   ②   ③   ④   ⑤

04 위 글의 밑줄 친 ⓑ를 대신하여 쓰기에 가장 적절한 것은?

① disappointing   ② annoying
③ painful   ④ burning
⑤ excited

[05~08] 다음 글을 읽고, 물음에 답하시오.

We Scare for Energy

In the animation, monsters scare children to get energy from their screams. Amazingly, their city ____ⓐ____ (power) by this sound! But could we actually produce electricity to light up a city from sound?

Yes, sound can be changed into electricity. But it would not be ____ⓑ____ in our everyday activities because the amount is too small. ____ⓒ____, the sound from a car horn only produces 50mv. That is only 1/4400 of the average 220v of electricity in our homes. So, we would need an unbelievable amount of screams to light up an entire city.

서답형

05 위 글의 주어진 단어를 빈칸 ⓐ에 어법에 맞게 쓰시오.

➡ _____

중요

06 위 글의 흐름상 빈칸 ⓑ에 들어갈 말로 가장 적절한 것은?

① grateful   ② thankful
③ thoughtful   ④ useful
⑤ wonderful

07 위 글의 빈칸 ⓒ에 들어갈 말로 가장 적절한 것은?

① As a result   ② Finally
③ For example   ④ However
⑤ On the other hand

08 다음 중 위 글의 내용과 일치하지 <u>않는</u> 것은?

① 괴물들은 에너지를 얻기 위해 아이들을 겁준다.

② 소리를 전기로 바꾸는 것이 가능하다.

③ 자동차 경적 소리는 50mv의 전기를 만들어 낼 수 있다.

④ 가정에서 사용하는 전기는 평균적으로 220v이다.

⑤ 소리를 이용해 전체 도시에 전기를 공급할 수 있는 기술을 개발 중이다.

[09~13] 다음 글을 읽고, 물음에 답하시오.

Up, Up and Away!

The house is lifted and flown __ⓐ__ thousands of balloons in the animation. Could that actually work?

Let's say that a house weighs __ⓑ__ 50,000kg. A normal balloon at an amusement park can lift __ⓒ__ 14g. So we need __ⓓ__ 3,570,000 balloons to lift up the house. We also have to think __ⓔ__ the weight of the balloons themselves and the strings. Then, we need to add a few more thousand balloons. Now, the biggest challenge is (A)<u>pumping</u> up all those balloons!

서답형

09 위 글의 빈칸 ⓐ~ⓔ에 들어갈 말이 <u>다른</u> 하나는?

① ⓐ   ② ⓑ   ③ ⓒ   ④ ⓓ   ⑤ ⓔ

서답형

10 다음과 같이 풀이되는 말을 위 글에서 찾아 쓰시오.

a film in which drawings appear to move

➡ _____

11 다음 중 글의 내용과 일치하는 것의 개수는?

ⓐ Thousands of balloons are used to lift and fly the house in the animation movie.

ⓑ Lifting a house with balloons is not an easy thing to do in real life.

ⓒ Pumping up millions of balloons is a piece of cake.

ⓓ The weight of the balloons themselves and the strings should be considered when we want to lift a house with balloons.

ⓔ The animation is about pumping up balloons to fly high in the sky.

① 1개   ② 2개   ③ 3개

④ 4개   ⑤ 5개

서답형

12 주어진 단어를 포함하여 7단어로 이루어진 문장으로 다음 물음에 답하시오.

Q: According to the passage, what is the hardest part of lifting a house with balloons? (them)

➡ _____

13 다음 중 밑줄 친 (A)와 쓰임이 같은 것은?

① She is <u>playing</u> the guitar.

② What is she <u>having</u> for lunch?

③ My goal is <u>winning</u> the race.

④ Jim is <u>making</u> fun of me.

⑤ The man is <u>pumping</u> up the tires.

[14~17] 다음 글을 읽고, 물음에 답하시오.

In animation movies, amazing things are possible. But are they actually possible in real life?

Let Down Your Hair, Rapunzel!

In the animation, Rapunzel must lower her long hair to let people in her tower. ① But could human hair really hold up a person?

Surprisingly, yes! ② A single hair can hold up 100g and an average head has ⓐabout 120,000 hairs. ③ With her hair, Rapunzel has the ability to hold up a person. ④ But she should wrap her hair around something strong and heavy. ⑤ If she ⓑdoesn't, she will get a very sore neck.

14 위 글의 ①~⑤ 중 주어진 문장이 들어가기에 가장 적절한 곳은?

All those hairs could hold up a couple of elephants!

①   ②   ③   ④   ⑤

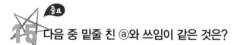

15 다음 중 밑줄 친 ⓐ와 쓰임이 같은 것은?

① This is a book about various trees.
② We wandered about the town for three hours.
③ The movie is about to begin.
④ What on earth are you talking about?
⑤ The tickets cost about 20 dollars.

서답형

16 위 글의 밑줄 친 ⓑ가 의미하는 것을 위 글에서 찾아 쓰시오.

➡ _____

17 다음 중 Rapunzel에 관한 내용으로 바르지 <u>않은</u> 것은?

① Her hair is very long.
② She is in her tower.
③ She has to use her hair to let in someone.
④ Her hair can hold up an elephant.
⑤ Her hair should be wrapped around something heavy when holding up someone.

[18~22] 다음 글을 읽고, 물음에 답하시오.

_____ⓐ_____

In the animation, monsters (A)[scare / are scared] children to get energy from their screams. Amazingly, (B)[its / their] city is powered by this sound! But could we actually produce electricity ___ⓑ___ a city (C)[from / into] sound?

Yes, sound can be changed into electricity. But it would not be helpful in our everyday activities because the amount is too small. For example, the sound from a car horn only produces 50mv. That is only 1/4400 of the average 220v of electricity in our homes. So, we would need _____ⓒ_____ to light up an entire city.

서답형

18 주어진 단어를 바르게 배열하여 빈칸 ⓐ에 들어갈 말을 완성하시오.

for / Scare / Energy / We

➡ _____

서답형

19 빈칸 ⓑ에 들어갈 말을 위 글에서 찾아 쓰시오.

➡ _____

20 위 글의 흐름상 빈칸 ⓒ에 들어갈 말로 가장 적절한 것은?

① a reasonable amount of car horns
② a believable amount of screams
③ an incredible amount of screams
④ a large amount of money
⑤ an unbelievable amount of monsters

21 다음 중 위 글을 읽고 답할 수 <u>없는</u> 질문은?

① What do monsters do to get energy?
② Is it possible to make electricity from sound?
③ How much electricity can a car horn make?
④ By what monsters' city is powered?
⑤ Why do we need electricity?

22 위 글의 (A)~(C)에서 어법상 옳은 것끼리 바르게 짝지어진 것은?

① scare – its – from
② are scared – their – into
③ scare – its – into
④ are scared – its – from
⑤ scare – their – from

[23~24] 다음 글을 읽고, 물음에 답하시오.

Up, Up and Away!

The house _____ⓐ_____ by thousands of balloons in the animation. Could that actually work?

Let's say that a house ①weighs about 50,000kg. A normal balloon at an amusement park can ②be lifted about 14g. So we need about 3,570,000 balloons ③to lift up the house. We also ④have to think about the weight of the balloons themselves and the strings. Then, we need ⑤to add a few more thousand balloons. Now, the biggest challenge is pumping up all those balloons!

23 위 글의 빈칸 ⓐ에 주어진 동사를 어법에 맞게 쓰시오.

lift and fly

➡ _____

24 위 글의 ①~⑤ 중 어법상 <u>틀린</u> 것을 골라 그 번호를 쓰고 바르게 고치시오.

➡ _____

25 주어진 문장에 자연스럽게 연결되도록 (A)~(C)를 바르게 나열한 것은?

In the animation, Rapunzel must lower her long hair to let people in her tower. But could human hair really hold up a person?

(A) All those hairs could hold up a couple of elephants! With her hair, Rapunzel has the ability to hold up a person.
(B) Surprisingly, yes! A single hair can hold up 100g and an average head has about 120,000 hairs.
(C) But she should wrap her hair around something strong and heavy. If she doesn't, she will get a very sore neck.

① (A) – (C) – (B)　② (B) – (A) – (C)
③ (B) – (C) – (A)　④ (C) – (A) – (B)
⑤ (C) – (B) – (A)

[01~05] 다음 글을 읽고, 물음에 답하시오.

In animation movies, amazing things are possible. But are they actually possible in real life?

Let Down Your Hair, Rapunzel!

In the animation, ⓐRapunzel must lower her long hair to let people in her tower. But could human hair really hold up a person?

Surprisingly, yes! A single hair can hold up 100g and an average head has about 120,000 hairs. ⓑAll those hairs could hold up a couple of elephants! With her hair, Rapunzel has the ability to hold up a person. But she should wrap her hair around something strong and heavy. If she doesn't, she will get a very sore neck.

01 위 글의 내용에 맞게 다음 물음에 대한 답을 완성하시오. 한 칸에 한 단어만 쓰시오.

Q: According to the passage, what kind of amazing thing does Rapunzel do in the movie?

A: The amazing thing that Rapunzel does in the movie is _____ _____ _____ _____ _____.

02 주어진 동사를 어법에 맞게 활용하여 밑줄 친 ⓐ와 같은 의미의 문장을 완성하시오.

Rapunzel must lower her long hair _____. (allow / enter)

03 위 글의 내용에 맞게 빈칸에 알맞은 말을 쓰시오.

Unless Rapunzel's hair _____ _____ around something _____ _____ _____, her neck will be sore.

04 주어진 단어를 이용하여 다음 물음에 완전한 문장의 영어로 답하시오.

Q: How much weight can a single hair hold up?

A: _____ (it)

05 밑줄 친 ⓑ와 같은 의미의 문장이 되도록 다음 문장을 완성하시오.

A couple of elephants could _____ _____ _____ by all those hairs!

[06~10] 다음 글을 읽고, 물음에 답하시오.

We Scare for Energy

In the animation, monsters scare children to get energy from ⓐtheir screams. Amazingly, ⓑtheir city is powered by this sound! But could we actually produce electricity to light up a city from sound?

Yes, _____ (A) _____. But it would not be helpful in our everyday activities because the amount is too small. For example, (B)the sound from a car horn only produces 50mv. That is only 1/4400 of the average 220v of electricity in our homes. So, we would need an unbelievable amount of screams to light up an entire city.

06 위 글의 밑줄 친 ⓐ와 ⓑ가 구체적으로 가리키는 것을 각각 우리말로 쓰시오.

ⓐ _____ ⓑ _____

07 다음 문장을 수동태로 만들어 빈칸 (A)에 쓰시오.

we can change sound into electricity

➡ _____

08 Write the reason why changing sound into electricity is not helpful in our everyday activities.

➡ _____

09 주어진 단어를 주어로 하여 밑줄 친 (B)와 같은 의미의 문장을 쓰시오.

only 50mv _____.

➡ _____

10 다음은 괴물들을 본 아이의 반응이다. 위 글의 단어를 어법에 맞게 활용하여 다음 빈칸에 쓰시오.

Mom, I am _____.

[11~13] 다음 글을 읽고, 물음에 답하시오.

Up, Up and Away!

(A) _____

Could that actually work?

Let's say that a house weighs about 50,000kg. A normal balloon at an amusement park can lift about 14g. So we need about 3,570,000 balloons to lift up the house. We also have to think about the weight of the balloons themselves and the strings. Then, we need to add a few more thousand balloons. Now, the biggest challenge is pumping up all those balloons!

11 다음 문장을 수동태로 전환하여 빈칸 (A)에 쓰시오.

Thousands of balloons lift and fly the house in the animation.

➡ _____
_____

12 적절한 대명사를 사용하여 다음 물음에 답하시오.

Q: How many grams can a normal balloon at an amusement park lift?

➡ _____

13 위 글의 내용에 맞게 대화의 빈칸을 채우시오.

Amelia: Jason, is it possible _____ _____ with balloons in real life?
Jason: Maybe it is. About 3,570,000 balloons _____ _____ to lift it. But can you imagine _____ _____ _____ _____ _____? I think it is the biggest challenge of all.

해석

Grammar in Real Life

This is Jack's plan for this week. There is a lot of work to do. He needs to go
<u>= much</u> <u>needs의 목적어</u>
to the library on Monday. He has two books to borrow from the library. Also
요일 앞에 전치사 on   two books를 수식하는 형용사적 용법
he has science homework to finish by Thursday. On Friday, he will be in the
                                    ~까지
school talent show. So, he will practice performing the songs at the talents
                                        practice의 목적어(동명사)
show all this week.
'all+this+명사'의 어순

구문해설 • plan: 계획 • there is ~: ~이 있다 • a lot of: 많은 • library: 도서관 • borrow: 빌리다

• finish: 끝내다 • talent: 재능 • practice: 연습하다

이것은 Jack의 이번 주 계획이다. 할 일이 많이 있다. 그는 월요일에 도서관에 가야 한다. 그는 도서관에서 빌려야 할 책 두 권이 있다. 또한. 그는 목요일까지 끝내야 할 과학 숙제가 있다. 금요일에 그는 학교 장기 자랑 대회에 나갈 것이다. 그래서 그는 이번 주 내내 장기 자랑 대회에서 공연할 노래들을 연습할 것이다.

Think & Write

Hello, my name is June. Today I'd like to talk about my new wearable
                        would like to V: V하고 싶다
technology, SuperEye. It is helpful to take pictures and video-record. It is also
                    = SuperEye   형용사 helpful을 수식하는 부사적 용법
useful to show me a map. Try it out and experience a new world!
4형식 동사+간접목적어+직접목적어 동사+대명사 목적어+부사(어순 주의)

구문해설 • talk about: ~에 관하여 이야기하다 • wearable: 착용할 수 있는 • technology: 기술

• take pictures: 사진을 찍다 • helpful: 유용한 • useful: 유용한 • try out: 시도하다

안녕, 내 이름은 June이야. 오늘 나는 나의 새로운 착용 가능한 기술인 SuperEye에 관해 말하고 싶어. 그것은 사진을 찍거나 녹화를 하는 데 유용해. 또한 나에게 지도를 보여 주는 데도 유용해. 한 번 사용해 보고 새로운 세계를 경험해 봐!

Wrap Up 3

Amy: Have you heard about the special event at the science museum?
      Have+p.p. = 현재완료

Brian: No, I haven't. What's the event?

Amy: There are science magic shows during the weekend, but only for this
      There are+복수명사   during+기간 명사   오직, 단지
      month.

Brian: Oh, thank you for the information. I'll visit there this weekend.
                                                = the science museum

구문해설 • Have you heard about ~?: ~에 대해 들어 본 적이 있니? • information: 정보

Amy: 너는 과학 박물관에서 하는 특별 이벤트에 대해 들어 본 적 있어?

Brian: 아니, 없어. 어떤 이벤트야?

Amy: 주말 동안 과학 마술 쇼가 있는데, 이번 달에만 있대.

Brian: 오, 정보 고마워. 이번 주말에 방문해야겠어.

01 다음 짝지어진 단어의 관계가 같도록 빈칸에 알맞은 말을 쓰시오.

actual : actually = surprising : _____

02 다음 문장의 빈칸에 들어갈 말을 〈보기〉에서 골라 적절한 형태로 쓰시오.

┌─ 보기 ┌
pump up / turn into /
look forward to / let's say that
└────────

(1) I'm _____ _____ _____ visiting the amusement park.

(2) You should _____ _____ all the balloons for the birthday party.

(3) _____ _____ _____ you have power to lift up an elephant.

(4) Grape juice will _____ _____ wine.

03 다음 중 밑줄 친 부분의 뜻풀이가 바르지 <u>않은</u> 것은?

① I have a <u>sore</u> throat. 아픈

② I didn't realize how <u>amazing</u> his work of art was. 놀라운

③ I got <u>average</u> grades in the mid-term test. 평균

④ Why don't you <u>lower</u> the price a little? 높이다

⑤ I hate the ghosts because they <u>scare</u> me. 겁을 주다

04 다음 주어진 문장의 밑줄 친 의미와 같은 의미로 쓰인 것은?

He must have <u>missed</u> a chance to go abroad.

① He completely <u>missed</u> the joke.

② I don't know why she didn't <u>miss</u> her mother so much.

③ What did you <u>miss</u> most when you were in Canada?

④ They don't want to <u>miss</u> a single note.

⑤ After my English teacher left, many students <u>missed</u> her.

05 다음 우리말을 주어진 단어를 이용하여 영작하시오.

(1) 제가 당신의 지혜를 빌려도 될까요?
(may, pick)

➡ _____

(2) 엄마는 내게 램프를 밝혀달라고 요청하셨다.
(ask, light, lamp)

➡ _____

(3) 나는 벤치에 앉아 있는 한 쌍의 새를 보았다.
(couple, sitting)

➡ _____

06 다음 대화의 우리말을 알맞게 영작하시오.

A: 너는 과학 축제에 대해 들어봤니?

B: Yes, I have. It will be held at the science museum this weekend.

➡ _____

[07~08] 다음 대화를 읽고, 물음에 답하시오.

Tom: Mom, have you heard ⓐabout the Chat Robot?

Mom: No, I ⓑhaven't. What is it?

Tom: It's a phone application. You can ask ⓒany questions and it will answer. Let me ⓓto show you. "Emily, what's the weather like today?"

Emily: "It's going to rain, so you'll need an umbrella."

Mom: Wow, ⓔwhat a great application!

07 위 대화의 밑줄 친 ⓐ~ⓔ 중 어법상 어색한 것을 고르고 바르게 고치시오.

➡ _____

08 엄마의 마지막 말로 보아 알 수 있는 엄마의 심정으로 적절한 것은?

① nervous
② surprised
③ disappointed
④ upset
⑤ indifferent

[09~11] 다음 대화를 읽고, 물음에 답하시오.

Jimmy: Lisa, what did you do last weekend?

Lisa: I made an egg ball with my brother.

Jimmy: An egg ball? What do you mean?

Lisa: _____(A)_____ Then, (B)the egg turns into a ball.

Jimmy: Wow, I want to make one, too!

09 위 대화의 빈칸 (A)에 들어갈 말을 주어진 단어를 모두 배열하여 완성하시오.

┌── 보기 ──┐
put / vinegar / for / days / we / an egg / in / two
└────────┘

➡ _____

10 위 대화의 밑줄 친 (B)와 의미가 같도록 change를 사용하여 다시 쓰시오.

➡ _____

11 위 대화를 읽고 알 수 없는 질문은?

① What did Lisa make last weekend?
② With whom did Lisa make an egg ball?
③ What did Lisa need to make an egg ball?
④ How long did Lisa put an egg in vinegar?
⑤ Why did an egg turn into a ball?

[12~13] 다음 대화를 읽고, 물음에 답하시오.

Minho: Anna, let's make a "Mystery Card" ⓐfor the science experiment.

Anna: A "Mystery Card?" What do you mean?

Minho: It's a special card. It can hide your message.

Anna: ⓑHow do you make it?

Minho: ⓒMix baking soda and water. Then, write a message on the card with it.

Anna: How can you read the card?

Minho: Paint ⓓover the card with grape juice, and then the message ⓔto appear.

12 위 대화의 밑줄 친 ⓐ~ⓔ 중 어법상 틀린 것을 찾아 바르게 고치시오.

➡ _____

13 위 대화를 읽고 대답할 수 없는 질문은?

① What are Minho and Anna making for the science experiment?
② What is the "Mystery Card"?
③ What should Minho and Anna prepare to make the "Mystery Card"?
④ How can Minho and Anna read a message on the "Mystery Card"?
⑤ What message do Minho and Anna want to write on the "Mystery Card"?

[14~15] 다음 대화를 읽고, 물음에 답하시오.

Jane: Have you heard about the Smart App Contest?

Minho: (A)응, 들어봤어. Are you going to enter it?

Jane: Yeah, I'm going to send my idea about a Pic Gardener App.

Minho: A Pic Gardener App? What do you mean?

Jane: When you take a picture of a plant, the app tells you how to take care of it.

Minho: It sounds like a very useful app.

14 위 대화의 밑줄 친 (A)의 우리말을 3단어를 사용하여 영어로 쓰시오.

➡ _____

15 위 대화의 내용과 일치하도록 빈칸을 완성하시오.

> Mon. Jun, 3rd. 2020.
> Today, I talked about the Smart App Contest with Jane. She said that she would enter it. I was impressed by her idea about (A)_____. It was the app that told me (B)_____, when I took a picture of a plant. I thought it was very (C)_____. I believe she will do well in the contest.

Grammar

16 다음 빈칸에 알맞은 것은?

> A: Who drew the picture?
> B: The picture _____ Jin.

① was drawn to   ② was drawn by
③ is drawn to   ④ is drawn by
⑤ was drawn in

17 다음 중 어법상 옳지 않은 것은?

① When was the concert held?
② My camera was disappeared from my car.
③ Is there anything to drink here?
④ The music was played by the most famous pianist.
⑤ Now the lights are turned on all at once.

18 다음 중 빈칸에 들어갈 말로 가장 적절한 것은?

> A: Is there _____ in New York?
> B: You should try visiting The Metropolitan Museum of Art.

① something to see interesting
② anything interested to see
③ something interesting seeing
④ anything interesting to see
⑤ seeing anything interesting

19 다음 문장을 수동태로 전환하시오.

> Lamon didn't allow his daughter to go to the park alone.

➡ _____
_____

20 다음 빈칸에 들어갈 말로 어법상 적절하지 <u>않은</u> 것은?

Jenny has many friends _____.

① to see   ② to talk to
③ to go   ④ to call
⑤ to remember

21 다음 문장에서 어법상 옳지 <u>않은</u> 것은?

Nothing ①was said ②about the accident ③since it ④was happened ⑤last night.

①   ②   ③   ④   ⑤

22 다음 중 밑줄 친 부분이 어법상 옳은 것은?

① Avery was made <u>clean</u> the room.
② My little sister <u>called</u> Puppy by her friends.
③ <u>Did</u> the lights in the room turned off?
④ Was the I-pad <u>borrowed</u> from Kevin?
⑤ The violin is <u>playing</u> by a famous violinist.

23 다음 우리말에 맞도록 빈칸에 알맞은 말을 쓰시오.

그에게 읽을 책 한 권과 마실 물, 앉을 의자 하나를 주세요.
➡ Please give him a book _____ _____, water _____ _____, and a chair _____ _____ _____.

24 다음 중 어법상 바르지 <u>않은</u> 것은?

① Mr. Cooper has many students to teach.
② Can I have a pen to write with?
③ They gave me a cushion to use.
④ They have many problems to discuss about.
⑤ I heard she had some work to do yesterday.

25 주어진 단어를 주어로 하여 다음 문장과 같은 의미의 문장을 쓰시오.

If he takes care of my sisters, we will be really relieved.
= If my sisters _____,
we will be really relieved.

26 다음 우리말을 영어로 바르게 옮긴 것은?

주워야 할 쓰레기가 너무 많아.

① There are so many trash to pick.
② There are so much trash to pick on.
③ There is too much trash to pick on.
④ There is too much trash to pick up.
⑤ There are too many trash to pick up.

Reading

[27~29] 다음 글을 읽고, 물음에 답하시오.

In animation movies, ____ⓐ____ things are possible. But are they actually possible in real life?

Let Down Your Hair, Rapunzel!

In the animation, Rapunzel must ____ⓑ____ her long hair to ____ⓒ____ people in her tower. But could human hair really hold up a person?

Surprisingly, yes! A single hair can hold up 100g and an average head has about 120,000 hairs. All those hairs could hold up a couple of elephants! With ____(A)____, Rapunzel has the ability to hold up a person. But she should ____ⓓ____ her hair around something strong and heavy. If she doesn't, she will get a very sore neck.

27 다음 중 빈칸 ⓐ~ⓓ에 들어갈 말이 <u>아닌</u> 것은?

① wrap   ② lower   ③ amazing
④ hold   ⑤ let

28 위 글의 빈칸 (A)에 들어갈 알맞은 말을 위 글에서 찾아 쓰시오.

➡ _____

29 다음 중 위 글을 읽고 답할 수 있는 것을 <u>모두</u> 고르면?

① How long is Rapunzel's hair?
② What made Rapunzel stay in the tower?
③ How many hairs does an average head have?
④ How much does an elephant weigh?
⑤ Why do people want to go to the tower?

[30~32] 다음 글을 읽고, 물음에 답하시오.

We Scare for Energy

In the animation, monsters scare children to get energy from their screams. ① Amazingly, their city is powered by this sound! ② But could we actually produce electricity ⓐto light up a city from sound?

Yes, sound can be changed into electricity. ③ But it would not be helpful in our everyday activities because the amount is too small. ④ For example, the sound from a car horn only produces 50mv. ⑤ So, we would need an unbelievable amount of screams to light up an entire city.

30 다음 중 주어진 문장이 들어가기에 가장 적절한 곳은?

> That is only 1/4400 of the average 220v of electricity in our homes.

①   ②   ③   ④   ⑤

31 다음 밑줄 친 ⓐ와 그 쓰임이 다른 것은?

① I want to have the ability <u>to speak</u> English well.
② Most people have a desire <u>to collect</u> things.
③ She will have a chance <u>to apply</u> for the job.
④ An attempt <u>to open</u> the jar turned out a failure.
⑤ We went to a grocery store <u>to buy</u> some milk.

32 위 글의 내용에 맞게 빈칸에 알맞은 말을 쓰시오.

> _____ would be needed to light up an entire city.

출제율 90%

01 다음 문장의 빈칸에 들어갈 말을 〈보기〉에서 골라 쓰시오.

┌─ 보기 ─┐
take care of / turn on /
take away / light up

(1) Would you _____ _____ these empty bottles?
(2) I have the power to _____ _____ lights.
(3) Do you know how to _____ _____ _____ this plant?
(4) Beautiful fireworks _____ _____ the sky.

출제율 90%

02 다음 영영풀이가 나타내는 말을 쓰시오.

a scientific test that is done in order to study what happens and to gain new knowledge

➡ _____

출제율 95%

03 다음 우리말에 맞게 빈칸에 알맞은 말을 쓰시오.

(1) 이 로봇이 스포츠카가 될 수 있다.
➡ This robot can _____ _____ a sports car.
(2) 너는 그 천을 무릎에 감쌀 필요가 있다.
➡ You need to _____ the cloth _____ your knee.
(3) 나는 이틀 전에 그 프로젝트를 끝냈다.
➡ I finished the project _____ _____ _____ days ago.

출제율 100%

04 다음 문장에 공통으로 들어갈 말을 고르시오.

• He _____(e)d his baby in his arms.
• The _____ in this building is being fixed.
• They watched the balloons _____ up.

① increase   ② jump
③ repair   ④ raise
⑤ lift

출제율 90%

05 다음 대화가 자연스럽게 이어지도록 순서대로 배열하시오.

(A) Oh, it sounds interesting.
(B) No, I haven't. What's it about?
(C) What show are you watching?
(D) The program uses science to explain magic tricks.
(E) I'm watching the Sci-Magic show. It's a new program. Have you heard about it?

➡ _____

[06~08] 다음 대화를 읽고, 물음에 답하시오.

Tom: Mom, _____(A)_____?
Mom: No, I haven't. What is it?
Tom: It's a phone application. You can ask any questions and it will answer. Let me show you. "Emily, what's the weather like today?"
Emily: "It's going to rain, so you'll need an umbrella."
Mom: Wow, what a great application!

06 위 대화의 빈칸 (A)에 들어갈 말을 〈보기〉에 주어진 단어를 모두 배열하여 완성하시오.

┌─── 보기 ───┐
you / about / Chat Robot / have /
the / heard

➡ _____

출제율 90%

07 위 대화에서 다음 영영풀이가 나타내는 말을 찾아 쓰시오.

a program designed to do a particular job

➡ _____

출제율 85%

08 위 대화의 내용과 일치하지 <u>않는</u> 것은?

① Tom is explaining the Chat Robot to his mom.
② Emily, the Chat Robot, is a phone application.
③ Tom's mom hasn't heard about the Chat Robot.
④ The Chat Robot answers the question about today's weather.
⑤ Tom's mom is surprised at the rain outside.

[09~10] 다음 대화를 읽고, 물음에 답하시오.

Mina: You know what? I made a potato clock yesterday!
Jack: A potato clock? What do you mean?
Mina: My clock works with potatoes, not with batteries. Potatoes can produce electricity.
Jack: That's interesting!

출제율 95%

09 What did Mina make yesterday?

➡ _____

출제율 95%

10 How can Mina's clock work? (Use the word 'because'.)

➡ _____

출제율 100%

11 다음 괄호 안에 주어진 단어의 형태가 바르게 짝지어진 것은?

I am not good at (make) friends, so I don't have a friend (depend on).

① make – to depend on
② making – depending on
③ to make – to depend on
④ making – to depend on
⑤ to make – depending on

출제율 95%

12 다음 중 어법상 바른 문장의 개수는?

ⓐ Ann's cup was broken by Ted.
ⓑ The money I put on the table was disappeared.
ⓒ Haiti was hit by strong earthquakes a few years ago.
ⓓ Emma is married a rich and honest man.
ⓔ Steve Jobs was born in 1955.

① 1개 ② 2개 ③ 3개
④ 4개 ⑤ 5개

출제율 90%

13 다음 중 빈칸에 들어갈 말을 바르게 배열한 것은?

How about looking for _____ for dinner?

① something eat tasty
② something to eat tasty
③ something tasty eat
④ something tasty to eat
⑤ something to tasty to eat

14 출제율 95%

다음 중 문장의 전환이 바르지 <u>않은</u> 것은?

① Two hundred people were employed by the company.
  → The company employed two hundred people.
② They didn't invite me to their party.
  → I was not invited to their party by them.
③ They canceled all flights because of the fog.
  → All flights are canceled by them because of the fog.
④ This road isn't used by us very often.
  → We don't use this road very often.
⑤ People speak English in many countries.
  → English is spoken in many countries.

15 출제율 85%

주어진 단어를 활용하여 다음 우리말을 조건에 맞게 영어로 쓰시오.

> 그가 너에게 그 사진을 보여 주었니?
> (shown / to you)

능동태로 ➡ _____
수동태로 ➡ _____

16 출제율 90%

주어진 단어를 활용하여 다음 우리말을 영어로 쓰시오.

> 연습은 영어에 통달하는 유일한 방법이다.
> (practice / mater)

➡ _____

[17~18] 다음 글을 읽고, 물음에 답하시오.

In animation movies, amazing things are possible. But are they actually possible in real life?

Let (A)[Up / Down] Your Hair, Rapunzel!

In the animation, Rapunzel must lower her long hair ⓐto let people in her tower. But could human hair really hold up a person?

Surprisingly, yes! A single hair can hold up 100g and an average head has about 120,000 hairs. All those hairs could hold up a couple of elephants! With her hair, Rapunzel has the ability (B)[hold up / to hold up] a person. But she should wrap her hair around something strong and heavy. (C)[If / Unless] she doesn't, she will get a very sore neck.

17 출제율 100%

위 글의 (A)~(C)에서 어법상 옳은 것끼리 바르게 짝지어진 것은?

① Up – hold up – If
② Up – to hold up – If
③ Down – to hold up – Unless
④ Down – hold up – If
⑤ Down – to hold up – If

18 출제율 95%

위 글의 밑줄 친 ⓐ와 쓰임이 같은 것은?

① He hoped <u>to be</u> elected president of his class.
② Kelly encouraged me <u>to do</u> my best all the time.
③ It is possible <u>to lift</u> a person with human hair.
④ Please give me a chair <u>to sit</u> on.
⑤ Jane flew from New York <u>to see</u> me again.

[19~21] 다음 글을 읽고, 물음에 답하시오.

We ①Scare for Energy

In the animation, monsters scare children to get energy from their screams. Amazingly, their city ②is powered by this sound! But ⓐ could we actually produce electricity to light up a city from sound?

Yes, sound can ③be changed into electricity. But it would not be helpful in our everyday activities ④because the amount is too small. For example, the sound from a car horn ⑤is produced only 50mv. That is only 1/4400 of the average 220v of electricity in our homes. So, we would need an unbelievable amount of screams to light up an entire city.

출제율 90%

19 위 글의 밑줄 친 ⓐ와 같은 의미의 문장은?

① could electricity be produced by a city?

② could electricity to light up a city be changed into sound?

③ could electricity to light up a city be made from sound?

④ could a city to produce electricity be produced by us?

⑤ could we actually make electricity to light up a city into sound?

출제율 100%

20 위 글의 ①~⑤ 중 어법상 바르지 <u>않은</u> 것은?

①   ②   ③   ④   ⑤

출제율 95%

21 위 글의 내용에 맞게 다음 물음에 답하시오.

> Q: In the animation movie, what do monsters do to get energy?
>
> A: _____

[22~24] 다음 글을 읽고, 물음에 답하시오.

Up, Up and Away!

The house is lifted and flown by thousands of balloons in the animation. Could ⓐthat actually work?

Let's say that a house weighs about 50,000kg. A normal balloon at an amusement park can lift about 14g. So we need about 3,570,000 balloons to lift up the house. We also have to think about the weight of the balloons themselves and the strings. Then, we need to add a few more thousand balloons. Now, the biggest challenge is pumping up all those balloons!

출제율 90%

22 다음 중 위 글을 읽고 답할 수 있는 질문은?

① When is the house lifted in the animation?

② Who pumped up all the balloons in the animation?

③ How many people do we need to pump up millions of balloons?

④ How many balloons do we need to lift up a house?

⑤ How many grams does a balloon string weigh?

출제율 95%

23 다음 주어진 어구를 바르게 배열하여 밑줄 친 ⓐ가 의미하는 것을 쓰시오. 필요하다면 어형을 바꾸시오.

> lift / a house / with / up / thousands of balloons

➡ _____

출제율 90%

24 위 글의 내용에 맞게 빈칸에 알맞은 말을 쓰시오.

> When we plan to lift up a house, we have to consider _____
>
> and _____.

[01~03] 다음 대화를 읽고, 물음에 답하시오.

Minho: Anna, let's make a "Mystery Card" for the science experiment.

Anna: A "Mystery Card?" What do you mean?

Minho: It's a special card. It can hide your message.

Anna: How do you make it?

Minho: Mix baking soda and water. Then, write a message on the card with it.

Anna: How can you read the card?

Minho: Paint over the card with grape juice, and then the message appears.

01 Why is a "Mystery Card" special?

➡ _____

02 What does Anna need to make a "Mystery Card"?

➡ _____

03 중요 "Mystery Card"의 메시지를 읽을 수 있는 방법을 우리말 20자 이내로 간략히 설명하시오.

➡ _____

04 주어진 어구를 활용하여 빈칸에 알맞은 말을 쓰시오.

A: You look very busy. What are you doing?

B: I'm going to throw a party for my parents. So (have / many things / plan).

➡ _____

05 다음 문장을 수동태로 바꿔 쓰시오.

(1) I made some mistakes.

➡ _____

(2) My friend made me a pretty doll.

➡ _____

(3) Jason always makes us bored.

➡ _____

06 중요 다음 중 어법상 틀린 것을 골라 바르게 고치시오.

That hotel has a pool to swim.

_____ ➡ _____

07 다음 두 문장이 같은 의미를 가지도록 빈칸에 알맞은 말을 쓰시오.

We didn't buy the oranges on the table.
= The oranges on the table _____ by us.

➡ _____

08 주어진 단어를 활용하여 다음 우리말을 7 단어로 이루어진 영어 문장으로 쓰시오.

결정할 충분한 시간이 너에게 주어졌어.
(be / give / decide)

➡ _____

In animation movies, amazing things are possible. But are they actually possible in real life?

Let Down Your Hair, Rapunzel!

In the animation, Rapunzel must lower her long hair to let people in her tower. ⓐBut could human hair really hold up a person? Surprisingly, yes! A single hair can hold up 100g and an average head has about 120,000 hairs. All those hairs could hold up a couple of elephants! With her hair, Rapunzel has the ability to hold up a person. But she should wrap her hair around something strong and heavy. If she doesn't, she will get a very sore neck.

09 According to the passage, what must be lowered so thatr people can enter Rapunzel's tower? Answer with 6 words.

➡ _____

10 위 글의 밑줄 친 ⓐ와 같은 의미가 되도록 빈칸에 알맞은 말을 쓰시오.

> But is it possible that a person _____
> _____ by human hair?

11 위 글의 내용에 맞게 빈칸에 알맞은 말을 쓰시오.

> Rapunzel: I need something _____
> _____ _____ my hair in order to
> let a friend in my tower. I want it to be
> _____ and _____. Do you have
> something like that?

We Scare for Energy

In the animation, monsters scare children to get energy from their screams. Amazingly, their city is powered by this sound! But could we actually produce electricity to light up a city from sound?

Yes, sound can be changed into electricity. But it would not be helpful in our everyday activities because the amount is too small. For example, the sound from a car horn only produces 50mv. That is only 1/4400 of the average 220v of electricity in our homes. So, we would need an unbelievable amount of screams to light up an entire city.

12 Why do monsters scare the children in the animation movie? Answer in English with a full sentence.

➡ _____

_____

13 위 글에 나오는 단어를 이용하여 빈칸에 알맞은 말을 쓰시오.

> A: Do you know that electricity _____
> _____ by a car horn?
> B: Oh, really? I didn't know that. How much amount of electricity is made?
> A: Only 50mv.

01 다음 담화문을 읽고 아래 표의 (A)~(C)를 완성하시오.

> W: Hello, students. Have you heard about the DIY Drone Class? You can make your own drone in the class. The Youth Community Center offers the class at 3 p.m. every Wednesday in May. Make your special drone and learn how to control it. Don't miss this great chance!

DIY Drone Class	
When	(A)
Where	(B)
What	You can (C)

02 〈보기〉의 동사를 활용하여 수동태로 문장을 쓰시오.

> 보기
>
> unlock   open   take away   hit   break   pour

(1) _____

(2) _____

(3) _____

(4) _____

(5) _____

(6) _____

03 주어진 단어를 알맞게 짝지어 〈보기〉와 같은 문장을 쓰시오.

> 보기
>
> I have no reason to give up.

> book   money   right   reason   chance   desire
> borrow   spend   speak   believe   win   have   give up   learn

(1) _____

(2) _____

(3) _____

(4) _____

(5) _____

(6) _____

단원별 모의고사

[01~02] 다음 대화를 읽고, 물음에 답하시오.

Hojin: Hey, Katy. Have you heard about the science fair?

Katy: Yeah, I'm going to go there.

Hojin: Me, too! I'm excited about doing different kinds of experiments.

Katy: Yeah, (A)I'm also looking forward to it! (wait)

01 위 대화의 밑줄 친 (A)와 의미가 같도록 주어진 단어를 사용하여 다시 쓰시오.

➡ _____

02 What can Hojin and Katy do at the science fair?

➡ _____

[03~04] 다음 대화를 읽고, 물음에 답하시오.

Emma: _____ (A) _____

David: "Dancing Beans?" What do you mean?

Emma: They are beans that move in the water like they're dancing.

David: Sounds interesting! What do we need?

Emma: We just need some water, vinegar, baking soda, and beans.

03 위 대화의 빈칸 (A)에 들어갈 말로 나머지와 의도가 다른 것은?

① Let's make "Dancing Beans" for the science project.

② Why don't we make "Dancing Beans" for the science project?

③ What about making "Dancing Beans" for the science project?

④ How about making "Dancing Beans" for the science project?

⑤ Why did you make "Dancing Beans" for the science project?

04 What David and Emma should prepare to make "Dancing Beans"?

➡ _____

_____

05 다음 담화문의 빈칸 (A)~(C)에 주어진 단어를 알맞은 형태로 쓰시오.

W: Hello, students. Have you (A)_____(hear) about the DIY Drone Class? You can make your own drone in the class. The Youth Community Center offers the class at 3 p.m. every Wednesday in May. (B)_____(make) your special drone and learn how (C)_____(control) it. Don't miss this great chance!

[06~07] 다음 대화를 읽고, 물음에 답하시오.

Jimmy: Lisa, what did you do last weekend?

Lisa: I made an egg ball ____(A)____ my brother.

Jimmy: An egg ball? What do you mean?

Lisa: We put an egg ____(B)____ vinegar ____(C)____ two days. Then, the egg turns ____(D)____ a ball.

Jimmy: Wow, ⓐI want to make one, too!

06 위 대화의 빈칸 (A)~(D)에 들어갈 말을 주어진 단어를 넣어 완성하시오.

┌─ 보기 ├─
for / with / into / in
└─────────────────┘

(A)_____ (B)_____ (C)_____ (D)_____

07 위 대화의 밑줄 친 ⓐ와 바꾸어 쓸 수 있는 것은?

① I'm good at making one, too.

② I'd like to make one, too.

③ I'm glad to make one, too.

④ I wish I could make one, too.

⑤ I like making one, too.

08 다음 대화의 내용과 일치하도록 빈칸을 명령문을 사용하여 완성하시오.

> Minho: Anna, let's make a "Mystery Card" for the science experiment.
>
> Anna: A "Mystery Card?" What do you mean?
>
> Minho: It's a special card. It can hide your message.
>
> Anna: How do you make it?
>
> Minho: Mix baking soda and water. Then, write a message on the card with it.
>
> Anna: How can you read the card?
>
> Minho: Paint over the card with grape juice, and then the message appears.

How to Make a Mystery Card	
step 1	Mix baking soda and water.
step 2	(A)
How to Read a Mystery Card	
step 1	(B)
step 2	Then, you can read the message.

(A) _____

(B) _____

[09~10] 다음 대화를 읽고, 물음에 답하시오.

> Jane: Have you heard about the Smart App Contest?
>
> Minho: Yes, I have. Are you going to (A)enter it?
>
> Jane: Yeah, I'm going to send my idea about a Pic Gardener App.
>
> Minho: A Pic Gardener App? What do you mean?
>
> Jane: When you take a picture of a plant, the app tells you how to take care of it.
>
> Minho: It sounds like a very useful app.

09 위 대화의 밑줄 친 (A)와 바꾸어 쓸 수 없는 것은? (2개)

① take part in   ② share

③ join   ④ participate in

⑤ exit

10 위 대화의 내용과 일치하지 않는 것은?

① Minho와 Jane은 Smart App Contest에 대해 알고 있다.

② Jane은 Smart App Contest에 참가할 것이다.

③ Jane은 Pic Gardener App을 고안해 냈다.

④ Pic Gardener App은 식물 관리에 대한 정보를 얻을 수 있는 앱이다.

⑤ Minho는 Pic Gardener App을 유용하게 사용하고 있다.

[11~12] 다음 대화를 읽고, 물음에 답하시오.

> Hojun: Hey, Katy. (A)과학 박람회에 대해 들어보았니? (about, fair)
>
> Katy: Yeah, I'm going to go there.
>
> Hojun: (B)Me, too! I'm excited about doing different kinds of experiments.
>
> Katy: Yeah, I'm also looking forward to it!

11 위 대화의 밑줄 친 (A)의 우리말을 주어진 단어를 이용하여 영작하시오.

➡ _____

12 위 대화의 밑줄 친 (B)와 바꾸어 쓸 수 있는 것은?

① So do I!　　② So am I!

③ Neither do I!　　④ Neither am I!

⑤ Me, neither!

13 주어진 어구를 바르게 배열하여 다음 우리말을 영어로 쓰시오. 필요하다면 단어를 추가하시오.

> 다른 사람에게 말할 기회를 주어라.
> (talk / the other / a chance / give / person)

➡ _____

14 다음 두 문장이 같은 의미가 되도록 빈칸에 알맞은 말을 쓰시오.

> Jason laughed at me.
> ➡ I _____.

15 다음 중 to부정사의 쓰임이 주어진 문장과 같은 것은?

> The school has strict rules to follow.

① Jim came to Korea to study Korean.

② People of the town were sad to hear the news.

③ The novelist needed something to write about.

④ His job is to make sure that everyone is safe.

⑤ I want to make more money than my friend does.

16 다음 중 어법상 바르지 않은 것은?

① My car was repaired by a mechanic.

② He has something curious to see.

③ Jason promised not to run away again.

④ I was deeply disappointed with the result.

⑤ Jessica had nothing eaten in the refrigerator.

17 다음 중 어법상 바르지 않은 것은?

① Kevin made a promise not to do it again.

② The blouse is made of silk.

③ By whom was the window shut?

④ The towels on the floor was found by Jim.

⑤ She has every reason to hate him.

[18~20] 다음 글을 읽고, 물음에 답하시오.

In animation movies, amazing things are possible. But are they actually possible ____ⓐ____ real life?

Let Down Your Hair, Rapunzel!

In the animation, Rapunzel must lower her long hair to let people in her tower. But could human hair really hold up a person?

Surprisingly, yes! A single hair can hold up 100g and an average head has about 120,000 hairs. All those hairs could hold up a couple of elephants! With her hair, Rapunzel has the ability ⓑto hold up a person. But she should wrap her hair around something strong and heavy. If she doesn't, she will get a very sore neck.

18 위 글의 빈칸 ⓐ에 들어갈 전치사와 같은 것은?

① You don't have to worry _____ it.
② I am waiting _____ my mom.
③ Life is full _____ wonders.
④ She is interested _____ history.
⑤ Mary is well known _____ her love for animals.

19 다음 중 밑줄 친 ⓑ와 쓰임이 같은 것은?

① The subject is difficult to talk about.
② I have something to tell you.
③ The man wanted to be a doctor.
④ The river is dangerous to swim in.
⑤ It is necessary to discuss the problem.

20 위 글의 내용을 참고하여 Rapunzel에게 해 줄 조언을 완성하시오.

_____ _____ _____ _____
_____ _____ _____ _____,
or you will get a very sore neck.

[21~24] 다음 글을 읽고, 물음에 답하시오.

We Scare for Energy

In the animation, monsters scare children to get energy from their screams. Amazingly, their city is powered by this sound! But could we actually produce electricity to light up a city from sound?

Yes, sound can be changed into electricity. But it would not be helpful in our everyday activities ___ⓐ___ the amount is too small. For example, the sound from a car horn only produces 50mv. That is only 1/4400 of the average 220v of electricity in our homes. So, we would need an unbelievable amount of screams ⓑto light up an entire city.

21 위 글의 빈칸 ⓐ에 들어갈 말로 가장 적절한 것은?

① while   ② because   ③ if
④ before   ⑤ until

22 위 글의 내용과 일치하는 것은?

① Monsters give children scares for fun.
② With the screams of children, monsters can light up their city.
③ Seeing monsters, children scream with joy.
④ Electricity can be changed into sound.
⑤ Changing sound into electricity is not difficult.

23 위 글의 내용에 맞게 빈칸에 알맞은 말을 쓰시오.

With the latest technology, we can actually produce _____ _____ _____. However, it is hard to say that _____ _____ _____ in our daily lives because the amount is too small.

24 위 글의 밑줄 친 ⓑ와 쓰임이 다른 하나는?

① She went to Italy to study music.
② We go to the river to catch fish.
③ He opened the door to welcome me.
④ You don't have a right to accept it.
⑤ We don't live to eat.

Lesson 4

Your Only Limit Is You

의사소통 기능

- 격려하기

  A: My serves were not strong enough.

  B: You're a great player. You'll do better next time.

- 상대방에게 도움 제안하기

  A: I can't wash this car alone. It's too big.

  B: Let me help you.

언어 형식

- 관계대명사

  There are people **who** are cheering excitedly.

- 지각동사

  Max **sees** the official waving a white flag.

교과서
Words & Expressions

Key Words

- **ahead** [əhéd] 부 앞에, 앞선
- **amazing** [əméiziŋ] 형 놀랄 정도의, 굉장한
- **beat** [biːt] 동 뛰다, 치다, 두드리다
- **block** [blak] 동 막다, 방해하다
- **cheer** [tʃiər] 동 갈채를 보내다, 환호성을 지르다
- **close match** 아슬아슬한 승부, 접전
- **complete** [kəmplíːt] 동 완성하다, 달성하다 형 완전한
- **count** [kaunt] 동 중요하다, (수를) 세다
- **crowd** [kraud] 명 군중, 관객
- **crowded** [kráudid] 형 복잡한, 붐비는
- **deep** [diːp] 형 깊은
- **engine** [éndʒin] 명 엔진, 기관
- **excitedly** [iksáitidli] 부 흥분하여, 기를 쓰고
- **finish line** 결승선
- **fix** [fiks] 동 수리하다, 고정시키다
- **flag** [flæg] 명 기, 깃발
- **gas pedal** (자동차의) 가속 페달
- **hang** [hæŋ] 동 매달다, 걸다
- **hit** [hit] 동 부딪치다
- **kart** [kaːrt] 명 소형 경주용 자동차

- **kick** [kik] 동 차다, 걷어차다
- **lap** [læp] 명 (경주에서 트랙의) 한 바퀴, 무릎
- **local** [lóukəl] 형 지방의
- **loud** [laud] 형 시끄러운, (소리가) 큰
- **memorable** [mémərəbl] 형 기억할 만한
- **official** [əfíʃəl] 명 (운동 경기의) 심판 형 공식의
- **pitching** [pítʃiŋ] 명 투구
- **pitcher** [pítʃər] 명 투수
- **place** [pleis] 명 장소, (경주, 대회 등의) 등위
- **press** [pres] 동 누르다, 밀어붙이다
- **punch** [pʌntʃ] 명 타격
- **rush** [rʌʃ] 동 돌진하다
- **seafood** [sifud] 명 해산물
- **straightaway** [streitəwei] 형 일직선의, 즉시의
- **tear** [tiər] 명 눈물
- **terrible** [térəbl] 형 무서운, 심한
- **three-pointer** 3점슛
- **track** [træk] 명 경주로, 트랙
- **voice** [vɔis] 명 목소리
- **volleyball** [válibɔːl] 명 배구

Key Expressions

- **be filled with** ~로 가득 차다
- **be satisfied with** ~에 만족하다
- **cheer up** 기운을 내다
- **do one's best** 최선을 다하다
- **keep up with** ~에 뒤떨어지지 않다
- **miss a chance** 기회를 놓치다

- **out of one's reach** ~에게 닿지 않는, ~의 힘이 미치지 않는
- **role model** 역할 모델
- **sit up** 자세를 바로 하다, 바로 앉다
- **take a chance** (모험 삼아) 해보다
- **win a race** 경주에 이기다

Word Power

※ 서로 반대되는 뜻을 가진 어휘

- □ **official** 공식적인 ↔ **unoffical** 비공식적인
- □ **crowded** 혼잡한 ↔ **uncrowded** 붐비지 않는
- □ **thin** 얇은 ↔ **thick** 두꺼운
- □ **satisfied** 만족한 ↔ **dissatisfied** 만족스럽지 않은
- □ **deep** 깊은 ↔ **shallow** 얕은
- □ **comfortable** 편안한 ↔ **uncomfortable** 불편한

- □ **complete** 완전한 ↔ **incomplete** 불완전한
- □ **finish** 끝내다 ↔ **begin** 시작하다
- □ **straight** 곧은, 일직선의 ↔ **curved** 굽은, 곡선의
- □ **filled** 가득 찬 ↔ **empty** 텅 빈
- □ **loud** 시끄러운 ↔ **silent** 고요한, 소리 없는
- □ **memorable** 기억할 만한 ↔ **forgettable** 잊을 만한

English Dictionary

- □ **cheer** 응원하다
  → to shout loudly, to show support or praise for somebody, or to give them encouragement
  누군가를 위해 지지나 칭찬을 보여주기 위해, 또는 용기를 북돋아 주기 위해 크게 소리 지르다

- □ **kart** 소형 경주용 자동차
  → a small motor vehicle used for racing
  경주를 위해 사용되는 작은 자동차

- □ **complete** 완성하다
  → to finish making or doing something
  무언가를 만들거나 하는 것을 끝내다

- □ **engine** 엔진
  → the part of a vehicle that produces power to make the vehicle move
  자동차를 움직이게 만드는 힘을 만들어 내는 자동차의 한 부분

- □ **pitcher** 투수
  → the player who throws the ball to the batter
  타자에게 공을 던지는 선수

- □ **tear** 눈물
  → a drop of liquid that comes out of your eye when you cry
  당신이 울 때 눈에서부터 나오는 액체 방울

- □ **track** 경주로, 트랙
  → a piece of ground with a special surface for people, cars, etc. to have races on
  사람이나 자동차 등이 경주하기 위한 특별한 표면을 가진 땅의 일부

- □ **voice** 목소리
  → the sound or sounds produced through the mouth by a person speaking or singing
  말을 하거나 노래를 부르는 사람에 의해 입을 통해 만들어지는 소리

- □ **memorable** 기억할 만한
  → special, good or unusual and therefore worth remembering or easy to remember
  특별하거나 좋거나 또는 유별나서 기억할 만한 가치가 있거나 또는 기억하기 쉬운

- □ **kick** 차다
  → to hit somebody/something with your foot
  발로 누군가나 무언가를 치다

- □ **block** 막다, 방해하다
  → to stop somebody from going somewhere or seeing something by standing in front of them or in their way
  누군가의 길이나 그들 앞에 서서 어딘가로 가거나 무언가를 보게 하는 것을 막다

- □ **crowd** 관객, 관중
  → a large number of people gathered together in a public place, for example in the streets or at a sports game
  예를 들어 거리나 스포츠 경기를 위해 공공장소에 모인 많은 사람들

- □ **finish line** 결승선
  → the line across a sports track, etc. that marks the end of a race
  경주의 끝을 표시하는 스포츠 경주로를 가로지르는 선

01 다음 영영풀이에 해당하는 말을 고르시오.

> the player who throws the ball to the batter

① catcher   ② coach
③ pitcher   ④ hitter
⑤ outfielder

02 다음 중 밑줄 친 부분의 뜻풀이가 바르지 않은 것은?

① I hear the voice of your children. 목소리
② The stadium is filled with the crowd. 사람들
③ Press the button to open the door. 누르다
④ Mike completed the final lap. 무릎
⑤ The red car hit the bus. 부딪치다

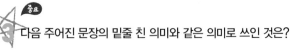

03 다음 주어진 문장의 밑줄 친 의미와 같은 의미로 쓰인 것은?

> It is the quality that counts.

① Every minute counts in the game.
② He began to count the number of guests.
③ Close your eyes and count to the number ten.
④ I was so surprised when my little daughter was able to count.
⑤ Mike, count to ten, and open your eyes.

서답형

04 다음 짝지어진 단어의 관계가 같도록 빈칸에 알맞은 말을 쓰시오.

> deep : shallow = _____ : forgettable

중요

05 다음 문장에 공통으로 들어갈 말을 고르시오.

> • Our team won a _____ victory at the soccer match.
> • Jane will _____ the task before going out.
> • He is a _____ stranger to me.

① comfortable   ② tear
③ complete   ④ straight
⑤ terrible

서답형

06 다음 문장의 빈칸에 들어갈 말을 〈보기〉에서 골라 쓰시오.

> ┤ 보기 ├
> gas pedal / finish line / cheer up /
> sit up / satisfied with

(1) When Emily saw Tom, she wanted to _____ him _____.
(2) Son, _____ _____ and look at this.
(3) My father was _____ _____ my present.
(4) Don't press the _____ _____.
(5) They are running toward the _____ _____.

01 다음 짝지어진 단어의 관계가 같도록 빈칸에 알맞은 말을 쓰시오.

> possible : impossible =
> comfortable : _____

02 다음 문장의 빈칸에 들어갈 말을 〈보기〉에서 골라 쓰시오.

┌─ 보기 ─┐
> lap / official / balance / hit

(1) As the _____ waved the flag, the race started.
(2) My car almost _____ the back of his car.
(3) Jimmy completed his tenth _____.
(4) It is important to keep the _____.

03 다음 우리말에 맞게 빈칸에 알맞은 말을 쓰시오.

(1) 우리는 경주에 우승하기 위해 최선을 다할 것이다.
➡ We will do our best to _____ _____ _____.
(2) 우리 회사의 최고 경영자를 만날 기회를 놓치지 마세요.
➡ Don't _____ _____ _____ to meet the CEO of our company.
(3) 그의 눈은 눈물로 가득 찼었다.
➡ His eyes _____ _____ _____ tears.

04 다음 우리말을 주어진 어구를 이용하여 영작하시오.

(1) 나는 그의 앞에서 걸었다. (ahead)
➡ _____
(2) 나는 여동생이 2등을 했다고 들었다. (place)
➡ _____
(3) 나는 그 유명한 가수를 만날 기회를 놓치고 싶지 않았다. (miss, chance, to meet)
➡ _____
_____

05 다음 대화의 우리말을 주어진 단어를 사용하여 영작하시오.

> A: (1)왜 시무룩한 얼굴이니? (long)
> B: I couldn't block the other players.
> A: Don't worry. (2)너는 다음에는 더 잘할 거야. (better, next)

(1) _____
(2) _____

06 다음 우리말을 주어진 단어를 배열하여 완성하시오.

(1) 프로젝트가 일주일 안에 완성되어야 한다.
(the project / be / in / should / a week / completed)
➡ _____
(2) 그는 가속페달을 세게 밟았다.
(down / pressed / on / gas / the / pedal / he / hard)
➡ _____
(3) 나는 나의 투구가 만족스럽지 않았다.
(pitching / not / I / with / my / was / satisfied)
➡ _____

Conversation

1 격려하기

> **A** My serves were not strong enough. 내 서브는 충분히 강하지 않았어.
> **B** You're a great player. You'll do better next time.
> 오, 너는 훌륭한 선수야. 다음번에는 더 잘할 거야.

■ 'You'll do better next time.'은 상대방을 격려해 주는 표현으로 Don't worry., There's always a next time., Cheer up! 또는 You can do it! 등으로 바꾸어 쓸 수 있다.

격려하기

- There's always a next time. 항상 다음 기회가 있어.
- Cheer up! 기운 내!
- You can do it! 너는 할 수 있어!
- Don't give up! 포기하지 마!
- Don't be so hard on yourself. 너무 자책하지 마.
- Don't take it too hard. 너무 상심하지 마.
- You are a great player. 너는 훌륭한 선수야.

핵심 Check

1. 다음 우리말과 일치하도록 빈칸에 알맞은 말을 쓰시오.

(1) **A:** I coudn't catch up with other runners today. (나는 오늘 다른 주자들을 따라잡을 수 없었어.)

　　B: ＿＿＿＿ ＿＿＿＿ ＿＿＿＿ ＿＿＿＿ ＿＿＿＿. You are a great player.

　　(너무 상심하지 마. 너는 훌륭한 선수야.)

(2) **A:** I didn't do well in the match. My punches were terrible.

　　(나는 시합에서 잘하지 못했어. 내 펀치는 형편없었어.)

　　B: ＿＿＿＿ ＿＿＿＿ ＿＿＿＿ ＿＿＿＿ ＿＿＿＿. (너무 자책하지 마.)

(3) **A:** I didn't jump high enough. (나는 충분히 높게 뛰어오르지 않았어.)

　　B: ＿＿＿＿ ＿＿＿＿! ＿＿＿＿ ＿＿＿＿ ＿＿＿＿ ＿＿＿＿! (기운 내! 너는 할 수 있어!)

② 상대방에게 도움 제안하기

A I can't wash this car alone. It's too big. 내가 혼자 이 차를 세차할 수 없어. 이건 너무 커.
B Let me help you. 내가 도와줄게.

■ 상대방에게 도움을 제안하고자 할 때 Let me help you., I'll help you. 또는 I'll give you a hand. 등으로 표현할 수 있다.

도움 요청하기

- Would you help me out? 나를 좀 도와주시겠어요?
- Could you do something for me? 좀 도와주시겠습니까?
- Would you give me a hand? 저 좀 도와주시겠어요?
- Would you mind helping me? 좀 도와주시겠습니까?

도움 제안하기

- Let me help you. 내가 도와줄게.
- Would you like me to help you? 내가 당신을 도와주길 원하나요?
- Do you need any help? 도움이 필요하세요?
- Can I give you a hand? 도와 드릴까요?
- May I help you? 제가 도와드릴까요?
- How can I help you? 무엇을 도와드릴까요?
- I'll help you. 제가 도와드릴게요.

핵심 Check

2. 다음 우리말과 일치하도록 빈칸에 알맞은 말을 쓰시오.

(1) **A:** I don't have a bottle-opener. I can't open the bottle. (나는 병따개가 없어. 병을 딸 수 없어.)

   B: Let _____ _____ _____ . (제가 도와드릴게요.)

(2) **A:** _____ _____ _____ _____ _____ ? (도움이 필요하신가요?)

   B: Yes. I can't fix the light. It's too high. (네. 저는 전등을 고칠 수 없어요. 너무 높아요.)

(3) **A:** I can't swim here. It's too _____ . (제가 여기서 수영을 못하겠어요. 너무 깊어요.)

   B: _____ _____ . I'll _____ _____ . (걱정 마세요. 제가 도와드릴게요.)

Conversation 교과서 대화문 익히기

A. Listen & Talk B-2

Emily: I heard your baseball team, the Reds, ❶won the match. Eight to seven, right? Congratulations, John!

John: Thanks. It was a ❷close game. I'm not happy with my pitching.

Emily: Why do you say ❸that?

John: I allowed two homeruns.

Emily: Oh, you're a great pitcher. ❹You'll do better next time.

Emily: 나는 너희 the Reds 야구팀이 시합에서 이겼다고 들었어. 8대 7이 맞니? 축하해, John!

John: 고마워. 정말 접전이었어. 나는 내 투구가 만족스럽지 않아.

Emily: 왜 그렇게 말하는 거야?

John: 홈런 두 개를 허용했거든.

Emily: 오. 너는 훌륭한 투수야. 다음번에는 더 잘할 거야.

❶ win the match: 시합에 이기다
❷ close: 우열을 가리기 힘든, 막상막하의
❸ that은 John이 자신의 투구에 만족스럽지 않다고 말한 것을 가리킨다.
❹ 낙담하고 있는 상대를 격려하는 것에 그치지 않고, 특정한 근거에 기초하여 상대방이 다음에는 '더 나아질 것'이라는 믿음을 표현할 때 쓴다.

Check(√) True or False

(1) John belongs to the Reds. T ☐ F ☐

(2) John hit two solo homeruns. T ☐ F ☐

B. Communication

Megan: ❶I'm worried about our next soccer match, James.

James: Why are you worried, Megan?

Megan: Well, I couldn't catch high balls in the last soccer match. I gave away too many goals.

James: I see. Here, ❷let me help you. I'll kick high balls to you.

Megan: Oh, that'll really help. I hope my skills ❸get better.

James: Don't worry. You'll do better next time.

Megan: James, 나는 다음 축구 시합이 걱정돼.

James: 왜 걱정하는 거야, Megan?

Megan: 음, 지난 축구 시합에서 나는 높은 공을 잡지 못했어. 너무 많은 골을 허용했어.

James: 알겠어. 자, 내가 도와줄게. 너에게 공을 높이 차 줄게.

Megan: 오, 그거 도움이 많이 되겠다. 내 기술이 나아지길 바라.

James: 걱정 마. 다음번에 더 잘할 거야.

❶ be worried about: ~을 걱정하다
❷ 상대방에게 도움을 제안할 때 쓰는 표현으로 Can I give you a hand?도 같은 의도로 쓰인다.
❸ get better: 좋아지다, 호전되다

Check(√) True or False

(3) Megan scored goals in the last soccer match. T ☐ F ☐

(4) James will kick high balls to Megan to practice for the next soccer match. T ☐ F ☐

Listen & Talk 1 A-1

Mom: David, how was your basketball game today?
David: We lost, Mom. I missed too many chances for a three-pointer.
Mom: Oh, ❶don't be so hard on yourself. You'll do better next time.
David: I hope so.

❶ '너무 자책하지 마.'라는 의미로 상대방을 격려하는 표현이다.

Listen & Talk 1 A-2

Jack: Did you come and watch my volleyball match yesterday?
Irene: Yeah, I did. That was a great volleyball match. You were great!
Jack: Thanks, but it was ❶a close match. My serves were not strong ❷enough.
Irene: Oh, you're a great player. You'll do better next time.

❶ a close match: 아슬아슬한 시합 ❷ enough: 충분히

Listen & Talk 2 A-1

Mike: Is it your first time riding a bike, Mina?
Mina: Yes, it is. I just can't ❶keep my balance.
Mike: Let me help you. I'll hold your bike.
Mina: Thanks, Mike. Don't ❷let go, okay?
Mike: Don't worry. Sit up and ❸look straight ahead.

❶ keep one's balance: 균형을 잡다 ❷ let go: 놓다 ❸ look straight ahead: 앞을 똑바로 보다

Listen & Talk 2 A-2

Tom: What are you doing, Sarah?
Sarah: I learned how to ❶stand on my head in PE class. So I'm trying ❷it now but it's not easy.
Tom: Let me help you. Kick your legs in the air again. I'll catch you.
Sarah: Oh, thanks. I'll try again.

❶ stand on one's head: 물구나무서다
❷ it은 물구나무 서는 것을 가리킨다.

Listen & Talk 2 B

Coach: Hey, Brian. Did you practice the *taegwondo* side kick?
Brian: Yes, Coach. But I'm still not comfortable with ❶it.
Coach: What problem are you having?
Brian: Well, I can't lift my leg high enough.
Coach: I see. Let me help you. I'll hold this kick pad for you. Show me your side kick.

❶ it은 taegwondo side kick(태권도 옆차기)을 가리킨다.

Wrap Up 1

Anna: Hi, Jake. Do you come to the ❶pool often?
Jake: Oh, hi, Anna. I ❷take a swimming class here ❸once a week.
Anna: When did you start the class?
Jake: Last month. But swimming is still not easy for me.
Anna: Oh, let me help you. I teach children how to swim in the school club.
Jake: Oh, that'll help me a lot. Thanks.

❶ pool: 수영장
❷ take a class: 수업을 듣다
❸ once a week: 일주일에 한번

Wrap Up 2

Emma: How was your soccer match last week?
Keine: We won, but ❶I'm not satisfied with our match.
Emma: Why do you say ❷that?
Keine: My passes were too short.
Emma: ❸Don't take it too hard. You're practicing a lot. You'll do better next time.

❶ be satisfied with: ~에 만족하다
❷ 이겼지만 경기에 만족하지 않는다고 말한 것을 가리킨다.
❸ Don't take it too hard.: 너무 상심하지 마.

다음 우리말과 일치하도록 빈칸에 알맞은 말을 쓰시오.

Listen & Talk 1 A-1

Mom: David, how was your basketball game today?

David: We lost, Mom. I _____ too many _____ for a _____-_____.

Mom: Oh, don't be so _____ on yourself. _____ _____ _____ next time.

David: I hope so.

 해석

Mom: David, 오늘 너희 농구 경기는 어땠니?
David: 저희가 졌어요, 엄마. 제가 3점 슛을 할 기회를 너무 많이 놓쳤어요.
Mom: 오, 너무 자책하지 마. 다음번에는 더 잘할 거야.
David: 저도 그러길 바라요.

Listen & Talk 1 A-2

Jack: Did you come and watch my _____ _____ yesterday?

Irene: Yeah, I did. That was a great volleyball match. You were great!

Jack: Thanks, but it was a _____ _____. My serves were not _____ _____.

Irene: Oh, _____ _____ _____ _____. You'll do better next time.

Jack: 어제 내 배구 시합 보러 왔어?
Irene: 응, 그랬어. 정말 멋진 배구 시합이었어. 너 정말 잘했어!
Jack: 고마워. 하지만 아슬아슬한 시합이었어. 내 서브는 충분히 강하지 않았어.
Irene: 오, 너는 훌륭한 선수야. 다음번에는 더 잘할 거야.

Listen & Talk 1 B

Emily: I heard your baseball team, the Reds, _____ _____ _____. Eight to seven, right? _____, John!

John: Thanks. It was a close game. I'm not happy with my _____.

Emily: Why do you say that?

John: I allowed two homeruns.

Emily: Oh, _____ _____ _____ _____. You'll _____ _____ next time.

Emily: 나는 너희 the Reds 야구팀이 시합에서 이겼다고 들었어. 8대 7이 맞니? 축하해, John!
John: 고마워. 정말 접전이었어. 나는 내 투구에 만족스럽지 않아.
Emily: 왜 그렇게 말하는 거야?
John: 홈런 두 개를 허용했거든.
Emily: 오, 너는 훌륭한 투수야. 다음번에는 더 잘할 거야.

Listen & Talk 2 A-1

Mike: Is it your _____ _____ riding a bike, Mina?

Mina: Yes, it is. I just can't _____ _____ _____.

Mike: Let me help you. I'll _____ your bike.

Mina: Thanks, Mike. _____ _____ go, okay?

Mike: Don't worry. _____ _____ and _____ _____ _____.

Mike: 미나야, 자전거 처음 타는 거야?
Mina: 응. 균형을 잘 못 잡겠어.
Mike: 내가 도와줄게. 네 자전거를 잡아 줄게.
Mina: 고마워, Mike. 놓으면 안 돼, 알았지?
Mike: 걱정 마. 앉아서 앞을 똑바로 봐.

Listen & Talk 2 A-1

Tom: What are you doing, Sarah?

Sarah: I learned _____ _____ _____ _____ _____

_____ in PE class. So I'm trying it now but it's not easy.

Tom: _____ _____ _____ _____. Kick your legs in the air

again. I'll _____ _____.

Sarah: Oh, thanks. I'll try again.

Listen & Talk 2 B

Coach: Hey, Brian. Did you practice the *taegwondo* side kick?

Brian: Yes, Coach. But _____ _____ _____ _____ _____

_____.

Coach: _____ _____ are you having?

Brian: Well, I can't _____ _____ _____ _____ _____.

Coach: I see. _____ _____ help you. I'll hold this kick pad for

you. Show me your _____ _____.

Communication

Megan: I'm _____ _____ our next soccer match, James.

James: _____ _____ you worried, Megan?

Megan: Well, I couldn't _____ _____ _____ in the last soccer

match. I _____ _____ too many goals.

James: I see. Here, _____ _____ _____ _____. I'll kick

high balls to you.

Megan: Oh, that'll really help. I hope _____ _____ _____

_____.

James: _____ _____. You'll do better next time.

Wrap Up 1

Anna: Hi, Jake. _____ _____ _____ to the pool often?

Jake: Oh, hi, Anna. I take a swimming class here _____ _____

_____.

Anna: When did you start the class?

Jake: Last month. But swimming is still not _____ _____ _____.

Anna: Oh, let me help you. I teach children _____ _____

in the school club.

Jake: Oh, _____ _____ _____ _____. Thanks.

Tom: Sarah, 뭐 하고 있어?
Sarah: 체육 시간에 물구나무 서는 법을 배웠거든. 그래서 지금 한번 해 보고 있는데, 쉽지 않네.
Tom: 내가 도와줄게. 다리를 공중에 차 올려봐. 내가 널 붙잡을게.
Sarah: 오, 고마워. 다시 해 볼게.

Coach: 저기, Brian. 태권도 옆 차기 연습했니?
Brian: 네, 코치님. 그런데 여전히 편하게 잘 안 돼요.
Coach: 어떤 문제가 있어?
Brian: 음, 다리를 충분히 높이 들어 올릴 수가 없어요.
Coach: 알겠다. 내가 도와줄게. 너를 위해 이 킥 패드를 잡아줄게. 너의 옆 차기를 보여주렴.

Megan: James, 나는 다음 축구 시합이 걱정돼.
James: 왜 걱정하는 거야, Megan?
Megan: 음, 지난 축구 시합에서 나는 높은 공을 잡지 못했어. 너무 많은 골을 허용했어.
James: 알겠어. 자, 내가 도와줄게. 너에게 공을 높이 차 줄게.
Megan: 오, 그거 도움이 많이 되겠다. 내 기술이 나아지길 바라.
James: 걱정 마. 다음번에는 더 잘할 거야.

Anna: 안녕, Jake. 너는 종종 수영장에 오니?
Jake: 오, 안녕, Anna. 나는 여기에서 일주일에 한 번 수영 수업을 들어.
Anna: 언제부터 수업을 시작했어?
Jake: 지난달부터. 그런데 수영은 여전히 나에게 쉽지 않아.
Anna: 오, 내가 도와줄게. 나는 학교 동아리에서 아이들에게 수영하는 법을 가르쳐 주거든.
Jake: 오, 그거 나에게 도움이 많이 되겠다. 고마워.

01 다음 대화의 밑줄 친 우리말을 영작하시오.

> A: My serves were not strong enough.
> B: You're a great player. <u>다음번에는 더 잘할 거야.</u>

➡ _____

02 다음 대화의 빈칸에 들어갈 말로 어색한 것은?

> A: I can't wash this car alone. It's too big.
> B: _____

① Let me help you.　　② Don't worry. I'll help you.
③ May I help you?　　④ Can I give you a hand?
⑤ It will be very grateful to me if you help me.

[03~04] 다음 대화를 읽고 물음에 답하시오.

> Emily: I heard your baseball team, the Reds, won the match. Eight to seven, right? Congratulations, John!
> John: Thanks. It was a close game. I'm not happy with my (A)_____ (pitch).
> Emily: Why do you say that?
> John: I allowed two homeruns.
> Emily: Oh, you're a great (B)_____(pitch). You'll do better next time.

03 위 대화의 빈칸 (A)와 (B)에 주어진 단어를 적절한 형태로 쓰시오.

　　(A) _____　　(B) _____

04 위 대화의 내용과 일치하지 <u>않는</u> 것은?

① John은 Reds팀의 투수이다.
② Reds팀은 8대 7로 경기에서 이겼다.
③ John은 어제 2점 홈런을 쳤다.
④ John은 자신의 투구에 만족하지 않는다.
⑤ Emily는 John이 좋은 투수라고 생각한다.

01 다음 대화의 우리말을 영작하시오.

> **A:** I can't wash this car alone. It's too big.
> **B:** 미안하지만 나는 너를 지금 도와줄 수 없어.

➡ _____

02 중요
다음 대화의 빈칸에 들어갈 말로 어색한 것은?

> **A:** My serves were not strong enough.
> **B:** You're a great player. _____

① There's always a next time.
② You'll do better next time.
③ You can do it better.
④ Don't give up! Try it again.
⑤ Would it be possible to serve more strongly?

[03~04] 다음 대화를 읽고 물음에 답하시오.

> **Jack:** Did you come and watch my volleyball match yesterday?
> **Irene:** Yeah, I did. That was a great volleyball match. You were great!
> **Jack:** Thanks, but it was a (A)close match. My serves were not strong enough.
> **Irene:** Oh, you're a great player. You'll do better next time.

03 위 대화의 밑줄 친 (A)close와 같은 의미로 쓰인 것은?

① What time does the museum close?
② My house is close to the bus stop.
③ My team finally won in a close game.
④ Would you close the windows for me?
⑤ Emily was my close friend.

04 위 대화의 내용과 일치하지 않는 것은?

① Irene은 어제 Jack의 배구 경기를 직접 관람하였다.
② 어제 Jack의 배구 경기는 아슬아슬한 경기였다.
③ Jack은 자신의 서브가 충분히 강하지 않았다고 생각한다.
④ Irene은 Jack이 훌륭한 선수라고 격려하였다.
⑤ Irene은 경기에 져서 낙담한 Jack을 위로하였다.

[05~06] 다음 대화를 읽고, 물음에 답하시오.

> **Emily:** I heard your baseball team, the Reds, (A)[win / won] the match. Eight to seven, right? Congratulations, John!
> **John:** Thanks. It was a (B)[close / closing] game. I'm not happy with my pitching.
> **Emily:** (C)[What / Why] do you say that?
> **John:** I allowed two homeruns.
> **Emily:** Oh, you're a great pitcher. You'll do better next time.

05 What was the score of the Reds in the baseball game?

➡ _____

06 중요
위 대화의 괄호 (A)~(C)에 들어갈 말로 바르게 짝지어진 것은?

① win – close – What
② win – closing – Why
③ won – closing – What
④ won – close – Why
⑤ won – close – What

서답형

07 다음 대화가 자연스럽게 이어지도록 순서대로 배열하시오.

> (A) Thanks, Mike. Don't let go, okay?
> (B) Is it your first time riding a bike, Mina?
> (C) Let me help you. I'll hold your bike.
> (D) Yes, it is. I just can't keep my balance.
> (E) Don't worry. Sit up and look straight ahead.

➡ _____

[08~09] 다음 대화를 읽고 물음에 답하시오.

Megan: I'm worried about our next soccer match, James.

James: Why are you worried, Megan?

Megan: Well, I couldn't catch high balls in the last soccer match. (A)<u>너무 많은 골을 허용했어</u>. (away)

James: I see. Here, let me help you. I'll kick high balls to you.

Megan: Oh, that'll really help. I hope my skills get better.

James: Don't worry. You'll do better next time.

서답형

08 위 대화의 (A)의 밑줄 친 우리말을 주어진 단어를 사용하여 영작하시오.

➡ _____

09 위 대화에서 Megan의 심정 변화로 적절한 것은?

① fearful → depressed
② anxious → hopeful
③ discouraged → upset
④ pleased → encouraged
⑤ relaxed → calm

[10~11] 다음 대화를 읽고 물음에 답하시오.

Anna: Hi, Jake. Do you come to the pool often?

Jake: Oh, hi, Anna. I take a swimming class here once a week.

Anna: When did you start the class?

Jake: Last month. But swimming is still not easy for me.

Anna: Oh, let me help you. I teach children how to swim in the school club.

Jake: Oh, that'll help me a lot. Thanks.

서답형

10 How many times does Jake take a swimming class a week?

➡ _____

서답형

11 What does Anna teach to children in the school club?

➡ _____

12 다음 대화의 빈칸에 들어갈 말로 어색한 것은?

> A: Why the long face?
> B: _____
> C: Don't worry. You'll do better next time.

① My serves were not strong enough.
② I couldn't keep up with other runners today.
③ I didn't do well in the match.
④ My punches were terrible.
⑤ I hit a two-run homerun.

01 다음 대화의 밑줄 친 우리말을 주어진 표현을 사용하여 영작하시오.

> A: I can't carry this bag. It's too heavy.
> B: 내가 도와줄까? (can, hand)

➡ _____

[02~03] 다음 대화를 읽고, 물음에 답하시오.

> Tom: What are you doing, Sarah?
> Sarah: I learned how to ___(A)___ on my head in PE class. So I'm trying it now but it's not easy.
> Tom: Let me help you. ___(B)___ your legs in the air again. I'll ___(C)___ you.
> Sarah: Oh, thanks. I'll try again.

02 위 대화의 빈칸 (A)~(C)에 들어갈 말을 보기에서 골라 쓰시오.

> ┤ 보기 ├
> catch / kick / stand / sit

(A) _____ (B) _____ (C) _____

03 What is Sarah trying to do now?

> She is trying to _____
> _____.

[04~05] 다음 대화를 읽고, 물음에 답하시오.

> Megan: I'm worried about our next soccer match, James.
> James: Why are you worried, Megan?
> Megan: Well, I couldn't catch high balls in the last soccer match. I gave away too many goals.
> James: I see. Here, let me help you. I'll kick high balls to you.

> Megan: Oh, that'll really help. I hope my skills get better.
> James: Don't worry. You'll do better next time.

04 What problem does Megan have?

➡ _____

05 What is James going to do to improve Megan's soccer skill?

➡ _____

06 다음 대화의 내용과 일치하도록 빈칸을 완성하시오.

> Coach: Hey, Brian. Did you practice the *taegwondo* side kick?
> Brian: Yes, Coach. But I'm still not comfortable with it.
> Coach: What problem are you having?
> Brian: Well, I can't lift my leg high enough.
> Coach: I see. Let me help you. I'll hold this kick pad for you. Show me your side kick.

> Mon June 24th, 2019
> I felt disappointed when I practiced _____. Though I practiced a lot, I was not comfortable with it. Especially I couldn't _____. That was my biggest problem. Fortunately, my coach helped me, holding _____. I showed him _____ and practiced it with him a lot. I really appreciated him for helping me.

Grammar

1 관계대명사

> • I know a man **who** makes pumpkin pies well. 나는 호박파이를 잘 만드는 남자를 안다.
> • The book **whose** cover is blue is his. 표지가 파란색인 그 책은 그의 것이다.

■ 관계대명사는 두 개의 문장을 하나로 이어주는 접속사 역할을 하면서 동시에 대명사 역할을 한다. 본래 문장에서 주격으로 쓰인 (대)명사는 주격 관계대명사로, 소유격으로 쓰인 (대)명사는 소유격 관계대명사로, 목적격으로 쓰인 (대)명사는 목적격 관계대명사로 바꾸어 준다.

- I thanked the boys. They told me how to get there.
  = I thanked the boys **who** told me how to get there.

- The glasses were under the table. My brother was looking for them.
  = The glasses **which** my brother was looking for were under the table.

■ 선행사에 따라서 사용되는 관계대명사의 종류는 다음과 같으며, 목적격 관계대명사는 생략 가능하다.

	주격	소유격	목적격
사람	who	whose	whom[who]
사물	which	whose[of which]	which

- Tell me about the people **who[whom]** you invited to your party. 너의 파티에 초대했던 사람들에 관해 말해줘.

- I know a doctor **whose** first name is the same as mine. 나는 내 이름과 똑같은 이름을 가진 의사를 안다.

- The plant **which** we bought yesterday needs water. 우리가 어제 산 식물은 물을 필요로 한다.

■ 관계대명사 that은 who, whom과 which를 대신하여 사용될 수 있으며 소유격은 없다.

- The kid **that[who]** I met yesterday was active. 내가 어제 만났던 아이는 활동적이었다.

- He is the only friend **that[whom]** Jina trusts. 그는 Jina가 신뢰하는 유일한 친구이다.

핵심 Check

1. 다음 우리말과 일치하도록 빈칸에 알맞은 말을 쓰시오.

(1) 경주에서 진 그 소년은 슬펐다.

➡ The boy _____ lost the race was sad.

(2) 나는 카메라를 도난당한 그 소녀를 안다.

➡ I know the girl _____ _____ was stolen.

2 지각동사

- I **saw** the boy **riding** a bike. 나는 그 소년이 자전거를 타는 것을 보았다.
- They **heard** Anna **sing** a song. 그들은 Anna가 노래 부르는 것을 들었다.

■ 지각동사는 원형부정사나 현재분사를 목적격보어로 사용하는 5형식 동사이다. 따라서 '동사+목적어 +V(ing)' 구조를 취하며, 목적격보어는 목적어를 설명한다.
  • She **saw** her son **enter**(또는 **entering**) his room. 그녀는 자기 아들이 방으로 들어가는 것을 보았다.
  • The man **felt** the ground **shake**(또는 **shaking**). 그 남자는 땅이 흔들리는 것을 느꼈다.

■ 보고, 듣고, 느끼는 것과 같이 감각을 나타내는 동사들이 지각동사에 해당하며 see, watch, hear, feel 등이 있다.
  • Kelly **heard** her friend **calling** her. Kelly는 그녀의 친구가 그녀를 부르는 것을 들었다.
  • Mary **saw** me **playing** a computer game. Mary는 내가 컴퓨터 게임을 하는 것을 보았다.

■ 목적어와 목적격보어와의 관계가 수동일 경우 목적격보어로 과거분사를 쓴다.
  • I **heard** my name **called**. 나는 내 이름이 불리는 것을 들었다.
  • Jimmy **saw** the vase **broken**. Jimmy는 그 화병이 깨진 것을 보았다.

핵심 Check

2. 다음 우리말과 같도록 빈칸에 알맞은 말을 쓰시오.

(1) 그들은 그 소년이 무대 위에서 춤추는 것을 보았다.
  ➡ They saw the boy _____ on the stage.

(2) 나는 아버지가 면도하시는 것을 지켜보았다.
  ➡ I watched my dad _____.

(3) 그녀는 누군가가 그녀를 보고 있는 것을 느꼈다.
  ➡ She felt someone _____ her.

(4) 우리는 무언가가 땅에 떨어지는 소리를 들었다.
  ➡ We heard something _____ to the ground.

(5) 그녀는 엄마가 커피 한 잔을 따르는 소리를 들었다.
  ➡ She heard her mother _____ a cup of coffee.

01 관계대명사를 이용하여 다음 두 문장을 하나의 문장으로 만드시오. (that은 쓰지 말 것.)

be located 위치해 있다

(1) I have a friend. He speaks English very well.

➡ _____

(2) We stayed in a hotel. It was located near the beach.

➡ _____

(3) Do you want to see the pictures? I took them.

➡ _____

(4) Jenny took care of a dog. Its tail was hurt. (whose를 이용)

➡ _____

02 다음 괄호 안의 동사를 어법에 맞게 빈칸에 쓰시오.

(1) Did you see her _____ the violin? (play)

(2) Jason heard his brother _____ a noise. (make)

(3) We heard them _____ about it. (talk)

(4) Jimmy watched us _____ the road.

03 다음 우리말에 맞게 주어진 단어를 바르게 배열하시오. (필요하면 어형을 바꿀 것.)

(1) 그녀가 너에게 사준 케이크를 먹었니?

(the cake / did / for / you / you / eat / that / she / buy)

➡ _____

(2) 보고 싶은 것이 있나요?

(see / there / to / is / you / anything / that / want)

➡ _____

(3) 그가 우는 것을 들었니?

(hear / cry / did / he / you)

➡ _____

(4) Kelly는 어떤 사람이 하얀색 깃발을 흔드는 것을 본다.

(see / wave / Kelly / a white flag / a person)

➡ _____

01 다음 빈칸에 적절한 것을 모두 고르시오.

> The people _____ I call most often on my cell phone are my mother and my sisters.

① which　　　② who

③ that　　　④ whose

⑤ whom

 02 다음 빈칸에 들어갈 말이 바르게 짝지어진 것은?

> • I watched Mrs. Han _____ beside a car.
> • Julian wants his parents _____ him some money.

① stand – give

② stand – giving

③ standing – giving

④ standing – to give

⑤ to stand – to give

03 다음 우리말을 영어로 바르게 옮기지 않은 것은?

① 나는 그녀가 울고 있는 것을 봤어.

　→ I saw her crying.

② 너는 머리가 긴 친구가 있니?

　→ Do you have a friend who has long hair?

③ Jane에게는 달리는 것이 취미인 언니가 한 명 있다.

　→ Jane has a sister who hobby is running.

④ Tom은 어제 그가 먹은 음식을 기억할 수 없었다.

　→ Tom couldn't remember the food which he ate yesterday.

⑤ 그가 무언가를 말하는 것을 들었니?

　→ Did you hear him say something?

서답형

04 적절한 관계대명사를 이용하여 다음 두 문장을 하나의 문장으로 쓰시오.

> • I like the boy.
> • He wanted to come to the party yesterday.

➡ _____

　_____

05 다음 문장의 빈칸에 알맞은 것을 모두 고르시오.

> We _____ the beautiful girl play the piano.

① heard　　　② wanted

③ encouraged　　④ allowed

⑤ watched

06 다음 빈칸에 들어갈 말이 나머지와 다른 하나는?

① He is the man _____ you can depend on.

② There lived a princess _____ fell in love with a begger.

③ You can see so many people _____ live near the Han river.

④ The man _____ arrived here first was Bill.

⑤ I know the boy _____ hobby is flying a drone.

서답형

07 주어진 동사를 이용하여 다음 우리말을 영어로 쓰시오.

> 그녀는 물이 흐르는 소리를 들었다.
> (hear / run)

➡ _____

08 다음 중 빈칸에 들어갈 동사 'fly'의 형태가 <u>다른</u> 하나는?

① Did you see the air balloon _____ high?
② The plane is _____ the tourists home.
③ Karen watched the kite _____ away in the sky.
④ He is not allowed _____ the plane yet.
⑤ I saw a bee _____ in through the window.

⭐ 중요
09 다음 중 밑줄 친 부분의 쓰임이 적절하지 <u>않은</u> 것은?

① He is the man <u>who</u> I look up to very much.
② I apologized to the girl <u>whose</u> orange juice I spilled.
③ Harvard is the best university <u>that</u> I have ever visited.
④ Vicky made friends with a boy <u>which</u> is in my class.
⑤ Did the woman <u>who</u> stepped on your toes just walk away?

10 다음 우리말을 바르게 영작한 것을 <u>모두</u> 고르시오.

> 나는 금발 머리인 저 소녀을 안다.

① I know the boy which has blond hair.
② I know the boy whose hair is blond.
③ I know the boy who is blond hair.
④ I know the boy that hair is blond.
⑤ I know the boy who has blond hair.

서답형
11 주어진 어구를 바르게 배열하여 다음 우리말을 영어로 쓰시오.

> 우리는 한밤중에 개 한 마리가 짖는 소리를 들었다.
> (barking / in the middle of / we / a dog / heard / the night)

➡ _____

⭐ 중요
12 다음 중 밑줄 친 부분의 어법상 쓰임이 바르지 <u>않은</u> 것은?

① I was listening to the music <u>played</u> by my friend.
② Can you hear someone <u>singing</u> a song?
③ Emily felt her shoulder <u>touched</u> by someone.
④ We watched the man <u>climb</u> Mount Everest.
⑤ Jessica saw a boy <u>bully</u> by some teenage boys.

서답형
13 관계대명사와 주어진 단어를 어법에 맞게 활용하여 다음 우리말을 영어로 쓰시오.

> 나는 수영하는 것을 정말로 즐기는 한 소녀를 안다.
> (know / enjoy / swim)

➡ _____

14 다음 문장에서 어법상 바르지 <u>않은</u> 것은?

> I ①saw a man ②enter the house ③who my friend ④lives ⑤in.

①   ②   ③   ④   ⑤

서답형

15 다음 빈칸에 알맞은 관계대명사를 쓰시오.

- Robert knows a woman _____ has six daughters.
- Everything _____ they told me was hard to believe.
- Did you see a girl and two dogs _____ walked together the other day?

서답형

16 다음 빈칸에 알맞은 말을 쓰시오.

I watched them _____ a new car park.
= I watched a new car park being built by them.

➡ _____

17 다음 밑줄 친 부분의 쓰임이 다른 하나는?

① This is the purse that Kelly lost on the bus.
② Does she have the cat that has blue eyes?
③ Jane couldn't remember the man that gave her his phone number.
④ Kyle knew that there was nothing he could do.
⑤ Jimmy bought some plants that clean the air in the house.

서답형

18 주어진 단어를 바르게 배열하여 다음 문장을 완성하시오.

August _____ September.
(before / that / the / comes / month / is)

➡ _____

서답형

19 다음 빈칸에 공통으로 들어갈 말을 쓰시오.

- Amelia is _____ with her friends.
- He saw the girls _____ chess.
- I enjoy _____ computer games.

➡ _____

20 다음 중 밑줄 친 부분을 생략할 수 없는 것은?

① The pants that you wanted to buy yesterday are sold out.
② The man who you wanted to meet was on vacation.
③ I don't want to hear the song which has a sad melody.
④ The doctor who you saw last week is my father.
⑤ Is this the card that you are looking for?

서답형

21 다음 주어진 단어를 문맥과 어법에 맞게 빈칸에 쓰시오.

say / come / paint / climb

- Kelly saw someone _____ close to her in the dark.
- I saw the famous man _____ a portrait with a brush.
- Clair heard someone _____ her name.
- We watched him _____ through the window, and then I called the police.

Grammar **181**

01 〈보기〉와 같이 하나의 문장을 두 개의 문장으로 쓰시오.

┤ 보기 ├

The people who love romantic music are usually kind.
➡ The people love romantic music.
➡ They are usually kind.

(1) Dan lectured on a topic which was very boring.

➡ _____

➡ _____

(2) I know the woman whose necklace was stolen.

➡ _____

➡ _____

02 다음 주어진 어구를 활용하여 우리말을 영어로 쓰시오.

당신은 이른 아침에 새들이 지저귀는 소리를 들을 것입니다.
(hear / sing / in the early morning)

➡ _____

03 다음 빈칸 ⓐ와 ⓑ에 공통으로 들어갈 말을 쓰고, 빈칸 ⓒ에는 'smile'을 어법에 맞게 쓰시오.

The town ___ⓐ___ I have lived in for three years is very small. People ___ⓑ___ live in the town are very nice. If you visit there, you will see many people ___ⓒ___ brightly.

➡ _____

04 다음 중 서로 관련 있는 문장을 연결하여 하나의 문장으로 쓰시오.

- A fire fighter is someone.
- The woman is in her home now.
- The bus was the last bus.
- A train has a number of cars.
- Milk is the white liquid.

- They are all connected together.
- It is produced by cows, goats, and some other animals.
- She was in the hospital.
- It left an hour ago.
- He or she puts out fires.

➡ _____
➡ _____

_____
➡ _____
➡ _____

➡ _____
_____

05 주어진 단어를 활용하여 다음 우리말을 영어로 쓰시오.

그녀는 자신의 심장이 더 빠르게 뛰는 것을 느꼈다.
(feel / beat)

➡ _____

06 다음 문장을 하나의 문장으로 만드시오.

- Is the chair comfortable?
- It was made by you.

➡ _____

07 동사 steal을 어법에 맞게 빈칸에 각각 쓰시오.

- Jimmy saw Tyler _____ a bunch of bananas.
- Jimmy found a bunch of bananas _____ by somebody.

08 다음 주어진 두 개의 문장을 하나의 문장으로 만드시오.

(1) I don't like stories.
   They have sad endings.
   ➡ _____
   _____

(2) Jason works for a company.
   It makes cars.
   ➡ _____
   _____

(3) We live in a world.
   It is changing all the time.
   ➡ _____
   _____

(4) There are people.
   They are cheering excitedly.
   ➡ _____
   _____

09 주어진 어구를 바르게 배열하여 다음 우리말을 영어로 쓰시오. 필요하다면 어형을 변형하시오.

우리는 한 남자가 기차에서 내리려고 애쓰는 것을 보았다. (get off / we / watch / the train / a man / to / try)

➡ _____

10 다음 문장의 빈칸에 알맞은 관계대명사를 쓰시오.

- This is the man _____ son I spoke to yesterday.
- The people _____ I work with are very nice and diligent.
- What is the name of the person _____ is very handsome?

11 주어진 단어를 활용하여 다음 우리말을 영어로 쓰시오.

그 창문이 잠긴 것을 보았니? (see / lock)

➡ _____

12 주어진 어구를 활용하여 다음 우리말을 영어로 쓰시오.

나는 너의 물고기들이 무리를 지어 헤엄치는 것을 보고 싶어.
(want / see / swim / in a group)

➡ _____

13 관계대명사를 이용하여 다음 빈칸을 알맞게 채우시오.

Is there anything _____ _____
_____ _____ _____ _____?
내가 널 위해 해 줄 수 있는 것이 있니?

Reading

Seconds from Winning

At the go-kart race track, there are many people who are cheering
고카트(작은 경주용 자동차)
주격 관계대명사: 불완전한 절을 이끌며 many people을 수식
excitedly. The karts that are making loud engine noises are waiting. An
주격 관계대명사: 불완전한 절을 이끌며 The karts를 수식
official waves a green flag and the race starts!

Max pushes his foot down hard on the gas pedal as he completes his
세게
접속사: '~하면서', '~할 때'
sixth lap on the track. On the straightaway, Max pulls right beside the
(자동차 등을) 바짝 대다, 바짝 놓다
race's leader, Simon. Last year, Simon won many races, but Max's best
동격
result in a race was coming in fifth place. This time, he has a chance
(경주, 대회 등의) 등위
to finish second. But he isn't going to be satisfied with second place
to부정사의 형용사적 용법: a chance를 수식   = won't be satisfied
today. The winner gets to meet the world famous racer L. J. Richards!
get to V: V하게 되다   동격
He doesn't want to miss the chance to meet his role model.
기회를 놓치다   to부정사의 형용사적 용법: the chance를 수식

Max completes the tenth lap and now has five more laps to go. Max
to부정사의 형용사적 용법: laps를 수식
sees Simon's kart ahead, just out of Max's reach. Max's kart gets closer
앞에서
and closer to Simon's. It almost hits the back end of Simon's kart. They
비교급 and 비교급: 점점 더 ~한   = Simon's kart
drive into the straightaway and Max presses harder on the gas pedal.
운전해 ~로 들어가다   더 세게

track 경주로, 트랙
cheer 환호하다, 응원하다
excitedly 흥분하여
noise 소음
official 심판
wave ~을 흔들다
push down ~을 꼭 누르다
straightaway 직선코스
right beside 바로 옆에
result 결과
fifth place 5등
be satisfied with ~에 만족하다
get to ~하게 되다
miss 놓치다
complete 끝내다, 완료하다
lap (경주에서 트랙의) 한 바퀴
out of one's reach ~에게 닿지 않는
비교급 and 비교급: 점점 더 ~한
press on ~을 누르다

확인문제

● 다음 문장이 본문의 내용과 일치하면 T, 일치하지 않으면 F를 쓰시오.

1 People are cheering at the go-kart race track. ☐

2 The karts are waiting without making noises. ☐

3 A green flag means that the race starts. ☐

4 Simon is the leader of the race until the sixth lap. ☐

5 Max won many races last year. ☐

6 Anyone can get a chance to meet L. J. Richards ☐

7 L. J. Richards is Simon's role model. ☐

"I can catch up," says Max.
= catch up (with Simon)

Max sees the official waving a white flag which means the last lap.
지각동사+목적어+Ving: 목적어가 V하는 것을 보다   주격 관계대명사(= that)

Max is right behind Simon. The finish line is getting closer, and the
바로   close의 비교급

cheering from the crowd is getting louder.
get+비교급: 점점 더 ~해지다

"I can do it!" Max says loudly. He can feel his heart beating hard. The
지각동사+목적어+Ving

karts rush across the finish line. Who is the winner?

Max's eyes are filled with tears as he finds out that he came in second.
접속사: '~할 때'   명사절을 이끄는 접속사

"No need for tears, kid," says a man's voice. Max can't believe his
= There is no need for tears   동사+주어: 도치 구문

eyes. The man who is standing in front of him is L. J. Richards! "Thank
주격 관계대명사(= that)   ~ 앞에

you, but I'm not the winner," says Max.

"It was a real close race. Even though you didn't win the race, you did
우열을 가릴 수 없는   '비록 ~이지만' (양보의 부사절을 이끎)

your best. That's the thing that counts!" says L. J. Richards.
주격 관계대명사: the thing을 수식하는 형용사절

'Did I do my best?' thinks Max. After a moment, he smiles. "Yeah, I
잠시 후에

guess I did."
= did my best

catch up 따라잡다	
mean 의미하다	
last 마지막의	
behind ~ 뒤에	
finish line 결승선	
cheering 환호	
beat 뛰다	
be filled with ~으로 가득 차다	
find out ~을 알게 되다	
need 필요	
voice 목소리	
believe 믿다	
stand 서 있다	
close 막상막하의	
even though 비록 ~일지라도	
count 중요하다	
do one's best 최선을 다하다	
guess 추측하다, 생각하다	

📎 **확인문제**

● 다음 문장이 본문의 내용과 일치하면 T, 일치하지 않으면 F를 쓰시오.

1 When a white flag is waved, racers know that it is the last lap. ☐

2 Simon is right in front of Max. ☐

3 As the finish line is getting closer, the sound of cheering is getting quieter. ☐

4 Max feels calm when he rushes across the finish line. ☐

5 L. J. Richards comes to Max to cheer him up. ☐

6 Max thinks that he did his best. ☐

● 우리말을 참고하여 빈칸에 알맞은 말을 쓰시오.

1 _____ the go-kart race _____, _____ _____ many people _____ _____ _____ excitedly.

2 The karts _____ _____ making loud engine noises _____ _____.

3 An official _____ a green _____ and the race _____!

4 Max _____ his foot _____ _____ on the gas pedal _____ he _____ his sixth lap on the track.

5 _____ the straightaway, Max _____ _____ _____ the race's leader, Simon.

6 Last year, Simon _____ _____ _____, but Max's best result in a race _____ _____ _____ fifth place.

7 This time, he has a _____ _____ _____ _____ .

8 But he isn't going to _____ _____ _____ second _____ today.

9 The winner _____ _____ _____ the world famous racer L. J. Richards!

10 He doesn't want _____ _____ the chance _____ _____ his role model.

11 Max _____ the tenth lap and now has five more laps _____ _____ .

12 Max _____ Simon's kart _____ , just _____ _____ Max's reach.

13 Max's kart gets _____ _____ _____ to Simon's.

14 It almost _____ _____ _____ _____ of Simon's kart.

15 They _____ _____ the straightaway and Max _____ _____ _____ the gas pedal.

16 "I can _____ _____ ," says Max.

17 Max sees the official _____ _____ _____ which _____ the last lap.

1 고카트 경기 트랙에 신이 나서 응원하고 있는 많은 사람들이 있다.

2 시끄러운 엔진 소음을 내고 있는 카트들이 기다리고 있다.

3 심판이 초록 깃발을 흔들고, 경기가 시작된다!

4 Max는 트랙을 여섯 바퀴 돌았을 때, 발로 가속 페달을 힘껏 누른다.

5 직선 구간에서 Max는 경기에서 선두를 달리고 있는 Simon의 바로 옆까지 다가간다.

6 작년에 Simon은 경기에서 여러 번 이겼지만 Max의 최고 경기 성적은 5등으로 들어온 것이었다.

7 이번에 그는 2등으로 끝낼 수 있는 기회를 잡았다.

8 그러나 그는 오늘 2등으로 만족하지 않을 것이다.

9 우승자는 세계적으로 유명한 경주 선수인 L.J. Richards를 만나게 된다!

10 그는 그의 역할 모델을 만날 수 있는 기회를 놓치길 원하지 않는다.

11 Max는 10바퀴를 다 돌고 이제 5바퀴를 더 돌아야 한다.

12 Max는 앞에 바로 닿을 듯한 거리에 있는 Simon의 카트를 본다.

13 Max의 카트는 Simon의 카트에 점점 더 가까워진다.

14 Max의 카트는 Simon의 카트의 뒷부분에 거의 닿을 것 같다.

15 그들은 직선 구간을 운전해가고, Max는 가속 페달을 더 세게 밟는다.

16 "나는 따라잡을 수 있어." Max가 말한다.

17 Max는 심판이 마지막 바퀴라는 것을 알려주는 흰색 깃발을 흔드는 것을 본다.

18 Max is _____ _____ Simon.

19 The finish line is _____ _____, and the cheering _____ _____ _____ is _____ _____.

20 "I _____ _____ _____!" Max says loudly.

21 He can _____ his heart _____ _____.

22 The karts _____ _____ the finish line.

23 _____ is the winner?

24 Max's eyes are _____ _____ _____ as he _____ _____ _____ he came in second.

25 "_____ _____ _____ _____, kid," says a man's voice.

26 Max _____ _____ his eyes.

27 The man _____ _____ _____ in front of him _____ L. J. Richards!

28 "Thank you, but I'm _____ _____ _____," says Max.

29 "It was _____ _____ _____.

30 Even though you _____ _____ _____ _____, you _____ your best.

31 That's the thing _____ _____!" says L. J. Richards.

32 '_____ I _____ _____ _____?' thinks Max.

33 _____ a moment, he _____.

34 "Yeah, I _____ I _____."

18 Max는 Simon 바로 뒤에 있다.

19 결승점이 점점 가까워지고, 관중으로부터 들리는 환호성이 점점 커진다.

20 "나는 할 수 있어!" Max는 큰 소리로 말한다.

21 그는 그의 심장이 세게 뛰는 것을 느낄 수 있다.

22 카트들이 돌진해 결승점을 지난다.

23 누가 승자인가?

24 Max는 자신이 2등으로 들어왔다는 것을 알았을 때, 눈에 눈물이 가득 찬다.

25 "울 필요 없단다, 얘야." 어떤 남자의 목소리가 말한다.

26 Max는 그의 눈을 믿을 수 없다.

27 그 앞에 서 있는 남자는 L.J. Richards이다!

28 "고마워요, 하지만 저는 일등이 아니에요." Max가 말한다.

29 "정말 아슬아슬한 경기였어.

30 네가 비록 경기를 이기지 못했지만, 너는 최선을 다했어.

31 중요한 것은 바로 그거란다!" L.J. Richards가 말한다.

32 '나는 최선을 다했을까?' Max는 생각한다.

33 잠시 후에, 그는 미소를 짓는다.

34 "네, 저는 최선을 다한 것 같아요."

● 우리말을 참고하여 본문을 영작하시오.

1 ▶ 고카트 경기 트랙에 신이 나서 응원하고 있는 많은 사람들이 있다.

➡ _____

2 ▶ 시끄러운 엔진 소음을 내고 있는 카트들이 기다리고 있다.

➡ _____

3 ▶ 심판이 초록 깃발을 흔들고, 경기가 시작된다!

➡ _____

4 ▶ Max는 트랙을 여섯 바퀴 돌았을 때, 발로 가속 페달을 힘껏 누른다.

➡ _____

5 ▶ 직선 구간에서 Max는 경기에서 선두를 달리고 있는 Simon의 바로 옆까지 다가간다.

➡ _____

6 ▶ 작년에 Simon은 경기에서 여러 번 이겼지만 Max의 최고 경기 성적은 5등으로 들어온 것이었다.

➡ _____

7 ▶ 이번에 그는 2등으로 끝낼 수 있는 기회를 잡았다.

➡ _____

8 ▶ 그러나 그는 오늘 2등으로 만족하지 않을 것이다.

➡ _____

9 ▶ 우승자는 세계적으로 유명한 경주 선수인 L. J. Richards를 만나게 된다!

➡ _____

10 ▶ 그는 그의 역할 모델을 만날 수 있는 기회를 놓치길 원하지 않는다.

➡ _____

11 ▶ Max는 10바퀴를 다 돌고 이제 5바퀴를 더 돌아야 한다.

➡ _____

12 ▶ Max는 앞에 바로 닿을 듯한 거리에 있는 Simon의 카트를 본다.

➡ _____

13 ▶ Max의 카트는 Simon의 카트에 점점 더 가까워진다.

➡ _____

14 ▶ Max의 카트는 Simon의 카트의 뒷부분에 거의 닿을 것 같다.

➡ _____

15 ▶ 그들은 직선 구간을 운전해가고, Max는 가속 페달을 더 세게 밟는다.

➡ _____

16 ▶ "나는 따라잡을 수 있어." Max가 말한다.

➡ _____

17 ▶ Max는 심판이 마지막 바퀴라는 것을 알려주는 흰색 깃발을 흔드는 것을 본다.

➡ _____

18 Max는 Simon 바로 뒤에 있다.

➡ _____

19 결승점이 점점 가까워지고, 관중으로부터 들리는 환호성이 점점 커진다.

➡ _____

20 "나는 할 수 있어!" Max는 큰 소리로 말한다.

➡ _____

21 그는 그의 심장이 세게 뛰는 것을 느낄 수 있다.

➡ _____

22 카트들이 돌진해 결승점을 지난다.

➡ _____

23 누가 승자인가?

➡ _____

24 Max는 자신이 2등으로 들어왔다는 것을 알았을 때, 눈에 눈물이 가득 찬다.

➡ _____

25 "울 필요 없단다, 얘야." 어떤 남자의 목소리가 말한다.

➡ _____

26 Max는 그의 눈을 믿을 수 없다.

➡ _____

27 그 앞에 서 있는 남자는 L. J. Richards이다!

➡ _____

28 "고마워요, 하지만 저는 일등이 아니에요." Max가 말한다.

➡ _____

29 "정말 아슬아슬한 경기였어.

➡ _____

30 네가 비록 경기를 이기지 못했지만, 너는 최선을 다했어.

➡ _____

31 중요한 것은 바로 그거란다!" L. J. Richards가 말한다.

➡ _____

32 '나는 최선을 다했을까?" Max는 생각한다.

➡ _____

33 잠시 후에, 그는 미소를 짓는다.

➡ _____

34 "네, 저는 최선을 다한 것 같아요."

➡ _____

[01~04] 다음 글을 읽고, 물음에 답하시오.

At the go-kart race track, (A)[there is / there are] many people ___ⓐ___ are cheering excitedly. The karts ___ⓑ___ are making loud engine noises (B)[is / are] waiting. An official (C)[waves / waving] a green flag and the race starts!

01 위 글의 (A)~(C)에서 어법상 옳은 것끼리 바르게 짝지어진 것은?

① there is – is – waves
② there are – is – waves
③ there is – are – waving
④ there are – are – waving
⑤ there are – are – waves

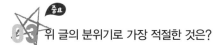

02 위 글의 빈칸 ⓐ와 ⓑ에 공통으로 들어갈 말을 쓰시오.

➡ _____

03 위 글의 분위기로 가장 적절한 것은?

① disappointing   ② boring
③ pleasing   ④ exciting
⑤ scaring

04 위 글의 내용과 일치하지 <u>않는</u> 것은?

① The passage is about a kart racing.
② A lot of people are there to watch the kart racing.
③ The engine noises are loud.
④ All the karts are running a race now.
⑤ There is a flag that gives a signal to start.

[05~08] 다음 글을 읽고, 물음에 답하시오.

Max pushes his foot down hard on the gas pedal ⓐas he completes his sixth lap on the track. ① On the straightaway, Max pulls right beside the race's leader, Simon. ② Last year, Simon won many races, but Max's best result in a race was coming in fifth place. ③ This time, he has a chance to finish second. ④ The winner gets to meet the world famous racer L. J. Richards! ⑤ He doesn't want to miss the chance to meet his role model.

05 위 글의 ①~⑤ 중 주어진 문장이 들어가기에 가장 적절한 곳은?

> But he isn't going to be satisfied with second place today.

①   ②   ③   ④   ⑤

06 다음 중 밑줄 친 ⓐ를 대신하여 쓸 수 있는 것은?

① but   ② because
③ when   ④ since
⑤ if

07 위 글을 읽고 답할 수 <u>없는</u> 것은?

① What does Max do on the straightaway?
② What is the name of the leader?
③ What was the best result of Max last year?
④ How many races did Simon win?
⑤ Who is L. J. Richards?

08 다음 중 위 글에서 유의어를 찾을 수 없는 것은?

① opportunity ② next to
③ well-known ④ press
⑤ lose

[09~14] 다음 글을 읽고, 물음에 답하시오.

Max completes the tenth lap and now has five more laps ①to go. Max sees Simon's kart ahead, just ②out of Max's reach. Max's kart gets closer and closer to Simon's. It almost ③hit the back end of Simon's kart. They drive ④into the straightaway and Max presses harder ⑤on the gas pedal.
"I can catch up," says Max.
Max sees the official waving a white flag which means the last lap. Max is right behind Simon. The finish line is _____(A)_____, and the cheering from the crowd is _____(B)_____.
"I can do it!" Max says loudly. He can feel his heart ____(C)____ (D)hard. The karts rush across the finish line. Who is the winner?

서답형

09 주어진 단어를 문맥과 어법에 맞게 활용하여 빈칸 (A)와 (B)에 쓰시오.

get / close / loud

(A)_____ (B)_____

서답형

10 다음 주어진 동사를 어법에 맞게 빈칸 (C)에 쓰시오.

beat

➡ _____

11 위 글의 밑줄 친 ①~⑤ 중 어법상 바르지 않은 것은?

① ② ③ ④ ⑤

서답형

12 위 글의 내용에 맞게 빈칸에 알맞은 말을 쓰시오.

People _____ _____ cheering see Max's cart _____ _____ _____ _____ to the kart which is right in front of his cart.

중요

13 다음 중 밑줄 친 (D)와 쓰임이 같은 것은?

① How about buying a hard mattress this time?
② It is hard to believe that she is only seven.
③ I heard that shoveling snow is a hard work.
④ Something cold and hard pressed into the back of my neck.
⑤ She kicked the door very hard and broke her toe.

14 다음 중 위 글의 내용과 일치하지 않는 것은?

① The total number of laps that racers have to finish is fifteen laps.
② It is not easy for Max to catch up with Simon.
③ Max presses harder on the gas pedal on the straightaway.
④ A white flag means that there is no lap left.
⑤ Max comes in second place in the race.

[15~18] 다음 글을 읽고, 물음에 답하시오.

Max's eyes are filled with tears as he finds out ⓐthat he came in second.

"No need for tears, kid," says a man's voice. Max can't believe his eyes. _____(A)_____

"Thank you, but I'm not the winner," says Max.

"It was a real close race. Even though you didn't win the race, you did your best. That's the thing that ⓑcounts!" says L. J. Richards.

'Did I do my best?' thinks Max. After a moment, he smiles. "Yeah, I guess ⓒI did."

서답형

15 다음 두 문장을 하나의 문장으로 만들어 빈칸 (A)에 쓰시오.

The man is L. J. Richards! He is standing in front of him.

➡ _____

_____

중요

16 다음 중 밑줄 친 ⓐ와 쓰임이 다른 것은?

① The fact that he has the data can be denied.

② I can see that he is crying with happiness.

③ Can I see the ticket that you bought online?

④ She thinks that he stole the money in her bag.

⑤ They said that Kelvin had to take part in the race.

17 다음 중 밑줄 친 ⓑ를 대신하여 쓸 수 있는 것은?

① adds　　② numbers　　③ matters

④ considers　　⑤ believes

서답형

18 위 글의 밑줄 친 ⓒ를 생략되지 않은 문장으로 쓰시오.

➡ _____

[19~22] 다음 글을 읽고, 물음에 답하시오.

Max pushes his foot down hard on the gas pedal as ⓐhe completes his sixth lap on the track. On the straightaway, Max pulls right beside the race's leader, Simon. Last year, ⓑhe won many races, but Max's best result in a race was coming in fifth place. This time, ⓒhe has a chance to finish second. But ⓓhe isn't going to be satisfied with second place today. The winner gets to meet the world famous racer L. J. Richards! He doesn't want to miss the chance (A)to meet ⓔhis role model.

중요

19 위 글의 밑줄 친 ⓐ~ⓔ 중 지칭하는 사람이 다른 하나는?

① ⓐ　② ⓑ　③ ⓒ　④ ⓓ　⑤ ⓔ

서답형

20 주어진 어구를 바르게 배열하여 다음 물음에 답하시오. 필요하다면 단어를 추가하거나 변형하시오.

Q: Why does Max want to win the race?

B: Because _____.

(the winner / the chance / have / meet / L. J. Richards)

➡ _____

서답형

21 위 글의 내용에 맞게 다음 빈칸에 알맞은 말을 쓰시오.

L. J. Richards _____ Max admires is

_____ _____ _____ _____ _____.

22 다음 중 밑줄 친 (A)와 쓰임이 같은 것은?

① Brad allowed his friend to use his USB.
② Did you go out to buy some flowers?
③ It is not easy to forgive you.
④ I have the ability to speak English well.
⑤ David hoped to become a dentist.

[23~25] 다음 글을 읽고, 물음에 답하시오.

Max completes the tenth lap and now has five more laps to go. Max sees Simon's kart ahead, just out of Max's reach. Max's kart gets closer and closer to Simon's. @It almost hits the back end of Simon's kart. They drive into the straightaway and Max presses harder on the gas pedal.

"I can catch up," says Max.

Max sees the official waving a white flag which means the last lap. Max is right behind Simon. The finish line is getting closer, and the cheering from the crowd is getting louder.

"I can do it!" Max says loudly. He can feel his heart beating hard. The karts rush across the finish line. Who is the winner?

23 위 글의 밑줄 친 문장 @의 의미로 가장 적절한 것은?

① Max's kart crashes Simon's kart.
② Max's kart is really close to Simon's kart.
③ Max's kart is right in front of Simon's kart.
④ Max wants to hit Simon's kart.
⑤ Max can barely see Simon's kart.

서답형
24 위 글의 내용에 맞게 빈칸에 알맞은 말을 쓰시오.

> When they are in the final lap, Simon is right _____ _____ _____ Max.

서답형
25 다음과 같이 풀이되는 말을 위 글에서 찾아 쓰시오.

> the place on the track or course where the race officially ends

➡ _____

26 다음 주어진 문장과 자연스럽게 이어지도록 (A)~(C)를 바르게 나열한 것은?

> An official waves a green flag and the race starts!

(A) But he isn't going to be satisfied with second place today. The winner gets to meet the world famous racer L. J. Richards! He doesn't want to miss the chance to meet his role model.

(B) Last year, he won many races, but Max's best result in a race was coming in fifth place. This time, he has a chance to finish second.

(C) Max pushes his foot down hard on the gas pedal as he completes his sixth lap on the track. On the straightaway, Max pulls right beside the race's leader, Simon.

① (A) – (C) – (B)   ② (B) – (A) – (C)
③ (B) – (C) – (A)   ④ (C) – (A) – (B)
⑤ (C) – (B) – (A)

[01~02] 다음 글을 읽고 물음에 답하시오.

At the go-kart race track, _____(A)_____. The karts that are making loud engine noises are waiting. An official waves a green flag and the race starts!

01 다음 두 문장을 하나의 문장으로 만들어 빈칸 (A)에 쓰시오.

There are many people. They are cheering excitedly.

➡ _____

02 When does the race starts? Answer in Korean.

➡ _____

[03~08] 다음 글을 읽고, 물음에 답하시오.

Max pushes his foot down hard on the gas pedal as he completes his sixth lap on the track. On the straightaway, Max pulls right beside the race's leader, Simon. Last year, Simon ___ⓐ___ many races, but Max's best result in a race was coming in fifth place. This time, he has a chance to finish second. But he isn't going to ___(A)___ with second place today. The winner gets ___ⓑ___ the world famous racer L. J. Richards! He doesn't want ___ⓒ___ the chance to meet his role model.

03 주어진 동사를 문맥과 어법에 맞게 빈칸 ⓐ~ⓒ에 쓰시오.

meet / miss / win

ⓐ_____ ⓑ_____ ⓒ_____

04 다음은 Simon에 관한 설명이다. 관계대명사를 이용하여 빈칸에 알맞은 말을 쓰시오.

Simon _____ last year is the race's leader.

05 주어진 동사를 어법에 맞게 빈칸 (A)에 쓰시오.

satisfy

➡ _____

06 위 글의 내용에 맞게 빈칸에 알맞은 말을 쓰시오.

Last year, when Max finished _____ _____ _____ in a race, it was Max's best result.

07 What does Max do on the straightaway? Answer in English with five words.

➡ _____

08 다음 빈칸에 들어갈 말을 위 글에서 찾아 쓰시오.

A _____ is the situation that exists at the end of a contest.

➡ _____

[09~11] 다음 글을 읽고, 물음에 답하시오.

Max completes the tenth lap and now has five more laps to go. (A)Max sees Simon's kart ahead,(see, go) just out of Max's reach. Max's kart gets closer and closer to Simon's. It almost hits the back end of Simon's kart. They drive into the straightaway and Max presses harder on the gas pedal. "I can catch up," says Max. Max sees the official waving a white flag which means the last lap. Max is right behind Simon. The finish line is getting closer, and the cheering from the crowd is getting louder. "I can do it!" Max says loudly. He can feel his heart beating hard. The karts rush across the finish line. Who is the winner?

09 주어진 단어를 활용하여 밑줄 친 (A)와 같은 의미의 문장을 쓰시오.

➡ _____

10 다음은 관중의 대화이다. 글의 내용에 맞게 빈칸에 알맞은 말을 쓰시오.

A: Do you see the official _____ _____ _____ _____? I don't know what it means.
B: _____ _____ that it is _____ _____ _____.

11 다음은 경기가 끝난 후 Max가 쓴 일기의 일부이다. 빈칸에 알맞은 말을 쓰시오.

When I got _____ to the finish line, I could hear the crowd _____. Also I started to feel my heart _____ very hard.

[12~14] 다음 글을 읽고, 물음에 답하시오.

The karts rush across the finish line. Who is the winner?
Max's eyes are filled with tears as he finds out that he came in second.
"No need for tears, kid." says a man's voice. Max can't believe his eyes. The man who is standing in front of him is L. J. Richards!
"Thank you, but I'm not the winner," says Max.
"It was a real close race. Even though you didn't win the race, you did your best. That's the thing that counts!" says L. J. Richards.
'Did I do my best?' thinks Max. After a moment, he smiles. "Yeah, I guess I did."

12 다음은 관중의 대화이다. 위 글의 내용에 맞게 빈칸에 알맞은 말을 쓰시오.

A: Can you see the man _____ _____ _____ _____ Max? Who is he?
B: Oh, he is L. J. Richards. I heard that Max looks up to him.

13 In what place did Max finish the race? Answer in English with a full sentence.

➡ _____

14 주어진 단어를 바르게 배열하여 위 글이 주는 교훈을 쓰시오.

the best / important / our best / than / being / doing / is / more

➡ _____
_____

구석구석

Listen & Talk C

Amy: Michael, why the long face?

Michael: I couldn't block the other player.
막다

Amy: Don't worry, Michael. You'll do better next time.
낙담하거나 실망한 사람을 격려하기 위해서 사용하는 표현이다.

구문해설 · long face: 시무룩한 얼굴

해석

Amy: Michael, 왜 시무룩한 얼굴이니?

Michael: 나는 다른 선수를 막지 못했어.

Amy: 걱정 마. Michael. 다음번에는 더 잘할 거야.

Grammar in Real Life

Ms. Green is a good cook who cooks delicious Italian food. She always goes
주격 관계대명사(= that)   빈도부사(일반동사 앞)
to the local store which has many fresh vegetables. Her restaurant is always
사물 선행사에 쓰이는 주격 관계대명사(= that)   빈도부사
crowded with people who like to eat her food. I want you to try her seafood
주격 관계대명사(= that)   want+목적어+to부정사
pizza which is the most popular.
사물 선행사에 쓰이는 주격 관계대명사(= that)

구문해설 · cook: 요리사 · delicious: 맛있는 · fresh: 신선한 · vegetables: 야채
· be crowded with: ～으로 붐비다

Green씨는 맛있는 이탈리아 음식을 만드는 훌륭한 요리사이다. 그녀는 항상 신선한 채소가 많이 있는 지역 상점에 간다. 그녀의 레스토랑은 그녀의 음식을 좋아하는 많은 사람들로 항상 붐빈다. 나는 네가 가장 인기 있는 그녀의 해산물 피자를 먹어 보기를 원한다.

Think & Write

A basketball match between Class 1 and Class 2 was held at school on Friday.
(둘) 사이의   수동태   요일 앞에 전치사 on
Class 1 won the game by a score. There are some memorable players. One
1점 차이로
of them was Sarah. She was the player who made a basket one second before
One에 수의 일치   주격 관계대명사   = before
the end of the game. It was a great match. We are looking forward to the next
the game ended   인칭대명사 It   전치사 to
match.

구문해설 · match: 경기 · be held: 개최되다 · by: ～ 차이로 · memorable: 기억에 남는
· make a basket: 득점을 올리다 · look forward to: ～을 기대하다

금요일에 학교에서 1반과 2반 사이의 농구 경기가 열렸습니다. 1반은 1점 차이로 그 경기에서 이겼습니다. 기억에 남는 몇 명의 선수가 있습니다. 그 중 한 명은 Sarah입니다. 그녀는 경기가 끝나기 1초 전에 득점을 올린 선수였습니다. 그것은 훌륭한 경기였습니다. 우리는 다음 경기를 기대하고 있습니다.

영역별 핵심문제

1 다음 영영풀이에 해당하는 말을 고르시오.

> to shout loudly, to show support or praise for somebody, or to give them encouragement

① cheer ② rush
③ press ④ block
⑤ kick

2 다음 중 밑줄 친 부분의 뜻풀이가 바르지 <u>않은</u> 것은?

① John and Tom met at the race track.
　　　　　　　　　　　　　　　　경마장
② Many people cheered for him excitedly.
　　　　　　　　　　　　　　　흥분하여
③ I stood at the starting line, waving the flag. 깃발
④ Suddenly, she burst into tears. 눈물
⑤ I watched your volleyball match yesterday.
　　　　　　　　　　　　　피구

3 다음 주어진 문장의 밑줄 친 의미와 같은 의미로 쓰인 것은?

> As an official waved the green flag, the race started.

① The official record cannot be changed.
② The official asked me to fill up the bottle with water.
③ Canada has two official languages.
④ I haven't written any official documents.
⑤ This is the President's official visit to Vietnam.

4 다음 문장의 빈칸에 공통으로 들어갈 말을 고르시오.

> • He won first _____ at the contest.
> • Ann, _____ the dishes on the table.
> • People gathered into a market _____.

① voice ② place ③ rush
④ press ⑤ count

5 다음 우리말과 일치하도록 주어진 말을 이용하여 완성하시오.

(1) Jake는 젊은 세대에게 뒤떨어지지 않기 위해 노력하고 있다. (keep)
　➡ Jake is trying to _____ _____ _____ the younger generation.
(2) 최선을 다하는 사람은 기회를 잡을 수 있다. (chance)
　➡ Those who _____ _____ _____ are able to _____ _____ _____.
(3) 이 상자는 많은 초콜릿과 사탕들로 채워져 있다. (fill)
　➡ This box _____ _____ _____ lots of chocolate and candies.

[06~07] 다음 대화를 읽고, 물음에 답하시오.

Mike: Is it your first time riding a bike, Mina?
Mina: Yes, it is. I just can't keep my balance.
Mike: (A)Let me help you. (hand) I'll hold your bike.
Mina: Thanks, Mike. Don't let go, okay?
Mike: Don't worry. Sit up and look straight ahead.

06 위 대화의 밑줄 친 (A)와 의미가 같도록 주어진 표현을 사용하여 다시 쓰시오.

➡ _____

07 위 대화의 내용과 일치하지 <u>않는</u> 것은?

① Mina는 자전거를 처음 타본다.
② Mina는 균형을 잡기 어려워한다.
③ Mike가 Mina의 자전거를 잡아 주려고 한다.
④ Mina는 Mike에게 자전거를 잡지 말라고 부탁하였다.
⑤ Mike는 Mina에게 똑바로 앉아 앞을 보라고 하였다.

[08~09] 다음 대화를 읽고, 물음에 답하시오.

Tom: What are you doing, Sarah?
Sarah: (A)<u>나는 체육 시간에 물구나무 서는 법을 배웠거든</u>. So I'm trying it now but it's not easy.
Tom: Let me help you. Kick your legs in the air again. I'll catch you.
Sarah: Oh, thanks. _____(B)

08 위 대화의 밑줄 친 (A)의 우리말과 일치하도록 〈보기〉에 주어진 모든 단어를 배열하여 완성하시오.

┌─ 보기 ┐
stand / head / in / I / how / learned / PE class / my / to / on
└──────┘

➡ _____

09 위 대화의 빈칸 (B)에 들어갈 말로 <u>어색한</u> 것은?

① Let me try it one more time.
② I'll do it again.
③ I'll give it a try.
④ I'll try again.
⑤ Don't give up!

[10~11] 다음 대화를 읽고, 물음에 답하시오.

Coach: Hey, Brian. Did you practice the *taegwondo* side kick?
Brian: Yes, Coach. But I'm still (A)[comfortable / uncomfortable] with it.
Coach: What problem are you having?
Brian: Well, I can't (B)[lift / drop] my leg high enough.
Coach: I see. Let me help you. I'll (C)[lose / hold] this kick pad for you. Show me your side kick.

10 다음 영영풀이가 나타내는 말을 위 대화에서 찾아 쓰시오.

┌─────────────────────────────────┐
│ to hit somebody/something with your foot │
└─────────────────────────────────┘

➡ _____

11 위 대화의 (A)~(C)에 들어갈 말로 바르게 짝지어진 것은?

① comfortable – lift – lose
② comfortable – drop – hold
③ uncomfortable – lift – hold
④ uncomfortable – drop – lose
⑤ uncomfortable – lift – lose

[12~13] 다음 대화를 읽고, 물음에 답하시오.

Anna: Hi, Jake. Do you come to the pool often?
Jake: Oh, hi, Anna. I take a swimming class here once a week.
Anna: When did you start the class?
Jake: Last month. But swimming is still not easy for me.
Anna: Oh, let me help you. _____(A)_____
Jake: Oh, that'll help me a lot. Thanks.

12 위 대화의 빈칸 (A)에 들어갈 말을 주어진 단어를 모두 배열하여 완성하시오.

┌─ 보기 ┐
swim / to / how / in / the / club /
teach / children / I / school
└─────────────────────────┘

➡ _____

13 위 대화의 내용과 일치하지 <u>않는</u> 것은?

① Jake는 일주일에 한 번씩 수영 수업을 듣는다.
② Jake는 지난달에 수영 수업을 듣기 시작했다.
③ Jake는 여전히 수영이 쉽지 않다.
④ Anna는 학교 동아리에서 아이들에게 수영을 가르친다.
⑤ Jake는 수영 수업이 만족스럽지 않다.

[14~15] 다음 대화를 읽고, 물음에 답하시오.

Jack: Did you come and ⓐwatch my volleyball match yesterday?

Irene: Yeah, I ⓑhave. That was a great volleyball match. You were great!

Jack: Thanks, but it was a ⓒclose match. My serves were not strong ⓓenough.

Irene: Oh, you're a great player. You'll do ⓔbetter next time.

14 위 대화의 ⓐ~ⓔ 중 어법상 어색한 것을 찾아 바르게 고치시오.

➡ _____

15 What was Jack not satisfied with?

➡ _____

Grammar

16 다음 빈칸에 공통으로 들어갈 말은?

┌─────────────────────────────┐
│ • The picture _____ my dad hang on │
│ the wall yesterday is painted by me. │
│ • This is a picture of a girl and dogs │
│ _____ are playing together in the │
│ garden. │
└─────────────────────────────┘

① who ② whose ③ which
④ what ⑤ that

17 다음 중 어법상 바르지 <u>않은</u> 것은?

① I saw my father washing his car.
② Did you hear about the woman that took part in the war?
③ She will hear the boys yelled at each other.
④ Julia saw her friend taking a selfie.
⑤ I met a man whose sister worked with you.

18 다음 우리말을 영어로 바르게 옮긴 것은?

┌─────────────────────────────┐
│ 나는 누군가가 우리를 따라오는 것을 느꼈다. │
└─────────────────────────────┘

① I heard us following someone.
② I heard us following him well.
③ I felt someone following us.
④ I felt me followed by somebody.
⑤ I felt myself following by someone.

19 주어진 단어를 이용하여 다음 우리말을 영어로 쓰시오.

┌─────────────────────────────┐
│ 네 전화기가 울리는 것을 들었니? │
│ (phone / ring) │
└─────────────────────────────┘

➡ _____

20 다음 중 주어진 문장의 빈칸에 들어갈 말과 <u>다른</u> 하나는?

> There were many children _____ were eating cotton candies.

① Did you see the movie _____ was about a woman's life?
② Many pictures _____ were painted by Vincent van Gogh are now very expensive.
③ I have twin babies _____ I should take care of.
④ Look at the house _____ fence is broken.
⑤ The man and the dog _____ are running together live next door to me.

21 다음 문장의 빈칸에 들어갈 말을 바르게 짝지은 것은?

> • We _____ some girls talking gladly.
> • I _____ my brothers to calm down.

① made – encouraged
② wanted – forced
③ heard – would like
④ saw – watched
⑤ listened to – finished

22 주어진 단어를 바르게 배열하여 문장을 완성하시오.

> A myth _____.
> (traditional / is / a / expresses / story / beliefs / which)

➡ _____

23 다음 중 어법상 옳은 것을 바르게 묶은 것은?

> ⓐ In our town, there are people aren't interested in other people at all.
> ⓑ The dress my friend is wearing is very expensive.
> ⓒ Thank you for the tip which is helpful.
> ⓓ Bradley enjoyed the show that I didn't like it.
> ⓔ Mr. Jang wanted to talk about the subject that was hard to understand.

① ⓐ, ⓑ, ⓓ   ② ⓑ, ⓒ, ⓓ   ③ ⓑ, ⓒ, ⓔ
④ ⓒ, ⓓ, ⓔ   ⑤ ⓐ, ⓓ, ⓔ

24 다음 우리말에 맞게 빈칸 ⓐ~ⓒ에 알맞은 말을 쓰시오.

> • Did you see _____?
> 그 비행기가 이륙하는 것을 보았니?
> • He heard _____.
> 그는 우리가 싸우는 소리를 들었어.
> • I watched _____.
> 나는 Jinna가 줄넘기를 하는 걸 보았어.

Reading

[25~28] 다음 글을 읽고, 물음에 답하시오.

An official waves a green flag and the race starts! Max pushes his foot ①down hard ___ⓐ___ the gas pedal as he ②completes his sixth lap ___ⓑ___ the track. On the straightaway, Max pulls right beside the race's leader, Simon. Last year, Simon ③won many races, but Max's best result in a race was coming in fifth place. This time, he has a chance to ④start second. But he isn't going to be satisfied ___ⓒ___ second place today. The winner gets to ⑤meet the world famous racer L. J. Richards! He doesn't want to miss ⓓ그의 역할 모델을 만날 그 기회.

25 위 글의 빈칸 ⓐ와 ⓑ에 공통으로 들어갈 말은?

① in   ② over   ③ about

④ on   ⑤ up

26 다음 중 빈칸 ⓒ에 들어갈 말과 같은 말이 들어가는 것은?

① Tom had to take care _____ his mother.

② I am afraid my idea is different _____ yours.

③ Are you interested _____ writing a poem?

④ Soon she got used _____ my smell.

⑤ The glass is filled _____ milk.

27 위 글의 ①~⑤ 중 글의 흐름상 어색한 것은?

①   ②   ③   ④   ⑤

28 주어진 단어를 활용하여 밑줄 친 우리말 ⓓ를 영어로 쓰시오.

chance / meet

➡ _____

[29~31] 다음 글을 읽고, 물음에 답하시오.

"I can do it!" Max says loudly. He can feel his heart beating hard. The karts rush across the finish line. Who is the winner?
Max's eyes are filled with tears as he finds out that he came in second.

"No need for tears, kid," says a man's voice. Max can't believe his eyes. The man who is standing in front of him is L. J. Richards! "Thank you, but I'm not the winner," says Max.
"It was a real close race. ____ⓐ____ you didn't win the race, you did your best. That's the thing that counts!" says L. J. Richards.
'Did I do my best?' thinks Max. After a moment, he smiles. "Yeah, I guess I did."

29 위 글의 빈칸 ⓐ에 들어갈 말로 가장 적절한 것은?

① Because   ② When

③ If   ④ Even though

⑤ While

30 다음 물음에 완전한 문장의 영어로 답하시오.

Q: What does Max feel when he gets near the finish line?

A: _____

➡ _____

31 다음 중 글의 내용과 일치하지 않는 것은?

① Max says that he can win the race.

② Max finishes the race in the second place.

③ Max talks with L. J. Richards.

④ Max is happy to know that he came in second.

⑤ Max thinks he did his best.

출제율 90%

01 다음 영영풀이에 해당하는 말을 고르시오.

> a piece of ground with a special surface for people, cars, etc. to have races on

① engine
② track
③ flag
④ tear
⑤ kart

출제율 95%

02 다음 우리말에 맞게 빈칸에 알맞은 말을 쓰시오.

(1) 기운 내! 너는 할 수 있어!

➡ _____ _____! You can do it!

(2) 모든 약은 아기의 손에 닿지 않는 곳에 보관하세요.

➡ Keep all the medicines _____ _____ _____ _____.

(3) 비록 접전이었지만 우리 팀은 경기에 우승하였다.

➡ Although it was a _____ _____, my team won the game.

출제율 100%

03 다음 주어진 문장의 밑줄 친 의미와 <u>다른</u> 의미로 쓰인 것은?

> Amy is wiping <u>tears</u> from her eyes.

① The sad story made her shed <u>tears</u>.
② Her eyes were filled with <u>tears</u>, listening to music.
③ <u>Tears</u> rolled down in my face.
④ Have you heard about the benefits of <u>tears</u>?
⑤ Be careful! This material <u>tears</u> easily.

[04~06] 다음 대화를 읽고, 물음에 답하시오.

Mom: David, how was your basketball game today?

David: We lost, Mom. I missed too many chances for a three-pointer.

Mom: Oh, don't be so hard on yourself. You'll do better next time.

David: _____

출제율 90%

04 위 대화의 빈칸에 들어갈 말로 알맞은 것은?

① No, thanks.
② I hope so.
③ Don't blame me.
④ It's all your fault.
⑤ Not at all.

출제율 95%

05 위 대화에서 David의 기분으로 적절한 것은?

① upset
② discouraged
③ pleased
④ nervous
⑤ lonely

출제율 100%

06 위 대화의 내용과 일치하지 <u>않는</u> 것은?

① David played the basketball game today.
② David's team lost the basketball game.
③ David blamed himself for his mistakes.
④ David's mom encouraged David to do better next time.
⑤ David's mom wanted to be so hard on herself.

[07~08] 다음 대화를 읽고, 물음에 답하시오.

Mike: (A) Is it your first time riding a bike, Mina?

Mina: (B) Yes, it is. I just can't keep my balance.

Mike: (C) I'll hold your bike.

Mina: (D) Thanks, Mike. Don't let go, okay?

Mike: (E) Don't worry. Sit up and look straight ahead.

출제율 90%

07 위 대화의 (A)~(E) 중 주어진 문장이 들어가기에 적절한 곳은?

> Let me help you.

① (A) ② (B) ③ (C) ④ (D) ⑤ (E)

출제율 90%

08 위 대화의 내용과 일치하도록 빈칸을 완성하시오.

A: What is Mina doing now?

B: She is learning how to _____ _____ _____.

[09~10] 다음 대화를 읽고, 물음에 답하시오.

Coach: (A) Hey, Brian. Did you practice the *taegwondo* side kick?

Brian: (B) Yes, Coach. But I'm still not comfortable with it.

Coach: (C) What problem are you having?

Brian: (D) Well, I can't lift my leg high enough.

Coach: (E) I'll hold this kick pad for you. Show me your side kick.

출제율 100%

09 위 대화의 (A)~(E) 중 주어진 문장이 들어가기에 적절한 곳은?

> I see. Let me help you.

① (A) ② (B) ③ (C) ④ (D) ⑤ (E)

출제율 95%

10 위 대화의 내용과 일치하지 않는 것은?

① Brain practiced the *taegwondo* side kick.

② Brain didn't feel comfortable with the *taegwondo* side kick.

③ Brain was not good at lifting his leg high enough.

④ The coach helped Brain practice the *taegwondo* side kick.

⑤ The coach showed the *taegwondo* side kick to Brain.

출제율 90%

11 다음 빈칸에 들어갈 말이 바르게 짝지어진 것은?

• There was a boy _____ dream was to be a pilot.

• I don't want to eat the bread _____ tastes sour.

① who – which   ② whom – that

③ whose – that   ④ whose – who

⑤ who – whose

출제율 95%

12 다음 중 빈칸에 들어갈 'play'의 형태가 다른 하나는?

① We saw the people in the park _____ catch.

② I heard the boys _____ cards in the living room.

③ Did you watch them _____ together last week?

④ I heard the music _____ by someone.

⑤ Have you seen the team _____ football in the stadium?

13 적절한 관계대명사를 이용하여 다음 두 문장을 하나의 문장으로 쓰시오.

출제율 90%

> • Unfortunately we couldn't go to the wedding.
> • We were invited to the wedding.

➡ _____

_____

14 다음 중 빈칸에 들어갈 말이 바르게 짝지어진 것은?

출제율 100%

> • Mrs. Brown heard someone _____ downstairs.
> • We watched a woman _____ behind the counter.

① come – to serve
② to come – to serve
③ coming – serve
④ comes – serving
⑤ to come – served

15 다음 중 밑줄 친 부분의 쓰임이 <u>다른</u> 하나는?

출제율 95%

① Do you know <u>that</u> Jason threw a ball to Kelly?
② I thought <u>that</u> telling the truth was important then.
③ He was the man <u>that</u> you mentioned about.
④ I know <u>that</u> you did your best on the test.
⑤ She believes <u>that</u> he will make her happy.

16 주어진 동사를 활용하여 다음 우리말을 영어로 쓰시오.

출제율 90%

> 우리는 한 B-boy가 무대 위에서 공연하는 것을 보았다. (watch / perform)

➡ _____

[17~19] 다음 글을 읽고, 물음에 답하시오.

> At the go-kart race track, there are many people ___ⓐ___ are cheering excitedly. The karts that are making loud engine noises are waiting. An official waves a green flag and the race starts!

17 다음 중 빈칸 ⓐ에 들어갈 말과 <u>다른</u> 하나는?

출제율 95%

① Do you know the woman _____ hair is curly and blond?
② Tom's dog _____ is walking with Tom looks happy.
③ He is not the man _____ always tells a lie.
④ This is the watch _____ Jenny bought last month.
⑤ Kelly will take part in the race _____ will be held next week.

18 위 글을 읽고 답할 수 있는 것은?

출제율 95%

① How many racers are there at the go-kart race?
② How many people are cheering?
③ What color of flag does an official wave?
④ Where is the go-kart track?
⑤ How long do the karts race?

19 위 글의 내용에 맞게 빈칸에 알맞은 말을 쓰시오. 〈출제율 95%〉

> You will hear the kart _____ _____
> _____ _____ in the go-kart race
> track.

[20~22] 다음 글을 읽고, 물음에 답하시오.

Max completes the tenth lap and now has five more laps to go. Max sees Simon's kart ahead, just out of Max's reach. Max's kart gets closer and closer to Simon's. It almost hits the back end of Simon's kart. They drive into the straightaway and Max presses harder on the gas pedal. "I can catch up," says Max.

_____(A)_____.

Max is right behind Simon. The finish line is getting closer, and the cheering from the crowd is getting louder.

"I can do it!" Max says loudly. He can feel his heart beating hard. The karts rush across the finish line. Who is the winner?

20 위 글의 빈칸 (A)에 다음 두 문장을 하나의 문장으로 바꿔 써 넣으시오. 〈출제율 85%〉

> Max sees the official waving a white flag.
> It means the last lap.

➡ _____

_____

21 다음과 같이 풀이되는 단어를 위 글에서 찾아 쓰시오. 〈출제율 90%〉

> a large group of people who have
> gathered together

➡ _____

22 위 글의 내용과 일치하는 문장의 개수를 고르시오. 〈출제율 90%〉

> ⓐ After finishing the tenth lap, there are still ten laps left.
> ⓑ Max can't see Simon's kart all the time.
> ⓒ Max's cart hits the back end of Simon's kart.
> ⓓ Max is at the back of Simon when the finish line is getting closer.
> ⓔ The crowd is holding their breath while watching the racing game.

① 1개　　② 2개　　③ 3개
④ 4개　　⑤ 5개

[23~24] 다음 글을 읽고, 물음에 답하시오.

Max's eyes are filled with tears as he finds out that he came in second.

"No need for tears, kid," says a man's voice. Max can't believe his eyes. The man ⓐ is standing in front of him is L. J. Richards!

"Thank you, but I'm not the ⓑwin," says Max.

"It was a real close race. Even though you didn't win the race, you did your best. That's the thing that counts!" says L. J. Richards.

'Did I do my best?' thinks Max. After a moment, he smiles. "Yeah, I guess I did."

23 위 글의 빈칸 ⓐ에 들어갈 말로 적절한 것을 <u>모두</u> 고르시오. 〈출제율 100%〉

① whom　　② who　　③ whose
④ which　　⑤ that

24 위 글의 밑줄 친 ⓑ를 알맞은 어형으로 고치시오. 〈출제율 95%〉

➡ _____

[01~03] 다음 대화를 읽고 물음에 답하시오.

> Emily: I heard your baseball team, the Reds, won the match. Eight to seven, right? Congratulations, John!
>
> John: Thanks. (A)그것은 접전이었어. I'm not happy with my pitching.
>
> Emily: Why do you say that?
>
> John: I allowed two homeruns.
>
> Emily: Oh, you're a great pitcher. You'll do better next time.

01 위 대화의 밑줄 친 (A)를 영작하시오.

➡ _____

02 위 대화에서 주어진 영영 풀이가 가리키는 말을 찾아 쓰시오.

> a sport event where people or teams compete against each other

➡ _____

03 Why was John unhappy with his pitching?

➡ _____

04 다음 우리말과 같은 뜻이 되도록 빈칸에 알맞은 말을 쓰시오.

(1) 나는 빠르게 결정하고 행동하는 사람을 좋아해.
➡ I like the person _____ _____ and _____ quickly.

(2) 그들은 꼬리를 가진 인형을 찾는 중이다.
➡ They are looking for _____ _____ _____ tails.

(3) 우리는 눈이 아름다운 소녀와 함께 이야기를 나누었다.
➡ We had a conversation with a girl _____ _____ _____ beautiful.

05 주어진 동사를 활용하여 다음 우리말을 영어로 쓰시오.

> 당신은 꽃들이 바람 속에서 춤추는 것을 볼 수 있습니다. (see / dance)

➡ _____
_____

06 다음 동사 'make'를 어법에 맞게 빈칸에 각각 쓰시오.

> • We saw Mom _____ cookies.
> • We ate cookies _____ by Mom.

07 적절한 관계대명사를 이용하여 다음 두 문장을 하나의 문장으로 쓰시오.

> • Where is the cheese?
> • I put it in the refrigerator.

➡ _____
_____

08 〈보기〉의 문장과 관계대명사를 이용하여 빈칸을 알맞게 채우시오.

> ┤ 보기 ├
> • You saw him driving a car.
> • They don't feel sorry for other people.
> • It has existed for a long time.

(1) A tradition is a custom _____
_____.

(2) What happened to the person _____
_____?

(3) I don't like people _____
_____.

[09~11] 다음 글을 읽고, 물음에 답하시오.

At the go-kart race track, there are many people who are cheering excitedly. ⓐThe karts that are making loud engine noises are waiting. An official waves a green flag and the race starts!

09 위 글의 내용에 맞게 빈칸에 알맞은 말을 쓰시오.

When you are at the go-kart race track, you can see many people _____ _____.

10 위 글의 밑줄 친 문장 ⓐ를 두 개의 문장으로 나누어 쓰시오.

➡ _____

_____

11 위 글의 내용에 맞게 빈칸에 알맞은 말을 쓰시오.

We will see the karts _____ on the track, making loud engine noises. As an official _____ _____ _____ _____, the go-kart race _____.

[12~13] 다음 글을 읽고, 물음에 답하시오.

Max's eyes are filled with tears as he finds out that he came in second.

"No need for tears, kid," says a man's voice. Max can't believe his eyes. The man who is standing in front of him is L. J. Richards!

"Thank you, but I'm not the winner," says Max.

"It was a real close race. Even though you didn't win the race, you did your best. That's the thing that counts!" says L. J. Richards.

'Did I do my best?' thinks Max. After a moment, he smiles. "Yeah, I guess I did."

12 위 글의 내용에 맞게 빈칸에 알맞은 말을 쓰시오.

At first, Max was not _____ with the result of the race _____ _____ he came in second.

13 위 글의 내용에 맞게 다음 물음에 완전한 문장의 영어로 답하시오.

Q: According to L. J. Richards, what is important to Max in the race?

A: _____

➡ _____

창의사고력 서술형 문제

01 다음 대화의 내용과 일치하도록 빈칸을 완성하시오.

> **Megan:** I'm worried about our next soccer match, James.
>
> **James:** Why are you worried, Megan?
>
> **Megan:** Well, I couldn't catch high balls in the last soccer match. I gave away too many goals.
>
> **James:** I see. Here, let me help you. I'll kick high balls to you.
>
> **Megan:** Oh, that'll really help. I hope my skills get better.
>
> **James:** Don't worry. You'll do better next time.

> Mon June 24th, 2019
>
> Today, I met Megan. She was worried about (A)_____ because she gave away too many goals in the last soccer match. She said she had trouble (B)_____. So, I decided to give (C)_____ to her. I (D)_____ for practice. She was satisfied with my help and wanted to improve her skills. I believe that she can do well next time.

02 〈보기〉와 같이 관계대명사를 이용하여 문장을 완성하시오.

> ── 보기 ──
>
> A soldier is a person who works in an army.

(1) Math teachers are people _____.
(2) Architects are people _____.
(3) Coffee is a drink _____.
(4) A car is a vehicle _____.
(5) King Sejong is the person _____.

03 주어진 동사의 동사원형이나 현재분사형을 써서 다양한 문장을 만드시오.

> ── 보기 ──
>
> see   hear   watch   listen to   feel

(1) _____
(2) _____
(3) _____
(4) _____
(5) _____
(6) _____

1 다음 문장의 빈칸에 들어갈 말을 보기에서 골라 적절한 형태로 쓰시오.

┌─ 보기 ┤
be satisfied with / be filled with /
keep up with / do one's best
└─────────────────────────┘

(1) I'll _____ to win this match.

(2) The street _____ cherry blossom now.

(3) I can't _____ you.

(4) He _____ his student's answer.

[02~03] 다음 대화를 읽고, 물음에 답하시오.

Emma: (A) How was your soccer match last week?

Keine: (B) We won, but I'm not ⓐsatisfying with our match.

Emma: (C) Why do you say ⓑthat?

Keine: (D) My passes were too ⓒshort.

Emma: (E) You're ⓓpracticing a lot. You'll do ⓔbetter next time.

2 위 대화의 (A)~(E) 중 주어진 문장이 들어가기에 적절한 곳은?

┌─────────────────────────┐
Don't take it too hard.
└─────────────────────────┘

① (A)   ② (B)   ③ (C)   ④ (D)   ⑤ (E)

3 위 대화의 ⓐ~ⓔ 중 어법상 어색한 것을 골라 바르게 고치시오.

➡ _____

[04~05] 다음 대화를 읽고, 물음에 답하시오.

Megan: I'm (A)worried about our next soccer match, James.

James: Why are you worried, Megan?

Megan: Well, I couldn't catch high balls in the last soccer match. I gave away too many goals.

James: I see. Here, let me help you. I'll kick high balls to you.

Megan: Oh, that'll really help. I hope my skills get better.

James: Don't worry. You'll do better next time.

4 위 대화의 밑줄 친 (A)worried와 바꾸어 쓸 수 있는 것을 모두 고르시오.

① concerned   ② comforted

③ anxious   ④ satisfied

⑤ alarmed

5 위 대화의 내용과 일치하지 않는 것은?

① Megan은 다음 축구 시합을 걱정하고 있다.

② Megan은 지난 축구 시합 때 많은 골을 내주었다.

③ James는 Megan에게 높은 공을 차 줄 것이다.

④ Megan은 자신의 실력이 점차 나아지길 바란다.

⑤ Megan은 James에게 공을 잡는 법을 알려줄 것이다.

[06~07] 다음 대화를 읽고, 물음에 답하시오.

Tom: What are you doing, Sarah?

Sarah: I learned how to stand on my head in PE class. So I'm trying it now but it's not easy.

Tom: Let me help you. Kick your legs in the air again. I'll catch you.

Sarah: Oh, thanks. I'll try again.

06 What did Sarah learn in PE class?

➡ _____

07 What did Tom tell Sarah to do to help her?

➡ _____

[08~09] 다음 대화를 읽고, 물음에 답하시오.

Mom: David, how was your basketball game today?
David: We lost, Mom. I missed too many chances for a three-pointer.
Mom: Oh, _____. You'll do better next time.
David: I hope so.

08 위 대화의 빈칸에 들어갈 말을 주어진 단어를 모두 배열하여 완성하시오.

┌─ 보기 ─┐
so / on / don't / hard / yourself / be
└─────┘

➡ _____

09 Why was David depressed after playing the basketball game?

➡ _____

_____

10 다음 대화의 (A)~(E) 중 주어진 문장이 들어가기에 알맞은 곳은?

You'll do better next time.

Emily: I heard your baseball team, the Reds, won the match. Eight to seven, right? Congratulations, John! (A)
John: Thanks. It was a close game. I'm not happy with my pitching. (B)
Emily: Why do you say that? (C)
John: I allowed two homeruns. (D)
Emily: Oh, you're a great pitcher. (E)

① (A)　② (B)　③ (C)　④ (D)　⑤ (E)

11 다음 빈칸에 공통으로 들어갈 말은?

• What is the name of the woman _____ legs are really long?
• I became friends with a girl _____ first language is the same as mine.

① who　　② that　　③ which
④ whose　⑤ whom

12 다음 빈칸에 알맞은 것을 모두 고르시오.

나는 누군가가 내 이름을 부르는 소리를 들었다.
➡ I heard _____.

① someone to call me
② someone call my name
③ my name calling me
④ someone calling me
⑤ my name called

13 다음 중 빈칸에 들어갈 말이 바르게 짝지어진 것은?

- Have you heard of a man _____ wallet was stolen?
- Maybe Jefferson is the person _____ is respected by every student.

① that – that
② who – whose
③ whose – whom
④ whom – that
⑤ whose – who

14 주어진 단어를 활용하여 다음 우리말을 영어로 쓰시오.

나는 Jason과 Helen이 함께 자전거를 타는 것을 봤어. (see / ride)

➡ _____

_____

15 다음 두 개의 문장을 하나의 문장으로 쓰시오.

- There are a girl and a goat.
- They are resting on the hill.

➡ _____

_____

[16~19] 다음 글을 읽고, 물음에 답하시오.

Max pushes his foot down ⓐhardly on the gas pedal as he completes his sixth lap on the track. On the straightaway, Max pulls ⓑright beside the race's leader, Simon. Last year, Simon won many races, but Max's best result in a race was (A)coming in fifth place. This time, he has a chance to finish ⓒsecond. But he isn't going to be satisfied with second place today. The winner ⓓgets to meet the world famous racer L. J. Richards! He doesn't want ⓔto miss the chance to meet his role model.

16 위 글의 ⓐ~ⓔ 중 어법상 바르지 않은 것은?

① ⓐ   ② ⓑ   ③ ⓒ   ④ ⓓ   ⑤ ⓔ

17 다음 중 위 글을 읽고 답할 수 없는 것은?

① What does Max do when he completes his sixth lap?
② What does Max do on the straightaway?
③ How many races did Simon win last year?
④ Why isn't Max going to be satisfied with second place today?
⑤ Who is Max's role model?

18 다음 중 밑줄 친 (A)와 쓰임이 다른 것은?

① Do you mind closing the door?
② His hobby is riding a bike alone.
③ Eating regularly is important.
④ We saw them jumping a rope.
⑤ The writer didn't finish writing a book.

19 다음은 Max와 엄마의 대화이다. 빈칸에 알맞은 말을 쓰시오.

Mom: Max, why do you want to win this race?
Max: Because only the winner gets the chance to meet L. J. Richards. If I win, you will see me _____ _____.

[20~23] 다음 글을 읽고, 물음에 답하시오.

"I can do it!" Max says loudly. He can feel his heart ⓐ<u>beating</u> hard. The karts rush across the finish line. Who is the winner?

Max's eyes _____(A)_____ tears as he finds out ⓑ<u>that</u> he came in second.

"No need for tears, kid." says a man's voice. Max can't believe his eyes. The man ⓒ<u>who</u> is standing in front of him is L. J. Richards!

"Thank you, but I'm not the winner," says Max.

"It was a real ⓓ<u>close</u> race. Even though you didn't win the race, you did your best. That's the thing ⓔ<u>that</u> counts!" says L. J. Richards.

'Did I do my best?' thinks Max. After a moment, he smiles. "Yeah, I guess I did."

20 동사 fill을 이용해 빈칸 (A)를 완성하시오. (3 words)

➡ _____

21 다음 중 밑줄 친 ⓐ~ⓔ에 대한 설명으로 바르지 <u>않은</u> 것은?

① ⓐ: 'beat'와 바꿔 쓸 수 있다.
② ⓑ: 목적어가 되는 명사절을 이끄는 접속사로 생략 가능하다.
③ ⓒ: 'that'을 대신 쓸 수 있다.
④ ⓓ: '가까운'이라는 의미이다.
⑤ ⓔ: 'which is important'와 같은 의미이다.

22 다음 중 글의 내용과 일치하는 것은?

① Max feels nothing when he rushes across the finish line.
② Max doesn't know who L. J. Richards is.
③ L. J. Richards wants Max to cry out loud.
④ Max regrets that he didn't do his best.
⑤ L. J. Richards cheers up Max.

23 위 글의 내용에 맞게 빈칸에 알맞은 말을 쓰시오.

L. J. Richards saw Max's kart _____ in second. He thought that Max _____ _____ _____. So he wanted to tell Max not to cry.

24 다음 대화가 자연스럽게 이어지도록 순서대로 배열하시오.

(A) Oh, thanks. I'll try again.
(B) What are you doing, Sarah?
(C) Let me help you. Kick your legs in the air again. I'll catch you.
(D) I learned how to stand on my head in PE class. So I'm trying it now but it's not easy.

➡ _____

25 주어진 문장과 자연스럽게 연결되도록 (A)~(C)를 바르게 나열하시오.

Max completes the tenth lap and now has five more laps to go.

(A) It almost hits the back end of Simon's kart. They drive into the straightaway and Max presses harder on the gas pedal. "I can catch up," says Max.

(B) Max sees Simon's kart ahead, just out of Max's reach. Max's kart gets closer and closer to Simon's.

(C) Max sees the official waving a white flag which means the last lap. Max is right behind Simon. The finish line is getting closer, and the cheering from the crowd is getting louder.

➡ _____

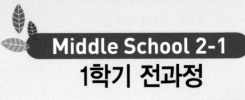

Middle School 2-1
1학기 전과정

중간 + 기말

영어 기출문제집

영어 중 2

비상 | 김진완

Best Collection

내용문의 중등영어발전소 적중100 편집부 TEL 070-7707-0457
인터넷 서비스 www.jj100.co.kr

Insight
on the textbook

교과서 파헤치기

영어 기출 문제집

적중 100 plus
1학기 전과정

영어 중 2

비상 | 김진완

INSIGHT
on the textbook

교과서 파헤치기

※ 다음 영어를 우리말로 쓰시오.

01	attractive		22	rule
02	view		23	seat
03	bake		24	balance
04	care		25	spike
05	corner		26	comment
06	decorate		27	scared
07	handy		28	mainly
08	shower		29	photography
09	place		30	peace
10	helpful		31	fantastic
11	pet		32	hedgehog
12	careful		33	wipe
13	cage		34	taste
14	suit		35	write down
15	macaron		36	be into
16	photographer		37	look around
17	hold		38	in person
18	repeat		39	be interested in
19	normally		40	come out
20	after-school class		41	go get
21	press		42	get used to
			43	pick up

※ 다음 우리말을 영어로 쓰시오.

01 균형

02 닦다

03 스케이트보드

04 연애 이야기, 로맨스

05 환상적인

06 사진술, 사진 찍기

07 로맨틱한, 낭만적인

08 블로그

09 배우

10 무서워하는, 겁먹은

11 영화관

12 논평, 견해

13 고슴도치

14 맛, 미각, 취향

15 비결, 묘책

16 주로

17 가시, 뾰족한 것

18 평화

19 가리키다, 지시하다

20 구석

21 예술의

22 재능, 재주

23 장식하다

24 보통

25 굽다

26 도움이 되는

27 주의 깊은

28 주의, 보살핌

29 누르다

30 반복하다

31 매력적인

32 새장, 우리

33 애완동물

34 사진사

35 처음부터 끝까지

36 약간의, 조금의

37 ～을 치우다[청소하다]

38 ～에 등록하다

39 ～을 둘러보다

40 ～에 익숙해지다

41 ～에 관심을 갖다

42 ～을 들어올리다[집다]

43 직접

※ 다음 영영풀이에 알맞은 단어를 <보기>에서 골라 쓴 후, 우리말 뜻을 쓰시오.

1 _____ : a small brown animal with stiff parts like needles covering its back: _____

2 _____ : a natural ability to do something well: _____

3 _____ : a type of popular music with a fast strong rhythm and words which are spoken fast, not sung: _____

4 _____ : a structure made of metal bars or wire in which animals or birds are kept: _____

5 _____ : a building in which films/movies are shown: _____

6 _____ : to say or write something again or more than once: _____

7 _____ : to make something look more attractive by putting things on it: _____

8 _____ : a place where you can sit, for example a chair: _____

9 _____ : to cook food in an oven without extra fat or liquid: _____

10 _____ : a situation or a period of time in which there is no war or violence in a country or an area: _____

11 _____ : a person who takes photographs, especially as a job: _____

12 _____ : to lift or move something to a higher level: _____

13 _____ : a small piece of advice about something practical: _____

14 _____ : to have somebody/something in your hand, arms: _____

15 _____ : having no or very little water or liquid: _____

16 _____ : a part of something where two or more sides, lines or edges join: _____

보기			
tip	hug	repeat	raise
talent	hedgehog	corner	photographer
theater	rap	dry	peace
seat	decorate	cage	bake

※ 다음 우리말과 일치하도록 빈칸에 알맞은 말을 쓰시오.

Listen & Talk 1 A

1. Mike: Betty, what are you _____ _____?

   Betty: I'm _____ the _____ on my blog.

   Mike: What do you _____ write _____ _____ about?

   Betty: I usually write about books. _____ _____ _____

   _____.

2. Jenny: Mike, _____ is the man _____ _____ _____?

   Mike: Oh, he is my _____ baseball player, John Luke. _____

   _____ _____ _____ baseball.

   Jenny: Wow, you _____ him _____ _____!

   Mike: Yeah, that was _____ _____ _____ of my life.

1. Mike: Betty, 뭐 보고 있어?
   Betty: 내 블로그에 달린 댓글을 읽어보는 중이야.
   Mike: 넌 평소에 무엇에 관해 블로그 게시물을 쓰니?
   Betty: 난 보통 책에 대해 써. 독서에 관심이 있거든.

2. Jenny: Mike, 네 SNS에 있는 남자는 누구야?
   Mike: 오, 그는 Jo□hn Luke라고 내가 제일 좋아하는 야구 선수야. 내가 야구에 정말 관심이 많거든.
   Jenny: 와, 그리고 너는 직접 그를 만났던 거고!
   Mike: 응, 그날이 내 인생 최고의 날이었지.

Listen & Talk 1 B

Jake: Hello, Elsa. _____ _____ _____ are you going to take?

Elsa: I'm _____ _____ _____ the drama class _____ Thursdays. What _____ you, Jake?

Jake: I'm _____ _____ taking the Tuesday _____ class. _____ _____ _____ _____ _____ _____.

Elsa: Oh, I _____ _____ the teacher is a famous _____.

Jake: Really? That's really _____!

Jake: 안녕, Elsa. 너 어떤 방과 후 수업을 들을 거야?
Elsa: 나는 목요일마다 하는 드라마 수업을 들을 거야. Jake, 너는 어때?
Jake: 화요일에 하는 사진 수업을 들으려고 생각 중이야. 난 사진 찍는 거에 관심이 있거든.
Elsa: 오, 그 선생님 유명한 사진작가라고 들었어.
Jake: 정말? 정말 멋지다!

Listen & Talk 2 A-1

W: I _____ this bread, but it _____ out too _____.

M: Oh, I _____ _____ _____ _____ _____ _____ without _____ it dry. _____ a glass of water _____ the oven.

W: That's a great _____. Where _____ you _____ that?

M: I saw it on _____ _____ _____.

W: 내가 이 빵을 구웠는데, 빵이 너무 마르게 나와 버렸어.
M: 오, 나 빵이 마르지 않도록 굽는 방법을 알고 있어. 오븐에 물 한 컵을 넣어봐.
W: 그거 정말 좋은 정보다. 너 그건 어디서 배웠어?
M: 요리 쇼에서 봤어.

Listen & Talk 2 A-2

M: Is that a 1000-piece _____?

W: Yeah, but _____ _____ so many pieces. It'll _____ a long
time _____ _____.

M: Oh, _____ _____ _____ _____ _____ _____
_____. Start _____ the corners, and then _____ the pieces
_____ the same colors.

W: I _____. Thanks.

Listen & Talk 2 B

Minsu: Oh, no. I _____ a dish.

Tina: _____ worry. I _____ _____ _____ _____ _____
the glass pieces _____ _____. I read the tip _____ _____
_____.

Minsu: _____ bread? _____?

Tina: You can _____ the area with it. It _____ _____ the small
pieces.

Minsu: Great tip! Thanks, Tina. I'll _____ _____ some bread in
the kitchen.

Communication

M: _____ _____ It's Your Stage! We _____ a great _____ for
you today. _____ _____ the people with _____ _____.

W: Hello. I'm Doremi. _____ _____ _____ _____ _____.

M: Great! What are you _____ _____ _____ today?

W: I know _____ _____ _____ _____ easily. I can
_____ _____ _____ _____ _____.

M: _____ interesting!

Wrap Up 1

Aron: Emily, _____ _____ are you going to _____?

Emily: I'm _____ _____ _____ the music club. I'm _____
music. What _____ you, Aron?

Aron: I _____ _____ the gardening club. I'm _____
_____ _____ _____ _____.

Emily: Oh, that _____ like an _____ _____.

M: 그거 조각이 1,000개짜리 퍼즐이야?

W: 응, 그런데 퍼즐 조각이 너무 많아.
다 맞추려면 한참 걸리겠어.

M: 아, 나 그 퍼즐 빨리 맞추는 방법 알아.
모서리들부터 맞추기 시작하고, 그런 다
음에 같은 색깔별로 조각들을 모아봐.

W: 알았어. 고마워.

Minsu: 오, 안 돼. 접시를 깨 버렸어.

Tina: 걱정 마. 빵으로 유리 조각을 치
우는 방법을 알아. 잡지에서 그
팁을 읽었거든.

Minsu: 빵으로? 어떻게?

Tina: 빵으로 그 부분을 닦으면 돼. 그
게 작은 조각들을 주워 모으거든.

Minsu: 훌륭한 팁이다! 고마워, Tina. 내가
부엌에 가서 빵을 좀 가져올게.

M: '당신의 무대입니다!'에 오신 걸 환영
합니다. 오늘 여러분을 위해 굉장한
볼거리를 마련했어요. 그럼 특별한
재능을 가진 사람들을 만나 볼게요.

W: 안녕하세요. 전 Doremi예요. 전 음
악에 관심이 있어요.

M: 좋아요! 오늘 우리에게 무엇을 보여
주실 건가요?

W: 전 높은 음을 쉽게 내는 방법을 알고
있어요. 제가 간단한 단계를 여러분
께 보여 드릴게요.

M: 흥미롭네요!

Aron: Emily, 너 어떤 동아리에 들 거야?

Emily: 음악 동아리에 들 거야. 나 음악
에 빠져 있거든. Aron, 넌 어때?

Aron: 난 정원 가꾸기 동아리에 들고
싶어. 식물이랑 꽃에 관심이 있
거든.

Emily: 오, 재미있는 동아리일 것 같은데.

※ 다음 우리말에 맞도록 대화를 영어로 쓰시오.

Listen & Talk 1 A

1. Mike: _____

   Betty: _____

   Mike: _____

   Betty: _____

2. Jenny: _____

   Mike: _____

   Jenny: _____

   Mike: _____

1. Mike: Betty, 뭐 보고 있어?
   Betty: 내 블로그에 달린 댓글을 읽어보는 중이야.
   Mike: 넌 평소에 무엇에 관해 블로그 게시물을 쓰니?
   Betty: 난 보통 책에 대해 써. 독서에 관심이 있거든.

2. Jenny: Mike, 네 SNS에 있는 남자는 누구야?
   Mike: 오, 그는 John Luke라고 내가 제일 좋아하는 야구 선수야. 내가 야구에 정말 관심이 많거든.
   Jenny: 와, 그리고 너는 직접 그를 만났던 거고!
   Mike: 응, 그날이 내 인생 최고의 날이었지.

Listen & Talk 1 B

Jake: _____

Elsa: _____

Jake: _____

_____

Elsa: _____

Jake: _____

Jake: 안녕, Elsa. 너 어떤 방과 후 수업을 들을 거야?
Elsa: 나는 목요일마다 하는 드라마 수업을 들을 거야. Jake, 너는 어때?
Jake: 화요일에 하는 사진 수업을 들으려고 생각 중이야. 난 사진 찍는 거에 관심이 있거든.
Elsa: 오, 그 선생님 유명한 사진작가라고 들었어.
Jake: 정말? 정말 멋지다!

Listen & Talk 2 A-1

W: _____

M: _____

_____

W: _____

M: _____

W: 내가 이 빵을 구웠는데, 빵이 너무 마르게 나와 버렸어.
M: 오, 나 빵이 마르지 않도록 굽는 방법을 알고 있어. 오븐에 물 한 컵을 넣어봐.
W: 그거 정말 좋은 정보다. 너 그건 어디서 배웠어?
M: 요리 쇼에서 봤어.

Listen & Talk 2 A-2

M: _____

W: _____

M: _____

_____

W: _____

M: 그거 조각이 1,000개짜리 퍼즐이야?
W: 응, 그런데 퍼즐 조각이 너무 많아. 다 맞추려면 한참 걸리겠어.
M: 아, 나 그 퍼즐 빨리 맞추는 방법 알아. 모서리들부터 맞추기 시작하고, 그런 다음에 같은 색깔별로 조각들을 모아봐.
W: 알았어. 고마워.

Listen & Talk 2 B

Minsu: _____

Tina: _____

_____

Minsu: _____

Tina: _____

Minsu: _____

Minsu: 오, 안 돼. 접시를 깨 버렸어.
Tina: 걱정 마. 빵으로 유리 조각을 치우는 방법을 알아. 잡지에서 그 팁을 읽었거든.
Minsu: 빵으로? 어떻게?
Tina: 빵으로 그 부분을 닦으면 돼. 그게 작은 조각들을 주워 모으거든.
Minsu: 훌륭한 팁이다! 고마워, Tina. 내가 부엌에 가서 빵을 좀 가져올게.

Communication

M: _____

_____

W: _____

M: _____

W: _____

M: _____

M: '당신의 무대입니다!'에 오신 걸 환영합니다. 오늘 여러분을 위해 굉장한 볼거리를 마련했어요. 그럼 특별한 재능을 가진 사람들을 만나 볼게요.
W: 안녕하세요. 전 Doremi예요. 전 음악에 관심이 있어요.
M: 좋아요! 오늘 우리에게 무엇을 보여 주실 건가요?
W: 전 높은 음을 쉽게 내는 방법을 알고 있어요. 제가 간단한 단계를 여러분께 보여 드릴게요.
M: 흥미롭네요!

Wrap Up 1

Aron: _____

Emily: _____

Aron: _____

Emily: _____

Aron: Emily, 너 어떤 동아리에 들 거야?
Emily: 음악 동아리에 들 거야. 나 음악에 빠져 있거든. Aron, 넌 어때?
Aron: 난 정원 가꾸기 동아리에 들고 싶어. 식물이랑 꽃에 관심이 있거든.
Emily: 오, 재미있는 동아리일 것 같은데.

※ 다음 우리말과 일치하도록 빈칸에 알맞은 것을 골라 쓰시오.

1 _____ It _____
A. Out   B. Rap

2 _____ your _____, Open your _____
A. heart   B. mind   C. open

3 Look _____ and _____ rap it _____
A. out   B. let's   C. around

4 Hey, I'm MC Joy. Do you want _____ _____ your _____ rap?
A. own   B. write   C. to

5 You _____ rap about _____ because _____ can _____ a story for a rap.
A. be   B. anything   C. can   D. everything

6 I get ideas _____ I'm _____ the bus, _____ the shower, or in my bed.
A. in   B. on   C. when

7 I _____ _____ my ideas and _____ them _____ I write my rap.
A. when   B. down   C. use   D. write

8 There _____ no _____ for _____ raps. You can start today!
A. writing   B. rules   C. are

9 _____ _____
A. Pets   B. Fantastic

10 _____ to *Fantastic Pets!* _____ a pet _____ great.
A. is   B. having   C. welcome

11 Today I'm _____ to _____ my _____ hedgehog, Polly.
A. pet   B. introduce   C. going

12 _____ I first _____ Polly, she was very _____.
A. got   B. scared   C. when

13 I couldn't _____ her _____ she _____ her spikes.
A. raised   B. because   C. hold

14 So, I _____ my T-shirt in her _____ and she got _____ to my smell.
A. used   B. case   C. placed

15 Finally, I was _____ to _____ her _____ my hands.
A. in   B. hold   C. able

16 Now, Polly is my _____ friend and always _____ me _____.
A. happy   B. makes   C. best

---

1 랩으로 표현해 봐

2 너의 생각을 열어 봐, 너의 마음을 열어 봐

3 주변을 둘러보고 랩으로 표현해 봐

4 안녕. 난 MC Joy야. 너만의 랩을 쓰고 싶니?

5 세상 모든 것들이 랩의 이야깃거리가 될 수 있기 때문에 넌 어떤 것에 대해서든 랩을 할 수 있어.

6 난 버스에서, 샤워 중에 또는 침대에서 아이디어들을 얻어.

7 내 아이디어들을 적어 두고 내가 랩을 쓸 때 그것들을 활용하지.

8 랩을 쓰는 데에는 어떤 규칙도 없어. 넌 오늘 당장 시작할 수 있어!

9 환상의 애완동물

10 '환상의 애완동물'에 온 걸 환영해! 애완동물을 기른다는 건 멋진 일이야.

11 오늘 난 나의 애완 고슴도치인 Polly를 소개할 거야.

12 내가 Polly를 처음 만났을 때, 그 애는 너무 겁을 먹었어.

13 그 애가 가시를 세워서 난 그 애를 손에 쥘 수가 없었어.

14 그래서 내가 그 애의 우리 안에 내 티셔츠를 두었더니 그 애가 내 냄새에 적응했어.

15 마침내, 난 손으로 그 애를 쥘 수 있게 되었지.

16 이제 Polly는 나의 가장 친한 친구이고 항상 나를 행복하게 해 줘.

17 _____ _____

A. Tips   B. Handy

18 _____ _____ to *Handy Tips*.

A. back   B. welcome

19 _____ do you _____ sit _____ a movie theater?

A. in   B. normally   C. where

20 _____ _____ a tip.

A. is   B. here

21 You will _____ it _____ and _____.

A. helpful   B. easy   C. find

22 Step 1 _____ your finger _____ something _____ from you.

A. far   B. point   C. at

23 Step 2 _____ one eye and _____ it.

A. open   B. close

24 Step 3 Repeat it _____ the _____ eye.

A. other   B. with

25 When _____ your finger _____?

A. move   B. does

26 Is it _____ you _____ your right eye?

A. close   B. when

27 Then you _____ _____ your right eye.

A. use   B. mainly

28 This _____ you should sit _____ the left _____ in the theater.

A. side   B. on   C. means

29 That _____, you can enjoy a full _____ of the screen _____.

A. better   B. view   C. way

30 This information is also _____ when you _____ a _____ in a classroom, _____.

A. choose   B. too   C. helpful   D. seat

---

17 쓸모 있는 팁

18 '쓸모 있는 팁'에 돌아온 걸 환영해.

19 넌 보통 영화관에서 어디에 앉니?

20 여기 팁이 하나 있어.

21 넌 이것이 쉽고 유용하다는 걸 알게 될 거야.

22 1단계: 멀리 떨어져 있는 물체를 손가락으로 가리켜 봐.

23 2단계: 한쪽 눈을 감았다가 떠 봐.

24 3단계: 반대쪽 눈으로 반복해 봐.

25 언제 네 손가락이 움직이니?

26 오른쪽 눈을 감았을 때니?

27 그렇다면 너는 주로 오른쪽 눈을 사용하는 거야.

28 그 말은 너는 영화관에서 왼편에 앉아야 한다는 걸 뜻해.

29 그렇게 하면, 너는 스크린의 꽉 찬 화면을 더 잘 즐길 수 있어.

30 이 정보는 네가 교실에서 자리를 고를 때도 도움이 될 거야.

※ 다음 우리말과 일치하도록 빈칸에 알맞은 말을 쓰시오.

1 Rap It _____

2 _____ your _____, _____ your _____

3 Look _____ and _____ _____ it _____

4 Hey, I'm MC Joy. Do you _____ _____ _____ your _____
_____?

5 You can rap _____ _____ because everything _____
_____ a story _____ _____ _____.

6 I get ideas _____ I'm _____ the bus, _____
_____, or _____ my bed.

7 I _____ _____ _____ _____ and _____ _____
when I _____ my rap.

8 There _____ _____ _____ for _____ raps. You
_____ _____ today!

9 _____ _____

10 _____ _____ _____ Pets! _____ a pet is great.

11 Today I'm _____ _____ _____ my pet _____, Polly.

12 _____ I first _____ Polly, she was very _____.

13 I _____ _____ her _____ she _____ her _____.

14 So, I _____ my T-shirt _____ _____ _____ and she
_____ _____ _____ my smell.

15 Finally, I _____ _____ _____ _____ her in my hands.

16 Now, Polly is _____ _____ _____ and always _____
_____ _____.

1 랩으로 표현해 봐

2 너의 생각을 열어 봐, 너의 마음을 열어 봐

3 주변을 둘러보고 랩으로 표현해 봐

4 안녕. 난 MC Joy야. 너만의 랩을 쓰고 싶니?

5 세상 모든 것들이 랩의 이야깃거리가 될 수 있기 때문에 넌 어떤 것에 대해서든 랩을 할 수 있어.

6 난 버스에서, 샤워 중에 또는 침대에서 아이디어들을 얻어.

7 내 아이디어들을 적어 두고 내가 랩을 쓸 때 그것들을 활용하지.

8 랩을 쓰는 데에는 어떤 규칙도 없어. 넌 오늘 당장 시작할 수 있어!

9 환상의 애완동물

10 '환상의 애완동물'에 온 걸 환영해! 애완동물을 기른다는 건 멋진 일이야.

11 오늘 난 나의 애완 고슴도치인 Polly를 소개할 거야.

12 내가 Polly를 처음 만났을 때, 그 애는 너무 겁을 먹었어.

13 그 애가 가시를 세워서 난 그 애를 손에 쥘 수가 없었어.

14 그래서 내가 그 애의 우리 안에 내 티셔츠를 두었더니 그 애가 내 냄새에 적응했어.

15 마침내, 난 손으로 그 애를 쥘 수 있게 되었지.

16 이제 Polly는 나의 가장 친한 친구이고 항상 나를 행복하게 해 줘.

17 _____ _____

18 _____ _____ to *Handy Tips*.

19 _____ do you _____ _____ _____ a movie theater?

20 _____ _____ a tip.

21 You will _____ it _____ _____ _____.

22 Step 1 _____ your finger _____ something _____ _____ you.

23 Step 2 _____ _____ _____ and _____ _____.

24 Step 3 Repeat it _____ _____ _____ _____.

25 When _____ your _____ _____?

26 Is it _____ you _____ your right eye?

27 _____ you _____ _____ your _____ _____.

28 This _____ you _____ _____ _____ the left side _____ _____ _____.

29 _____ _____, you can _____ a _____ _____ of the screen _____.

30 _____ _____ is also _____ when you _____ _____ _____ in a classroom, _____.

17 쓸모 있는 팁

18 '쓸모 있는 팁'에 돌아온 걸 환영해.

19 넌 보통 영화관에서 어디에 앉니?

20 여기 팁이 하나 있어.

21 넌 이것이 쉽고 유용하다는 걸 알게 될 거야.

22 1단계: 멀리 떨어져 있는 물체를 손가락으로 가리켜 봐.

23 2단계: 한쪽 눈을 감았다가 떠 봐.

24 3단계: 반대쪽 눈으로 반복해 봐.

25 언제 네 손가락이 움직이니?

26 오른쪽 눈을 감았을 때니?

27 그렇다면 너는 주로 오른쪽 눈을 사용하는 거야.

28 그 말은 너는 영화관에서 왼편에 앉아야 한다는 걸 뜻해.

29 그렇게 하면, 너는 스크린의 꽉 찬 화면을 더 잘 즐길 수 있어.

30 이 정보는 네가 교실에서 자리를 고를 때도 도움이 될 거야.

※ 다음 문장을 우리말로 쓰시오.

1 Rap It Out

➡ _____

2 Open your mind, Open your heart

➡ _____

3 Look around and let's rap it out

➡ _____

4 Hey, I'm MC Joy. Do you want to write your own rap?

➡ _____

5 You can rap about anything because everything can be a story for a rap.

➡ _____

6 I get ideas when I'm on the bus, in the shower, or in my bed.

➡ _____

7 I write down my ideas and use them when I write my rap.

➡ _____

8 There are no rules for writing raps. You can start today!

➡ _____

9 Fantastic Pets

➡ _____

10 'Welcome to *Fantastic Pets*! Having a pet is great.

➡ _____

11 Today I'm going to introduce my pet hedgehog, Polly.

➡ _____

12 When I first got Polly, she was very scared.

➡ _____

13 I couldn't hold her because she raised her spikes.

➡ _____

14 So, I placed my T-shirt in her case and she got used to my smell.

➡ _____

15 Finally, I was able to hold her in my hands.

➡ _____

16 Now, Polly is my best friend and always makes me happy.

➡ _____

17 Handy Tips

➡ _____

18 Welcome back to *Handy Tips*.

➡ _____

19 Where do you normally sit in a movie theater?

➡ _____

20 Here is a tip.

➡ _____

21 You will find it easy and helpful.

➡ _____

22 Step 1 Point your finger at something far from you.

➡ _____

23 Step 2 Close one eye and open it.

➡ _____

24 Step 3 Repeat it with the other eye.

➡ _____

25 When does your finger move?

➡ _____

26 Is it when you close your right eye?

➡ _____

27 Then you mainly use your right eye.

➡ _____

28 This means you should sit on the left side in the theater.

➡ _____

29 That way, you can enjoy a full view of the screen better.

➡ _____

30 This information is also helpful when you choose a seat in a classroom, too.

➡ _____

※ 다음 괄호 안의 단어들을 우리말에 맞도록 바르게 배열하시오.

1 (Out / It / Rap)
➡ _____

2 (mind, / your / open / heart / open / your)
➡ _____

3 (around / look / and / rap / out / let's / it)
➡ _____

4 (hey, / MC / I'm / Joy. / you / do / to / want / your / write / rap? / own)
➡ _____

5 (can / you / about / rap / anything / because / can / everything / be / story / a / rap. / for / a)
➡ _____

6 (when / I / ideas / get / I'm / the / on / bus, / the / shower, / in / or / bed. / my / in)
➡ _____

7 (I / down / write / ideas / my / and / them / use / when / write / rap. / my / I)
➡ _____

8 (are / there / no / for / rules / raps. / writing / you / start / today! / can)
➡ _____

9 (Pets / Fantastic)
➡ _____

10 (to / Pets! / welcome / Fantastic / a / having / great. / is / pet)
➡ _____

11 (I'm / going / today / to / introduce / pet / my / Polly. / hedgehog,)
➡ _____

12 (I / when / first / Polly, / got / she / scared. / very / was)
➡ _____

13 (couldn't / I / hold / because / her / raised / spikes. / she)
➡ _____

14 (so, / placed / I / T-shirt / my / her / in / case / and / she / used / got / to / smell. / my)
➡ _____

15 (finally, / was / I / able / hold / to / her / hands. / in / my)
➡ _____

16 (now, / is / Polly / best / my / friend / and / always / happy. / me / makes)
➡ _____

---

1 랩으로 표현해 봐

2 너의 생각을 열어 봐, 너의 마음을 열어 봐

3 주변을 둘러보고 랩으로 표현해 봐

4 안녕. 난 MC Joy야. 너만의 랩을 쓰고 싶니?

5 세상 모든 것들이 랩의 이야깃거리가 될 수 있기 때문에 넌 어떤 것에 대해서든 랩을 할 수 있어.

6 난 버스에서, 샤워 중에 또는 침대에서 아이디어들을 얻어.

7 내 아이디어들을 적어 두고 내가 랩을 쓸 때 그것들을 활용하지.

8 랩을 쓰는 데에는 어떤 규칙도 없어. 넌 오늘 당장 시작할 수 있어!

9 환상의 애완동물

10 '환상의 애완동물'에 온 걸 환영해! 애완동물을 기른다는 건 멋진 일이야.

11 오늘 난 나의 애완 고슴도치인 Polly를 소개할 거야.

12 내가 Polly를 처음 만났을 때, 그 애는 너무 겁을 먹었어.

13 그 애가 가시를 세워서 난 그 애를 손에 쥘 수가 없었어.

14 그래서 내가 그 애의 우리 안에 내 티셔츠를 두었더니 그 애가 내 냄새에 적응했어.

15 마침내, 난 손으로 그 애를 쥘 수 있게 되었지.

16 이제 Polly는 나의 가장 친한 친구이고 항상 나를 행복하게 해 줘.

17 (Tips / Handy)

➡ _____

18 (back / welcome / to / Tips. / Handy)

➡ _____

19 (do / where / normally / you / in / sit / a / theater? / movie)

➡ _____

20 (is / here / tip. / a)

➡ _____

21 (will / you / find / easy / it / helpful. / and)

➡ _____

22 (step 1 / your / point / finger / at / far / you. / something / from)

➡ _____

23 (step 2 / one / close / eye / and / it. / open)

➡ _____

24 (step 3 / it / repeat / the / with / eye. / other)

➡ _____

25 (does / when / finger / move? / your)

➡ _____

26 (it / you / is / when / your / eye? / close / right)

➡ _____

27 (then / mainly / you / use / eye. / right / your)

➡ _____

28 (means / this / should / you / sit / the / on / side / left / theater. / the / in)

➡ _____

29 (way, / that / can / you / enjoy / full / a / view / of / better. / screen / the)

➡ _____

30 (information / this / also / is / helpful / when / choose / you / seat / a / in / classroom, / too. / a)

➡ _____

17	쓸모 있는 팁
18	'쓸모 있는 팁'에 돌아온 걸 환영해.
19	넌 보통 영화관에서 어디에 앉니?
20	여기 팁이 하나 있어.
21	넌 이것이 쉽고 유용하다는 걸 알게 될 거야.
22	1단계: 멀리 떨어져 있는 물체를 손가락으로 가리켜 봐.
23	2단계: 한쪽 눈을 감았다가 떠 봐.
24	3단계: 반대쪽 눈으로 반복해 봐.
25	언제 네 손가락이 움직이니?
26	오른쪽 눈을 감았을 때니?
27	그렇다면 너는 주로 오른쪽 눈을 사용하는 거야.
28	그 말은 너는 영화관에서 왼편에 앉아야 한다는 걸 뜻해.
29	그렇게 하면, 너는 스크린의 꽉 찬 화면을 더 잘 즐길 수 있어.
30	이 정보는 네가 교실에서 자리를 고를 때도 도움이 될 거야.

※ 다음 우리말을 영어로 쓰시오.

1 랩으로 표현해 봐

➡ _____

2 너의 생각을 열어 봐, 너의 마음을 열어 봐

➡ _____

3 주변을 둘러보고 랩으로 표현해 봐

➡ _____

4 안녕. 난 MC Joy야. 너만의 랩을 쓰고 싶니?

➡ _____

5 세상 모든 것들이 랩의 이야깃거리가 될 수 있기 때문에 넌 어떤 것에 대해서든 랩을 할 수 있어.

➡ _____

6 난 버스에서, 샤워 중에 또는 침대에서 아이디어들을 얻어.

➡ _____

7 내 아이디어들을 적어 두고 내가 랩을 쓸 때 그것들을 활용하지.

➡ _____

8 랩을 쓰는 데에는 어떤 규칙도 없어. 넌 오늘 당장 시작할 수 있어!

➡ _____

9 환상의 애완동물

➡ _____

10 '환상의 애완동물'에 온 걸 환영해! 애완동물을 기른다는 건 멋진 일이야.

➡ _____

11 오늘 난 나의 애완 고슴도치인 Polly를 소개할 거야.

➡ _____

12 내가 Polly를 처음 만났을 때, 그 애는 너무 겁을 먹었어.

➡ _____

13 그 애가 가시를 세워서 난 그 애를 손에 쥘 수가 없었어.

➡ _____

14 그래서 내가 그 애의 우리 안에 내 티셔츠를 두었더니 그 애가 내 냄새에 적응했어.

➡ _____

15 마침내, 난 손으로 그 애를 쥘 수 있게 되었지.

➡ _____

16 이제 Polly는 나의 가장 친한 친구이고 항상 나를 행복하게 해 줘.

➡ _____

17 쓸모 있는 팁

➡ _____

18 '쓸모 있는 팁'에 돌아온 걸 환영 해.

➡ _____

19 넌 보통 영화관에서 어디에 앉니?

➡ _____

20 여기 팁이 하나 있어.

➡ _____

21 넌 이것이 쉽고 유용하다는 걸 알게 될 거야.

➡ _____

22 1단계: 멀리 떨어져 있는 물체를 손가락으로 가리켜 봐.

➡ _____

23 2단계: 한쪽 눈을 감았다가 떠 봐.

➡ _____

24 3단계: 반대쪽 눈으로 반복해 봐.

➡ _____

25 언제 네 손가락이 움직이니?

➡ _____

26 오른쪽 눈을 감았을 때니?

➡ _____

27 그렇다면 너는 주로 오른쪽 눈을 사용하는 거야.

➡ _____

28 그 말은 너는 영화관에서 왼편에 앉아야 한다는 걸 뜻해.

➡ _____

29 그렇게 하면, 너는 스크린의 꽉 찬 화면을 더 잘 즐길 수 있어.

➡ _____

30 이 정보는 네가 교실에서 자리를 고를 때도 도움이 될 거야.

➡ _____

※ 다음 우리말과 일치하도록 빈칸에 알맞은 말을 쓰시오.

Communication Step B

1. A: _____ _____ *It's Your Stage*! Can you introduce _____?

2. B: Hello. I'm Bob. I'm _____ _____ _____.

3. A: What _____ you _____ _____ show us today?

4. B: I know _____ _____ draw a face quickly. I can _____ you easy _____.

5. A: Sounds _____!

1. A: '당신의 무대입니다!'에 오신 걸 환영합니다. 자기소개를 해주겠어요?
2. B: 안녕하세요. 전 Bob예요. 전 그림 그리기에 관심이 있어요.
3. A: 오늘 우리에게 무엇을 보여 주실 건가요?
4. B: 전 얼굴을 빠르게 그리는 방법을 알고 있어요. 제가 간단한 단계를 여러분께 보여 드릴게요.
5. A: 흥미롭네요!

Look and Write

1. MOVIE REVIEW – SPY COUPLE

2. Thomas: Great action scenes _____ me _____ from beginning _____ end.

3. Kelly: I _____ the main actor _____.

4. He is a great actor, _____!

5. Ria: I _____ the music _____ the movie.

6. It _____ everything _____.

1. 영화 리뷰 – SPY COUPLE
2. Thomas: 멋진 액션 장면이 시종일관 나를 흥분되게 만들었다.
3. Kelly: 나는 주연 남배우가 매력적이라는 것을 알았다.
4. 그는 훌륭한 배우이기도 하다.
5. Ria: 나는 영화 속 음악을 즐겼다.
6. 그 음악이 모든 것을 낭만적으로 만들었다.

Think and Write

1. _____ _____ Cooking Class!

2. Are you _____ in _____ cookies?

3. I can _____ you some _____ _____!

4. In this _____, you will learn _____ cooking _____.

5. _____ can bake cookies _____ only _____ _____.

6. This class is _____ and everything is _____ _____ you.

7. _____ _____ today!

1. 요리 수업에 오신 것을 환영합니다!
2. 쿠키를 굽는 것에 흥미가 있나요?
3. 내가 몇 가지 유용한 팁을 줄게요.
4. 이 수업에서, 당신은 기본적인 요리 기술을 배울 겁니다.
5. 누구든지 단 하루 만에 쿠키를 구울 수 있어요.
6. 이 수업은 무료이고 당신을 위해 모든 것이 준비되어 있습니다.
7. 오늘 등록하세요!

※ 다음 우리말을 영어로 쓰시오.

Communication Step B

1. A: '당신의 무대입니다!'에 오신 걸 환영합니다. 자기소개를 해주겠어요?
   ➡ _____

2. B: 안녕하세요. 전 Bob예요. 전 그림 그리기에 관심이 있어요.
   ➡ _____

3. A: 오늘 우리에게 무엇을 보여 주실 건가요?
   ➡ _____

4. B: 전 얼굴을 빠르게 그리는 방법을 알고 있어요. 제가 간단한 단계를 여러분께 보여 드릴게요.
   ➡ _____

5. A: 흥미롭네요!
   ➡ _____

Look and Write

1. 영화 리뷰 – SPY COUPLE
   ➡ _____

2. Thomas: 멋진 액션 장면이 시종일관 나를 흥분되게 만들었다.
   ➡ _____

3. Kelly: 나는 주연 남배우가 매력적이라는 것을 알았다.
   ➡ _____

4. 그는 훌륭한 배우이기도 하다.
   ➡ _____

5. Ria: 나는 영화 속 음악을 즐겼다.
   ➡ _____

6. 그 음악이 모든 것을 낭만적으로 만들었다.
   ➡ _____

Think and Write

1. 요리 수업에 오신 것을 환영합니다!
   ➡ _____

2. 쿠키를 굽는 것에 흥미가 있나요?
   ➡ _____

3. 내가 몇 가지 유용한 팁을 줄게요.
   ➡ _____

4. 이 수업에서, 당신은 기본적인 요리 기술을 배울 겁니다.
   ➡ _____

5. 누구든지 단 하루 만에 쿠키를 구울 수 있어요.
   ➡ _____

6. 이 수업은 무료이고 당신을 위해 모든 것이 준비되어 있습니다.
   ➡ _____

7. 오늘 등록하세요!
   ➡ _____

※ 다음 영어를 우리말로 쓰시오.

01 bead _____

02 chimney _____

03 wrap _____

04 excellent _____

05 cross _____

06 stranger _____

07 express _____

08 fair _____

09 warm-up exercise _____

10 wedding _____

11 foreign _____

12 lucky _____

13 monster _____

14 drum _____

15 present _____

16 mask _____

17 Mongolia _____

18 sunlight _____

19 material _____

20 chimney sweep _____

21 system _____

22 tribe _____

23 traditional _____

24 treasure _____

25 dependent _____

26 following _____

27 traditional _____

28 palace _____

29 excel _____

30 different _____

31 wealth _____

32 performance _____

33 fireplace _____

34 fancy _____

35 check out _____

36 stand for _____

37 by the way _____

38 first of all _____

39 turn off _____

40 get into _____

41 put away _____

42 put on _____

43 sign up for _____

※ 다음 우리말을 영어로 쓰시오.

01 보물

02 장식하다, 꾸미다

03 악단, 밴드

04 의지하는, 의존하는

05 인형

06 다양한, 다른

07 민속 음악

08 텐트, 천막

09 뛰어나다, 탁월하다

10 소개하다

11 장식이 많은, 화려한

12 궁전, 왕궁

13 솜브레로

14 부, 재산

15 다음에 나오는

16 벽난로

17 머무르다

18 (밧)줄, 끈

19 공연

20 다양한

21 전통적인

22 결혼식, 결혼

23 햇빛

24 굴뚝

25 모르는[낯선] 사람

26 나타내다, 표현하다

27 싸다, 포장하다

28 운 좋은, 행운의

29 선물; 현재의

30 전통적인

31 훌륭한, 우수한

32 재료

33 괴물, 요괴

34 외국의

35 ~와 의사소통하다

36 ~을 입어 보다

37 무료로

38 ~ 덕분에

39 ~을 고대하다

40 나라마다

41 우선, 가장 먼저

42 확인하다, 살펴보다

43 ~을 상징하다

※ 다음 영영풀이에 알맞은 단어를 <보기>에서 골라 쓴 후, 우리말 뜻을 쓰시오.

1 _____ : a child's toy in the shape of a person, especially a baby or a child:

_____

2 _____ : an open space for a fire in the wall of a room: _____

3 _____ : a collection of valuable things such as gold, silver and jewellery:

_____

4 _____ : a covering for part or all of the face, worn to hide or protect it:

_____

5 _____ : to make something look more attractive by putting things on it:

_____

6 _____ : that is/are going to be mentioned next: _____

7 _____ : traditional and typical of the ordinary people of a country or community:

_____

8 _____ : a person that you do not know: _____

9 _____ : needing somebody/something in order to survive or be successful:

_____

10 _____ : to cover something completely in paper or other material, for example

when you are giving it as a present: _____

11 _____ : to show or make known a feeling, an opinion, etc. by words, looks or

actions: _____

12 _____ : to go across; to pass from one side to the other: _____

13 _____ : having good luck: _____

14 _____ : being part of the beliefs, customs or way of life of a particular group of

people, that have not changed for a long time: _____

15 _____ : something that you give to someone especially as a way of showing

affection or thanks: _____

16 _____ : a strong, thick string that is made by twisting many thin strings or fibers

together: _____

보기			
cross	treasure	express	wrap
mask	present	dependent	following
fireplace	folk	lucky	decorate
doll	rope	stranger	traditional

※ 다음 우리말과 일치하도록 빈칸에 알맞은 말을 쓰시오.

Listen and Talk 1 A-1

Mike: Elsa, _____ _____ your Hula dance class _____?

Elsa: Oh, it's great. We _____ _____ _____ _____ at the ACB Hall _____ _____.

Mike: Wow, that _____ _____ a big day for you!

Elsa: Yeah, I'm _____ _____ _____ the performance.

Mike: Elsa, 너희 훌라댄스 수업은 어때?
Elsa: 오, 아주 좋아. 우리 이번 주말에 ACB 홀에서 공연을 할 거야.
Mike: 와, 너에게 정말 중요한 날로 들리는 걸!
Elsa: 맞아, 나는 공연이 정말 기대가 돼.

Listen and Talk 1 A-2

Sora: Chris, what _____ _____ _____ _____ _____ this Sunday?

Chris: _____ _____ _____ _____ _____ the World Food Fair.

Sora: Oh, I was there _____ _____. There were _____ _____ _____ from _____ _____ the world.

Chris: Great! I'm _____ _____ _____ _____ them.

Sora: Chris, 이번 주 일요일에 뭐 할 거야?
Chris: 세계 음식 박람회에 갈 거야.
Sora: 오, 나 지난 주말에 거기 갔었어. 전 세계의 전통 음식이 많이 있었어.
Chris: 멋지다! 그 음식을 먹어 보는 것이 기대돼.

Listen and Talk 1 B

Tom: Jane, what _____ you _____?

Jane: I'm _____ _____ for a program at the African Museum.

Tom: _____ there an _____ one?

Jane: Yeah, I'm _____ _____ _____ an _____ _____ and a _____ _____.

Tom: Oh, _____ _____!

Jane: Yeah, I'm looking forward to _____ _____ _____.

Tom: Jane, 뭐 하고 있니?
Jane: 아프리카 박물관에서 하는 프로그램을 신청하고 있어.
Tom: 흥미로운 것이 있니?
Jane: 응, 나는 아프리카의 북과 전통 가면을 만들 거야.
Tom: 오, 재미있겠다!
Jane: 맞아, 난 박물관에 가는 것이 기대가 돼.

Listen and Talk 2 A-1

W: I _____ this tea _____ Wang's birthday. _____ he like it?

M: Sure, he _____. Wang _____ _____ _____.

W: Great. Then I'll _____ _____ _____.

M: _____ _____ _____ it _____. Red _____ _____ wealth in China.

W: Wang의 생일을 위해 이 차를 샀어. 그 애가 좋아할까?
M: 물론, 좋아할 거야. Wang은 차를 즐겨 마시잖아.
W: 잘됐다. 그러면 선물을 포장할게.
M: 빨간색으로 포장하는 것을 잊지 마. 빨간색은 중국에서 부를 상징하거든.

Listen and Talk 2 A-2

Elsa: Our _____ _____ Gyengbokgung is this Friday. _____ _____ at two.

Jake: Okay, I'll _____ _____ at the bus stop.

Elsa: Oh, and _____ _____ _____ _____ a *hanbok*. we can _____ _____ the palace for free in our *hanboks*.

Jake: Right. I _____ _____.

Elsa: 우리 경복궁 방문이 이번 주 금요일이지. 두 시에 만나자.
Jake: 알겠어, 버스 정류장에서 보자.
Elsa: 오, 한복 입는 것을 잊지 마. 한복을 입으면 궁에 무료로 들어갈 수 있어.
Jake: 맞다, 하마터면 잊을 뻔했네.

Listen and Talk 2 B

Amy: Look, Brandon. A horse _____ _____ the street _____ there.

Brandon: Yes, there is _____ _____ _____ for horses here in London.

Amy: Oh, I _____ _____ that. That's interesting. Now _____ _____ _____ _____.

Brandon: Wait! Cars _____ _____ the _____ _____ in London.

Amy: Right, I _____ _____ that.

Brandon: Yeah, it's different _____ _____ _____ _____. _____ before _____ _____ in London.

Amy: 봐, Brandon. 저기 말이 길을 건너고 있어.
Brandon: 맞아, 여기 런던에는 말을 위한 교통 신호등이 있어.
Amy: 오, 난 몰랐는걸. 흥미롭다. 이제 우리도 길을 건너자.
Brandon: 기다려! 런던에는 차가 오른쪽에서 와.
Amy: 맞다, 깜박했어.
Brandon: 응, 나라마다 다르잖아. 런던에서는 길을 건너기 전에 오른쪽을 보는 것을 잊지 마.

Communication

Sue: _____ was your _____ _____ here in Mongolia?

Jake: It was great. _____ _____ _____, where _____ _____ _____ tonight?

Sue: You're _____ _____ _____ in a *ger*, a Mongolian _____.

Jake: Oh, _____ _____ _____ _____ _____ _____.

Sue: You'll like it. _____ _____ a fireplace in the *ger*. So, _____ _____ _____ your things _____ from the fireplace.

Jake: I _____. Thank you.

Sue: 여기 몽골에서의 첫날은 어떠셨나요?
Jake: 아주 좋았어요. 그런데 오늘 밤 어디에서 머무르게 되나요?
Sue: 몽골 천막인 '게르'에서 주무시게 될 거예요.
Jake: 오, 정말 기대가 되네요.
Sue: 마음에 드실 거예요. 게르에는 난로가 있어요. 그러니 물건을 난로에서 치워 두는 것을 잊지 마세요.
Jake: 알겠습니다. 감사합니다.

※ 다음 우리말에 맞도록 대화를 영어로 쓰시오.

Listen and Talk 1 A-1

Mike: _____

Elsa: _____

Mike: _____

Elsa: _____

Mike: Elsa, 너희 홀라댄스 수업은 어때?
Elsa: 오, 아주 좋아. 우리 이번 주말에 ACB 홀에서 공연을 할 거야.
Mike: 와, 너에게 정말 중요한 날로 들리는 걸!
Elsa: 맞아, 나는 공연이 정말 기대가 돼.

Listen and Talk 1 A-2

Sora: _____

Chris: _____

Sora: _____

_____

Chris: _____

Sora: Chris, 이번 주 일요일에 뭐 할 거야?
Chris: 세계 음식 박람회에 갈 거야.
Sora: 오, 나 지난 주말에 거기 갔었어. 전 세계의 전통 음식이 많이 있었어.
Chris: 멋지다! 그 음식을 먹어 보는 것이 기대돼.

Listen and Talk 1 B

Tom: _____

Jane: _____

Tom: _____

Jane: _____

Tom: _____

Jane: _____

Tom: Jane, 뭐 하고 있니?
Jane: 아프리카 박물관에서 하는 프로그램을 신청하고 있어.
Tom: 흥미로운 것이 있니?
Jane: 응, 나는 아프리카의 북과 전통 가면을 만들 거야.
Tom: 오, 재미있겠다!
Jane: 맞아, 난 박물관에 가는 것이 기대가 돼.

Listen and Talk 2 A-1

W: _____

M: _____

W: _____

M: _____

W: Wang의 생일을 위해 이 차를 샀어. 그 애가 좋아할까?
M: 물론, 좋아할 거야. Wang은 차를 즐겨 마시잖아.
W: 잘됐다. 그러면 선물을 포장할게.
M: 빨간색으로 포장하는 것을 잊지 마. 빨간색은 중국에서 부를 상징하거든.

Listen and Talk 2 A-2

Elsa: _____

Jake: _____

Elsa: _____

_____

Jake: _____

Elsa: 우리 경복궁 방문이 이번 주 금요일이지. 두 시에 만나자.
Jake: 알겠어, 버스 정류장에서 보자.
Elsa: 오, 한복 입는 것을 잊지 마. 한복을 입으면 궁에 무료로 들어갈 수 있어.
Jake: 맞다, 하마터면 잊을 뻔했네.

Listen and Talk 2 B

Amy: _____

Brandon: _____

Amy: _____

Brandon: _____

Amy: _____

Brandon: _____

Amy: 봐, Brandon. 저기 말이 길을 건너고 있어.
Brandon: 맞아, 여기 런던에는 말을 위한 교통 신호등이 있어.
Amy: 오, 난 몰랐는걸. 흥미롭다. 이제 우리도 길을 건너자.
Brandon: 기다려! 런던에는 차가 오른쪽에서 와.
Amy: 맞다, 깜박했어.
Brandon: 응, 나라마다 다르잖아. 런던에서는 길을 건너기 전에 오른쪽을 보는 것을 잊지 마.

Communication

Sue: _____

Jake: _____

Sue: _____

Jake: _____

Sue: _____

_____

Jake: _____

Sue: 여기 몽골에서의 첫날은 어떠셨나요?
Jake: 아주 좋았어요. 그런데 오늘 밤 어디에서 머무르게 되나요?
Sue: 몽골 천막인 '게르'에서 주무시게 될 거예요.
Jake: 오, 정말 기대가 되네요.
Sue: 마음에 드실 거예요. 게르에는 난로가 있어요. 그러니 물건을 난로에서 치워 두는 것을 잊지 마세요.
Jake: 알겠습니다. 감사합니다.

※ 다음 우리말과 일치하도록 빈칸에 알맞은 것을 골라 쓰시오.

1 _____ _____.
　A. Sweepy　　　　B. I'm

2 I'm _____ Germany and my job is _____ _____ chimneys.
　A. clean　　　B. to　　　C. from

3 _____ winter, chimney sweeps _____ people _____ warm and safe.
　A. keep　　　B. to　　　C. during　　　D. help

4 So people think chimney _____ _____ them good _____.
　A. luck　　　B. bring　　　C. sweeps

5 People even _____ chimney sweeps _____ be _____ their weddings!
　A. at　　　B. to　　　C. want

6 _____ you _____ me, it is your _____ day.
　A. lucky　　　B. see　　　C. if

7 My name is José and _____ _____ my mariachi band _____.
　A. members　　　B. are　　　C. these

8 We play _____ music and _____ _____ our sombreros, or big hats.
　A. wear　　　B. always　　　C. folk

9 In Mexico, people wear these hats _____ stay _____ under the _____ and strong _____.
　A. sunlight　　　B. hot　　　C. cool　　　D. to

10 We mariachi players _____ our sombreros _____ fancy.
　A. look　　　B. to　　　C. want

11 So we _____ _____ them _____ a lot of different _____.
　A. materials　　　B. decorate　　　C. often　　　D. with

12 _____ of _____ sombreros do you like _____?
　A. best　　　B. our　　　C. which

1　나는 Sweepy야.

2　나는 독일에서 왔고, 내 직업은 굴뚝을 청소하는 거야.

3　겨울에 굴뚝 청소부들은 사람들이 따뜻하고 안전하게 지낼 수 있도록 도와주지.

4　그래서 사람들은 굴뚝 청소부들이 자신들에게 행운을 가져다준다고 생각해.

5　사람들은 심지어 굴뚝 청소부들이 자신의 결혼식에 있기를 바란단다!

6　네가 만일 나를 본다면, 그날은 너의 행운의 날인 거야.

7　내 이름은 José이고, 이 사람들은 마리아치 악단 단원들이야.

8　우리는 민속 음악을 연주하고 항상 솜브레로라는 큰 모자를 쓰지.

9　멕시코에서 사람들은 뜨겁고 강한 햇볕 아래서 시원하게 지내기 위해 이 모자들을 써.

10　우리 마리아치 연주자들은 우리의 솜브레로가 화려하게 보이길 원해.

11　그래서 우리는 종종 여러 가지 재료들을 많이 이용해서 그것들을 장식하지.

12　우리 솜브레로 중 어느 것이 가장 마음에 드니?

13 _____ name is Ayanda and I'm _____ _____.

   A. Zulu   B. a   C. My

14 We are a _____ in _____ Africa.

   A. South   B. tribe

15 _____ do you _____ _____ my beads?

   A. of   B. think   C. what

16 Zulu people _____ _____ clothes _____ beads.

   A. with   B. making   C. enjoy

17 They are beautiful and _____ color _____ a special _____.

   A. meaning   B. has   C. each

18 When we did not have our _____ writing system, we used beads _____ _____ with each _____.

   A. other   B. own   C. communicate   D. to

19 If you want _____ _____ the meaning of the colors, _____ _____, check out the following box.

   A. out   B. to   C. check   D. know

Color	Good Meaning	Bad Meaning
Black	_____	death
_____	wealth	_____
Red	love	_____
White	love	—

   A. anger   B. marriage   C. badness   D. yellow

20 If you want to _____ someone a _____ message, you can _____ yourself with these _____.

   A. beads   B. express   C. send   D. special

21 _____ _____ do you want _____ _____?

   A. make   B. message   C. to   D. what

---

13 내 이름은 Ayanda이고 나는 줄루 사람이야.

14 우리는 남아프리카의 부족이지.

15 내 구슬들에 대해 어떻게 생각하니?

16 줄루족 사람들은 구슬로 옷 만드는 것을 즐겨.

17 그것들은 아름답고 각각의 색깔에는 특별한 의미가 있어.

18 우리 자신의 문자 체계가 없었을 때, 우리는 서로 의소통하기 위해서 구슬들을 이용했어.

색	좋은 의미	나쁜 의미
검은색	결혼	죽음
노란색	부	나쁨
빨간색	사랑	분노
흰색	사랑	-

19 만약 네가 그 색깔들의 의미를 알고 싶다면, 다음에 나오는 네모를 확인해 봐.

20 만약 네가 누군가에게 특별한 메시지를 보내고 싶다면, 이 구슬들로 네 자신을 표현할 수 있어.

21 너는 어떤 메시지를 만들고 싶니?

※ 다음 우리말과 일치하도록 빈칸에 알맞은 말을 쓰시오.

1 _____ Sweepy.

2 I'm _____ _____ and my job _____ _____ _____ _____.

3 _____ winter, chimney sweeps _____ people _____ _____ _____ and _____.

4 _____ people _____ chimney sweeps _____ _____ _____ _____.

5 People _____ _____ chimney sweeps _____ _____ at _____ _____!

6 _____ you _____ _____, it is _____ _____ _____.

7 My name is José and _____ _____ my mariachi _____ _____.

8 We _____ _____ _____ and _____ _____ our sombreros, or _____ _____.

9 _____ _____, people _____ these hats _____ _____ under the _____ and _____ _____.

10 We mariachi players _____ our sombreros _____ _____ _____.

11 So we _____ _____ them _____ a lot of _____.

12 _____ _____ our sombreros do you _____ _____?

---

1 나는 Sweepy야.

2 나는 독일에서 왔고, 내 직업은 굴뚝을 청소하는 거야.

3 겨울에 굴뚝 청소부들은 사람들이 따뜻하고 안전하게 지낼 수 있도록 도와주지.

4 그래서 사람들은 굴뚝 청소부들이 자신들에게 행운을 가져다준다고 생각해.

5 사람들은 심지어 굴뚝 청소부들이 자신의 결혼식에 있기를 바란단다!

6 네가 만일 나를 본다면, 그날은 너의 행운의 날인 거야.

7 내 이름은 José이고, 이 사람들은 마리아치 악단 단원들이야.

8 우리는 민속 음악을 연주하고 항상 솜브레로라는 큰 모자를 쓰지.

9 멕시코에서 사람들은 뜨겁고 강한 햇볕 아래서 시원하게 지내기 위해 이 모자들을 써.

10 우리 마리아치 연주자들은 우리의 솜브레로가 화려하게 보이길 원해.

11 그래서 우리는 종종 여러 가지 재료들을 많이 이용해서 그것들을 장식하지.

12 우리 솜브레로 중 어느 것이 가장 마음에 드니?

13 _____ _____ is Ayanda and I'm _____ _____.

14 We are _____ _____ _____ _____ Africa.

15 _____ do you _____ _____ my beads?

16 Zulu people _____ _____ _____ _____ beads.

17 _____ _____ beautiful and _____ _____ has a _____ _____.

18 _____ we did not have _____ _____ _____ _____, we used beads _____ _____ with each other.

19 If you want _____ _____ _____ _____ _____ _____ _____, check out the following box.

Color	_____ _____	_____ _____
Black	_____	_____
_____	_____	badness
Red	love	_____
_____	_____	—

20 If you _____ _____ _____ someone a _____ _____, you can _____ _____ _____ these beads.

21 _____ _____ do you _____ _____ _____?

---

13 내 이름은 Ayanda이고 나는 줄루 사람이야.

14 우리는 남아프리카의 부족이지.

15 내 구슬들에 대해 어떻게 생각하니?

16 줄루족 사람들은 구슬로 옷 만드는 것을 즐겨.

17 그것들은 아름답고 각각의 색깔에는 특별한 의미가 있어.

18 우리 자신의 문자 체계가 없었을 때, 우리는 서로 의소통하기 위해서 구슬들을 이용했어.

색	좋은 의미	나쁜 의미
검은색	결혼	죽음
노란색	부	나쁨
빨간색	사랑	분노
흰색	사랑	-

19 만약 네가 그 색깔들의 의미를 알고 싶다면, 다음에 나오는 네모를 확인해 봐.

20 만약 네가 누군가에게 특별한 메시지를 보내고 싶다면, 이 구슬들로 네 자신을 표현할 수 있어.

21 너는 어떤 메시지를 만들고 싶니?

※ 다음 문장을 우리말로 쓰시오.

1 ▶ I'm Sweepy.

➡ _____

2 ▶ I'm from Germany and my job is to clean chimneys.

➡ _____

3 ▶ During winter, chimney sweeps help people to keep warm and safe.

➡ _____

4 ▶ So people think chimney sweeps bring them good luck.

➡ _____

5 ▶ People even want chimney sweeps to be at their weddings!

➡ _____

6 ▶ If you see me, it is your lucky day.

➡ _____

7 ▶ My name is José and these are my mariachi band members.

➡ _____

8 ▶ We play folk music and always wear our sombreros, or big hats.

➡ _____

9 ▶ In Mexico, people wear these hats to stay cool under the hot and strong sunlight.

➡ _____

10 ▶ We mariachi players want our sombreros to look fancy.

➡ _____

11 ▶ So we often decorate them with a lot of different materials.

➡ _____

12 ▶ Which of our sombreros do you like best?

➡ _____

13 My name is Ayanda and I'm a Zulu.

➡ _____

14 We are a tribe in South Africa.

➡ _____

15 What do you think of my beads?

➡ _____

16 Zulu people enjoy making clothes with beads.

➡ _____

17 They are beautiful and each color has a special meaning.

➡ _____

18 When we did not have our own writing system, we used beads to communicate with each other.

➡ _____

19 If you want to know the meaning of the colors, check out the following box.

➡ _____

색	_____	좋은 의미	_____ _____	나쁜 의미	_____ _____
검은색	_____	결혼	_____	죽음	_____
노란색	_____	부	_____	나쁨	_____
빨간색	_____	사랑	_____	분노	_____
흰색	_____	사랑	_____		—

20 If you want to send someone a special message, you can express yourself with these beads.

➡ _____

21 What message do you want to make?

➡ _____

※ 다음 괄호 안의 단어들을 우리말에 맞도록 바르게 배열하시오.

1 (Sweepy. / I'm)

➡ _____

2 (I'm / Germany / from / and / job / my / to / is / chimneys. / clean)

➡ _____

3 (winter, / during / sweeps / chimney / people / help / keep / to / safe. / and / warm)

➡ _____

4 (people / so / chimney / think / sweeps / bring / luck. / good / them)

➡ _____

5 (even / people / want / chimney / to / sweeps / be / at / weddings! / their)

➡ _____

6 (you / if / me, / see / is / it / day. / lucky / your)

➡ _____

7 (name / my / is / José / and / are / these / mariachi / my / members. / band)

➡ _____

8 (play / we / music / folk / and / wear / always / sombreros, / our / hats. / big / or)

➡ _____

9 (Mexico, / in / people / these / wear / hats / stay / to / cool / under / hot / the / and / sunlight. / strong)

➡ _____

➡ _____

10 (mariachi / we / players / want / sombreros / our / fancy. / look / to)

➡ _____

11 (we / so / often / them / decorate / with / lot / a / of / materials. / different)

➡ _____

12 (of / which / sombreros / our / best? / like / you / do)

➡ _____

1 나는 Sweepy야.

2 나는 독일에서 왔고, 내 직업은 굴뚝을 청소하는 거야.

3 겨울에 굴뚝 청소부들은 사람들이 따뜻하고 안전하게 지낼 수 있도록 도와주지.

4 그래서 사람들은 굴뚝 청소부들이 자신들에게 행운을 가져다준다고 생각해.

5 사람들은 심지어 굴뚝 청소부들이 자신의 결혼식에 있기를 바란단다!

6 네가 만일 나를 본다면, 그날은 너의 행운의 날인 거야.

7 내 이름은 José이고, 이 사람들은 마리아치 악단 단원들이야.

8 우리는 민속 음악을 연주하고 항상 솜브레로라는 큰 모자를 쓰지.

9 멕시코에서 사람들은 뜨겁고 강한 햇볕 아래서 시원하게 지내기 위해 이 모자들을 써.

10 우리 마리아치 연주자들은 우리의 솜브레로가 화려하게 보이길 원해.

11 그래서 우리는 종종 여러 가지 재료들을 많이 이용해서 그것들을 장식하지.

12 우리 솜브레로 중 어느 것이 가장 마음에 드니?

13 (name / my / is / Ayanda / a / and / Zulu. / I'm)

➡ _____

14 (are / we / tribe / a / Africa. / South / in)

➡ _____

15 (you / do / what / of / think / beads? / my)

➡ _____

16 (people / Zulu / making / enjoy / beads. / with / clothes)

➡ _____

17 (are / they / beautiful / and / color / each / has / meaning. / a / special)

➡ _____

18 (when / we / have / not / did / our / writing / own / system, / we / beads / used / to / each / other. / with / communicate)

➡ _____

_____

19 (you / if / know / to / want / meaning / the / of / colors, / the / check / box. / the / following / out)

➡ _____

※ (Meaning / Good / Color / Meaning / Bad / death / marriage / Black / wealth / Yellow / badness / love / Red / anger / love / White)

_____	_____	_____
_____	_____	_____
_____	_____	_____
_____	_____	_____
_____	_____	—

20 (you / if / send / to / want / someone / message, / a / special / can / you / yourself / express / beads. / with / these)

➡ _____

_____

21 (message / what / you / do / want / make? / to)

➡ _____

13 내 이름은 Ayanda이고 나는 줄루 사람이야.

14 우리는 남아프리카의 부족이지.

15 내 구슬들에 대해 어떻게 생각하니?

16 줄루족 사람들은 구슬로 옷 만드는 것을 즐겨.

17 그것들은 아름답고 각각의 색깔에는 특별한 의미가 있어.

18 우리 자신의 문자 체계가 없었을 때, 우리는 서로 의소소통하기 위해서 구슬들을 이용했어.

색	좋은 의미	나쁜 의미
검은색	결혼	죽음
노란색	부	나쁨
빨간색	사랑	분노
흰색	사랑	-

19 만약 네가 그 색깔들의 의미를 알고 싶다면, 다음에 나오는 네모를 확인해 봐.

20 만약 네가 누군가에게 특별한 메시지를 보내고 싶다면, 이 구슬들로 네 자신을 표현할 수 있어.

21 너는 어떤 메시지를 만들고 싶니?

※ **다음 우리말을 영어로 쓰시오.**

1 나는 Sweepy야.

➡ _____

2 나는 독일에서 왔고, 내 직업은 굴뚝을 청소하는 거야.

➡ _____

3 겨울에 굴뚝 청소부들은 사람들이 따뜻하고 안전하게 지낼 수 있도록 도와주지.

➡ _____

4 그래서 사람들은 굴뚝 청소부들이 자신들에게 행운을 가져다준다고 생각해.

➡ _____

5 사람들은 심지어 굴뚝 청소부들이 자신의 결혼식에 있기를 바란단다!

➡ _____

6 네가 만일 나를 본다면, 그날은 너의 행운의 날인 거야.

➡ _____

7 내 이름은 José이고, 이 사람들은 마리아치 악단 단원들이야.

➡ _____

8 우리는 민속 음악을 연주하고 항상 솜브레로라는 큰 모자를 쓰지.

➡ _____

9 멕시코에서 사람들은 뜨겁고 강한 햇볕 아래서 시원하게 지내기 위해 이 모자들을 써.

➡ _____

10 우리 마리아치 연주자들은 우리의 솜브레로가 화려하게 보이길 원해.

➡ _____

11 그래서 우리는 종종 여러 가지 재료들을 많이 이용해서 그것들을 장식하지.

➡ _____

12 우리 솜브레로 중 어느 것이 가장 마음에 드니?

➡ _____

13 내 이름은 Ayanda이고 나는 줄루 사람이야.

➡ _____

14 우리는 남아프리카의 부족이지.

➡ _____

15 내 구슬들에 대해 어떻게 생각하니?

➡ _____

16 줄루족 사람들은 구슬로 옷 만드는 것을 즐겨.

➡ _____

17 그것들은 아름답고 각각의 색깔에는 특별한 의미가 있어.

➡ _____

18 우리 자신의 문자 체계가 없었을 때, 우리는 서로 의소소통하기 위해서 구슬들을 이용했어.

➡ _____

19 만약 네가 그 색깔들의 의미를 알고 싶다면, 다음에 나오는 네모를 확인해 봐.

➡ _____

색 _____	좋은 의미 _____ _____	나쁜 의미 _____ _____
검은색 _____	결혼 _____	죽음 _____
노란색 _____	부 _____	나쁨 _____
빨간색 _____	사랑 _____	분노 _____
흰색 _____	사랑 _____	—

20 만약 네가 누군가에게 특별한 메시지를 보내고 싶다면, 이 구슬들로 네 자신을 표현할 수 있어.

➡ _____

21 너는 어떤 메시지를 만들고 싶니?

➡ _____

※ 다음 우리말과 일치하도록 빈칸에 알맞은 말을 쓰시오.

Grammar in Real Life

1. Mom: Mike, I'm _____ to be _____. _____ you make dinner _____ Sam?

2. Mike: Okay, _____ worry. Sam, come _____ early.

3. Sam: Okay.

4. Mom: Mike and Sam, _____ _____ to do your homework.

5. Sam: I will, Mom. Can you _____ _____ _____ _____ _____?

6. Mom: Sure.

1. 엄마: Mike, 나 오늘 늦을 거야. Sam 에게 저녁식사를 차려 주겠니?
2. Mike: 알았어요, 걱정 마세요. Sam, 집에 일찍 와.
3. Sam: 알았어.
4. 엄마: Mike, Same. 반드시 숙제를 하렴.
5. Sam: 할게요, 엄마. 우리에게 아이스 크림을 사 오실 수 있어요?
6. 엄마: 물론이지.

Think & Write

1. A: _____ festival do you want to _____ to your _____ _____?

2. B: I _____ _____ _____ the *Haenyeo* festival.

3. A: Where and when _____ your _____ friends enjoy the festival?

4. B: They can enjoy the festival _____ Jeju _____ September.

5. A: What _____ your foreign friends do _____ they visit the festival?

6. B: They can _____ _____ _____ their hands and learn old *haenyeo* songs.

1. A: 너의 외국인 친구들에게 어느 축제 를 소개하고 싶니?
2. B: 나는 해녀 축제를 소개하고 싶어.
3. A: 너의 외국인 친구들이 언제 어디서 그 축제를 즐길 수 있어?
4. B: 그들은 9월에 제주에서 그 축제를 즐길 수 있지.
5. A: 외국인 친구들이 축제에 방문한다 면, 무엇을 할 수 있을까?
6. B: 그들은 손으로 물고기를 잡고 해녀 노래를 배울 수 있지.

Wrap Up 3

1. A: What _____ you _____ _____ do this Saturday?

2. B: I'm going _____ _____ my friend, Lashi. He's _____ in Korea _____ the vacation.

3. A: Oh, he's _____ India, _____ _____?

4. B: Yeah, he is. I'm _____ _____ to showing him _____ Seoul.

5. A: Great. _____ a good time _____ your friend.

1. A: 이번 주 토요일에 뭐 할 거야?
2. B: 나는 내 친구인 Lashi를 만날 거야. 그는 방학 동안에 한국에 머물고 있어.
3. A: 오, 인도에서 온 친구 맞지?
4. B: 맞아. 나는 그에게 서울을 구경시켜 주고 싶어.
5. A: 멋지다. 친구와 좋은 시간 보내.

※ 다음 우리말을 영어로 쓰시오.

Grammar in Real Life

1. 엄마: Mike, 나 오늘 늦을 거야. Sam에게 저녁식사를 차려 주겠니?
➡ _____

2. Mike: 알았어요, 걱정 마세요. Sam, 집에 일찍 와.
➡ _____

3. Sam: 알았어.
➡ _____

4. 엄마: Mike, Same. 반드시 숙제를 하렴.
➡ _____

5. Sam: 할게요, 엄마. 우리에게 아이스크림을 사 오실 수 있어요?
➡ _____

6. 엄마: 물론이지.
➡ _____

Think & Write

1. A: 너의 외국인 친구들에게 어느 축제를 소개하고 싶니?
➡ _____

2. B: 나는 해녀 축제를 소개하고 싶어.
➡ _____

3. A: 너의 외국인 친구들이 언제 어디서 그 축제를 즐길 수 있어?
➡ _____

4. B: 그들은 9월에 제주에서 그 축제를 즐길 수 있지.
➡ _____

5. A: 외국인 친구들이 축제에 방문한다면, 무엇을 할 수 있을까?
➡ _____

6. B: 그들은 손으로 물고기를 잡고 해녀 노래를 배울 수 있지.
➡ _____

Wrap Up 3

1. A: 이번 주 토요일에 뭐 할 거야?
➡ _____

2. B: 나는 내 친구인 Lashi를 만날 거야. 그는 방학 동안에 한국에 머물고 있어.
➡ _____

3. A: 오, 인도에서 온 친구 맞지?
➡ _____

4. B: 맞아. 나는 그에게 서울을 구경시켜 주고 싶어.
➡ _____

5. A: 멋지다. 친구와 좋은 시간 보내.
➡ _____

※ 다음 영어를 우리말로 쓰시오.

01 produce	_____	
02 useful	_____	
03 vinegar	_____	
04 appear	_____	
05 balloon	_____	
06 bean	_____	
07 car horn	_____	
08 drone	_____	
09 entire	_____	
10 experiment	_____	
11 average	_____	
12 hide	_____	
13 unbelievable	_____	
14 impossible	_____	
15 lower	_____	
16 application	_____	
17 ability	_____	
18 monster	_____	
19 record	_____	
20 normal	_____	
21 collector	_____	

22 scare	_____
23 single	_____
24 scream	_____
25 electricity	_____
26 amusement	_____
27 explain	_____
28 unlock	_____
29 entire	_____
30 miss	_____
31 fold	_____
32 activity	_____
33 sore	_____
34 string	_____
35 a couple of	_____
36 hold up	_____
37 let's say that	_____
38 paint over	_____
39 pump up	_____
40 take care of	_____
41 take away	_____
42 what's more	_____
43 wrap ~ around	_____

※ 다음 우리말을 영어로 쓰시오.

01 놀랍게도 _____

02 전체의 _____

03 무게가 ~이다 _____

04 양 _____

05 풍선 _____

06 전기, 전류 _____

07 평균 _____

08 활동 _____

09 박람회; 공정한 _____

10 재미, 놀이 _____

11 접다 _____

12 그러나 _____

13 충고, 조언 _____

14 들어 올리다 _____

15 놓치다, 그리워하다 _____

16 아픈 _____

17 설명하다 _____

18 가능한, 있을 수 있는 _____

19 건전지, 배터리 _____

20 실 _____

21 더하다 _____

22 따다, 집다 _____

23 도전; 도전하다 _____

24 자물쇠를 열다 _____

25 반지; 울리다 _____

26 믿을 수 없는 _____

27 나타나다 _____

28 내리다, 낮추다 _____

29 기록하다 _____

30 보통의, 평범한 _____

31 괴물, 요괴 _____

32 능력 _____

33 유용한 _____

34 비명, 외침(소리) _____

35 ~을 제거하다 _____

36 예를 들어 _____

37 ~을 끄다 _____

38 ~을 환하게 하다 _____

39 주입하다, 채워 넣다 _____

40 ~의 지혜를 빌리다 _____

41 ~가 되다 _____

42 ~의 앞에 _____

43 ~을 돌보다 _____

※ 다음 영영풀이에 알맞은 단어를 <보기>에서 골라 쓴 후, 우리말 뜻을 쓰시오.

1 _____ : to measure how heavy somebody/something is, usually by using scales: _____

2 _____ : a person who collects things, either as a hobby or as a job: _____

3 _____ : calculated by adding several amounts together, finding a total, and dividing the total by the number of amounts: _____

4 _____ : a new or difficult task that tests somebody's ability and skill: _____

5 _____ : that can be done or achieved: _____

6 _____ : to become frightened: _____

7 _____ : to put something together with something else so as to increase the size, number, amount, etc.: _____

8 _____ : a scientific test that is done in order to study what happens and to gain new knowledge: _____

9 _____ : a loud high cry made by somebody who is hurt, frightened, excited, etc.: _____

10 _____ : to put or keep something/somebody in a place where it cannot be seen or found: _____

11 _____ : an aircraft without a pilot, controlled from the ground: _____

12 _____ : a device that is placed inside a car engine, clock, radio, etc. and that produces the electricity that makes it work: _____

13 _____ : to raise somebody/something or be raised to a higher position or level: _____

14 _____ : to let or make something/somebody go down: _____

15 _____ : the feeling that you have when you think that something is funny: _____

16 _____ : an event at which many people gather to buy things or to get information about a product or activity: _____

보기			
amusement	lower	drone	collector
fair	scare	scream	lift
experiment	challenge	add	average
possible	weigh	battery	hide

※ 다음 우리말과 일치하도록 빈칸에 알맞은 말을 쓰시오.

Listen and Talk 1 A-1

Mike: _____ _____ are you _____, Sally?

Sally: I'm _____ the Sci-Magic show. it's a new program. _____
_____ _____ _____ _____?

Mike: No, I _____. What's it _____?

Sally: The program uses _____ _____ _____ magic tricks.

Mike: Oh, it _____ _____.

Mike: Sally, 무슨 쇼 프로그램을 보고 있니?
Sally: '과학 마술 쇼'를 보고 있어. 새로 하는 프로그램이야. 너 그것에 대해 들어 본 적 있어?
Mike: 아니, 없어. 무엇에 관한 거야?
Sally: 그 프로그램에서는 마술 묘기를 설명하기 위해 과학을 이용해.
Mike: 오, 흥미로울 것 같아.

Listen and Talk 1 A-2

Tom: Mom, _____ you _____ _____ the Chat Robot?

Mom: _____, _____ _____ _____. What is it?

Tom: It's a _____ _____. You _____ _____ any questions
and it will answer. _____ _____ _____ _____ _____. "Emily,
_____ the weather _____ today?"

Emily: "It's _____ _____ _____, so you'll _____ an umbrella."

Mom: Wow, _____ _____ _____ _____ _____!

Tom: 엄마, Chat Robot에 관해 들어 본 적 있으세요?
Mom: 아니, 없어. 그게 뭐니?
Tom: 그건 휴대폰 앱이에요. 어떤 질문이든 물으면 그것을 대답해 줘요. 보여 드릴게요. "Emily, 오늘 날씨는 어때?"
Emily: "비가 올 예정이니까, 당신은 우산이 필요할 것입니다."
Mom: 와, 정말 멋진 앱이구나!

Listen and Talk 1 B

W: Hello, students. _____ _____ _____ _____ the DIY
Drone Class? You can make your _____ _____ in the _____.
The Youth Community Center _____ the class at 3 p.m. _____
_____ in May. _____ your _____ _____ and learn
_____ _____ _____. _____ this great
chance!

W: 학생 여러분, 안녕하세요. DIY 무인기(드론) 수업에 관해 들어 본 적이 있나요? 그 수업에서 여러분은 자신만의 무인기를 만들 수 있어요. 청소년 지역 문화 회관에서 5월에 수요일마다 오후 3시에 수업이 있어요. 여러분의 특별한 무인기를 만들고, 조종하는 방법을 배워 보세요. 이 좋은 기회를 놓치지 마세요.

Listen and Talk 2 A-1

Mina: You know _____? I _____ a potato clock yesterday!

Jack: A potato clock? _____ _____ _____ _____?

Mina: My clock _____ _____ potatoes, _____ batteries.
Potatoes can produce _____.

Jack: That's _____!

Mina: 그거 알아? 나 어제 감자 시계를 만들었어!
Jack: 감자 시계? 무슨 말이야?
Mina: 내 시계는 건전지가 아니라 감자로 작동을 해. 감자로 전기를 만들 수 있거든.
Jack: 그거 흥미롭다!

Listen and Talk 2 A-2

Jimmy: Lisa, _____ _____ _____ _____ _____ _____ _____?

Lisa: I _____ an egg ball _____ my brother.

Jimmy: An egg ball? _____ do you _____?

Lisa: We _____ an egg _____ _____ _____ two days. Then, the egg _____ _____ a ball.

Jimmy: Wow, I _____ _____ make one, _____!

Listen and Talk 2 B

Minho: Anna, _____ make a "Mystery Card" for the _____ _____.

Anna: A "Mystery Card?" _____ _____ _____ _____?

Minho: It's a _____ card. It can _____ _____ _____.

Anna: _____ do you _____ it?

Minho: _____ baking soda and water. Then, write a message _____ _____ _____ _____ it.

Anna: _____ _____ _____ _____ _____?

Minho: _____ _____ the card _____ grape juice, _____ _____ the message _____.

Communication

Jane: _____ _____ _____ _____ the Smart App Contest?

Minho: _____, _____ _____. Are you _____ _____ enter it?

Jane: Yeah, I'm _____ _____ _____ my idea _____ a Pic Gardener App.

Minho: A Pic Gardener App? _____ _____ _____ _____ _____?

Jane: When you _____ _____ _____ _____ a plant, the app _____ you _____ _____ _____.

Minho: It _____ _____ a very _____ app.

Wrap Up 1

Hojin: Hey, Katy. _____ you _____ _____ the science fair?

Katy: Yeah, I'm _____ _____ there.

Hojin: Me, _____! I'm _____ about doing different _____ _____ _____.

Katy: Yeah, I'm also _____ _____ _____ it!

Jimmy: Lisa, 지난 주말에 뭐 했어?
Lisa: 남동생이랑 달걀 공을 만들었어.
Jimmy: 달걀 공? 무슨 말이야?
Lisa: 우리는 달걀을 이틀 동안 식초에 담가놨어. 그러면 달걀이 공으로 변해.
Jimmy: 와, 나도 하나 만들고 싶어!

Minho: Anna, 우리 과학 실험으로 '미스터리 카드'를 만들자.
Anna: 미스터리 카드? 무슨 말이야?
Minho: 그건 특별한 카드야. 그 카드는 너의 메시지를 숨길 수 있어.
Anna: 어떻게 만드는데?
Minho: 베이킹 소다랑 물을 섞어. 그러고 나서 그걸로 카드 위에 메시지를 써.
Anna: 카드를 어떻게 읽을 수 있어?
Minho: 카드를 포도 주스로 칠하면 메시지가 나타나.

Jane: 너 스마트 앱 대회에 대해 들어 본 적 있어?
Minho: 응, 들어 봤어. 너 거기 나갈 거야?
Jane: 응, Pic Gardener 앱에 관한 내 아이디어를 보내 보려고.
Minho: Pic Gardener 앱? 무슨 말이야?
Jane: 식물의 사진을 찍으면, 그 앱이 그 식물을 가꾸는 법을 알려 주는 거야.
Minho: 매우 유용한 앱 같아.

Hojin: 저기, Katy. 너 과학 박람회에 대해 들어 본 적 있어?
Katy: 응, 나 거기에 갈 거야.
Hojin: 나도! 난 다양한 종류의 실험들을 할 생각을 하니 신나.
Katy: 맞아, 나도 그게 정말 기대돼!

※ 다음 우리말에 맞도록 대화를 영어로 쓰시오.

Listen and Talk 1 A-1

Mike: _____

Sally: _____

_____

Mike: _____

Sally: _____

Mike: _____

Mike: Sally, 무슨 쇼 프로그램을 보고 있니?
Sally: '과학 마술 쇼'를 보고 있어. 새로 하는 프로그램이야. 너 그것에 대해 들어 본 적 있어?
Mike: 아니, 없어. 무엇에 관한 거야?
Sally: 그 프로그램에서는 마술 묘기를 설명하기 위해 과학을 이용해.
Mike: 오, 흥미로울 것 같아.

Listen and Talk 1 A-2

Tom: _____

Mom: _____

Tom: _____

_____

Emily: _____

Mom: _____

Tom: 엄마, Chat Robot에 관해 들어 본 적 있으세요?
Mom: 아니, 없어. 그게 뭐니?
Tom: 그건 휴대폰 앱이에요. 어떤 질문이든 물으면 그것을 대답해 줘요. 보여 드릴게요. "Emily, 오늘 날씨는 어때?"
Emily: "비가 올 예정이니까, 당신은 우산이 필요할 것입니다."
Mom: 와, 정말 멋진 앱이구나!

Listen and Talk 1 B

W: _____

_____

_____

_____

W: 학생 여러분, 안녕하세요. DIY 무인기(드론) 수업에 관해 들어 본 적이 있나요? 그 수업에서 여러분은 자신만의 무인기를 만들 수 있어요. 청소년 지역 문화 회관에서 5월에 수요일마다 오후 3시에 수업이 있어요. 여러분의 특별한 무인기를 만들고, 조종하는 방법을 배워 보세요. 이 좋은 기회를 놓치지 마세요.

Listen and Talk 2 A-1

Mina: _____

Jack: _____

Mina: _____

_____

Jack: _____

Mina: 그거 알아? 나 어제 감자 시계를 만들었어!
Jack: 감자 시계? 무슨 말이야?
Mina: 내 시계는 건전지가 아니라 감자로 작동을 해. 감자로 전기를 만들 수 있거든.
Jack: 그거 흥미롭다!

Listen and Talk 2 A-2

Jimmy: _____

Lisa: _____

Jimmy: _____

Lisa: _____

Jimmy: _____

Jimmy: Lisa, 지난 주말에 뭐 했어?
Lisa: 남동생이랑 달걀 공을 만들었어.
Jimmy: 달걀 공? 무슨 말이야?
Lisa: 우리는 달걀을 이틀 동안 식초에 담가놨어. 그러면 달걀이 공으로 변해.
Jimmy: 와, 나도 하나 만들고 싶어!

Listen and Talk 2 B

Minho: _____

Anna: _____

Minho: _____

Anna: _____

Minho: _____

Anna: _____

Minho: _____

Minho: Anna, 우리 과학 실험으로 '미스터리 카드'를 만들자.
Anna: 미스터리 카드? 무슨 말이야?
Minho: 그건 특별한 카드야. 그 카드는 너의 메시지를 숨길 수 있어.
Anna: 어떻게 만드는데?
Minho: 베이킹 소다랑 물을 섞어. 그러고 나서 그걸로 카드 위에 메시지를 써.
Anna: 카드를 어떻게 읽을 수 있어?
Minho: 카드를 포도 주스로 칠하면 메시지가 나타나.

Communication

Jane: _____

Minho: _____

Jane: _____

Minho: _____

Jane: _____

Minho: _____

Jane: 너 스마트 앱 대회에 대해 들어 본 적 있어?
Minho: 응, 들어 봤어. 너 거기 나갈 거야?
Jane: 응, Pic Gardener 앱에 관한 내 아이디어를 보내 보려고.
Minho: Pic Gardener 앱? 무슨 말이야?
Jane: 식물의 사진을 찍으면, 그 앱이 그 식물을 가꾸는 법을 알려 주는 거야.
Minho: 매우 유용한 앱 같아.

Wrap Up 1

Hojin: _____

Katy: _____

Hojin: _____

Katy: _____

Hojin: 저기, Katy. 너 과학 박람회에 대해 들어 본 적 있어?
Katy: 응, 나 거기에 갈 거야.
Hojin: 나도! 난 다양한 종류의 실험들을 할 생각을 하니 신나.
Katy: 맞아, 나도 그게 정말 기대돼!

※ 다음 우리말과 일치하도록 빈칸에 알맞은 것을 골라 쓰시오.

1 In _____ movies, _____ things are _____.
A. possible   B. amazing   C. animation

2 But are they _____ possible in _____ life?
A. real   B. actually

3 _____ _____ Your Hair, Rapunzel!
A. Down   B. Let

4 In the animation, Rapunzel _____ _____ her long hair to _____ people _____ her tower.
A. in   B. let   C. lower   D. must

5 But could _____ hair really _____ up a _____?
A. person   B. hold   C. human

6 Surprisingly, yes! A _____ hair can hold up 100g and an _____ head has _____ 120,000 hairs.
A. about   B. average   C. single

7 _____ _____ hairs could hold up a _____ _____ elephants!
A. of   B. couple   C. those   D. all

8 _____ her hair, Rapunzel has the _____ to hold _____ a person.
A. up   B. ability   C. with

9 But she should _____ her hair _____ something strong and _____.
A. heavy   B. around   C. wrap

10 If she _____, she _____ get a very _____ neck.
A. sore   B. will   C. doesn't

11 We _____ _____ Energy
A. for   B. scare

12 In the animation, monsters _____ children _____ _____ energy _____ their screams.
A. from   B. to   C. scare   D. get

13 _____, their city is _____ _____ this sound!
A. by   B. amazingly   C. powered

14 But could we actually _____ electricity to _____ a city _____ sound?
A. from   B. light   C. produce   D. up

1 만화 영화에서는 놀라운 일들이 가능하다.

2 하지만 그런 일들이 실생활에서 정말 가능할까?

3 라푼젤, 네 머리카락을 내려!

4 만화 영화에서 라푼젤은 사람들이 탑에 들어오게 하기 위해서 그녀의 긴 머리카락을 내려야 한다.

5 하지만 인간의 머리카락이 정말로 사람을 들어 올릴 수 있을까?

6 놀랍게도 그렇다! 머리카락 한 가닥은 100그램의 무게를 들어 올릴 수 있고 보통 머리에는 12만 개 정도의 머리카락이 있다.

7 그 모든 머리카락은 코끼리 두 마리를 들어 올릴 수 있다!

8 라푼젤에게는 머리카락으로 사람을 들어 올릴 수 있는 능력이 있다.

9 하지만 그녀는 머리카락을 어떤 강하고 무거운 것에 감아야 한다.

10 만약 그렇게 하지 않으면 그녀는 목이 많이 아플 것이다.

11 우리는 에너지를 얻기 위해 겁을 준다

12 만화 영화에서 괴물들은 아이들의 비명에서 에너지를 얻기 위해 아이들을 겁준다.

13 놀랍게도 그들의 도시는 이 소리로 동력을 공급받는다!

14 하지만 정말 소리로부터 도시를 밝히는 전기를 만들 수 있을까?

15 Yes, sound can _____ _____ _____ electricity.
  A. into   B. changed   C. be

16 But it would not be _____ in our everyday activities _____ the _____ is too _____.
  A. small   B. because   C. helpful   D. amount

17 _____ _____, the sound _____ a car horn only _____ 50mv.
  A. produces   B. for   C. from   D. example

18 That is _____ 1/4400 of the _____ 220v of _____ in our homes.
  A. electricity   B. average   C. only

19 So, we would need an _____ amount of _____ to light up an _____ city.
  A. entire   B. screams   C. unbelievable

20 Up, _____ and _____!
  A. Away   B. Up

21 The house is _____ and _____ by _____ of balloons in the animation.
  A. thousands   B. flown   C. lifted

22 _____ that _____ work?
  A. actually   B. could

23 _____ say that a house _____ _____ 50,000kg.
  A. about   B. weighs   C. let's

24 A _____ balloon at an _____ park can _____ about 14g.
  A. lift   B. amusement   C. normal

25 So we need _____ 3,570,000 balloons _____ _____ _____ the house.
  A. up   B. lift   C. to   D. about

26 We also _____ to think _____ the weight of the balloons _____ and the _____.
  A. themselves   B. about   C. strings   D. have

27 Then, we _____ to _____ a _____ more thousand balloons.
  A. few   B. add   C. need

28 Now, the biggest _____ is _____ up _____ _____ balloons!
  A. those   B. pumping   C. all   D. challenge

15 그렇다. 소리는 전기로 바뀔 수 있다.

16 그렇지만 그 양이 너무 적기 때문에 그것은 우리의 일상 활동에서는 도움이 되지 않을 것이다.

17 예를 들어. 자동차 경적 소리는 겨우 50밀리볼트를 만들어 낸다.

18 그것은 우리 가정에서 사용하는 일반적인 220볼트 전기의 1/4400밖에 되지 않는다.

19 그래서 도시 전체를 밝히기 위해서는 믿기 어려운 정도로 많은 양의 비명이 필요할 것이다.

20 높이. 높이 그리고 멀리!

21 만화 영화에서 집은 수천 개의 풍선에 의해 들려 올라가고 날아간다.

22 이게 실제로 가능할까?

23 집 한 채의 무게가 5만 킬로그램 정도라고 가정해 보자.

24 놀이공원에 있는 보통의 풍선은 대략 14그램을 들어 올릴 수 있다.

25 그래서 집을 들어 올리기 위해 우리는 약 3.570.000개의 풍선이 필요하다.

26 우리는 또한 풍선 자체와 줄의 무게에 대해서도 생각해야 한다.

27 그렇게 되면. 수천 개의 풍선을 더 추가할 필요가 있다.

28 이제 가장 큰 어려움은 그 모든 풍선에 바람을 넣는 일이다!

※ 다음 우리말과 일치하도록 빈칸에 알맞은 말을 쓰시오.

1 In _____ movies, _____ _____ _____ _____.

2 But are they _____ _____ in _____ _____?

3 _____ _____ Your Hair, Rapunzel!

4 _____ the animation, Rapunzel _____ _____ her long hair _____ _____ _____ _____ her tower.

5 But _____ human hair really _____ _____ _____ _____?

6 _____, yes! A _____ hair can _____ _____ 100g and an _____ head _____ _____ 120,000 hairs.

7 _____ _____ _____ could _____ _____ a couple of elephants!

8 _____ _____ _____, Rapunzel has _____ _____ _____ _____ _____ a person.

9 But she should _____ _____ _____ _____ something _____ and _____.

10 If she _____, she _____ _____ a very _____ _____.

11 We _____ _____ Energy

12 In the animation, monsters _____ _____ _____ energy _____ _____ _____.

13 _____, their city _____ _____ _____ this sound!

14 But _____ we actually _____ _____ _____ _____ _____ a city _____ sound?

1 만화 영화에서는 놀라운 일들이 가능하다.

2 하지만 그런 일들이 실생활에서 정말 가능할까?

3 라푼젤, 네 머리카락을 내려!

4 만화 영화에서 라푼젤은 사람들이 탑에 들어오게 하기 위해서 그녀의 긴 머리카락을 내려야 한다.

5 하지만 인간의 머리카락이 정말로 사람을 들어 올릴 수 있을까?

6 놀랍게도 그렇다! 머리카락 한 가닥은 100그램의 무게를 들어 올릴 수 있고 보통 머리에는 12만 개 정도의 머리카락이 있다.

7 그 모든 머리카락은 코끼리 두 마리를 들어 올릴 수 있다!

8 라푼젤에게는 머리카락으로 사람을 들어 올릴 수 있는 능력이 있다.

9 하지만 그녀는 머리카락을 어떤 강하고 무거운 것에 감아야 한다.

10 만약 그렇게 하지 않으면 그녀는 목이 많이 아플 것이다.

11 우리는 에너지를 얻기 위해 겁을 준다

12 만화 영화에서 괴물들은 아이들의 비명에서 에너지를 얻기 위해 아이들을 겁준다.

13 놀랍게도 그들의 도시는 이 소리로 동력을 공급받는다!

14 하지만 정말 소리로부터 도시를 밝히는 전기를 만들 수 있을까?

15 Yes, sound can _____ _____ _____ _____ .

16 But it _____ _____ be _____ _____ our everyday activities _____ _____ _____ _____ too _____ .

17 _____ _____ , the sound _____ a _____ _____ only _____ 50mv.

18 That is only 1/4400 _____ _____ _____ 220v of _____ _____ _____ _____ .

19 So, we would need _____ _____ _____ _____ _____ to _____ _____ an _____ city.

20 _____ , _____ and _____ !

21 The house _____ _____ _____ _____ by _____ _____ _____ in the animation.

22 _____ that _____ _____ ?

23 _____ _____ that a house _____ _____ 50,000kg.

24 A _____ balloon at _____ _____ _____ _____ can _____ 14g.

25 So we _____ _____ 3,570,000 balloons _____ _____ _____ the house.

26 We also _____ _____ _____ _____ the _____ of the balloons _____ and the _____ .

27 Then, we need to _____ _____ _____ _____ balloons.

28 Now, the _____ _____ is _____ _____ _____ _____ balloons!

---

15 그렇다. 소리는 전기로 바뀔 수 있다.

16 그렇지만 그 양이 너무 적기 때문에 그것은 우리의 일상 활동에서는 도움이 되지 않을 것이다.

17 예를 들어, 자동차 경적 소리는 겨우 50밀리볼트를 만들어 낸다.

18 그것은 우리 가정에서 사용하는 일반적인 220볼트 전기의 1/4400밖에 되지 않는다.

19 그래서 도시 전체를 밝히기 위해서는 믿기 어려운 정도로 많은 양의 비명이 필요할 것이다.

20 높이, 높이 그리고 멀리!

21 만화 영화에서 집은 수천 개의 풍선에 의해 들려 올라가고 날아간다.

22 이게 실제로 가능할까?

23 집 한 채의 무게가 5만 킬로그램 정도라고 가정해 보자.

24 놀이공원에 있는 보통의 풍선은 대략 14그램을 들어 올릴 수 있다.

25 그래서 집을 들어 올리기 위해 우리는 약 3.570.000개의 풍선이 필요하다.

26 우리는 또한 풍선 자체와 줄의 무게에 대해서도 생각해야 한다.

27 그렇게 되면, 수천 개의 풍선을 더 추가할 필요가 있다.

28 이제 가장 큰 어려움은 그 모든 풍선에 바람을 넣는 일이다!

50 Lesson 3. I Wonder Why, I Wonder How

※ 다음 문장을 우리말로 쓰시오.

1 In animation movies, amazing things are possible.

➡ _____

2 But are they actually possible in real life?

➡ _____

3 Let Down Your Hair, Rapunzel!

➡ _____

4 In the animation, Rapunzel must lower her long hair to let people in her tower.

➡ _____

5 But could human hair really hold up a person?

➡ _____

6 Surprisingly, yes! A single hair can hold up 100g and an average head has about 120,000 hairs.

➡ _____

7 All those hairs could hold up a couple of elephants!

➡ _____

8 With her hair, Rapunzel has the ability to hold up a person.

➡ _____

9 But she should wrap her hair around something strong and heavy.

➡ _____

10 If she doesn't, she will get a very sore neck.

➡ _____

11 We Scare for Energy

➡ _____

12 In the animation, monsters scare children to get energy from their screams.

➡ _____

13 Amazingly, their city is powered by this sound!

➡ _____

14 But could we actually produce electricity to light up a city from sound?

➡ _____

15 Yes, sound can be changed into electricity.

➡ _____

16 But it would not be helpful in our everyday activities because the amount is too small.

➡ _____

17 For example, the sound from a car horn only produces 50mv.

➡ _____

18 That is only 1/4400 of the average 220v of electricity in our homes.

➡ _____

19 So, we would need an unbelievable amount of screams to light up an entire city.

➡ _____

20 Up, Up and Away!

➡ _____

21 The house is lifted and flown by thousands of balloons in the animation.

➡ _____

22 Could that actually work?

➡ _____

23 Let's say that a house weighs about 50,000kg.

➡ _____

24 A normal balloon at an amusement park can lift about 14g.

➡ _____

25 So we need about 3,570,000 balloons to lift up the house.

➡ _____

26 We also have to think about the weight of the balloons themselves and the strings.

➡ _____

27 Then, we need to add a few more thousand balloons.

➡ _____

28 Now, the biggest challenge is pumping up all those balloons!

➡ _____

Step4

※ 다음 괄호 안의 단어들을 우리말에 맞도록 바르게 배열하시오.

1 (movies, / animation / in / things / are / possible. / amazing)
➡ _____

2 (are / but / actually / they / in / possible / life? / real)
➡ _____

3 (Down / Let / Hair, / Your / Rapunzel!)
➡ _____

4 (the / animation, / in / Rapunzel / lower / must / long / her / hair / people / let / to / tower. / her / in)
➡ _____
_____

5 (but / human / could / really / hair / up / hold / person? / a)
➡ _____

6 (surprisingly, / yes! / a / hair / single / hold / can / 100g / up / and / an / head / average / has / hairs. / 120,000 / about)
➡ _____
_____

7 (those / all / hairs / hold / could / up / couple / a / elephants! / of)
➡ _____

8 (hair, / with / her / Rapunzel / the / has / a / ability / hold / to / person. / up)
➡ _____

9 (but / she / wrap / should / hair / her / something / around / heavy. / and / strong)
➡ _____

10 (she / doesn't, / if / she / get / will / sore / a / neck. / very)
➡ _____

11 (for / Scare / we / Energy)
➡ _____

12 (the / in / animation, / scare / monsters / to / children / energy / got / screams. / their / from)
➡ _____

13 (amazingly, / city / their / powered / this / is / sound! / by)
➡ _____

14 (but / we / could / produce / actually / to / electricity / up / light / sound? / from / a / city)
➡ _____

1 만화 영화에서는 놀라운 일들이 가능하다.

2 하지만 그런 일들이 실생활에서 정말 가능할까?

3 라푼젤, 네 머리카락을 내려!

4 만화 영화에서 라푼젤은 사람들이 탑에 들어오게 하기 위해서 그녀의 긴 머리카락을 내려야 한다.

5 하지만 인간의 머리카락이 정말로 사람을 들어 올릴 수 있을까?

6 놀랍게도 그렇다! 머리카락 한 가닥은 100그램의 무게를 들어 올릴 수 있고 보통 머리에는 12만 개 정도의 머리카락이 있다.

7 그 모든 머리카락은 코끼리 두 마리를 들어 올릴 수 있다!

8 라푼젤에게는 머리카락으로 사람을 들어 올릴 수 있는 능력이 있다.

9 하지만 그녀는 머리카락을 어떤 강하고 무거운 것에 감아야 한다.

10 만약 그렇게 하지 않으면 그녀는 목이 많이 아플 것이다.

11 우리는 에너지를 얻기 위해 겁을 준다

12 만화 영화에서 괴물들은 아이들의 비명에서 에너지를 얻기 위해 아이들을 겁준다.

13 놀랍게도 그들의 도시는 이 소리로 동력을 공급받는다!

14 하지만 정말 소리로부터 도시를 밝히는 전기를 만들 수 있을까?

15 (yes, / can / sound / be / electricity. / into / changed)
➡ _____

16 (but / it / be / not / would / helpful / our / in / everyday / activities / the / because / amount / too / small. / is)
➡ _____
_____

17 (example, / for / sound / the / from / car / a / horn / 50mv. / produces / only)
➡ _____

18 (is / that / 1/4400 / only / of / average / the / 220v / electricity / of / homes. / in / our)
➡ _____

19 (so, / we / need / would / an / amount / unbelievable / screams / of / light / up / to / city. / entire / an)
➡ _____

20 (Away! / Up / and / Up,)
➡ _____

21 (house / the / lifted / is / and / flown / thousands / by / balloons / of / the / animation. / in)
➡ _____

22 (that / could / work? / actually)
➡ _____

23 (say / let's / that / house / a / weighs / 50,000kg. / about)
➡ _____

24 (normal / a / balloon / at / amusement / an / park / lift / can / 14g. / about)
➡ _____

25 (so / need / we / 3,570,000 / about / balloons / lift / to / up / house. / the)
➡ _____

26 (we / have / also / think / to / the / about / weight / of / balloons / the / themselves / strings. / the / and)
➡ _____
_____

27 (then, / need / we / add / to / a / more / few / balloons. / thousand)
➡ _____

28 (now, / biggest / the / challenge / is / up / pumping / balloons! / those / all)
➡ _____

15 그렇다, 소리는 전기로 바뀔 수 있다.

16 그렇지만 그 양이 너무 적기 때문에 그것은 우리의 일상 활동에서는 도움이 되지 않을 것이다.

17 예를 들어, 자동차 경적 소리는 겨우 50밀리볼트를 만들어 낸다.

18 그것은 우리 가정에서 사용하는 일반적인 220볼트 전기의 1/4400밖에 되지 않는다.

19 그래서 도시 전체를 밝히기 위해서는 믿기 어려운 정도로 많은 양의 비명이 필요할 것이다.

20 높이, 높이 그리고 멀리!

21 만화 영화에서 집은 수천 개의 풍선에 의해 들려 올라가고 날아간다.

22 이게 실제로 가능할까?

23 집 한 채의 무게가 5만 킬로그램 정도라고 가정해 보자.

24 놀이공원에 있는 보통의 풍선은 대략 14그램을 들어 올릴 수 있다.

25 그래서 집을 들어 올리기 위해 우리는 약 3.570.000개의 풍선이 필요하다.

26 우리는 또한 풍선 자체와 줄의 무게에 대해서도 생각해야 한다.

27 그렇게 되면, 수천 개의 풍선을 더 추가할 필요가 있다.

28 이제 가장 큰 어려움은 그 모든 풍선에 바람을 넣는 일이다!

※ **다음 우리말을 영어로 쓰시오.**

1 만화 영화에서는 놀라운 일들이 가능하다.

➡ _____

2 하지만 그런 일들이 실생활에서 정말 가능할까?

➡ _____

3 라푼젤, 네 머리카락을 내려!

➡ _____

4 만화 영화에서 라푼젤은 사람들이 탑에 들어오게 하기 위해서 그녀의 긴 머리카락을 내려야 한다.

➡ _____

5 하지만 인간의 머리카락이 정말로 사람을 들어 올릴 수 있을까?

➡ _____

6 놀랍게도 그렇다! 머리카락 한 가닥은 100그램의 무게를 들어 올릴 수 있고 보통 머리에는 12만 개 정도의 머리카락이 있다.

➡ _____

7 그 모든 머리카락은 코끼리 두 마리를 들어 올릴 수 있다!

➡ _____

8 라푼젤에게는 머리카락으로 사람을 들어 올릴 수 있는 능력이 있다.

➡ _____

9 하지만 그녀는 머리카락을 어떤 강하고 무거운 것에 감아야 한다.

➡ _____

10 만약 그렇게 하지 않으면 그녀는 목이 많이 아플 것이다.

➡ _____

11 우리는 에너지를 얻기 위해 겁을 준다

➡ _____

12 만화 영화에서 괴물들은 아이들의 비명에서 에너지를 얻기 위해 아이들을 겁준다.

➡ _____

13 놀랍게도 그들의 도시는 이 소리로 동력을 공급받는다!

➡ _____

14 하지만 정말 소리로부터 도시를 밝히는 전기를 만들 수 있을까?

➡ _____

15 그렇다. 소리는 전기로 바뀔 수 있다.

➡ _____

16 그렇지만 그 양이 너무 적기 때문에 그것은 우리의 일상 활동에서는 도움이 되지 않을 것이다.

➡ _____

17 예를 들어, 자동차 경적 소리는 겨우 50밀리볼트를 만들어 낸다.

➡ _____

18 그것은 우리 가정에서 사용하는 일반적인 220볼트 전기의 1/4400밖에 되지 않는다.

➡ _____

19 그래서 도시 전체를 밝히기 위해서는 믿기 어려운 정도로 많은 양의 비명이 필요할 것이다.

➡ _____

20 높이, 높이 그리고 멀리!

➡ _____

21 만화 영화에서 집은 수천 개의 풍선에 의해 들려 올라가고 날아간다.

➡ _____

22 이게 실제로 가능할까?

➡ _____

23 집 한 채의 무게가 5만 킬로그램 정도라고 가정해 보자.

➡ _____

24 놀이공원에 있는 보통의 풍선은 대략 14그램을 들어 올릴 수 있다.

➡ _____

25 그래서 집을 들어 올리기 위해 우리는 약 3,570,000개의 풍선이 필요하다.

➡ _____

26 우리는 또한 풍선 자체와 줄의 무게에 대해서도 생각해야 한다.

➡ _____

27 그렇게 되면, 수천 개의 풍선을 더 추가할 필요가 있다.

➡ _____

28 이제 가장 큰 어려움은 그 모든 풍선에 바람을 넣는 일이다!

➡ _____

※ 다음 우리말과 일치하도록 빈칸에 알맞은 말을 쓰시오.

Grammar in Real Life

1. This is Jack's _____ _____ this week.

2. There is _____ _____ _____ work to do.

3. He needs _____ _____ to the library _____ Monday.

4. He has two books _____ _____ from the library.

5. Also he has _____ _____ to finish _____ Thursday.

6. _____ Friday, he will be in the school _____ _____.

7. So, he will _____ _____ the songs at the _____ _____ all this week.

1. 이것은 Jack의 이번 주 계획이다.
2. 할 일이 많이 있다.
3. 그는 월요일에 도서관에 가야 한다.
4. 그는 도서관에서 빌려야 할 책 두 권이 있다.
5. 또한, 그는 목요일까지 끝내야 할 과학 숙제가 있다.
6. 금요일에 그는 학교 장기 자랑 대회에 나갈 것이다.
7. 그래서 그는 이번 주 내내 장기 자랑 대회에서 공연할 노래들을 연습할 것이다.

Think & Write

1. Hello, _____ _____ is June.

2. Today _____ _____ to _____ _____ my new _____ technology, SuperEye.

3. It is _____ _____ _____ pictures and video-record.

4. It is also useful to _____ _____ _____ _____.

5. _____ _____ _____ and experience a new world!

1. 안녕, 내 이름은 June이야.
2. 오늘 나는 나의 새로운 착용 가능한 기술인 SuperEye에 관해 말하고 싶어.
3. 그것은 사진을 찍거나 녹화를 하는 데 유용해.
4. 또한 나에게 지도를 보여 주는 데도 유용해.
5. 한 번 사용해 보고 새로운 세계를 경험해 봐!

Wrap Up 3

1. Amy: _____ _____ _____ about the _____ event at the _____ _____?

2. Brian: No, I _____. What's the event?

3. Amy: _____ _____ science magic shows _____ the weekend, but _____ _____ this month.

4. Brian: Oh, _____ you _____ the information. I'll visit _____ this weekend.

1. Amy: 너는 과학 박물관에서 하는 특별 이벤트에 대해 들어 본 적 있어?
2. Brian: 아니, 없어. 어떤 이벤트야?
3. Amy: 주말 동안 과학 마술쇼가 있는데, 이번 달에만 있대.
4. Brian: 오, 정보 고마워. 이번 주말에 방문해야겠어.

※ 다음 우리말을 영어로 쓰시오.

Grammar in Real Life

1. 이것은 Jack의 이번 주 계획이다.

   ➡ _____

2. 할 일이 많이 있다.

   ➡ _____

3. 그는 월요일에 도서관에 가야 한다.

   ➡ _____

4. 그는 도서관에서 빌려야 할 책 두 권이 있다.

   ➡ _____

5. 또한, 그는 목요일까지 끝내야 할 과학 숙제가 있다.

   ➡ _____

6. 금요일에 그는 학교 장기 자랑 대회에 나갈 것이다.

   ➡ _____

7. 그래서 그는 이번 주 내내 장기 자랑 대회에서 공연할 노래들을 연습할 것이다.

   ➡ _____

Think & Write

1. 안녕, 내 이름은 June이야.

   ➡ _____

2. 오늘 나는 나의 새로운 착용 가능한 기술인 SuperEye에 관해 말하고 싶어.

   ➡ _____

3. 그것은 사진을 찍거나 녹화를 하는 데 유용해.

   ➡ _____

4. 또한 나에게 지도를 보여 주는 데도 유용해.

   ➡ _____

5. 한 번 사용해 보고 새로운 세계를 경험해 봐!

   ➡ _____

Wrap Up 3

1. Amy: 너는 과학 박물관에서 하는 특별 이벤트에 대해 들어 본 적 있어?

   ➡ _____

2. Brian: 아니, 없어. 어떤 이벤트야?

   ➡ _____

3. Amy: 주말 동안 과학 마술쇼가 있는데, 이번 달에만 있대.

   ➡ _____

4. Brian: 오, 정보 고마워. 이번 주말에 방문해야겠어.

   ➡ _____

Step1

※ 다음 영어를 우리말로 쓰시오.

01	amazing	_____
02	terrible	_____
03	voice	_____
04	place	_____
05	engine	_____
06	block	_____
07	excitedly	_____
08	cheer	_____
09	close match	_____
10	local	_____
11	gas pedal	_____
12	hit	_____
13	lap	_____
14	loud	_____
15	official	_____
16	punch	_____
17	hang	_____
18	straightaway	_____
19	three-pointer	_____
20	kick	_____
21	count	_____

22	deep	_____
23	crowded	_____
24	memorable	_____
25	seafood	_____
26	rush	_____
27	beat	_____
28	complete	_____
29	finish line	_____
30	crowd	_____
31	pitcher	_____
32	fix	_____
33	ahead	_____
34	press	_____
35	take a chance	_____
36	sit up	_____
37	miss a chance	_____
38	be satisfied with	_____
39	cheer up	_____
40	be filled with	_____
41	do one's best	_____
42	keep up with	_____
43	out of one's reach	_____

※ 다음 우리말을 영어로 쓰시오.

01	뛰다, 치다	
02	중요하다, (수를) 세다	
03	앞에, 앞선	
04	배구	
05	경주로, 트랙	
06	투구	
07	결승선	
08	기, 깃발	
09	해산물	
10	깊은	
11	완성하다; 완전한	
12	수리하다, 고정시키다	
13	복잡한, 붐비는	
14	기억할 만한	
15	소형 경주용 자동차	
16	군중, 관객	
17	돌진하다	
18	투수	
19	눈물	
20	누르다, 밀어붙이다	
21	무서운, 심한	

22	갈채를 보내다	
23	흥분하여, 기를 쓰고	
24	목소리	
25	아슬아슬한 승부, 접전	
26	막다, 방해하다	
27	3점슛	
28	매달다, 걸다	
29	타격	
30	시끄러운, (소리가) 큰	
31	놀랄 정도의, 굉장한	
32	일직선의, 즉시의	
33	지방의	
34	(경주, 대회 등의) 등위	
35	~에 만족하다	
36	기운을 내다	
37	최선을 다하다	
38	경주에 이기다	
39	~로 가득 차다	
40	~에 뒤떨어지지 않다	
41	기회를 놓치다	
42	자세를 바로 하다, 바로 앉다	
43	(모험 삼아) 해 보다	

※ 다음 영영풀이에 알맞은 단어를 <보기>에서 골라 쓴 후, 우리말 뜻을 쓰시오.

1   _____ : a small motor vehicle used for racing: _____

2   _____ : to have value or importance: _____

3   _____ : to finish making or doing something: _____

4   _____ : to hit somebody/something with your foot: _____

5   _____ : the player who throws the ball to the batter: _____

6   _____ : a drop of liquid that comes out of your eye when you cry: _____

7   _____ : a piece of ground with a special surface for people, cars, etc. to have

   races on: _____

8   _____ : fish and shellfish that live in the ocean and are used for food: _____

9   _____ : the sound or sounds produced through the mouth by a person speaking or

   singing: _____

10 _____ : the part of a vehicle that produces power to make the vehicle move:

   _____

11 _____ : a game in which two teams of players hit a large ball back and forth over

   a high net: _____

12 _____ : special, good or unusual and therefore worth remembering or easy to

   remember: _____

13 _____ : to shout loudly, to show support or praise for somebody, or to give them

   encouragement: _____

14 _____ : to stop somebody from going somewhere or seeing something by standing

   in front of them or in their way: _____

15 _____ : a large number of people gathered together in a public place, for example

   in the streets or at a sports game: _____

16 _____ : the line across a sports track, etc. that marks the end of a race: _____

보기			
crowd	count	finish line	track
cheer	tear	pitcher	seafood
voice	memorable	complete	kart
block	kick	volleyball	engine

※ 다음 우리말과 일치하도록 빈칸에 알맞은 말을 쓰시오.

Listen & Talk 1 A-1

Mom: David, _____ was your _____ _____ today?

David: We _____, Mom. I _____ too many _____ for a _____ -_____.

Mom: Oh, _____ _____ _____ _____ on yourself. _____ _____ _____ next time.

David: I _____ _____.

Mom: David, 오늘 너희 농구 경기는 어땠니?
David: 저희가 졌어요, 엄마. 제가 3점 슛을 할 기회를 너무 많이 놓쳤어요.
Mom: 오, 너무 자책하지 마. 다음번에는 더 잘할 거야.
David: 저도 그러길 바라요.

Listen & Talk 1 A-2

Jack: Did you come and watch my _____ _____ yesterday?

Irene: Yeah, I did. That was a great volleyball match. _____ _____!

Jack: Thanks, _____ it was a _____ _____. My serves _____ _____ _____ _____.

Irene: Oh, _____ _____ _____ _____. You'll _____ _____ next time.

Jack: 어제 내 배구 시합 보러 왔어?
Irene: 응, 그랬어. 정말 멋진 배구 시합이었어. 너 정말 잘했어!
Jack: 고마워. 하지만 아슬아슬한 시합이었어. 내 서브는 충분히 강하지 않았어.
Irene: 오, 너는 훌륭한 선수야. 다음번에는 더 잘할 거야.

Listen & Talk 1 B

Emily: I _____ your baseball team, the Reds, _____ _____ _____. _____ _____ _____, right? _____, John!

John: Thanks. It was _____ _____ _____. I'm _____ _____ _____ my _____.

Emily: _____ do you _____ that?

John: I _____ _____ _____.

Emily: Oh, _____ _____ _____ _____. You'll _____ _____ next time.

Emily: 나는 너희 the Reds 야구팀이 시합에서 이겼다고 들었어. 8 대 7이 맞니? 축하해, John!
John: 고마워. 정말 접전이었어. 나는 내 투구에 만족스럽지 않아.
Emily: 왜 그렇게 말하는 거야?
John: 홈런 두 개를 허용했거든.
Emily: 오, 너는 훌륭한 투수야. 다음번에는 더 잘할 거야.

Listen & Talk 2 A-1

Mike: Is it your _____ _____ _____ a bike, Mina?

Mina: Yes, it is. I just _____ _____ _____ _____.

Mike: _____ _____ _____ you. I'll _____ your bike.

Mina: Thanks, Mike. _____ _____ go, okay?

Mike: Don't worry. _____ _____ and _____ _____ _____ _____.

Mike: 미나야, 자전거 처음 타는 거야?
Mina: 응. 균형을 잘 못 잡겠어.
Mike: 내가 도와줄게. 네 자전거를 잡아 줄게.
Mina: 고마워, Mike. 놓으면 안 돼, 알았지?
Mike: 걱정 마. 앉아서 앞을 똑바로 봐.

Listen & Talk 2 A-1

Tom: What _____ you _____, Sarah?

Sarah: I learned _____ _____ _____ _____ _____ _____

in PE class. So I'm _____ it now but it's _____ _____.

Tom: _____ _____ _____ _____. _____ your legs in the

air again. I'll _____ _____.

Sarah: Oh, thanks. I'll _____ _____.

Listen & Talk 2 B

Coach: Hey, Brian. _____ you _____ the *taegwondo* side kick?

Brian: Yes, Coach. But _____ _____ _____ _____ _____ _____

_____.

Coach: _____ _____ are you _____?

Brian: Well, I _____ _____ _____ _____ _____ _____ _____.

Coach: I see. _____ _____ help you. I'll _____ this kick pad

for you. _____ me your _____ _____.

Communication

Megan: I'm _____ _____ _____ next soccer match, James.

James: _____ _____ you _____, Megan?

Megan: Well, I _____ _____ _____ _____ in the last soccer

match. I _____ _____ too many goals.

James: I see. Here, _____ _____ _____ _____ _____. I'll _____

_____ _____ to you.

Megan: Oh, that'll really help. I hope _____ _____ _____

_____.

James: _____ _____. You'll _____ _____ next time.

Wrap Up 1

Anna: Hi, Jake. _____ _____ _____ _____ _____ the pool often?

Jake: Oh, hi, Anna. I _____ _____ _____ _____ here

_____ _____.

Anna: _____ did you _____ _____ _____?

Jake: _____ _____. But swimming is still not _____ _____

_____.

Anna: Oh, _____ _____ _____ you. I teach children _____

_____ _____ in the school club.

Jake: Oh, _____ _____ _____ _____ _____ _____. Thanks.

Tom: Sarah, 뭐 하고 있어?

Sarah: 체육 시간에 물구나무 서는 법을 배웠거든. 그래서 지금 한번 해 보고 있는데, 쉽지 않네.

Tom: 내가 도와줄게. 다리를 공중에 차 올려봐. 내가 널 붙잡을게.

Sarah: 오, 고마워. 다시 해 볼게.

Coach: 저기, Brian. 태권도 옆 차기 연습했니?

Brian: 네, 코치님. 그런데 여전히 편하게 잘 안 돼요.

Coach: 어떤 문제가 있어?

Brian: 음, 다리를 충분히 높이 들어 올릴 수가 없어요.

Coach: 알겠다. 내가 도와줄게. 너를 위해 이 킥 패드를 잡아줄게. 너의 옆 차기를 보여주렴.

Megan: James, 나는 다음 축구 시합이 걱정돼.

James: 왜 걱정하는 거야, Megan?

Megan: 음, 지난 축구 시합에서 나는 높은 공을 잡지 못했어. 너무 많은 골을 허용했어.

James: 알겠어. 자, 내가 도와줄게. 너에게 공을 높이 차 줄게.

Megan: 오, 그거 도움이 많이 되겠다. 내 기술이 나아지길 바라.

James: 걱정 마. 다음번에는 더 잘할 거야.

Anna: 안녕, Jake. 너는 종종 수영장에 오니?

Jake: 오, 안녕, Anna. 나는 여기에서 일주일에 한 번 수영 수업을 들어.

Anna: 언제부터 수업을 시작했어?

Jake: 지난달부터. 그런데 수영은 여전히 나에게 쉽지 않아.

Anna: 오, 내가 도와줄게. 나는 학교 동아리에서 아이들에게 수영하는 법을 가르쳐 주거든.

Jake: 오, 그거 나에게 도움이 많이 되겠다. 고마워.

※ 다음 우리말에 맞도록 대화를 영어로 쓰시오.

Listen & Talk 1 A-1

Mom: _____

David: _____

Mom: _____

David: _____

Mom: David, 오늘 너희 농구 경기는 어땠니?
David: 저희가 졌어요, 엄마. 제가 3점 슛을 할 기회를 너무 많이 놓쳤어요.
Mom: 오, 너무 자책하지 마. 다음번에는 더 잘할 거야.
David: 저도 그러길 바라요.

Listen & Talk 1 A-2

Jack: _____

Irene: _____

Jack: _____

Irene: _____

Jack: 어제 내 배구 시합 보러 왔어?
Irene: 응, 그랬어. 정말 멋진 배구 시합이었어. 너 정말 잘했어!
Jack: 고마워. 하지만 아슬아슬한 시합이었어. 내 서브는 충분히 강하지 않았어.
Irene: 오, 너는 훌륭한 선수야. 다음번에는 더 잘할 거야.

Listen & Talk 1 B

Emily: _____

_____

John: _____

Emily: _____

John: _____

Emily: _____

Emily: 나는 너희 the Reds 야구팀이 시합에서 이겼다고 들었어. 8 대 7이 맞니? 축하해, John!
John: 고마워. 정말 접전이었어. 나는 내 투구에 만족스럽지 않아.
Emily: 왜 그렇게 말하는 거야?
John: 홈런 두 개를 허용했거든.
Emily: 오, 너는 훌륭한 투수야. 다음번에는 더 잘할 거야.

Listen & Talk 2 A-1

Mike: _____

Mina: _____

Mike: _____

Mina: _____

Mike: _____

Mike: 미나야, 자전거 처음 타는 거야?
Mina: 응. 균형을 잘 못 잡겠어.
Mike: 내가 도와줄게. 네 자전거를 잡아 줄게.
Mina: 고마워, Mike. 놓으면 안 돼, 알았지?
Mike: 걱정 마. 앉아서 앞을 똑바로 봐.

Listen & Talk 2 A-1

Tom: _____

Sarah: _____

_____

Tom: _____

Sarah: _____

Tom: Sarah, 뭐 하고 있어?
Sarah: 체육 시간에 물구나무 서는 법
을 배웠거든. 그래서 지금 한번
해 보고 있는데, 쉽지 않네.
Tom: 내가 도와줄게. 다리를 공중에 차
올려봐. 내가 널 붙잡을게.
Sarah: 오, 고마워. 다시 해 볼게.

Listen & Talk 2 B

Coach: _____

Brian: _____

Coach: _____

Brian: _____

Coach: _____

_____

Coach: 저기, Brian. 태권도 옆 차기 연
습했니?
Brian: 네, 코치님. 그런데 여전히 편하
게 잘 안 돼요.
Coach: 어떤 문제가 있어?
Brian: 음, 다리를 충분히 높이 들어 올
릴 수가 없어요.
Coach: 알겠다. 내가 도와줄게. 너를
위해 이 킥 패드를 잡아줄게.
너의 옆 차기를 보여주렴.

Communication

Megan: _____

James: _____

Megan: _____

_____

James: _____

Megan: _____

James: _____

Megan: James, 나는 다음 축구 시합이
걱정돼.
James: 왜 걱정하는 거야, Megan?
Megan: 음, 지난 축구 시합에서 나는
높은 공을 잡지 못했어. 너무
많은 골을 허용했어.
James: 알겠어. 자, 내가 도와줄게. 너
에게 공을 높이 차 줄게.
Megan: 오, 그거 도움이 많이 되겠다.
내 기술이 나아지길 바라.
James: 걱정 마. 다음번에는 더 잘할 거야.

Wrap Up 1

Anna: _____

Jake: _____

Anna: _____

Jake: _____

Anna: _____

Jake: _____

Anna: 안녕, Jake. 너는 종종 수영장에
오니?
Jake: 오, 안녕, Anna. 나는 여기에서
일주일에 한 번 수영 수업을 들어.
Anna: 언제부터 수업을 시작했어?
Jake: 지난달부터. 그런데 수영은 여전
히 나에게 쉽지 않아.
Anna: 오, 내가 도와줄게. 나는 학교 동
아리에서 아이들에게 수영하는
법을 가르쳐 주거든.
Jake: 오, 그거 나에게 도움이 많이 되
겠다. 고마워.

※ 다음 우리말과 일치하도록 빈칸에 알맞은 것을 골라 쓰시오.

1 _____ the go-kart race track, _____ are many people _____ are _____ excitedly.

    A. there   B. cheering   C. who   D. at

2 The karts _____ are _____ loud engine noises _____ .

    A. waiting   B. making   C. are   D. that

3 An official _____ a green _____ and the race _____ !

    A. starts   B. flag   C. waves

4 Max _____ his foot _____ hard on the gas pedal _____ he _____ his sixth lap on the track.

    A. completes   B. down   C. as   D. pushes

5 _____ the straightaway, Max _____ right _____ the race's leader, Simon.

    A. pulls   B. beside   C. on

6 Last year, Simon _____ many races, but Max's best _____ in a race was _____ in fifth _____ .

    A. place   B. result   C. won   D. coming

7 This time, he has a _____ to _____ .

    A. second   B. chance   C. finish

8 But he isn't _____ to be _____ with second _____ today.

    A. satisfied   B. place   C. going

9 The winner _____ to _____ the world _____ racer L. J. Richards!

    A. gets   B. famous   C. meet

10 He doesn't want to _____ the _____ to meet his _____ model.

    A. role   B. chance   C. miss

11 Max _____ the _____ lap and now has five more _____ to go.

    A. tenth   B. laps   C. completes

12 Max sees Simon's kart _____ , just _____ of Max's _____ .

    A. ahead   B. reach   C. out

13 Max's kart _____ closer and _____ to Simon's.

    A. closer   B. gets

14 It _____ _____ the back _____ of Simon's kart.

    A. almost   B. end   C. hits

15 They _____ _____ the straightaway and Max _____ _____ on the gas pedal.

    A. into   B. presses   C. drive   D. harder

16 "I can _____ _____ ," says Max.

    A. up   B. catch

17 Max sees the _____ _____ a white flag which _____ the last lap.

    A. waving   B. means   C. official

---

1 고카트 경기 트랙에 신이 나서 응원하고 있는 많은 사람들이 있다.

2 시끄러운 엔진 소음을 내고 있는 카트들이 기다리고 있다.

3 심판이 초록 깃발을 흔들고, 경기가 시작된다!

4 Max는 트랙을 여섯 바퀴 돌았을 때, 발로 가속 페달을 힘껏 누른다.

5 직선 구간에서 Max는 경기에서 선두를 달리고 있는 Simon의 바로 옆까지 다가간다.

6 작년에 Simon은 경기에서 여러 번 이겼지만 Max의 최고 경기 성적은 5등으로 들어온 것이었다.

7 이번에 그는 2등으로 끝낼 수 있는 기회를 잡았다.

8 그러나 그는 오늘 2등으로 만족하지 않을 것이다.

9 우승자는 세계적으로 유명한 경주 선수인 L.J. Richards를 만나게 된다!

10 그는 그의 역할 모델을 만날 수 있는 기회를 놓치길 원하지 않는다.

11 Max는 10바퀴를 다 돌고 이제 5바퀴를 더 돌아야 한다.

12 Max는 앞에 바로 닿을 듯한 거리에 있는 Simon의 카트를 본다.

13 Max의 카트는 Simon의 카트에 점점 더 가까워진다.

14 Max의 카트는 Simon의 카트의 뒷부분에 거의 닿을 것 같다.

15 그들은 직선 구간을 운전해가고, Max는 가속 페달을 더 세게 밟는다.

16 "나는 따라잡을 수 있어." Max가 말한다.

17 Max는 심판이 마지막 바퀴라는 것을 알려주는 흰색 깃발을 흔드는 것을 본다.

18 Max is _____ _____ Simon.

    A. behind   B. right

19 The finish line is _____ closer, and the _____ from the _____ is getting _____.

    A. louder   B. getting   C. crowd   D. cheering

20 "I _____ _____ it!" Max says _____.

    A. loudly   B. do   C. can

21 He can _____ his heart _____ _____.

    A. hard   B. beating   C. feel

22 The karts _____ _____ the _____ line.

    A. across   B. rush   C. finish

23 _____ is the _____?

    A. winner   B. who

24 Max's eyes are _____ _____ tears as he finds _____ that he came in second.

    A. filled   B. out   C. with

25 "No _____ for _____, kid," says a man's _____.

    A. need   B. voice   C. tears

26 Max _____ _____ his eyes.

    A. believe   B. can't

27 The man who is _____ in _____ of him _____ L. J. Richards!

    A. standing   B. is   C. front

28 "Thank you, _____ I'm _____ the _____," says Max.

    A. winner   B. not   C. but

29 "It was a _____ _____ _____.

    A. close   B. race   C. real

30 _____ though you didn't _____ the race, you did your _____.

    A. win   B. best   C. even

31 That's the thing _____ _____!" says L. J. Richards.

    A. counts   B. that

32 '_____ I do my _____?' thinks Max.

    A. best   B. did

33 _____ a moment, he _____.

    A. smiles   B. after

34 "Yeah, I _____ I _____."

    A. did   B. guess

---

18 Max는 Simon 바로 뒤에 있다.

19 결승점이 점점 가까워지고, 관중으로부터 들리는 환호성이 점점 커진다.

20 "나는 할 수 있어!" Max는 큰 소리로 말한다.

21 그는 그의 심장이 세게 뛰는 것을 느낄 수 있다.

22 카트들이 돌진해 결승점을 지난다.

23 누가 승자인가?

24 Max는 자신이 2등으로 들어왔다는 것을 알았을 때, 눈에 눈물이 가득 찬다.

25 "울 필요 없단다, 얘야." 어떤 남자의 목소리가 말한다.

26 Max는 그의 눈을 믿을 수 없다.

27 그 앞에 서 있는 남자는 L.J. Richards이다!

28 "고마워요, 하지만 저는 일등이 아니에요." Max가 말한다.

29 "정말 아슬아슬한 경기였어.

30 네가 비록 경기를 이기지 못했지만, 너는 최선을 다했어.

31 중요한 것은 바로 그거란다!" L.J. Richards가 말한다.

32 '나는 최선을 다했을까?' Max는 생각한다.

33 잠시 후에, 그는 미소를 짓는다.

34 "네, 저는 최선을 다한 것 같아요."

※ 다음 우리말과 일치하도록 빈칸에 알맞은 말을 쓰시오.

1 _____ the go-kart race _____, _____ _____ many people _____ _____ _____ _____.

2 The karts _____ _____ _____ _____ engine noises _____ _____.

3 An _____ _____ a green _____ and the race _____!

4 Max _____ his foot _____ _____ on the gas pedal _____ he _____ his _____ on the track.

5 _____ _____ _____ _____, Max _____ _____ _____ the race's leader, Simon.

6 Last year, Simon _____ _____ _____, but Max's best result in a race _____ _____ _____ _____ _____ _____.

7 This time, he has a _____ _____ _____ _____.

8 But he isn't going to _____ _____ today.

9 The winner _____ _____ _____ the world famous racer L. J. Richards!

10 He doesn't want _____ _____ the chance _____ _____ _____ _____ _____.

11 Max _____ _____ _____ _____ and now has five more laps _____ _____.

12 Max _____ Simon's kart _____, just _____ _____ Max's reach.

13 Max's kart _____ _____ _____ _____ to Simon's.

14 It almost _____ _____ _____ _____ of Simon's kart.

15 They _____ _____ the straightaway and Max _____ _____ _____ _____ _____ _____.

16 "I _____ _____ _____," says Max.

17 Max sees the official _____ _____ _____ which _____ _____ _____ _____.

---

1 고카트 경기 트랙에 신이 나서 응원하고 있는 많은 사람들이 있다.

2 시끄러운 엔진 소음을 내고 있는 카트들이 기다리고 있다.

3 심판이 초록 깃발을 흔들고, 경기가 시작된다!

4 Max는 트랙을 여섯 바퀴 돌았을 때, 발로 가속 페달을 힘껏 누른다.

5 직선 구간에서 Max는 경기에서 선두를 달리고 있는 Simon의 바로 옆까지 다가간다.

6 작년에 Simon은 경기에서 여러 번 이겼지만 Max의 최고 경기 성적은 5등으로 들어온 것이었다.

7 이번에 그는 2등으로 끝낼 수 있는 기회를 잡았다.

8 그러나 그는 오늘 2등으로 만족하지 않을 것이다.

9 우승자는 세계적으로 유명한 경주 선수인 L.J. Richards를 만나게 된다!

10 그는 그의 역할 모델을 만날 수 있는 기회를 놓치길 원하지 않는다.

11 Max는 10바퀴를 다 돌고 이제 5바퀴를 더 돌아야 한다.

12 Max는 앞에 바로 닿을 듯한 거리에 있는 Simon의 카트를 본다.

13 Max의 카트는 Simon의 카트에 점점 더 가까워진다.

14 Max의 카트는 Simon의 카트의 뒷부분에 거의 닿을 것 같다.

15 그들은 직선 구간을 운전해가고, Max는 가속 페달을 더 세게 밟는다.

16 "나는 따라잡을 수 있어." Max가 말한다.

17 Max는 심판이 마지막 바퀴라는 것을 알려주는 흰색 깃발을 흔드는 것을 본다.

18 Max is _____ _____ Simon.

19 The finish line is _____ _____, and the _____ _____ _____ _____ is _____ _____.

20 "I _____ _____ _____!" Max _____ _____.

21 He _____ _____ his heart _____ _____.

22 The karts _____ _____ _____ _____ _____ _____.

23 _____ is the _____?

24 Max's eyes are _____ _____ _____ as he _____ _____ _____ he came _____ _____.

25 "_____ _____ _____ _____ _____, kid," says a man's voice.

26 Max _____ _____ _____ _____ _____.

27 The man _____ _____ _____ _____ _____ him _____ L. J. Richards!

28 "Thank you, but I'm _____ _____ _____," says Max.

29 "It was _____ _____ _____ _____.

30 _____ _____ you _____ _____ _____ _____, you _____ your best.

31 That's the thing _____ _____!" says L. J. Richards.

32 '_____ I _____ _____ _____?' _____ Max.

33 _____ _____ _____, he _____.

34 "Yeah, I _____ I _____."

---

18 Max는 Simon 바로 뒤에 있다.

19 결승점이 점점 가까워지고, 관중으로부터 들리는 환호성이 점점 커진다.

20 "나는 할 수 있어!" Max는 큰 소리로 말한다.

21 그는 그의 심장이 세게 뛰는 것을 느낄 수 있다.

22 카트들이 돌진해 결승점을 지난다.

23 누가 승자인가?

24 Max는 자신이 2등으로 들어왔다는 것을 알았을 때, 눈에 눈물이 가득 찬다.

25 "울 필요 없단다, 얘야." 어떤 남자의 목소리가 말한다.

26 Max는 그의 눈을 믿을 수 없다.

27 그 앞에 서 있는 남자는 L.J. Richards이다!

28 "고마워요, 하지만 저는 일등이 아니에요." Max가 말한다.

29 "정말 아슬아슬한 경기였어.

30 네가 비록 경기를 이기지 못했지만, 너는 최선을 다했어.

31 중요한 것은 바로 그거란다!" L.J. Richards가 말한다.

32 '나는 최선을 다했을까?' Max는 생각한다.

33 잠시 후에, 그는 미소를 짓는다.

34 "네, 저는 최선을 다한 것 같아요."

※ 다음 문장을 우리말로 쓰시오.

1 At the go-kart race track, there are many people who are cheering excitedly.

➡ _____

2 The karts that are making loud engine noises are waiting.

➡ _____

3 An official waves a green flag and the race starts!

➡ _____

4 Max pushes his foot down hard on the gas pedal as he completes his sixth lap on the track.

➡ _____

5 On the straightaway, Max pulls right beside the race's leader, Simon.

➡ _____

6 Last year, Simon won many races, but Max's best result in a race was coming in fifth place.

➡ _____

7 This time, he has a chance to finish second.

➡ _____

8 But he isn't going to be satisfied with second place today.

➡ _____

9 The winner gets to meet the world famous racer L. J. Richards!

➡ _____

10 He doesn't want to miss the chance to meet his role model.

➡ _____

11 Max completes the tenth lap and now has five more laps to go.

➡ _____

12 Max sees Simon's kart ahead, just out of Max's reach.

➡ _____

13 Max's kart gets closer and closer to Simon's.

➡ _____

14 It almost hits the back end of Simon's kart.

➡ _____

15 They drive into the straightaway and Max presses harder on the gas pedal.

➡ _____

16 "I can catch up," says Max.

➡ _____

17 Max sees the official waving a white flag which means the last lap.

➡ _____

18 Max is right behind Simon.

➡ _____

19 The finish line is getting closer, and the cheering from the crowd is getting louder.

➡ _____

20 "I can do it!" Max says loudly.

➡ _____

21 He can feel his heart beating hard.

➡ _____

22 The karts rush across the finish line.

➡ _____

23 Who is the winner?

➡ _____

24 Max's eyes are filled with tears as he finds out that he came in second.

➡ _____

25 "No need for tears, kid," says a man's voice.

➡ _____

26 Max can't believe his eyes.

➡ _____

27 The man who is standing in front of him is L. J. Richards!

➡ _____

28 "Thank you, but I'm not the winner," says Max.

➡ _____

29 "It was a real close race.

➡ _____

30 Even though you didn't win the race, you did your best.

➡ _____

31 That's the thing that counts!" says L. J. Richards.

➡ _____

32 'Did I do my best?' thinks Max.

➡ _____

33 After a moment, he smiles.

➡ _____

34 "Yeah, I guess I did."

➡ _____

※ 다음 괄호 안의 단어들을 우리말에 맞도록 바르게 배열하시오.

1 (the / at / race / go-kart / track, / are / there / people / many / are / who / excitedly. / cheering)
➡ _____

2 (karts / the / that / making / are / engine / loud / waiting. / are / noises)
➡ _____

3 (official / an / waves / green / a / flag / the / and / starts! / race)
➡ _____

4 (pushes / Max / foot / his / hard / down / the / on / pedal / gas / as / he / his / completes / sixth / on / track. / the / lap)
➡ _____

5 (the / on / straightaway, / pulls / Max / beside / right / race's / the / Simon. / leader,)
➡ _____

6 (year, / last / won / Simon / races, / many / but / best / Max's / result / a / in / race / coming / was / place. / fifth / in)
➡ _____

7 (time, / this / has / he / chance / a / second. / finish / to)
➡ _____

8 (he / but / going / isn't / be / to / satisfied / second / with / today. / place)
➡ _____

9 (winner / the / gets / meet / to / world / the / racer / Richards! / L. / famous / J.)
➡ _____

10 (doesn't / he / to / want / miss / chance / the / meet / to / model. / role / his)
➡ _____

11 (Max / the / completes / tenth / and / lap / now / five / has / laps / go. / more / to)
➡ _____

12 (sees / Max / kart / Simon's / ahead, / out / just / reach. / of / Max's)
➡ _____

13 (kart / Max's / closer / gets / and / Simon's. / to / closer)
➡ _____

14 (almost / it / hits / back / the / of / end / kart. / Simon's)
➡ _____

15 (drive / they / into / straightaway / the / and / presses / Max / on / harder / pedal. / gas / the)
➡ _____

16 (can / "I / up," / catch / Max. / says)
➡ _____

17 (sees / Max / official / the / waving / white / a / flag / means / which / lap. / last / the)
➡ _____

1 고카트 경기 트랙에 신이 나서 응원하고 있는 많은 사람들이 있다.

2 시끄러운 엔진 소음을 내고 있는 카트들이 기다리고 있다.

3 심판이 초록 깃발을 흔들고, 경기가 시작된다!

4 Max는 트랙을 여섯 바퀴 돌았을 때, 발로 가속 페달을 힘껏 누른다.

5 직선 구간에서 Max는 경기에서 선두를 달리고 있는 Simon의 바로 옆까지 다가간다.

6 작년에 Simon은 경기에서 여러 번 이겼지만 Max의 최고 경기 성적은 5등으로 들어온 것이었다.

7 이번에 그는 2등으로 끝낼 수 있는 기회를 잡았다.

8 그러나 그는 오늘 2등으로 만족하지 않을 것이다.

9 우승자는 세계적으로 유명한 경주 선수인 L.J. Richards를 만나게 된다!

10 그는 그의 역할 모델을 만날 수 있는 기회를 놓치길 원하지 않는다.

11 Max는 10바퀴를 다 돌고 이제 5바퀴를 더 돌아야 한다.

12 Max는 앞에 바로 닿을 듯한 거리에 있는 Simon의 카트를 본다.

13 Max의 카트는 Simon의 카트에 점점 더 가까워진다.

14 Max의 카트는 Simon의 카트의 뒷부분에 거의 닿을 것 같다.

15 그들은 직선 구간을 운전해가고, Max는 가속 페달을 더 세게 밟는다.

16 "나는 따라잡을 수 있어." Max가 말한다.

17 Max는 심판이 마지막 바퀴라는 것을 알려주는 흰색 깃발을 흔드는 것을 본다.

18 (is / Max / behind / right / Simon.)

➡ _____

19 (finish / the / line / getting / is / closer, / and / cheering / the / from / crowd / louder. / getting / is)

➡ _____

➡ _____

20 (can / "I / do / it!" / loudly. / says / Max)

➡ _____

21 (can / he / feel / heart / his / hard. / beating)

➡ _____

22 (karts / the / rush / across / line. / finish / the)

➡ _____

23 (is / who / winner? / the)

➡ _____

24 (eyes / Max's / filled / are / tears / with / as / finds / he / that / out / came / he / second. / in)

➡ _____

25 (need / "no / tears, / for / kid," / a / voice. / man's / says)

➡ _____

26 (can't / Max / eyes. / his / believe)

➡ _____

27 (man / the / is / who / standing / front / in / of / Richards! / him / L. / J. / is)

➡ _____

28 (you, / "thank / I'm / but / not / winner," / Max. / says)

➡ _____

29 ("it / a / was / real / race. / close)

➡ _____

30 (though / even / didn't / you / the / win / race, / did / you / best. / your)

➡ _____

31 (the / that's / thing / counts!" / that / Richards. / L. / J. / says)

➡ _____

32 (I / 'did / my / do / best?' / Max. / thinks)

➡ _____

33 (a / after / moment, / smiles. / he)

➡ _____

34 ("yeah, / guess / I / did." / I)

➡ _____

18 Max는 Simon 바로 뒤에 있다.

19 결승점이 점점 가까워지고, 관중으로부터 들리는 환호성이 점점 커진다.

20 "나는 할 수 있어!" Max는 큰 소리로 말한다.

21 그는 그의 심장이 세게 뛰는 것을 느낄 수 있다.

22 카트들이 돌진해 결승점을 지난다.

23 누가 승자인가?

24 Max는 자신이 2등으로 들어왔다는 것을 알았을 때, 눈에 눈물이 가득 찬다.

25 "울 필요 없단다, 얘야." 어떤 남자의 목소리가 말한다.

26 Max는 그의 눈을 믿을 수 없다.

27 그 앞에 서 있는 남자는 L.J. Richards이다!

28 "고마워요, 하지만 저는 일등이 아니에요." Max가 말한다.

29 "정말 아슬아슬한 경기였어.

30 네가 비록 경기를 이기지 못했지만, 너는 최선을 다했어.

31 중요한 것은 바로 그거란다!" L.J. Richards가 말한다.

32 '나는 최선을 다했을까?' Max는 생각한다.

33 잠시 후에, 그는 미소를 짓는다.

34 "네, 저는 최선을 다한 것 같아요."

※ 다음 우리말을 영어로 쓰시오.

1 고카트 경기 트랙에 신이 나서 응원하고 있는 많은 사람들이 있다.

➡ _____

2 시끄러운 엔진 소음을 내고 있는 카트들이 기다리고 있다.

➡ _____

3 심판이 초록 깃발을 흔들고, 경기가 시작된다!

➡ _____

4 Max는 트랙을 여섯 바퀴 돌았을 때, 발로 가속 페달을 힘껏 누른다.

➡ _____

5 직선 구간에서 Max는 경기에서 선두를 달리고 있는 Simon의 바로 옆까지 다가간다.

➡ _____

6 작년에 Simon은 경기에서 여러 번 이겼지만 Max의 최고 경기 성적은 5등으로 들어온 것이었다.

➡ _____

7 이번에 그는 2등으로 끝낼 수 있는 기회를 잡았다.

➡ _____

8 그러나 그는 오늘 2등으로 만족하지 않을 것이다.

➡ _____

9 우승자는 세계적으로 유명한 경주 선수인 L. J. Richards를 만나게 된다!

➡ _____

10 그는 그의 역할 모델을 만날 수 있는 기회를 놓치길 원하지 않는다.

➡ _____

11 Max는 10바퀴를 다 돌고 이제 5바퀴를 더 돌아야 한다.

➡ _____

12 Max는 앞에 바로 닿을 듯한 거리에 있는 Simon의 카트를 본다.

➡ _____

13 Max의 카트는 Simon의 카트에 점점 더 가까워진다.

➡ _____

14 Max의 카트는 Simon의 카트의 뒷부분에 거의 닿을 것 같다.

➡ _____

15 그들은 직선 구간을 운전해가고, Max는 가속 페달을 더 세게 밟는다.

➡ _____

16 "나는 따라잡을 수 있어." Max가 말한다.

➡ _____

17 Max는 심판이 마지막 바퀴라는 것을 알려주는 흰색 깃발을 흔드는 것을 본다.

➡ _____

18 Max는 Simon 바로 뒤에 있다.

➡ _____

19 결승점이 점점 가까워지고, 관중으로부터 들리는 환호성이 점점 커진다.

➡ _____

20 "나는 할 수 있어!" Max는 큰 소리로 말한다.

➡ _____

21 그는 그의 심장이 세게 뛰는 것을 느낄 수 있다.

➡ _____

22 카트들이 돌진해 결승점을 지난다.

➡ _____

23 누가 승자인가?

➡ _____

24 Max는 자신이 2등으로 들어왔다는 것을 알았을 때, 눈에 눈물이 가득 찬다.

➡ _____

25 "울 필요 없단다, 얘야." 어떤 남자의 목소리가 말한다.

➡ _____

26 Max는 그의 눈을 믿을 수 없다.

➡ _____

27 그 앞에 서 있는 남자는 L. J. Richards이다!

➡ _____

28 "고마워요, 하지만 저는 일등이 아니에요." Max가 말한다.

➡ _____

29 "정말 아슬아슬한 경기였어.

➡ _____

30 네가 비록 경기를 이기지 못했지만, 너는 최선을 다했어.

➡ _____

31 중요한 것은 바로 그거란다!" L. J. Richards가 말한다.

➡ _____

32 '나는 최선을 다했을까?'' Max는 생각한다.

➡ _____

33 잠시 후에, 그는 미소를 짓는다.

➡ _____

34 "네, 저는 최선을 다한 것 같아요."

➡ _____

※ 다음 우리말과 일치하도록 빈칸에 알맞은 말을 쓰시오.

Listen & Talk C

1. Amy: Michael, _____ _____ _____ _____?

2. Michael: I _____ _____ the _____ _____.

3. Amy: _____ _____, Michael. You'll _____ _____ next time.

1. Amy: Michael, 왜 시무룩한 얼굴이니?
2. Michael: 나는 다른 선수를 막지 못했어.
3. Amy: 걱정 마. Michael. 다음번에는 더 잘할 거야.

Grammar in Real Life

1. Ms. Green is a good _____ _____ _____ _____ Italian food.

2. She _____ _____ to the local store _____ has many _____ vegetables.

3. Her restaurant _____ _____ _____ _____ people _____ like to eat her food.

4. I _____ _____ _____ _____ her seafood pizza which is the _____ _____.

1. Green씨는 맛있는 이탈리아 음식을 만드는 훌륭한 요리사이다.
2. 그녀는 항상 신선한 채소가 많이 있는 지역 상점에 간다.
3. 그녀의 레스토랑은 그녀의 음식을 좋아하는 많은 사람들로 항상 붐빈다.
4. 나는 네가 가장 인기 있는 그녀의 해산물 피자를 먹어 보기를 원한다.

Think & Write

1. A basketball match _____ Class 1 _____ Class 2 _____ at school _____ Friday.

2. Class 1 _____ the game _____ _____ _____.

3. There are some _____ _____.

4. _____ _____ them _____ Sarah.

5. She was the player who _____ _____ _____ one second before _____ _____ _____ the game.

6. It was a _____ _____.

7. We _____ _____ _____ to the next match.

1. 금요일에 학교에서 1반과 2반 사이의 농구 경기가 열렸습니다.
2. 1반은 1점 차이로 그 경기에서 이겼습니다.
3. 기억에 남는 몇 명의 선수가 있습니다.
4. 그 중 한 명은 Sarah입니다.
5. 그녀는 경기가 끝나기 1초 전에 득점을 올린 선수였습니다.
6. 그것은 훌륭한 경기였습니다.
7. 우리는 다음 경기를 기대하고 있습니다.

※ 다음 우리말을 영어로 쓰시오.

Listen & Talk C

1. Amy: Michael, 왜 시무룩한 얼굴이니?

➡ _____

2. Michael: 나는 다른 선수를 막지 못했어.

➡ _____

3. Amy: 걱정 마. Michael. 다음번에는 더 잘할 거야.

➡ _____

Grammar in Real Life

1. Green씨는 맛있는 이탈리아 음식을 만드는 훌륭한 요리사이다.

➡ _____

2. 그녀는 항상 신선한 채소가 많이 있는 지역 상점에 간다.

➡ _____

3. 그녀의 레스토랑은 그녀의 음식을 좋아하는 많은 사람들로 항상 붐빈다.

➡ _____

4. 나는 네가 가장 인기 있는 그녀의 해산물 피자를 먹어 보기를 원한다.

➡ _____

Think & Write

1. 금요일에 학교에서 1반과 2반 사이의 농구 경기가 열렸습니다.

➡ _____

2. 1반은 1점 차이로 그 경기에서 이겼습니다.

➡ _____

3. 기억에 남는 몇 명의 선수가 있습니다.

➡ _____

4. 그 중 한 명은 Sarah입니다.

➡ _____

5. 그녀는 경기가 끝나기 1초 전에 득점을 올린 선수였습니다.

➡ _____

6. 그것은 훌륭한 경기였습니다.

➡ _____

7. 우리는 다음 경기를 기대하고 있습니다.

➡ _____

MEMO

MEMO

적중100^{plus}
1학기 전과정
영어 기출 문제집

영어 기출 문제집

1학기

정답 및 해설

비상 | 김진완

중 2

영어 기출 문제집

적중100

1학기

정답 및 해설

비상 | 김진완

중 2

적중100

Suit Your Taste!

시험대비 실력평가
p.08

01 romantic 02 hedgehog 03 talent 04 ②
05 (1) write down (2) get used to (3) in person
06 ④ 07 ①

01 명사와 형용사와의 관계를 나타내므로 romance의 형용사 형태인 romantic이 알맞다.

02 등을 덮고 있는 바늘과 같은 뻣뻣한 부분을 가진 작은 갈색의 동물을 가리키는 말은 hedgehog(고슴도치)이다.

03 무언가를 잘하는 천부적 능력을 가리키는 말은 talent(재능)이다.

04 ② attractive는 매력적인을 뜻한다.

05 in person: 직접 get used to: ~에 익숙해지다 write down: ~을 적다

06 주어진 rule은 규칙을 나타내지만 ④번은 동사로 '지배하다, 통치하다'를 뜻한다

07 view: 시야, 보는 것; 전망; 관점

서술형 시험대비
p.09

01 photographer
02 rap
03 cage
04 (1) shower (2) Point (3) repeat (4) normally
05 (1) clean up (2) come out
　　(3) look around (4) go get
06 (1) Everything can be a story for a rap.
　　(2) My sister is scared of going out alone.
　　(3) This information is very helpful when you choose a seat
　　(4) I usually take a shower before going to bed.

01 law: 법, lawyer: 변호사, photograph: 사진, photographer: 사진사

02 빠르고 강한 리듬과 노래하지 않고 빠르게 이야기하는 가사를 가진 인기 있는 음악의 한 종류를 가리키는 말은 rap(랩)이다.

03 동물이나 새를 가두기 위해 금속 막대기나 철사로 이루어진 구조를 가리키는 말은 cage(우리)이다.

04 normally: 보통, repeat: 반복하다, point: 가리키다, take a

shower: 샤워를 하다

05 come out: 나오다, clean up: 치우다, 청소하다, go get: ~을 가져오다, look around: 둘러보다

교과서 Conversation

핵심 Check
p.10~11

1 (1) What, interested / interested
　(2) Are you interested in / into
2 (1) take / I know how to
　(2) problems / Don't worry, How about
　(3) don't know how to / how to

교과서 대화문 익히기

Check(√) True or False
p.12

1 T 2 F 3 T 4 F

교과서 확인학습
p.14~15

Listen & Talk 1 A
1 looking at / comments / I'm intereste in reading
2 I'm really interested in / in person

Listen & Talk 1 B
Which after-school class / take / photography, I'm interested in taking pictures / photographer

Listen & Talk 2 A-1
dry / know how to bake bread / tip / a cooking show

Listen & Talk 2 A-2
I know how to do it quickly / group

Listen & Talk 2 B
know how to clean up / How / wipe / picks up / go get

Communication
I'm interested in music / going to show us / how to sing high notes

Wrap Up 1
what club / join / into / interested in plants and flowers / interesting club

시험대비 기본평가   p.16

01 What are you interested in?

02 ④   03 ①   04 ②

01 be interested in: ~에 관심이 있다

02 ④번을 제외한 나머지는 모두 문제 해결 방법을 알려 주려는 의도를 갖고 있다.

03 Mike는 John Luke를 만난 날을 인생 최고의 날이라고 표현한 것으로 보아 매우 신이 났음을 알 수 있다. excited: 신이 난, depressed: 우울한, upset: 화난, disappointed: 실망한, nervous: 긴장한

04 Mike는 야구에 관심을 갖고 있지만 Jenny가 야구에 관심이 있는지는 알 수 없다.

시험대비 실력평가   p.17~18

01 ①   02 bread   03 ⑤   04 ③

05 ④   06 (C) – (B) – (A) – (D)   07 ⑤

08 빵을 구울 때 오븐에 물 한 컵을 넣기   09 Which
after-school class are you going to take?   10 ②

11 (B) – (C) – (D) – (A)

01 나머지는 모두 관심 있는 것에 대한 질문이지만 ①번은 '어떻게 이자를 받을 수 있나요?'라는 뜻을 나타낸다.

03 민수가 어떻게 그 부분을 닦기 위해 깨진 그릇을 사용할 수 있는지는 알 수 없다.

04 주어진 문장은 방과 후 수업으로 사진 수업을 듣는 것을 생각 중인 이유로 적절하기 때문에 (C)에 들어가야 한다.

05 Jake가 사진 수업의 교사가 누구인지 이미 알고 있다는 설명은 대화의 내용과 일치하지 않는다.

06 (C) 무엇을 보고 있는지 질문 → (B) 하고 있는 일 설명 → (A) 무엇을 쓰는지에 대한 구체적 질문 → (D) 구체적 대답 및 흥미 설명

07 (A) 어떻게 빵을 굽는지 알고 있다고 말하고 있으므로 '의문사+to부정사'의 형태가 적절하다. (B) 명령문을 나타내고 있으므로 동사 Put이 알맞다. (C) cooking show: 요리 프로, cook: 요리사

10 대화의 흐름상 '너는 언제?'라는 의미의 ②번이 적합하다.

11 (B) 사실 확인 질문 → (C) 대답 및 어려움 설명 → (D) 조언 및 방법 알려주기 → (A) 반응 및 감사 표현

서술형 시험대비   p.19

01 I'm interested in Spanish.

02 I know how to bake bread without making it dry.

03 I'm really interested in baseball.

04 in person

05 모서리들부터 맞추기 시작하고, 같은 색깔별로 조각들을 모은다.

06 What are you going to show us today?

07 She knows how to sing high notes easily.

07 Doremi의 특별한 재능은 높은 음을 쉽게 부르는 법을 알고 있다는 것이다.

교과서
Grammar

핵심 Check   p.20~21

1 (1) Leave, open   (2) me lucky   (3) call him Mike

2 (1) Laughing   (2) studying hard   (3) writing

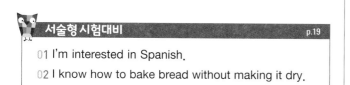

시험대비 기본평가   p.22

01 (1) sadly → sad   (2) to climb → climbing
   (3) see → seeing   (4) to go → going

02 (1) upset   (2) Playing[To play]   (3) smiling
   (4) taking   (5) smart

03 (1) Riding[To ride] a bike is exciting.
   (2) Kelly was surprised at seeing him.
   (3) What makes you so happy?
   (4) You thought this book easy.
   (5) We named our puppy Tommy.

01 (1) 부사는 보어 역할을 할 수 없다. (2) give up은 동명사를 목적어로 취하는 동사이다. (3), (4) 전치사의 목적어 자리이므로 동명사 형태를 써야 한다.

02 (1) 5형식 동사의 목적보어이므로 형용사를 쓴다. (2) 주어 자리이므로 동명사나 to부정사 형태가 옳다. (3) cannot help는 동명사를 목적어로 취하는 동사로 '~하지 않을 수 없다'는 의미로 쓰인다. (4) 전치사의 목적어이므로 동명사를 쓰는 것이 옳다. (5) 5형식 동사의 목적보어 자리이므로 형용사를 쓰는 것이 옳다.

03 (1) '자전거를 타는 것'이 주어이므로 ride를 동명사나 to부정사로 만든다. (2) 전치사 at의 목적어로 동명사를 쓰는 것에 유의한다. (3) 5형식 동사로 쓰인 make이다. 따라서 목적보어로 형용사를 쓰는 것이 옳다. (4) '책이 쉬운' 것이므로 5형식으로 문장을 만든다. (5) name은 목적어와 목적 보어를 취하는 5형식 동사이다.

01 ⑤　02 ⑤　03 ③　04 ③

05 speaking　06 ①, ④　07 ②　08 Walking with you makes me happy. 09 ①　10 ②

11 ④　12 being late 13 ③　14 ⑤

15 ④　16 ③　17 warmly → warm

18 ②　19 ②　20 I enjoy going to museums. 21 ④　22 Larry isn't used to wearing a suit every day. 23 ④　24 ③

01 know는 형용사를 목적보어로 취할 수 없다.

02 <보기>의 밑줄은 동명사이다. ⑤번은 '~하는 중'이라고 해석되는 현재분사이다.

03 4형식과 5형식으로 모두 쓰일 수 있는 동사는 make이다.

04 appoint: 임명하다

05 전치사 of의 목적어 자리이므로 동명사를 써야 한다.

06 동명사를 목적어로 취하는 동사가 들어가야 한다.

07 ② 방을 깨끗하게 유지했다는 의미이므로 clean을 형용사로 쓰는 것이 옳다.

08 동명사 주어는 단수 취급하는 것에 유의한다.

09 ⓒ suggest는 동명사를 목적어로 취한다. ⓓ keep은 5형식 동사로 쓰였으므로 목적보어로 형용사를 취해야 한다. lovely: 사랑스러운

10 stop은 동명사를 목적어로 취하며, stop 뒤에 to부정사가 오는 경우 '~을 하기 위하여 멈추다'라는 의미로 쓰인다.

11 want는 to부정사를 목적어를 취하는 동사이다. 나머지는 동명사를 목적어로 취하는 동사이다.

12 전치사의 목적어 역할을 하므로 be동사를 동명사로 만든다.

13 mind는 동명사를 목적어로 취하며, 전치사 about의 목적어로 동명사를 쓰는 것이 옳다.

14 ① imagine은 동명사를 목적어로 취한다. ② 전치사 about의 목적어로 skipping을 쓰는 것이 옳다. ③ postpone은 목적어로 동명사를 취한다. run an errand: 심부름을 하다 ④ 경치를 깨끗하게 볼 수 있게 해주므로 make를 5형식으로 썼다. 따라서 clear가 옳다.

15 ④번은 '~하는 중'이라고 해석되는 현재분사이지만 나머지는 모두 동명사이다.

16 ③번은 4형식 문장이고, 나머지 문장은 5형식 문장이다.

17 keep이 5형식 동사로 쓰였으므로 목적보어로 형용사를 쓰는 것이 옳다.

18 첫 번째 문장은 5형식으로 쓰였으며 두 번째 문장은 4형식으로 쓰였다. 어법과 내용상 left가 들어가는 것이 옳다.

19 라디오 소리를 줄여달라는 요청의 문장이다. mind의 목적어로 동명사를 이용하여 요청의 문장을 만든 ②번이 옳다.

20 enjoy는 동명사를 목적어로 취하는 동사이다.

21 unless는 부정어를 이끌 수 없다. unless: ~하지 않으면, stop+Ving: V하는 것을 멈추다

22 be used to Ving: V하는 것에 익숙하다

23 '명사+ly'는 형용사이지만 '형용사+ly'는 부사이다. 부사는 보어로 쓰일 수 없다.

24 cannot help Ving: V하지 않을 수 없다. It is no use Ving: V하는 것은 소용없다. have difficulty Ving: V하는 데에 어려움이 있다

01 speaking

02 You can consider it just a part of American culture.

03 I keep losing something.

04 (1) spending (2) writing (3) standing

05 my skin healthy

06 going to the zoo

07 living

08 driving during the rush hour

09 Walking[To walk] a long distance makes us hungry.

10 doesn't mind waiting

11 painting the house, next weekend

12 breaking Kevin's smart phone

13 (1) His father made him a famous soccer player.
   (2) You will find the experience important and valuable.
   (3) The shoes will keep you warm.

14 Kathy made her friend upset by using bad words.

15 Anxiety made her awake all night long.

16 Meeting you makes me happy.

01 be good at: ~에 능숙하다

02 consider A B: A를 B라고 여기다

03 keep Ving: 계속해서 V하다

04 (1) from의 목적어로 동명사가 적절하다. prevent A from B: A가 B를 못하게 하다 (2), (3) put off, mind는 동명사를 목적어로 취하는 동사이다.

05 keep은 5형식 동사이다.

06 suggest는 동명사를 목적어로 취한다.

07 Sam은 자신의 일상을 바꿀 필요가 있다고 생각하며 계속해서 이렇게 살 수 없다고 말한다. go on은 동명사를 목적어로 취한다.

08 avoid는 동명사를 목적어로 취한다.

09 주어진 어구를 동명사나 to부정사로 주어를 만들어 주고, 동명사나 to부정사 주어를 단수 취급하는 것에 유의한다.

10 Jackson은 Adrian을 기다리는 것을 꺼려하지 않는다.

11 postpone은 동명사를 목적어로 취하는 동사이다.

12 Emma는 Kevin의 스마트폰을 망가트린 것을 부인했다. deny는 동명사를 목적어로 취하는 동사이다.

13 make, find, keep은 모두 5형식 동사이다.

14 나쁜 말을 함으로써 친구를 화나게 했다는 의미이다. by+Ving: V함으로써

15 anxiety: 불안

16 '너를 만나는 것'이 주어이므로 동사 meet을 이용하여 동명사 주어를 만든다.

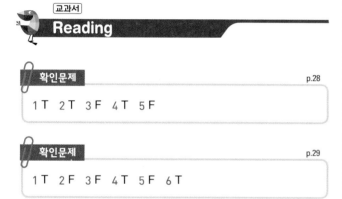

Reading

확인문제 p.28

1 T 2 T 3 F 4 T 5 F

확인문제 p.29

1 T 2 F 3 F 4 T 5 F 6 T

교과서 확인학습 A p.30~31

01 Out　　02 Open, Open　03 around, out

04 want to write　05 about anything, can be

06 when, on, in, in

07 write down, use them

08 are no rules, writing　　09 Fantastic

10 Fantastic, Having　　11 introduce, pet

12 When, got, scared

13 hold, because, raised

14 placed, in her case, got used to

15 was able to hold

16 makes me happy　　17 Handy

18 Welcome back

19 Where, normally sit in

20 Here is　　21 find it easy and helpful

22 Point, at, far from　　23 Close, open it

24 it, the other　25 does, move

26 when, close　27 mainly use　28 means, sit on

29 That way, enjoy, full view

30 This information, helpful, choose a seat, too

교과서 확인학습 B p.32~33

1 Rap It Out

2 Open your mind, Open your heart

3 Look around and let's rap it out

4 Hey, I'm MC Joy. Do you want to write your own rap?

5 You can rap about anything because everything can be a story for a rap.

6 I get ideas when I'm on the bus, in the shower, or in my bed.

7 I write down my ideas and use them when I write my rap.

8 There are no rules for writing raps. You can start today!

9 Fantastic Pets

10 Welcome to *Fantastic Pets*! Having a pet is great.

11 Today I'm going to introduce my pet hedgehog, Polly

12 When I first got Polly, she was very scared.

13 I couldn't hold her because she raised her spikes.

14 So, I placed my T-shirt in her case and she got used to my smell.

15 Finally, I was able to hold her in my hands.

16 Now, Polly is my best friend and always makes me happy.

17 Handy Tips

18 Welcome back to *Handy Tips* .

19 Where do you normally sit in a movie theater?

20 Here is a tip.

21 You will find it easy and helpful.

22 Step 1 Point your finger at something far from you.

23 Step 2 Close one eye and open it.

24 Step 3 Repeat it with the other eye.

25 When does your finger move?

26 Is it when you close your right eye?

27 Then you mainly use your right eye.

28 This means you should sit on the left side in the theater.

29 That way, you can enjoy a full view of the screen better.

30 This information is also helpful when you choose a seat in a classroom, too.

시험대비 실력평가 p.34~37

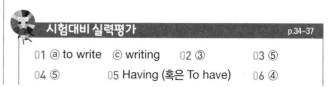

01 ⓐ to write　ⓒ writing　　02 ③　　03 ⑤

04 ⑤　　　05 Having (혹은 To have)　　06 ④

07 ③　　　08 ②　　　09 she raised her spikes

10 ②　　　11 ①　　　12 ④　　　13 a tip

14 helpful, in a movie theater, in a classroom, a seat

15 easy and helpful　　　16 ④　　　17 ①

18 ③　　　19 She gets ideas for her rap.　20 my

ideas　　　21 ③　　　22 ①, ④　　　23 ③

24 ①, ④　　　25 are spikes　26 introducing 27 ②

28 ③　　　29 repeating it with the other eye

01 want는 to부정사를 목적어로 취하는 동사이며, ⓒ에는 전치사 for의 목적어 역할을 하는 동명사가 들어가야 한다.

02 MC Joy는 자신의 아이디어를 버스에서, 샤워할 때, 그리고 잠자리에서 얻는다고 하였다.

03 '버스를 타고 있을 때'이므로 on the bus라고 하는 것이 옳다.

04 (A) '무엇이든'이라는 의미이므로 anything, (B) 복수명사 my ideas를 지칭하므로 them, (C) no rules가 주어이므로 are가 옳다.

05 주어 자리이므로 주어진 동사를 to부정사 혹은 동명사로 만드는 것이 옳다.

06 Polly가 나의 냄새에 익숙해진 후에 마침내 그녀를 잡을 수 있었다고 보는 것이 옳다.

07 Polly가 글쓴이의 최초 애완동물인지는 나와 있지 않다.

08 ⓐ Polly의 우리 안에 옷을 넣어 두는 것이므로 전치사 in, ⓑ get used to: ~에 익숙해지다

09 글쓴이가 처음에 Polly를 잡을 수 없었던 이유는 Polly가 가시를 곤두세웠기 때문이다.

10 (A) sit은 자동사로 '앉다'는 의미이고, seat은 타동사로 '~를 앉히다'는 의미이다. (B) one eye를 지칭하므로 단수를 지칭하는 대명사 it을 써야 한다. (C) 둘 중 다른 하나는 the other이다.

11 평소에 어떤 눈을 사용하는지 알아내기 위한 세 가지 단계가 있다는 것을 제외하고는 모두 글의 내용과 일치하지 않는다.

12 handy는 유용하다는 의미이다. 따라서 useful이 옳다.

13 it은 앞 문장의 a tip을 가리키는 인칭대명사이다.

14 당신이 좌석을 선택할 때, 이 정보는 극장에서 뿐만 아니라 교실에서도 유용하다.

15 내용과 어법상 쉽고 유용하다는 말이 들어가는 것이 옳다.

16 오늘 랩을 시작할 수 있다고 하였으므로 ④번은 일치하지 않는다.

17 since는 '~이기 때문에'라는 의미로 쓰일 수 있다.

18 '가능'을 의미하는 조동사가 들어가는 것이 가장 적절하다.

19 Joy는 버스에 있을 때 랩을 위한 아이디어를 얻는다고 하였다.

20 Joy는 아이디어를 적어두었다가 랩을 쓸 때 그것을 이용한다고 하였다.

21 밑줄 친 ⓐ는 동명사로 '~하는 것'이라고 해석된다. ③번은 '~하는 중'이라고 해석되는 현재분사이다.

22 get[become] used to: ~에 익숙해지다

23 (A) Polly가 두려움을 느낀 것이므로 scared (B) raise: ~을

올리다, rise: 오르다 (C) make가 5형식 동사로 쓰였으므로 목적격보어로 형용사

24 ⓒ는 '마침내, 드디어'라는 의미이다. 따라서 ①, ④가 옳다.

25 Polly는 등에 가시가 있다.

26 이 글은 글쓴이의 애완동물 Polly를 소개하는 것에 집중되어 있다.

27 오른쪽 눈을 감았을 때 손가락이 움직인다면 오른쪽 눈을 주로 사용한다는 의미이므로 극장 왼쪽 편에 앉아야 한다는 문장 앞에 오는 것이 옳다.

28 far from: ~에서 먼 ① depend on: ~에 의존하다 ② turn down: (소리를) 낮추다 ③ be made from: ~으로 만들어지다 ④ look after: ~를 돌보다 ⑤ put off: 미루다, 연기하다

29 동명사를 이용하여 빈칸을 채운다. 세 번째 단계는 두 번째 단계에서 했던 것을 다른 쪽 눈으로 반복하는 것이다.

서술형 시험대비

p.38~39

01 everything can be a story for a rap　02 Do you want to write your own rap?　03 When do you usually get your ideas?　04 There are no rules for writing raps.　05 to write raps　06 Having a pet is great　07 ⓐ to introduce ⓑ to hold　08 Raising her spikes　09 She looked scared.　10 Placing your T-shirt in her case　11 always makes me happy　12 Here is a tip to choose a better seat.　13 한 쪽 눈을 감았다가 뜨는 것　14 I have to sit on the right side in the theater.　15 sitting on the left side in the theater　16 I mostly use my left eye.　17 Choosing a seat in a classroom is easy.

01 주위를 둘러보라고 한 이유는 모든 것이 랩을 위한 이야기가 될 수 있기 때문이다.

02 want는 to부정사를 목적어로 취하는 동사이다.

03 자신이 아이디어를 얻을 때에 관하여 이야기하고 있으므로 주로 언제 아이디어를 얻는지를 묻는 것이 옳다.

04 랩 쓰는 것에 규칙은 없다고 하였다.

05 오늘부터 랩을 쓰기 시작할 수 있다는 의미이다.

06 동명사를 주어로 한 문장을 쓰면 된다.

07 ⓐ be going to V: V할 예정이다, V하려고 하다 ⓑ be able to V: V할 수 있다

08 가시를 세우는 것은 글쓴이가 그녀를 잡기 힘들게 만들었다.

09 글쓴이가 처음에 Polly를 데리고 왔을 때, 그녀는 두려워하였다.

10 Jane은 자신의 애완동물 고슴도치와 친해지고 싶다고 하였다. 냄

새에 익숙해지면 친해지므로 티셔츠를 두도록 조언할 수 있다.

11 make는 목적어와 목적격보어를 취하는 5형식 동사이다.

12 더 나은 좌석을 선택하기 위한 팁이 있다.

13 'Close one eye and open it.'을 가리키는 것이다.

14 질문: 왼쪽 눈을 감았을 때 손가락이 움직인다면, 너는 극장에서 어디에 앉아야 할까?

15 당신이 오른쪽 눈을 주로 사용한다면, 극장에서 왼쪽 편에 앉는 것이 당신으로 하여금 스크린 전체를 즐길 수 있도록 한다. enable+목적어+to V: 목적어가 V하는 것을 가능하게 하다

16 극장 오른편에 앉아서 스크린을 더 잘 볼 수 있었다면 주로 사용하는 눈이 왼쪽 눈이다.

17 '교실에서 자리를 선택하는 것'을 동명사로 하여 문장을 만든다.

영역별 핵심문제
p.41~45

01 photographer 02 normally 03 (1) getting used to (2) go get (3) sign up 04 ①
05 ① 06 ④ 07 She is really into them. 08 ② 09 talent 10 ②
11 I know how to clean up the glass pieces with bread. 12 ③ 13 ③ 14 I'm interested in taking pictures. 15 ②
16 She knows that the teacher is a famous photographer.
17 ⑤ 18 ④ 19 ① 20 ⑤
21 Using(또는 To use) a smart watch will make your life convenient. 22 ②, ④ 23 ④
24 ④ 25 Jimmy denied playing computer games too much. 26 ③ 27 the work easier 28 ④ 29 ② 30 ③
31 my ideas 32 ④ 33 ② 34 He placed his T-shirt in her case.

---

01 특히 직업으로 사진을 찍는 사람을 가리키는 말은 photographer(사진사)이다.

02 짝지어진 단어는 반의어 관계를 나타내므로 abnormally(비정상적으로)의 반의어 normally(보통, 정상적으로)가 알맞다.

04 place는 동사로 쓰여 '~에 두다'를 의미한다.

05 close: (눈을) 감다, (문을) 닫다; 가까운

06 상대방을 안도시키기 위해 쓰이는 말이므로 상대방이 가진 문제를 설명한 다음에 이어지는 (D)가 적절하다.

07 be into: ~을 좋아하다

08 (A)는 음표를 나타내며 이와 같은 의미로 쓰인 것은 ②번이다. ① 노트 ③ 필기, 기록 ④ 노트 ⑤ 편지, 쪽지

09 무언가를 잘하는 천부적 능력을 나타내는 말은 talent(재능)이다.

10 위 대화는 쇼 진행자(host)와 출연자(guest)와의 관계를 나타낸다.

12 Minsu는 그릇을 깨서 걱정하였지만 Tina의 조언을 통해 안심했음을 알 수 있다.

13 빵이 작은 유리 조각을 집어내므로 손으로 집어야 한다는 것을 잘못된 설명이다.

16 Elsa가 사진 수업에 대해 알고 있는 것은 선생님이 유명한 사진사라는 것이다.

17 ⑤번을 제외한 나머지는 모두 뻑뻑하게 만들지 않고 빵을 굽는 방법을 알고 있음을 나타내는 표현이다.

18 idea: 생각, advice: 조언, information: 정보, rap: 랩, guidance: 지침

19 전치사의 목적어는 동명사이며, keep은 목적보어로 현재분사를 쓴다. 따라서 waiting이 옳다.

20 be busy Ving: V하느라 바쁘다, 동사 quit의 목적어는 동명사이다.

21 '스마트 시계를 사용하는 것'이 주어이므로 use를 동명사나 to 부정사로 쓰는 것이 옳다.

22 냉장고는 음식을 시원하게 유지해 주거나, 음식을 시원하게 만든다.

23 ④번의 위 문장은 'Kelly는 그를 보고 웃지 않을 수 없었다.'는 의미이지만 아래 문장은 'Kelly는 그가 웃도록 도울 수 없었다.'는 의미이다.

24 <보기>의 raining은 현재분사이다. ④번은 '~하는 것'으로 해석되는 동명사이다.

25 deny는 동명사를 목적어로 취하는 동사이다.

26 stop+~ing: ~하는 것을 멈추다, stop+to~: ~하기 위해 멈추다

27 '그 일이 더 쉬운' 것이므로 find는 5형식 동사로 쓰였다.

28 ① keep은 5형식 동사로 쓰였으므로 목적보어로 형용사를 쓴다. ② 전치사의 목적어로 동명사를 써야 하므로 using이 옳다. ③, ⑤ finish, suggest는 동명사를 목적어로 취하므로 doing, having으로 고쳐야 한다.

29 내용상 '~할 때'를 뜻하는 접속사가 들어가는 것이 옳다.

30 어떠한 것에 관해서든 랩을 할 수 있다고 하였으므로 모든 것 (everything)이 랩을 위한 이야기가 될 수 있다고 하는 것이 옳다.

31 적어둔 자신의 생각을 사용한다는 말이다.

32 Polly가 어떤 종류의 티셔츠를 좋아하는지는 알 수 없다.

33 밑줄 친 ⓐ는 5형식 동사로 쓰였다. 이때 목적어를 보충 설명하기 위하여 목적격보어를 필요로 한다. 의견을 분명히 하는 것이므로 ②번이 5형식으로 쓰인 make이다.

34 Sam은 Polly의 우리 안에 자신의 티셔츠를 두었다.

단원별 예상문제
p.46~49

01 (A) in (B) up (C) for 02 (A) interested (B) interesting 03 ⓓ → interested 04 (B) → (D) → (E) → (C) → (A) 05 ① 06 ③
07 She baked the bread but it came out too dry.
08 She can solve it by putting a glass of water in the oven. 09 He got it from a cooking show.

10 Gloves keep our hands warm.　　11 ⑤
12 ④　　　13 ④　　　14 ③　　　15 (1)
having　(2) listening to　(3) spending　16 waiting
17 t(T)aking　18 ③　　　19 Writing raps 20 ④
21 ⑤　　　22 a pet, Polly, get used to　23 (A)
Write　(B) Care for　(C) Choose　24 ⑤
25 pointing your finger at something

01 put A in B: A를 B에 넣다, sign up for: ~에 신청하다, look for: ~을 찾다

02 (A) be interested in ~: ~에 관심이 있다　(B) interesting: 흥미로운

03 be interested in ~: ~에 관심이 있다

04 (B) 어떤 방과 후 수업을 들을지 질문 → (D) 대답 및 상대방에게도 질문 → (E) 대답 → (C) 사진 수업에 관한 추가 설명 → (A) 기대감 표현

05 이어지는 대화에서 특별한 재능을 가진 사람이 나와야 하므로 (A)가 적절하다.

06 ③ Doremi는 높은 음을 연주하는 것이 아니라 부를 것이다.

07 소녀의 문제는 빵을 구웠는데 너무 뻑뻑해져서 나온 것이다.

08 소년의 충고에 따르면 오븐에 물 한 컵을 넣음으로써 문제를 해결할 수 있다.

09 소년은 요리 프로를 통해 빵 굽기에 관한 유용한 정보를 얻었다.

10 장갑은 짝을 이루는 명사이므로 복수 명사로 쓰는 것이 옳다.

11 by+Ving: V함으로써

12 주어 역할을 하는 동명사는 to부정사로 대체할 수 있으며, 전치사의 목적어로 동명사를 쓰는 것이 옳다.

13 ④ keep이 5형식 동사로 쓰이고 있으므로 anxious라고 쓰는 것이 옳다.

14 I am looking forward to going home next month.

15 (1) be used to Ving: V하는 것에 익숙하다 (2) instead of의 목적어이므로 동명사 형태를 쓰는 것이 옳다. (3) avoid는 동명사를 목적어로 취하는 동사이다.

16 전치사의 목적어로 동명사를 쓰는 것이 옳다.

17 동사 take는 take pictures와 함께 쓰이면 '사진을 찍다'라는 의미가 되고, 목적어로 salt를 받아서 '섭취하다'는 의미도 된다. 전치사의 목적어와 주어 역할을 하는 것은 동명사이므로 taking[Taking]을 쓴다.

18 위 글은 랩을 쓰는 방법에 관한 글이다.

19 'Joy는 모든 것이 랩을 위한 이야기가 될 수 있다고 하였으므로, 랩을 쓰는 것은 쉽다고 답하는 것이 옳다.

20 Joy는 아이디어를 적어두었다가 나중에 사용한다고 하였다.

21 Polly가 Sam의 냄새에 익숙해져서 마침내 손으로 Polly를 잡을 수 있었고, 따라서 지금 둘은 친한 친구가 되었다고 보는 것이 옳다.

22 Sam에게는 애완동물 한 마리가 있고, 그것은 Polly라고 이름 지어진 고슴도치이다. Sam이 처음에 그녀를 데리고 왔을 때, Sam은 그녀가 자신의 냄새에 익숙해질 시간이 필요하겠다고 생각했고, 얼마 후 둘은 친한 친구가 되었다.

23 랩을 쓰고, 고슴도치를 돌보고, 더 나은 자리를 선택하는 방법에 관한 글이다.

24 고슴도치가 가시를 세우는 이유는 알 수 없다.

25 어떤 눈을 주로 사용하는지 알고 싶다면, 첫 번째로 해야 하는 것은 손가락으로 무엇을 가리키는 것이다.

서술형 실전문제
p.50~51

01 (A) at　(B) about　(C) in
02 He likes John Luke best.
03 He is interested in baseball.
04 Overeating(또는 To overeat) makes him ill.
05 keep asking, leave
06 Seeing is believing. (또는 To see is to believe.)
07 Drinking lots of water makes us healthy.
08 He found the movie educational.
09 writing your own rap
10 do you enjoy writing raps?
11 Where do you usually sit in a movie theater?
12 in choosing a seat in a classroom
13 pointing[to point] your finger, closing[to close] one eye, repeating[to repeat], the other eye

01 look at: ~을 보다, write about: ~에 대해 쓰다, be interested in~: ~에 관심이 있다

02 Mike가 가장 좋아하는 야구 선수는 John Luke이다.

03 Mike는 야구에 관심을 갖고 있다.

04 주어가 '과식'이므로 overeat을 동명사로 만들어 문장을 쓴다. 동명사 주어는 단수 취급을 하는 것에 유의한다.

05 keep Ving: 계속해서 V하다

06 백 번 듣는 것은 한 번 보는 것보다 못하다는 속담이다. '보는 것이 믿는 것이다'라는 영어 속담과 그 뜻을 함께 한다.

07 동명사 주어는 단수 취급하는 것이 옳다.

08 educational: 교육적인

09 give up은 동명사를 목적어로 취하는 동사이다.

10 Joy는 랩을 쓰는 것을 즐긴다. enjoy는 동명사를 목적어로 취한다.

11 usually는 빈도부사로 일반 동사 앞, be동사나 조동사 뒤에 위치한다.

12 전치사 in의 목적어 역할을 해야 하므로 choose를 동명사 형태로 바꾸어야 한다.

13 첫 번째 단계는 손가락으로 무언가를 가리키는 것이고, 두 번째 단계는 한 쪽 눈을 감았다가 뜨는 것이며, 세 번째 단계는 다른 한

쪽 눈으로 두 번째 단계를 반복하는 것이다. 동사 뒤에서 보어 역할을 해야 하므로 동명사나 to부정사 형태로 빈칸을 채우는 것에 유의한다.

 창의사고력 서술형 문제 p.52

|모범답안|

01 (A) take the drama class on Thursdays
　(B) taking the Tuesday photography class
　(C) he has an interest in taking pictures
　(D) the teacher is a famous photographer

02 (1) I found the town peaceful.
　(2) The dress made her attractive.
　(3) The noise kept me awake.
　(4) The sofa made me comfortable.
　(5) I found the jewelry valuable.

03 (1) I can't stop thinking about you.
　(2) I postponed cleaning my room.
　(3) I practice playing the violin every day.
　(4) I feel like having some snacks.
　(5) I often avoid answering my phone.

 단원별 모의고사 p.53~56

01 (1) careful　(2) artistic　(3) romantic　(4) peaceful
02 (1) interested in　(2) into　(3) look around　03 why don't you make some macarons for her?　04 I don't know how to cut this image.　05 (1) It takes time to get used to other cultures.　(2) I'll tell you when I meet you in person.　(3) How can I sign up for this program?　06 Her blog is usually about books.　07 She has an interest in reading.
08 ⓑ → how　09 ④　10 what club are you going to join?　11 ⑤　12 He will make some macarons for her.　13 But I don't know how to make them.　14 ⓔ → group　15 She can finish it quickly by starting from the corners, and then grouping the pieces with the same colors.
16 He makes me crazy.　17 ⑤　18 ④
19 Keep, open, sleeping　20 ①　21 ⑤
22 used　23 pet　24 ③　25 ②
26 useful　27 ④　28 ③

01 careful: 조심하는, 주의 깊은, artistic: 예술적인, romantic: 로맨틱한, peaceful: 평화로운
06 Betty는 주로 블로그에 책에 관해 쓰고 있다.
07 Betty는 책 읽기에 관심을 갖고 있다.

08 대화의 흐름상 어떻게 빵을 구워야 하는지 알려주고 있으므로 방법을 나타내는 how가 적절하다.
09 Mike는 Sue에게 오븐에 물을 한 컵 넣어 줄 것을 조언해 주었다.
11 be into: ~에 관심이 있다, ~을 좋아하다 ⑤번은 음악에 관심이 없다는 뜻이다.
12 Mike와 Lisa는 Clara를 위해 마카롱을 만들 것이다.
14 Start와 병렬구조를 이루므로 동사원형 형태인 group이 적절하다.
15 Emma는 구석에서부터 시작해서 같은 색의 조각들을 모아 빨리 1000개 조각의 퍼즐을 끝낼 수 있다.
16 '나를 미치도록' 만드는 것이므로 make를 5형식 동사로 활용하여 문장을 만든다.
17 '나를 초조하도록' 만드는 것이므로 make를 5형식 동사로 보는 것이 옳다. 따라서 nervous로 고쳐야 한다.
18 keep은 '목적어를 어떠한 상태로 유지하다'라는 의미로 쓰는 동사이다. 따라서 make를 5형식 동사로 사용하여 문장을 만든다.
19 feel like는 동명사를 목적어로 취하는 동사이다.
20 ①번은 '~하는 중'이라는 의미의 현재분사로 쓰였으나 나머지는 모두 동명사이다.
21 주어가 Polly이므로 단수 동사를 쓰는 것이 옳다.
22 get used to: ~에 익숙해지다.
23 당신과 함께하며 당신에게 즐거움을 주기 위해 집에 데리고 있는 동물은 애완동물이다.
24 Polly가 처음부터 Sam과 잘 지냈던 것은 아니다.
25 동사 means의 목적어 역할을 하면서, 동시에 명사절을 이끌어야 하므로 접속사 that이 들어가는 것이 옳다.
26 유용하다는 의미의 형용사가 들어가야 하므로 useful을 쓰는 것이 옳다.
27 mainly는 '주로'라는 의미이지만 hardly는 '거의 ~않다'라는 의미의 부사이다.
28 간단한 방법으로 자신에게 가장 좋은 자리를 찾는 방법에 관한 글이다. 따라서 ③번이 옳다.

Half a World Away

시험대비 실력평가   p.60

01 noisy   02 stranger   03 ④

04 ④   05 ③

06 (1) check out   (2) put on   (3) stand for   (4) try on

07 Don't forget to write letters.

01 주어진 단어는 명사와 형용사의 관계를 나타내고 있으므로 noise의 형용사 noisy(시끄러운)가 적절하다.

02 '당신이 모르는 사람'을 가리키는 말은 stranger(낯선 사람)이다.

03 cross: 십자가; 건너다

04 chimney는 굴뚝을 의미한다.

05 주어진 문장에서 present는 선물을 뜻하며 이와 같은 의미로 쓰인 것은 ③번이다. ①, ⑤번은 '출석한'을 뜻하며 ②번은 '제시하다' ④번은 '발표하다'를 뜻한다.

06 check out: 확인하다, put on: ~을 입다, 쓰다, stand for: ~을 상징하다, try on: ~을 입어 보다

서술형 시험대비   p.61

01 excellent   02 wrap   03 (1) cross   (2) performance

   (3) wedding   (4) fair   04 I can't wait to try

various foods.   05 (1) communicate with

(2) for free   (3) put away   06 (1) We used English to

communicate with each other.   (2) People are dancing

to folk music.   (3) My father wore a hat to look fancy.

01 주어진 단어의 관계는 동사와 형용사의 관계를 나타내므로 excel의 형용사 excellent(우수한, 훌륭한)가 적절하다.

02 '예를 들어 당신이 선물을 줄 때 종이나 다른 재료로 무언가를 완전히 덮다'는 wrap(싸다, 포장하다)이다.

03 cross: 건너다, performance: 공연, wedding: 결혼식, fair: 박람회

04 look forward to는 '~을 기대하다, ~을 학수고대하다'라는 의미를 나타내므로 'I can't wait to ~ (몹시 ~하고 싶다)'로 바꾸어 쓸 수 있다.

05 communicate with: ~와 의사소통하다, for free: 무료로, put away: ~을 치우다

Conversation   교과서

핵심 Check   p.62~63

1 (1) looking forward to meeting   (2) can't wait to

   (3) can't wait for

2 (1) Don't forget to   (2) Remember to

   (3) Make sure to

교과서 대화문 익히기

Check(√) True or False   p.64

1 T   2 F   3 T   4 F

교과서 확인학습   p.66~67

Listen and Talk 1 A-1

how is, going / perform / like / looking forward to

Listen and Talk 1 A-2

are you going to do / I'm going to go to / traditional foods / trying

Listen and Talk 1 B

signing up / interesting / African drum / traditional mask / how fun / visiting the museum

Listen and Talk 2 A-1

for / will / drinking tea / wrap the present / Don't forget to wrap it in red / stands for

Listen and Talk 2 A-2

Let's meet / see you / don't forget to wear / get into the palace

Listen and Talk 2 B

a crossing light / let's cross the street / right side / from country to country. Don't forget to look to the right

Communication

By the way / I'm looking forward to it / fireplace / put / away

시험대비 기본평가   p.68

01 Remember   02 I'm looking forward to the new year.

03 ③   04 ④

01 Remember는 기억하다를 의미하므로 Don't forget과 의미가

같다.

03 (A)는 훌라 댄스 수업이 어떻게 되어 가는지 질문하고 있으므로 how, (B)는 동사가 와야 하므로 sounds, (C)는 'look forward to: ~을 기대하다'를 의미하므로 forward가 적절하다.

04 Elsa는 공연을 기대하고 있으므로 excited(신난, 흥분한)가 적절하다. nervous: 긴장한, depressed: 우울한, upset: 화난, disappointed: 실망한

01 ⑤   02 I'm looking forward to seeing you again in Seoul.   03 They are going to meet at the bus stop at two.   04 They should wear a hanbok because they can get into the palace for free.   05 ①, ⑤   06 stands for   07 ④   08 ①, ③   09 ⓐ to cook ⓑ eating   10 ⑤   11 (A) a horse crossing the street (B) a crossing light for horses (C) look to the right before I cross   12 (B) – (D) – (A) – (C)

01 ⑤번을 제외한 나머지는 모두 기대감을 드러낸다.

03 Elsa와 Jake는 버스 정류장에서 두 시에 만날 것이다.

04 Elsa와 Jake는 무료로 궁전에 들어갈 수 있기 때문에 한복을 입어야 한다.

05 'don't forget'은 remember(기억하다)와 keep in mind(명심하다)로 바꾸어 쓸 수 있다. remind: 상기시키다

06 stand for: ~을 상징하다

07 Jake는 Sora에게 선물을 빨간색으로 포장할 것을 잊지 말라고 이야기하였다.

08 이어지는 대화의 내용으로 보아 기대감을 나타내는 표현이 적절하므로 ①, ③번이 맞다.

09 be going to+동사원형, enjoy의 목적어로 동명사가 적절하다.

11 런던에서의 내 인생의 첫날이라 나는 매우 흥분되었다. Brandon과 길을 걸을 때 나는 길을 건너는 말을 보았다. 놀랍게도 런던에는 말을 위한 신호등이 있었다. 길을 건널 때 나는 런던에서는 길을 건너기 전에 오른쪽을 보아야 한다는 것을 거의 잊었었다. Brandon이 이것을 내게 상기시켜 주었다. 내일 나는 런던에서 길을 건널 때 더욱 조심할 것이다.

12 (B) 훌라 춤 수업에 대해 질문 - (D) 대답 및 이번 주말 계획 설명 - (A) 반응 - (C) 기대감 표현

01 I'm looking forward to trying traditional foods.

02 many   03 wait to try them   04 He is going to go to the World Food Fair.   05 (A) 런던에는 말을 위한 교통 신호등이 있다. (B) 런던에서는 차가 오른쪽에서 온다.   06 She should remember to look to the right before she crosses in London.   07 (B) – (A) – (E) – (D) – (C)

01 look forward to: ~을 기대하다

02 lots of: 많은

03 can't wait to: ~를 몹시 바라다

04 Chris는 이번 주 일요일에 세계 음식 박람회에 갈 예정이다.

06 Amy가 런던에서 길을 건널 때 기억해야 하는 것은 길을 건너기 전에 오른쪽을 보아야 한다는 것이다.

07 (B) 다음 시간에 만들 음식 설명 → (A) 음식에 대한 구체적 질문 → (E) 음식에 대한 구체적 설명 → (D) 기대감 표현 → (C) 기쁨 및 확신 표현

교과서
Grammar

1 (1) If, are   (2) If, rains, will stay
    (3) Unless, will you come
2 (1) persuaded, to go   (2) expects, to arrive
    (3) told, not to run

01 (1) leaving → to leave   (2) will want → want
    (3) to not → not to   (4) If → Unless
02 (1) to be   (2) will give   (3) to drink   (4) to use
03 (1) My parents want me to be an architect.
    (2) If you finish your homework, you can go out.
    (3) These shoes enable me to walk comfortably.
    (4) They begged us to come back.

01 (1) want의 목적격보어는 to부정사이며, (2) 조건의 부사절에서 현재가 미래를 대신하므로 want, (3) to부정사의 부정형은 'not to V' 형태이다. (4) hurry를 don't hurry로 바꾸어도 좋다.

02 (1), (3), (4) ask, advise, allow는 to부정사를 목적격보어로 취하는 동사이다. (2) Kelly에게 메시지를 전달하는 것은 미래이므로 미래시제를 쓰는 것이 옳다.

03 (1), (3), (4)의 동사 want, enable, beg는 모두 to부정사를 목적격보어로 취하는 동사이다. (2) 조동사 can은 '가능' 외에도 허가를 나타내며 '~해도 좋다'는 뜻으로 해석된다.

01 ③	02 ③	03 ④	04 allowed, to go
05 ⑤	06 ③		07 Unless
08 ③	09 I need you to help me with the dishes.		
10 ③	11 ④	12 ⑤	13 want you to be upset
		14 ④	15 ⑤
16 ⑤	17 talking, to talk		18 ③
19 ⑤	20 Molly let her children splash around in the pool for a while.	21 ③	22 ⑤
23 Linda to come and stay with them		24 If I meet you in person, I will ask you many questions.	

01 ask는 목적격보어로 to부정사를 사용한다.

02 ③번은 '~인지 아닌지'로 해석되는 명사절을 이끄는 접속사 if이다. 나머지는 모두 조건절을 이끄는 if이다.

03 현재시제로 미래를 표현하는 조건의 부사절이므로 give를 쓰는 것이 옳다.

04 allow는 to부정사를 목적격보어로 취하는 동사이다.

05 빈칸에는 to부정사를 목적격보어로 취할 수 있는 동사가 들어가야 한다.

06 일찍 자는 주체는 손님이므로 5형식을 사용하고, would like는 to부정사를 목적격보어로 취하므로 ③번이 적절하다.

07 if not은 unless와 같다.

08 명사절과 부사절을 모두 이끌면서 '~인지 아닌지', '~라면'이라고 해석될 수 있는 것은 접속사 if이다.

09 도와주는 주체가 you이므로 need you to help를 써서 5형식 틀을 갖추어야 한다.

10 ①, ④, ⑤번의 동사는 to부정사를 목적격보어로 취하는 동사들이며, ②번에는 목적어로 쓰이는 to부정사가 들어간다. ③번은 조동사 뒤에 위치하는 동사원형의 자리이다.

11 encourage와 want는 모두 to부정사를 목적격보어로 취하는 동사이므로 빈칸에는 to부정사가 들어가는 것이 적절하다. get along well: 잘 지내다

12 조건절의 시제가 현재이므로, 현재나 미래를 나타내는 주절을 쓰는 것이 옳다.

13 want는 목적격보어로 to부정사를 사용한다

14 ④ have trouble (in) Ving: ~하는 데에 어려움이 있다 ①, ③, ⑤는 목적격보어로 쓰인 to부정사가 들어가며 ②는 형용사로 사용된 to부정사가 들어간다.

15 빈칸이 이끄는 절은 현재형이지만, 주절은 미래이므로 빈칸에는 시간•조건의 부사절이 들어가야 한다. 따라서 양보절 접속사인 ⑤번은 적절하지 않다.

16 ⑤번의 warn은 to부정사를 목적격보어로 취하는 동사이다.

17 stop은 동명사를 목적어로 취하는 동사이며 ask는 목적격 보어로 to부정사를 취한다.

18 ⓐ, ⓑ, ⓓ는 부사절을 이끄는 if로 '만약 ~라면'이라고 해석하고, ⓒ, ⓔ는 명사절을 이끄는 접속사 if로 '~인지 아닌지'라고 해석한다.

19 consider는 동명사를 목적어로 취하는 동사이며, persuade는 목적격보어로 to부정사를 취한다. 조건절에서는 현재형으로 미래를 표현하므로 meet을 쓰는 것이 옳다.

20 splash around: 물장구치다, 첨벙거리다

21 ⓐ avoid는 동명사를 목적어로 취하는 동사이므로 answering으로 쓰는 것이 옳다. ⓑ '금지하다'라는 의미인 forbid는 목적격보어로 to부정사를 취하므로 옳은 문장이다. ⓒ 전치사 of의 목적어로 동명사를 썼으므로 옳은 문장이다. ⓓ would like는 5형식으로 쓰일 때 목적격보어로 to부정사를 취하므로 옳은 문장이다. ⓔ teach는 목적격보어로 to부정사를 취하는 동사이다. 따라서 to drive로 쓰는 것이 옳다.

22 want는 목적격보어로 to부정사를 취하는 동사이다.

23 Ann이 Linda에게 그들과 함께 머물자고 초대하는 상황이다. 목적격보어로 to부정사를 취하는 invite를 이용하여 문장을 만든다.

24 in person: 직접, 몸소

01 I don't know what we will do if we don't find the way.

02 If you need money, I will lend you some.
If you want those pictures, you can have them.
If you are busy now, I will call you later.

03 (1) get up　(2) will plant　(3) will buy, have

04 Unless, will miss / will be very surprised / will go / to be

05 She asked me to drop by her house.

06 Jason to see a doctor

07 If there is a fire, the alarm will ring.
If you want me to help you, I will help you.
If I don't feel well tomorrow, I will stay at home.

08 me to accept Kelly's apology

09 you to go to any place you want to go

10 If you get up early tomorrow, what will you do?

11 They don't allow people to park in front of the building.

12 (1) to throw → throwing　(2) taking → to take
(3) Unless → If　(4) help → to help

13 closing the window / to close the window

01 부사절 if는 현재시제로 미래를 표현한다.

02 네가 돈이 필요하다면 내가 좀 빌려줄게. / 네가 그 그림들을 원한

다면, 네가 가져도 좋아. / 네가 지금 바쁘다면 내가 나중에 전화할게.

03 (1) 조건절이므로 현재시제, (2) 명사절 접속사 if가 이끄는 절이므로 내용과 시제를 일치시켜 미래시제, (3) '가욋돈이 있으면'이라는 조건절은 현재형으로 쓰고, 컴퓨터를 사는 것은 다음 달의 일이므로 주절에 미래시제를 쓰는 것이 옳다.

04 miss: 놓치다 be surprised: 놀라다 be crowded with: ~으로 붐비다 on time: 정각에

05 ask+목적어+to부정사: 목적어가 V하도록 요청하다

06 advise는 목적격보어로 to부정사를 사용한다.

07 feel well: 건강하다

08 accept an apology: 사과를 받아들이다

09 차를 가지고 있는 것은 당신이 가길 원하는 어떠한 곳이건 갈 수 있게 한다. enable은 to부정사를 목적격보어로 취하는 동사이다.

10 조건의 부사절에서 현재시제가 미래를 나타내는 것에 유의하여 문장을 만든다.

11 allow는 to부정사를 목적격보어로 취하는 동사이다. 부정어와 to를 추가하여 문장을 만든다.

12 (1) practice는 동명사를 목적어로 취하는 동사이다. (2) tell은 목적격보어로 to부정사를 취한다. (3) '바쁘지 않다면 날 좀 도와줄래?'라는 의미가 자연스러우므로 unless를 if로 고치거나 not을 빼는 것이 옳다. (4) get은 목적격보어로 to부정사를 취하는 동사이다.

13 mind는 동명사를 목적어로 취하는 동사이고, would like 는 5형식으로 쓰일 때 목적격보어로 to부정사를 취한다.

교과서
Reading

확인문제
p.80

1 T 2 T 3 F 4 T 5 F

확인문제
p.81

1 T 2 T 3 F 4 F 5 F 6 T

교과서 확인학습 A
p.82~83

02 from Germany, is to clean
03 During, help, to keep
04 bring them good luck   05 want, to be
06 see me, lucky day   07 these are

08 folk music, always wear
09 wear, to stay cool, hot, strong sunlight
10 want, to look fancy
11 often decorate, with, materials
12 Which, best   13 a Zulu   14 a tribe in
15 What do you think
16 making clothes with
17 They are, each color has
18 When, our own writing system, to communicate
19 to know the meaning of the colors / Good Meaning, Bad Meaning, marriage, death, Yellow, wealth, anger, White, love
20 express yourself with
21 What message, to make

교과서 확인학습 B
p.84~85

1 I'm Sweepy.
2 I'm from Germany and my job is to clean chimneys.
3 During winter, chimney sweeps help people to keep warm and safe.
4 So people think chimney sweeps bring them good luck.
5 People even want chimney sweeps to be at their weddings!
6 If you see me, it is your lucky day.
7 My name is José and these are my mariachi band members.
8 We play folk music and always wear our sombreros, or big hats.
9 In Mexico, people wear these hats to stay cool under the hot and strong sunlight.
10 We mariachi players want our sombreros to look fancy.
11 So we often decorate them with a lot of different materials.
12 Which of our sombreros do you like best?
13 My name is Ayanda and I'm a Zulu.
14 We are a tribe in South Africa.
15 What do you think of my beads?
16 Zulu people enjoy making clothes with beads.
17 They are beautiful and each color has a special meaning.
18 When we did not have our own writing system, we used beads to communicate with each other.
19 If you want to know the meaning of the colors,

check out the following box. / Color, Good Meaning, Bad Meaning / Black, marriage, death / Yellow, wealth, badness / Red, love, anger / White, love

20 If you want to send someone a special message, you can express yourself with these beads.

21 What message do you want to make?

시험대비 실력평가
p.86~89

01 ①, ④　　02 ③　　03 ②　　04 good luck　　05 to look fancy　　06 ④
07 ④　　08 Mexican people wear sombreros to stay cool.　　09 ③　　10 a tribe　　11 ③
12 ⑤　　13 ⑤　　14 people　　15 ③
16 Germany, warm, chimney sweeps　　17 ②, ④
18 ⑤　　19 ③　　20 It looks fancy.
21 mariachi band members　22 ②　　23 beads
24 ④　　25 ④

01 be동사의 보어 자리이므로 '굴뚝을 청소하는 것'이라는 의미를 만들어 주기 위하여 to부정사나 동명사를 사용하는 것이 옳다.

02 굴뚝 청소부는 겨울 동안 사람들을 따뜻하고 안전하게 지낼 수 있도록 돕는다고 하였다.

03 '~한 채로 유지하다'는 의미이므로 stay가 가장 알맞다.

04 위 글에서 chimney sweeps가 결혼식에서 행운을 가져다준다고 하였다.

05 want는 목적격보어로 to부정사를 취하는 동사이다.

06 sombrero를 멋지게 보이도록 만들기 위해서 여러 가지 장식을 한다고 볼 수 있다. 따라서 ④번에 들어가는 것이 가장 옳다.

07 솜브레로는 모자이다.

08 멕시코 사람들이 솜브레로를 쓰는 이유는 시원함을 유지하기 위해서이다.

09 색깔에 따라 서로 다른 의미를 가지는 구슬(beads)에 관한 내용이 주를 이루고 있다. 따라서 ③번이 가장 옳다.

10 같은 종족의 사람들, 같은 언어를 사용하고 같은 풍습을 갖는 사람들의 무리는 '부족'이다.

11 ③ Zulu족은 과거에 문자 체계를 가지고 있지 않았다고 하였다.

12 Sweepy가 몇 살인지는 알 수 없다.

13 want는 to부정사를 목적격보어로 취하는 동사이다. 따라서 to be로 쓰는 것이 옳다.

14 사람들을 가리키고 있다.

15 사람들은 Sweepy가 그들에게 행운을 가져다 줄 것이라고 생각하기 때문이다.

16 굴뚝 청소부 덕분에 독일 사람들은 겨울에 따뜻하고 안전하게

지낸다.

17 ② mariachi 밴드는 민속 음악을 연주한다.

18 (A) 주어가 We이므로 복수동사 wear, (B) '뜨거운 태양빛 아래에서'라는 의미가 옳으므로 under, (C) 지칭하는 명사가 sombreros이므로 복수대명사 them을 쓰는 것이 옳다.

19 밑줄 친 ⓐ와 ③은 부사로 쓰인 to부정사이며 '~하기 위해서'라고 해석된다. ① want의 목적어, ② 진주어, ④ 목적격 보어, ⑤ 형용사로 쓰인 to부정사이다.

20 솜브레로를 멋지게 만들기 위해서 여러 가지 장식을 한다고 하였다. 따라서 솜브레로가 어떤지를 묻는 말에 멋지다고 답할 수 있다.

21 mariachi 밴드 멤버들을 가리키는 대명사이다.

22 빈칸에는 enjoy의 목적어로 동명사가 들어가야 한다. ②번에는 전치사 in의 목적어로 동명사가 들어가며, 나머지는 모두 to부정사를 목적어로 취하는 동사들이다.

23 They는 앞에서 나온 beads를 가리키는 인칭대명사이다.

24 전치사 with는 '~와 함께'라는 의미와 '~으로'라는 의미를 갖는다.

25 주어진 문장의 mariachi 밴드 멤버를 소개하는 문장인 (C)가 처음으로 나오고, (C)에서 언급한 큰 모자를 설명하는 (A)가 나온 후, 모자를 멋지게 보이기 위하여 여러 가지 재료로 모자를 꾸민다는 내용인 (B) 순서로 나열하는 것이 옳다.

서술형 시험대비
p.90~91

01 cleaning chimneys　　02 During winter, chimney sweeps help people (to) keep warm and safe.
03 People think chimney sweeps bring them good luck.　　04 lucky　　05 German, warm, safe
06 They always wear their sombreros.
07 decorating, to look fancy　　08 hot and strong, to wear　　09 enables people to stay cool　　10 Which of our sombreros do you like best?　　11 ⓐ making ⓑ to make　12 each color has its own meaning　13 to communicate with each other　14 express, to, use, beads, White
15 I will use red beads.

01 주어나 보어로 쓰인 to부정사를 동명사로 쓸 수 있다.

02 help는 to부정사나 원형부정사를 목적격보어로 취하는 동사이다. 따라서 keeping을 to keep 혹은 keep으로 고쳐 쓰는 것이 옳다.

03 질문: 사람들은 굴뚝 청소부가 무엇을 가져다준다고 생각하나요?

04 명사 luck을 형용사형으로 만들어 답을 쓴다.

05 Sweepy는 독일 인형으로 그것의 직업은 굴뚝을 청소하는 것이다. 만약 당신이 겨울을 따뜻하고 안전하게 보내길 원한다면, Sweepy가 당신을 도와 줄 것이다.

06 mariachi 밴드 멤버들은 항상 솜브레로를 쓴다고 하였다.

07 솜브레로를 장식하는 이유는 멋지게 보이기 위해서이다.

08 멕시코의 태양빛은 뜨겁고 강하기 때문에 솜브레로를 쓴다고 하였다. advise는 목적격보어로 to부정사를 취하므로 어법에 유의하여 빈칸을 채운다.

09 enable은 목적격보어로 to부정사를 취하는 동사로 '목적어가 V하는 것을 가능하게 하다'라고 해석된다.

10 best: 가장

11 enjoy는 동명사를 목적어로 취하는 동사이며, want는 to부정사를 목적어로 취하는 동사이다.

12 one's own: 자기 자신의, 자기만의

13 enable은 to부정사를 목적격보어로 취하는 동사이다. 구슬은 줄루족이 서로 소통하는 것을 가능하게 한다.

14 Jimmy: 나는 Jane과 사랑에 빠졌어. 무언가로 내 마음을 표현하고 싶어. 무엇을 이용해야 할까? Helen: 나는 네게 구슬을 사용하라고 조언하겠어. 흰색 구슬은 사랑을 의미해. 그리고 어떠한 나쁜 의미도 가지지 않아.

15 화가 났음을 표현하는 색깔은 빨간색이라고 하였다.

영역별 핵심문제　　　　　　p.93~97

01 weak　　02 doll　　03 ④　　04 (1) materials (2) stay (3) introduce (4) fireplace 05 (1) get in (2) turn off (3) put on　　06 Don't forget to wrap it in red.　07 Because he enjoys drinking tea. 08 ①　　09 ④　　10 I'm looking forward to visiting the museum.　11 make an African drum and a traditional mask　12 (A) – (C) – (D) – (B)　　　13 By the way 14 ⑤
15 ④　　　16 ③　　　17 ②　　　18 ②
19 ②　　　20 ②　　　21 ③　　　22 don't, stop, playing, won't, allow, you, to　23 ⑤
24 ④　　　25 If you run up the hill, your heart will beat fast.　　26 ④　　27 don't have any homework to do, will go surfing 28 ②
29 ⑤　　　30 ③　　　31 ②　　　32 our sombreros　33 to stay cool　　　34 ⑤
35 (A) What　(B) to communicate　(C) yourself

01 주어진 단어의 관계는 반의어 관계를 나타낸다. strong(강한)의 반의어인 weak(약한)이 적절하다.

02 '사람, 특히 아기나 어린 아이의 모양을 한 어린이 장난감'을 가리키는 말은 doll(인형)이다.

03 excel은 '뛰어나다, 탁월하다'라는 뜻이다.

04 material: 재료, stay: 머무르다, introduce: 소개하다, fireplace: 벽난로

05 get in: ~에 들어가다, turn off: ~을 끄다, put on: ~을 바르다

06 don't forget to: ~하기를 잊지 않다

07 Wang이 Sora의 선물을 좋아할 것이라고 Jack이 확신한 이유는 그가 차 마시는 것을 즐기기 때문이다.

08 stand for는 '상징하다'라는 뜻을 나타내며 이와 바꾸어 쓸 수 있는 말은 symbolize이다.

09 (A)에 들어갈 말로 프로그램에 대한 기대를 나타내는 표현이 적절하지만 ④번은 '상관없어'라는 의미이다.

11 Jane은 아프리카 박물관에서 아프리카 드럼과 전통 가면을 만들 수 있다.

12 (A) 이번 주 일요일 계획 질문 → (C) 계획 설명 → (D) 자신의 경험 및 박람회 정보 제공 → (B) 기대감 표현

15 주어진 문장은 언제까지 축제가 열리는지에 대한 대답으로 적절하므로 (D)번이 적절하다.

16 Harry가 기모노를 입은 채 Jina와 사진을 찍었다는 설명은 대화의 내용과 일치하지 않는다.

17 빈칸이 이끄는 절은 현재시제이지만 주절은 미래이므로 빈칸에는 조건을 나타내는 접속사 if가 알맞다.

18 많은 짐을 들고 있는 Angela가 Jason에게 도움을 요청하는 상황이므로 ②번이 적절하다.

19 오늘 밤에 늦게 온다면 기다리지 않을 것이라는 의미로. 조건의 부사절이므로 현재형으로 미래를 나타낼 수 있다. 따라서 ②번이 가장 적절하다.

20 자신의 전화기를 사용하지 말라고 했으므로 forbade는 to use 로, told는 not to use를 쓰는 것이 옳다. forbid 금지하다

21 ③번은 명사절을 이끄는 접속사 if이다.

22 won't allow you to를 대신하여 will not let you를 써도 좋다.

23 want는 to부정사를 목적격보어로 취하는 동사이다.

24 encourage와 advise는 모두 to부정사를 목적격보어로 취하는 동사이므로 빈칸에는 to부정사가 들어가는 것이 옳다.

25 run up: ~을 뛰어오르다 beat: 뛰다

26 enable은 to부정사를 목적격보어로 취하는 동사이다. 따라서 to live로 쓰는 것이 옳다.

27 서핑하러 갈 시간이 있느냐는 물음에 아직 숙제가 있는지 없는지 모른다며, 만약 할 숙제가 없다면 함께 가겠다고 답할 수 있다.

28 겨울 동안 사람들이 따뜻하게 지낼 수 있도록 돕는다고 보는 것이 옳다.

29 빈칸 ⓐ에는 출신을 나타내는 전치사 from이 들어간다.

30 mariachi 밴드는 민속음악을 연주한다고 하였다.

31 fancy는 '화려한'이란 의미이다. 따라서 '소박한'이란 의미의 simple이 반대되는 말이다. decorative: 장식용의

32 멤버들의 솜브레로를 가리키는 대명사이다. 솜브레로를 멋지게 만들기 위해서 여러 가지 장식을 하는 것이다

33 help는 원형부정사나 to부정사를 목적격보어로 취하는 동사이다. 솜브레로는 강한 햇빛 아래에서 멕시코 사람들이 시원함을 유지하도록 돕는다.

34 줄루족이 언제 그들 자신의 문자 체계를 갖기 시작했는지는 알 수 없다.

35 (A) 상대방의 의견을 물을 때 쓰는 표현은 'What do you think of ~?'이다. (B) '~하기 위해서'라고 해석되는 to부정사가 들어가는 것이 옳다. 이때 to부정사는 부사적 용법으로 사용되었다. (C) 주어와 목적어가 같을 때 목적어로 재귀대명사를 쓴다.

단원별 예상문제

p.98~101

01 ⑤ 02 ③ 03 (1) I'm looking forward to the school festival. (2) You should put the toys away before having dinner. (3) Can I download this app for free? 04 (D) – (B) – (E) – (A) – (C) 05 I'm looking forward to the performance. 06 She is going to perform at the ACB Hall. 07 Because red stands for wealth in China. 08 ② 09 don't forget to wear a *hanbok* 10 ⑤ 11 ④ 12 ③ 13 ④ 14 Julia's mother taught Julia to play the violin. 15 have, will choose 16 ①, ③ 17 ② 18 ④ 19 chimney sweeps help people to keep warm and safe 20 ③ 21 ④ 22 The hot sunlight forces people to wear sombreros. 23 ② 24 told him to use yellow color 25 ①

01 fair: 공정한; 박람회

02 주어진 문장에서 express는 '표현하다'를 뜻한다. ③번은 '급행열차'를 의미한다.

03 put ~ away: ~을 치우다, for free: 무료로

04 (D) 프로그램을 신청하고 있음을 설명함 - (B) 프로그램에 대해 질문 - (E) 구체적인 설명 - (A) 흥미 표현 - (C) 기대감 표현

05 look forward to: ~을 기대하다, 고대하다

06 Elsa는 이번 주말에 ACB 홀에서 공연을 할 것이다.

07 Jack이 Sora가 선물을 빨간색으로 포장하길 원하는 이유는 중국에서는 빨간색이 부를 상징하기 때문이다.

08 (A) buy 뒤에 전치사 for가 이어진다. (B) enjoy는 동명사를 목적어로 취한다. (C) forget to: ~할 것을 잊다, forget ~ing: ~한 것을 잊다

10 대화를 통해 한복 대여에 관한 것은 알 수 없다.

11 시간 • 조건의 부사절에서 현재시제로 미래를 나타낸다. 따라서 rains로 쓰는 것이 옳다.

12 ⓐ would like는 5형식으로 쓰일 때 목적격보어로 to부정사를 취하므로 to run으로 쓰는 것이 옳다. ⓓ order는 목적격보어로 to부정사를 취하는 동사이다.

13 ④번에는 전치사의 목적어로 동명사 having이 들어가지만 나머

지는 모두 to have가 들어간다.

14 teach는 목적격보어로 to부정사를 사용한다.

15 조건의 부사절에서 현재시제로 미래를 표현할 수 있으므로 if절 동사는 have로 쓰고 주절은 미래시제를 쓴다.

16 allow와 permit은 '허용[허락]하다'라는 의미로 쓰이는 동사이다. 모두 to부정사를 목적격보어로 취한다.

17 ⓐ, ⓑ, ⓒ는 글의 내용과 일치하지만, Sweepy는 사람들이 겨울 동안 따뜻하고 안전하게 지낼 수 있도록 돕는다고 하였으므로 ⓓ, ⓔ는 옳지 않다.

18 4형식을 3형식으로 전환할 때 bring은 전치사 to를 사용하여 간접목적어를 뒤로 보낸다.

20 stay는 2형식 동사로 형용사를 보어로 취한다. 따라서 cool 로 쓰는 것이 옳다.

21 a great deal of는 셀 수 없는 명사를 수식한다.

22 뜨거운 햇빛은 사람들로 하여금 솜브레로를 쓰도록 강요한다.

23 빈칸 ⓐ에는 때를 나타내는 접속사 When이 들어간다. ① Although[Though], ② when, ③ If, ④ Unless, ⑤ Although[Though]가 들어가는 것이 자연스럽다.

24 표에 따르면 노란색 구슬은 부를 의미한다. tell은 목적격보어로 to부정사를 취하는 것에 유의한다.

25 Zulu 족의 삶에서 구슬이 여러 용도로 쓰이고 있다는 내용의 글이다.

서술형 실전문제

p.102~103

01 ⓔ → trying

02 She went there last weekend.

03 He can enjoy lots of traditional foods from all over the world.

04 find, will tell

05 caused the rumor to spread

06 I have enough pineapples, I will bake

07 enables older people to study at college

08 wearing, (to) stay cool

09 decorate, (to) look fancy

10 we communicated with each other by using beads.

11 want, to, to, use, red, used, express

12 Because they didn't have their own writing system.

13 (B) – (C) – (A)

---

01 look forward to의 to는 전치사이므로 trying이 적절하다.

02 Mina는 지난 주말에 세계 음식 박람회를 방문하였다.

03 Chris는 세계 음식 박람회에서 전 세계로부터 온 많은 전통적인 음식을 즐길 수 있다.

04 시간 • 조건의 부사절에서 현재시제가 미래를 대신한다는 것에

---

16 정답 및 해설

유의하여 빈칸을 채운다.

05 cause+목적어+to V: 목적어가 V하도록 야기하다

06 조건의 부사절에서 현재시제로 미래를 나타낼 수 있으므로 have enough pineapples를 쓴다.

07 enable은 to부정사를 목적격보어로 취하는 동사이다. study를 to부정사로 만들어 문장을 쓴다.

08 A: 너무 더워. 솜브레로를 쓰지 않을 수 없어. B: 넌 그걸 써야 해. 그건 네가 시원함을 유지하도록 도와.

09 많은 재료들로 솜브레로를 장식하면 멋지게 보이도록 만들 수 있다고 하였다.

10 구슬을 사용함으로써 우리는 서로 소통했습니다.

12 줄루족이 의사소통을 위해 구슬을 사용했던 이유는 그들 자신의 문자 체계가 존재하지 않았기 때문이었다.

13 (C)의 these hats가 (B)의 sombreros를 가리키므로 (B) 다음에 (C)가 이어지고 (A)의 So가 (C)의 결과를 말하므로 (C) 다음에 (A)가 이어지는 것이 자연스럽다.

창의사고력 서술형 문제 p.104

|모범답안|

01 (A) tea (B) he enjoys drinking tea
(C) wrap it in red (D) wealth in China

02 (1) If it is sunny tomorrow, I will go on a picnic.
(2) If it is windy tomorrow, I'll wear my coat.
(3) If you need my computer, you can use it.
(4) If I have much money, I will travel to Rome.
(5) If you buy some flour, I can make you a cake.

03 (1) My mom encourages me to live a happy life.
(2) Mr. Hudson allowed me to go home early today.
(3) Oxygen in the air causes a fire to spread.
(4) The teacher persuaded me to accept the apology from my friend.
(5) My brother advised me to get up early.
(6) My car enables me to go anywhere I want to go.

단원별 모의고사 p.105~108

01 (A) away (B) on (C) for
02 (1) stands for (2) try on (3) looking forward to
03 wealth 04 ⑤ 05 signing up for
06 (B) interesting (C) visiting 07 palace
08 ④ 09 I'm looking forward to trying them.
10 ⑤ 11 He is looking forward to sleeping in a ger, a Mongolian tent. 12 He should remember to put his things away from the fireplace. 13 you lend me, I will pay, back 14 ①, ④ 15 ③
16 ⑤ 17 take, will get 18 We

play folk music and always wear our sombreros, or big hats. 19 ④ 20 What do you think of my beads? 21 ③ 22 The bad meaning of yellow is badness. 23 ③ 24 ⓐ to know ⓑ to send ⓒ to make 25 ②

01 put away: ~을 치우다, try on: ~을 입어 보다, stand for: ~을 상징하다

02 stand for: ~을 상징하다, try on: ~을 입어 보다, look forward to ~ing: ~을 기대하다

03 부유한 상태를 가리키는 말은 wealth(부, 부유)이다.

04 Wang이 평소에 무슨 종류의 차를 즐기는지는 알 수 없다.

05 sign up for: ~을 신청[가입]하다

06 interesting: 흥미로운, look forward to ~ing: ~을 기대하다

07 왕, 여왕, 대통령 등의 공식적인 집을 가리키는 말은 palace(궁전, 왕궁)이다.

08 한복을 입어야 함을 상기키는 말로 이어지는 대화에서 한복을 입어야 할 필요성을 설명하고 있으므로 (D)가 적절하다.

09 look forward to ~ing: ~을 기대하다

11 Jake는 몽골 텐트인 게르에서 잠을 자는 것을 기대하고 있다.

12 Jake는 난로 주변에서 그의 물건을 치워야 한다는 것을 기억해야 한다.

13 pay somebody back: (빌린 돈을) 갚다, 돌려주다

14 주어진 문장에는 3형식과 5형식으로 모두 쓰일 수 있으면서, 동시에 to부정사를 목적어와 목적격보어로 각각 취하는 동사를 넣어야 한다. 따라서 ①, ④가 옳다.

15 ① '~인지 아닌지'로 해석되는 명사절이다. tomorrow가 있으므로 will accept를 쓰는 것이 옳다. ② teach는 to부정사를 목적격보어로 취하는 동사이다. 따라서 to swim 으로 써야 한다. ④ to부정사의 부정은 not to V이다. ⑤ advise는 to부정사를 목적격보어로 취하는 동사이므로 to learn으로 쓰는 것이 옳다.

16 빈칸에는 to부정사를 목적격보어로 취할 수 있는 동사가 들어가야 한다. keep은 해당하지 않는다.

17 조건절에서 현재시제로 미래를 나타낸다.

18 빈도부사 always는 일반동사 앞, be동사나 조동사 뒤에 위치하는 것이 옳다.

19 솜브레로를 장식하여 멋져 보이게 할 수 있다고 하였다. 사람들이 멋져 보이는 것은 아니다.

20 What do you think of ~?는 누군가의 의견을 묻는 표현이다.

21 each는 단수명사를 이끈다. 따라서 color라고 쓰는 것이 옳다.

22 노란색이 가진 나쁜 의미는 '나쁨, 해로움'이다.

23 ③ 네 개의 색에 일곱 가지 의미가 있다.

24 want는 to부정사를 목적어로 취한다.

25 Sweepy 소개 → 굴뚝 청소부가 하는 일이 사람들을 도움 → 그래서 사람들은 굴뚝 청소부가 행운을 가져다준다고 생각함 → 심지어 결혼식에도 굴뚝 청소부가 있기를 원함

I Wonder Why,
I Wonder How

시험대비 실력평가   p.112

01 impossible 02 weigh   03 ①   04 ②
05 (1) challenge (2) amusement (3) add (4) amount
06 ③   07 (A) of (B) up (C) up

01 주어진 관계는 반의어를 나타낸다. possible: 가능한, impossible 불가능한

02 주로 저울을 사용해서 어떤 사람이나 사물이 얼마나 무거운지 측정하다를 나타내는 말은 weigh(무게를 재다)이다.

03 ① experiment: 실험

04 lock은 동사로 '잠그다', 명사로는 '자물쇠'라는 의미를 나타낸다. lock ~ in one's arms는 '~를 꼭 껴안다, 끌어안다'를 의미한다.

05 challenge: 도전, amusement park: 놀이 공원, add: 더하다, amount: 양

06 주어진 문장에서 fair는 '박람회'를 뜻한다. 이와 같은 의미로 쓰인 것은 ③번이고 나머지는 모두 '공정한'을 의미한다.

07 take care of: ~을 돌보다, pick up: ~을 집다, light up: ~을 밝히다

서술형 시험대비   p.113

01 unlock   02 collector   03 hide
04 (1) Let's say that (2) pump up (3) light up
05 (1) car horn (2) unbelievable (3) scare
06 (A) possibility (B) amazingly (C) ability
07 (1) Let's paint evenly over the wall with yellow.
   (2) Have you heard about the special event at the science museum?
   (3) Let's say that potatoes produce electricity.

01 주어진 관계는 반의어를 나타낸다. lock: 잠그다, unlock: 자물쇠를 풀다

02 취미나 일로 무언가를 수집하는 사람을 가리키는 말은 collector(수집가)이다.

03 무언가를 보이지 않거나 찾을 수 없는 장소에 놓거나 보관하는 것은 hide(숨기다)이다.

04 let's say that ~라고 가정해 보자, pump up: 바람을 넣다, light up: ~을 환하게 밝히다, 점등하다

05 car horn: 자동차 경적, unbelievable: 믿을 수 없는, scare: 겁을 주다

06 possibility: 가능성, amazingly: 놀랍게도, ability: 능력

교과서
Conversation

핵심 Check   p.114~115

1 (1) Have you heard about (2) Yes, I have. Have you
  (3) No, I haven't
2 (1) What do you mean (2) What is it (3) tell, more

교과서 대화문 익히기

Check(√) True or False   p.116

1 T   2 F   3 T   4 F

교과서 확인학습   p.118~119

Listen & Talk 1 A-1

What show / Have you heard about it / science / interesting

Listen & Talk 1 A-2

No, I haven't / Let me show you / what a great application

Listen & Talk 1 B

Have you heard about / offers / how to control it

Listen & Talk 2 A-1

What do you mean / electricity

Listen & Talk 2 A-2

what did you do last weekend / put / in vinegar / turns into

Listen & Talk 2 B

What do you mean / hide / Mix / How can you read the card / appears

Communication

Have you heard about / Yes, I have / What do you mean / how to take care of it / useful

Wrap Up 1

excited / experiments / looking forward to

시험대비 기본평가　　　　　　　　p.120

01 What do you mean?　　02 ⑤　　　03 ②
04 ③

02 경험 여부를 묻는 질문에 대한 대답으로 'Yes, I have.' 또는 'No, I haven't.'가 적절하다.

03 주어진 문장은 경험 여부를 묻고 있으며 이에 대해 적절한 대답 (No, I haven't.)이 이어지므로 (B)가 적절하다.

04 Mike가 무엇에 관심이 있는지는 알 수 없다.

시험대비 실력평가　　　　　　　　p.121~122

01 (B) – (A) – (E) – (D) – (C)　02 Have you heard about the DIY Drone Class?03 ①　　04 We can make our own special drone and learn how to control it.　　05 No, I haven't.　　06 ①
07 ⑤　　　08 ⑤　　　09 ③　　　10 달걀을 이틀 동안 식초에 담가 놓는다.　11 ②　　12 ④

01 (B) 경험 질문 - (A) 대답 및 구체적인 설명 요구 - (E) 구체적인 설명 및 시범 - (D) 질문에 대한 대답 - (C) 놀라움 표현

02 경험을 묻는 현재완료를 쓴다.

03 advertise: 홍보하다, apologize: 사과하다, appreciate: 고마워하다, celebrate: 축하하다, protest: 항의하다

04 DIY 드론 수업에서 당신만의 특별한 드론을 만들고 어떻게 이를 조종하는지 배울 수 있다.

06 문맥상 '설명하다'라는 뜻의 explain이 알맞다. produce: 생산하다, challenge: 도전하다, pump: 물을 퍼 올리다, decorate: 장식하다

07 나머지는 모두 흥미로움을 표현하지만 ⑤번은 관심이 없음을 이야기한다.

09 이어지는 문장에서 egg ball에 대한 자세한 설명이 이어져야 하므로 (C)가 적절하다.

11 (A)는 메시지를 숨길 수 있다는 의미가 되어야 하므로 hide, (B)는 베이킹 소다와 물을 섞으라는 의미가 되어야 하므로 Mix(섞다), (C)는 그러면 메시지가 보인다는 의미가 되어야 하므로 appears가 적절하다.

서술형 시험대비　　　　　　　　p.123

01 Have you heard about the Sci-Magic show?

---

02 What do you mean?
03 ⓓ → to explain
04 It is about using science to explain magic tricks.
05 mean
06 (A) phone application　　(B) any questions
　　(C) the weather

02 이어지는 대화에서 BFF를 구체적으로 설명하고 있으므로 빈칸에 구체적인 정보를 요청하는 표현이 알맞다.

03 목적을 나타내는 to부정사 형태가 알맞다.

04 과학 마술 쇼는 마술 묘기를 설명하기 위해 과학을 사용하는 것에 관한 것이다.

05 potato clock이 무슨 의미냐고 묻는 표현이므로 mean이 적절하다.

06 오늘 나의 사랑스러운 아들 Tom이 새로운 휴대폰 어플리케이션 Chat Robot을 소개해 주었다. 이것은 어떠한 질문에도 대답할 수 있었다. Tom은 내게 어떻게 작동하는지 날씨에 대해 물어보며 보여주었다. 놀랍게도 이것은 우리에게 날씨에 대해 알려주었고 우리가 무엇이 필요할지 알려주었다. 나는 이 어플리케이션에 매우 놀랐다.

교과서

Grammar

핵심 Check　　　　　　　　p.124~125

1 (1) is covered with　　(2) is run by
2 (1) to read　　(2) to win　　(3) to write on

시험대비 기본평가　　　　　　　　p.126

01 (1) read about → read　　(2) born → was born
　　(3) choose → to choose　　(4) for her → to her
02 (1) was invited　　(2) to achieve　　(3) are caused
　　(4) to hurt　　(5) were found
03 (1) I want something to eat.
　　(2) We have a trip to plan.
　　(3) The new highway was completed last month.
　　(4) The ink is washed off easily with water.

01 (1) 'read a book'이 성립하므로 전치사 없이 수식하는 것이 옳다. (2) be born 태어나다 (3) options를 수식해야 하므로 to부정사 형태로 써야 한다. (4) 4형식 동사의 수동태가 직접목적어를 주어로 할 경우 간접목적어에 전치사를 붙이며, give는 전치사 to를 쓰는 동사이다. 단, 이때의 to는 생략하기도 한다.

19

02 (1) 주어가 회의에 초대받는 것이므로 수동태, (2) the goal을 수식해야 하므로 to부정사, (3) 사고가 야기되는 것이므로 수동태, (4) anything을 수식해야 하므로 to부정사, (5) 열쇠가 발견되는 것이며 이틀 전의 일이므로 과거형 수동태를 쓰는 것이 옳다.

03 (1) '먹을 것'이므로 to eat이 something을 수식하게 한다. (2) '계획할 여행'이므로 to plan이 a trip을 수식하도록 만든다. (3) 고속도로가 '완공되는 것'이므로 수동태, (4) 잉크가 '지워지는 것'이므로 수동태를 쓰는 것이 옳다.

01 ④   02 ②   03 ④
04 something to play with   05 ④   06 ②, ⑤
07 ⑤   08 There is nothing to see here.
09 borrow, to read   10 ③   11 ③
12 ④   13 ③   14 is expected   15 ④
16 ②   17 ④   18 I wasn't seen singing
a song with my friends by anybody.   19 was
discovered by   20 ③   21 ②
22 ②, ③   23 Do you have a story to tell?
24 I was told to taste the food by Mom.

01 'take care of twin sisters', 'ask many questions'라고 표현하므로 ④번이 옳다.

02 ① be filled with: ~으로 가득 차 있다 ③ 형용사와 to부정사가 동시에 명사를 수식할 때 '형용사+to부정사' 순서로 수식한다. ④ 5형식 동사의 목적격보어가 원형부정사인 경우 수동태를 만들 때 to부정사화한다. 따라서 made to do가 옳다. ⑤ make는 직접목적어를 주어로 한 수동태에서 간접목적어에 전치사 for를 붙이는 동사이므로 for me로 쓰는 것이 옳다.

03 모두 to부정사가 형용사로 사용되고 있으나 ④번은 목적을 나타내는 부사로 사용되었다.

04 play with something: 무언가를 가지고 놀다

05 ④ 구동사의 수동태에서 'by+행위자'를 생략하기 쉬우므로 이에 유의한다. was looked after by her라고 쓰는 것이 옳다.

06 주어진 문장은 4형식 동사의 과거 수동태이다. 따라서 능동태 시제를 과거로 고르는 것이 옳으며, 간접목적어가 주어로 쓰일 경우 별도로 전치사를 사용하지 않는다.

07 ①~④는 모두 수동태로 쓰여 made가 들어가는 것이 옳으며, ⑤번은 진행형으로 쓰여 making이 들어간다.

08 '볼만한 것'이므로 see를 to부정사로 만들어 nothing을 수식하게 만든다.

09 journey: 여행

10 by 이외의 다른 전치사를 쓰는 수동태 문제이다. be filled with: ~로 가득 차다 be pleased with: ~으로 기뻐하다

11 주어진 문장을 수동태로 바르게 만드는 문제이다. The child는 단수 주어이고, 시제가 saw로 과거형이므로 수동태를 만들 때 was seen으로 쓰고, 목적격보어 playing은 그대로 써주면 된다.

12 '백명의 손님을 대접할 점심'이므로 점심을 수식하면서 동시에 동사원형 serve를 취하기 위해서는 전치사 for가 아니라 to부정사를 쓰는 것이 옳다.

13 건물이 디자인된 것이냐고 묻고 있으므로 수동태를 써야 한다. 따라서 Did가 아닌 Was를 쓰는 것이 옳다.

14 정시에 도착하리라고 예상된다는 의미가 옳으므로 expect의 수동태를 써야 한다.

15 직접목적어를 주어로 할 때 간접목적어에 전치사 for를 붙이는 동사는 ④번이다. 나머지 동사들은 모두 to를 사용한다.

16 '친구에게 줄 어떤 것'이란 의미가 적절하므로 to give가 something을 수식하는 ②번이 옳다.

17 주어진 문장과 ④번은 형용사로 쓰인 to부정사이다. ① 부사적 용법, ②, ③, ⑤ 명사적 용법

18 주어진 문장의 의미는 '누구도 내가 내 친구들과 함께 노래 부르는 것을 보지 못했다.'는 의미이다.

19 누가 그 보물을 발견했는지를 묻고 있다. 수동태를 사용하여 Jackson 선장에 의해 발견되었다고 답할 수 있다.

20 deal with a problem이라고 쓰는 것이 옳으므로 to deal with가 정답이다. high blood pressure: 고혈압 deal with: ~을 다루다, ~을 대처하다

21 'play with friends'이므로 전치사 with를 쓰는 것이 옳다.

22 밑줄 친 offered는 4형식 동사로 직접목적어를 주어로 한 수동태에서는 간접목적어에 전치사 to를 붙이는 동사이다. 따라서 ②, ③번이 옳다.

23 '들려줄 이야기'이므로 to부정사가 a story를 수식하도록 문장을 만든다.

24 동사 told는 과거형이며 능동태의 목적어를 주어로 사용하여 수동태 문장을 만들어야 하므로 I에 수의 일치를 하여 was told를 쓴다.

01 was written by
02 (1) to read   (2) to study   (3) to worry about
03 I was given the watch by my father a few years ago. / The watch was given (to) me by my father a few years ago.
04 was made to laugh a lot by Helen's brother
05 was built / was invented / was divided / is surrounded / were surprised
06 something to say to you
07 I don't have enough time to work out these days.

08 ⓐ to do ⓑ was thrown

09 ⓐ to walk ⓑ set ⓒ were taken ⓓ were brought

10 I have no reason to refuse his request.

11 (1) A tree was planted by the Emperor himself.

　(2) A French company made us this car.

　(3) The young girls look up to the man.

　(4) Honey is made by worker bees.

12 Do you have any samples to give out?

13 (1) to do (2) to eat (3) to talk about

　(4) to ride (5) to read

14 The brave young man caught the thief.

　The thief was caught by the brave young man.

---

01 햄릿은 누가 썼는지에 관한 질문이므로 셰익스피어에 의해 쓰여진 것이라고 답하면 된다.

02 (1) a magazine을 수식하는 to부정사가 와야 한다. (2) 공부할 '많은 과목들'을 의미하므로 to부정사를 쓰는 것이 옳다. (3) '~에 관하여 걱정하다'는 'worry about ~'이므로 전치사 about을 써야 한다.

03 4형식 동사의 수동태를 묻는 문제이다. 동사 give는 직접목적어를 주어로 하는 수동태에서 간접목적어에 전치사 to를 붙인다. 이때의 to는 생략할 수 있다.

04 목적보어가 원형부정사인 경우 수동태를 만들 때 to부정사화한다.

05 건설 비용이 비싸지 않기 때문에 한씨 가족이 새 기숙사를 지었다. / 야구 경기는 미국인들에 의해 만들어졌다. / 우리나라는 두 나라로 나뉘었다. / 한국은 삼면이 물로 둘러싸여 있다. / 우리는 그들이 회의에 오리라고 기대하지 않았지만 그들이 그곳에 있었다. 우리는 그들을 보고 놀랐다.

06 '말할 어떤 것'이라는 의미로 작문을 하는 것이 좋다. to부정사가 something을 꾸미도록 문장을 만든다.

07 '운동할 시간'이므로 time to work out의 어순이 옳다.

08 '해야 할 많은 것'이므로 to부정사 형태로 many things를 수식하는 것이 옳으며 throw a party는 '파티를 열다'는 의미이다.

09 ⓐ '달 위를 걸은 최초의 인간'이라는 의미이므로 to부정사로 만들어 the first man을 수식하게 한다. ⓑ Neil이 달에 발을 디딘 것이므로 능동태 과거시제로 쓴다. ⓒ 사진이 찍혀서 지구로 가져다진 것은 수동태를 쓰는 것이 옳다.

10 거절할 이유라고 하였으므로 refuse를 to부정사로 만들어 reason을 수식하게 만든다.

11 (1) Emperor: 황제 (2) 4형식으로 쓰인 make이다. 직접목적어를 주어로 사용하고 있으므로 간접목적어에 전치사 for를 붙인다. 능동태로 A French company made this car for us.로 써도 좋다. (3) look up to: ~을 존경하다 (4) worker bee: 일벌

12 나눠주는 샘플이 있나요? give out: 나눠주다

13 (1) many boring things를 수식하는 to부정사 가 와야 하며,

'지겨운 일을 하다'는 'do boring things'이므로 to do가 오는 것이 옳다. (2) '먹을 것'이므로 something을 수식하는 'to eat'을 쓰는 것이 옳다. (3) '~에 관하여 말하다'는 표현은 'talk about ~'이다. (4) a bicycle을 수식하는 to부정사를 써야 한다. (5) '읽을 시간'이므로 to read를 써서 time을 수식한다.

14 catch: ~을 붙잡다

교과서 Reading

확인문제　　　　　　　　　　　　p.132

1 T 2 T 3 F 4 T 5 F

확인문제　　　　　　　　　　　　p.133

1 F 2 T 3 T 4 F 5 F 6 T

교과서 확인학습 A　　　　　　p.134~135

01 amazing things are possible

02 are they actually possible　　03 Let Down

04 must lower, to let people in

05 could, hold up a person

06 hold up, has about

07 All those hairs, hold up

08 the ability to hold up

09 wrap her hair around

10 doesn't, will get, sore　　　11 Scare for

12 scare children to get, from　　13 is powered by

14 produce electricity to light up, from

15 be changed into

16 helpful in, because the amount is, small

17 For example, from, produces

18 of the average, electricity

19 an unbelievable amount of screams, entire

20 Away　　　　21 is lifted and flown by

22 actually work 23 weighs about

24 normal, an amusement park

25 about, to lift up

26 have to think about, themselves

27 add a few more thousand

28 challenge, pumping up all those

1 In animation movies, amazing things are possible.

2 But are they actually possible in real life?

3 Let Down Your Hair, Rapunzel!

4 In the animation, Rapunzel must lower her long hair to let people in her tower.

5 But could human hair really hold up a person?

6 Surprisingly, yes! A single hair can hold up 100g and an average head has about 120,000 hairs.

7 All those hairs could hold up a couple of elephants!

8 With her hair, Rapunzel has the ability to hold up a person.

9 But she should wrap her hair around something strong and heavy.

10 If she doesn't, she will get a very sore neck.

11 We Scare for Energy

12 In the animation, monsters scare children to get energy from their screams.

13 Amazingly, their city is powered by this sound!

14 But could we actually produce electricity to light up a city from sound?

15 Yes, sound can be changed into electricity.

16 But it would not be helpful in our everyday activities because the amount is too small.

17 For example, the sound from a car horn only produces 50mv.

18 That is only 1/4400 of the average 220v of electricity in our homes.

19 So, we would need an unbelievable amount of screams to light up an entire city.

20 Up, Up and Away!

21 The house is lifted and flown by thousands of balloons in the animation.

22 Could that actually work?

23 Let's say that a house weighs about 50,000kg.

24 A normal balloon at an amusement park can lift about 14g.

25 So we need about 3,570,000 balloons to lift up the house.

26 We also have to think about the weight of the balloons themselves and the strings.

27 Then, we need to add a few more thousand balloons.

28 Now, the biggest challenge is pumping up all those balloons!

01 amazing things   02 ④   03 ③

04 ③   05 is powered   06 ④   07 ③

08 ⑤   09 ①   10 animation   11 ③

12 The hardest part is pumping them up.   13 ③

14 ③   15 ⑤   16 doesn't wrap her hair around something strong and heavy   17 ④

18 We Scare for Energy   19 to light up   20 ③

21 ⑤   22 ⑤   23 is lifted and flown

24 ② → lift   25 ②

01 애니메이션 영화 속에서 벌어지는 놀라운 것들을 가리키는 대명사이다.

02 머리카락으로 코끼리도 들어 올릴 수 있다고 하였으므로 ④번은 글의 내용과 일치하지 않는다.

03 ③ Rapunzel의 머리카락으로 사람들을 들어 올릴 수 있는 것이므로 With라고 쓰는 것이 옳다.

04 '아픈 목'이라는 의미이므로 painful이 옳다.

05 소리에 의해서 동력 공급을 받는다는 의미가 자연스러우므로 수동태를 쓰는 것이 옳다.

06 소리가 전기로 바뀌는 양이 너무 적으므로 유용하지 않을 것이라는 말이 들어가는 것이 가장 적절하다. 따라서 ④번이 옳다. ①, ②: 감사하는 ③: 사려 깊은 ⑤: 훌륭한

07 소리로 전기를 만드는 것이 일상생활에 도움이 되지 않는 이유를 설명하기 위한 예를 들고 있다. 따라서 For example이 옳다.

08 ⑤번은 글에 나와 있지 않는 내용이다.

09 ⓐ에는 수동태에 쓰이는 전치사 by가 들어가고, ⓑ, ⓒ, ⓓ는 '대략'의 의미를 갖는 부사 about이 들어간다. ⓔ 전치사 about이 들어간다.

10 그림이 움직이는 것처럼 보이는 영화는 애니메이션이다.

11 ⓐ, ⓑ, ⓓ가 글의 내용과 일치한다. a piece of cake: 식은 죽 먹기

12 가장 큰 어려움은 모든 풍선에 바람을 넣는 것이라고 하였다.

13 (A)는 '~하는 것'이라고 해석되는 동명사이다. 따라서 ③번이 옳다.

14 주어진 문장의 All those hairs가 가리키는 것은 120,000 hairs이다.

15 밑줄 친 ⓐ는 '대략'이라는 의미로 쓰인 부사 about이다. 따라서 ⑤번이 정답이다. ①, ④ ~에 관한 ② 여기저기 ③ 지금 막 ~하려고 하여

16 앞 문장에서 언급한 것을 하지 않을 경우에 대하여 말하고 있다.

17 Rapunzel이 코끼리를 들어 올릴 수 있다는 말은 나와 있지 않다.

18 '우리는 에너지를 얻기 위해 겁준다.'는 의미이다.

19 도시를 밝혀주는 전기를 소리로부터 만들어 내는 것에 관한 글이다.

20 소리를 전기로 바꾸는 양이 매우 적기 때문에 전체 도시를 밝히기 위해서는 엄청난 양의 비명소리가 필요하다는 의미가 옳다. 따라서 ③번이 가장 적절하다. reasonable: 합리적인 incredible: 놀라운, 믿기 힘든

21 우리에게 전기가 필요한 이유는 글에 나와 있지 않다.

22 (A) 괴물들이 아이들을 겁주는 것이므로 능동태, (B) 괴물들의 도시를 지칭하는 것이므로 their, (C) 소리로부터 전기를 생산하는 것이므로 from이 옳다. into를 쓰면 전기를 소리로 바꾼다는 의미가 되므로 글의 내용상 옳지 않다.

23 수 천 개의 풍선이 집을 들어 올린 것이므로, 수동태를 쓰는 것이 옳다.

24 풍선이 대략 14g의 무게를 들어 올릴 수 있다는 의미이다. 따라서 수동태가 아닌 능동태로 쓰는 것이 옳다.

25 사람의 머리카락이 사람을 들어 올릴 수 있는지 물음 → (B) 머리카락 한 개가 들어 올릴 수 있는 무게와 사람의 평균 머리카락 개수 → (A) Rapunzel이 머리카락으로 사람을 들어 올릴 수 있음 → (C) 하지만 목이 아프지 않으려면 머리카락을 강하고 무거운 것에 감아야 함

서술형 시험대비 p.142~143

01 holding up a person with her hair 02 to allow people to enter her tower 03 is wrapped, strong and heavy 04 It can hold up 100g. 05 be held up 06 ⓐ 아이들의 ⓑ 괴물들의 07 sound can be changed into electricity 08 Because the amount is too small. 09 is produced by the sound from a car horn 10 scared 11 The house is lifted and flown by thousands of balloons in the animation. 12 It can lift about 14g. 13 to lift a house / are needed, pumping up all those balloons

01 Rapunzel이 영화 속에서 하는 놀라는 일은 그녀의 머리카락으로 사람을 들어 올리는 것이다.

02 allow+목적어+to부정사: 목적어가 V하는 것을 허락하다. enter: ~로 들어가다

03 주어가 Rapunzel의 머리카락이므로 수동태를 써서 표현한다. Rapunzel의 머리카락이 강하고 무거운 것에 감겨 있지 않으면 그녀의 목이 아플 것이다.

04 질문: 한 올의 머리카락은 얼마만큼의 무게를 지탱할 수 있나요?

05 밑줄 친 문장 ⓑ를 수동태로 만드는 문제이다. 조동사 뒤에는 동사원형을 써야 하므로 be동사를 원형으로 바꿔 답을 쓰는 것에 유의한다.

06 아이들이 비명소리로부터 에너지를 얻어 괴물들의 도시에 전기를 공급받는다.

07 목적어가 sound이므로 sound를 주어로 하여 수동태를 만든다. 행위자가 중요한 대상이 아닐 경우 'by+행위자'는 생략해도 무방하다.

08 질문: 소리를 전기로 바꾸는 것이 우리들의 일상적인 활동에 왜 유용하지 않은지 그 이유를 쓰시오.

09 목적어를 주어로 두었으므로, 수동태 문장을 만든다. 50mv는 셀 수 없는 양이므로 be동사를 단수로 쓰는 것에 유의한다.

10 be scared: 겁먹다

11 목적어 the house를 주어로 하고, the house는 단수이므로 수의 일치에 유의하여 수동태를 만든다.

12 놀이공원에 있는 보통의 풍선은 몇 그램의 무게를 들어 올릴 수 있는지 묻고 있다.

13 풍선으로 집을 들어 올리는 것이 가능하냐는 질문에, 대략 357만개의 풍선이 필요하지만 그 모든 풍선에 바람을 넣는 것은 힘든 도전이라고 말한다. imagine은 동명사를 목적어로 취하는 동사이다.

영역별 핵심문제 p.145~149

01 surprisingly 02 (1) looking forward to (2) pump up (3) Let's say that (4) turn into 03 ④ 04 ④ 05 (1) May I pick your brain? (2) My mother asked me to light up the lamp. (3) I saw a couple of birds sitting on the bench. 06 Have you heard about the science festival? 07 ⓓ → show 08 ② 09 We put an egg in vinegar for two days. 10 the egg is changed into a ball 11 ⑤ 12 ⓔ appears 13 ⑤ 14 Yes, I have. 15 (A) a Pic Gardener App (B) how to take care of the plant (C) useful 16 ② 17 ② 18 ④ 19 Lamon's daughter was not allowed to go to the park alone by Lamon. 20 ③ 21 ④ 22 ④ 23 to read, to drink, to sit on[in] 24 ④ 25 are taken care of by him 26 ④ 27 ④ 28 her hair 29 ③, ④ 30 ⑤ 31 ⑤ 32 An unbelievable amount of screams

01 주어진 관계는 형용사와 부사의 관계를 나타낸다.

02 look forward to: ~을 기대하다, pump up: 바람을 넣다, let's say that: ~을 가정해 보자, turn into: ~가 되다

03 lower: 낮추다

04 주어진 문장에서 miss는 '놓치다'를 의미하며 이와 같은 의미로 쓰인 것은 '그들은 단 하나의 음도 놓치고 싶어 하지 않는다.'라는 의미로 쓰인 ④번이다. ①번은 '이해하지 못하다', ②, ③, ⑤번은 '그리워하다'를 의미한다.

05 pick one's brain: ~의 지혜를 빌리다

23

07 사역동사 let 뒤에 원형부정사 show가 적절하다.

08 엄마가 Tom의 시범을 통해 놀라움을 나타냈음을 알 수 있으므로 surprised(놀란)가 적절하다.

10 change를 사용하여 수동태로 바꾸어 쓸 수 있다. turn into: ~가 되다

11 왜 달걀이 공으로 변했는지는 알 수 없다.

12 동사가 오는 자리이므로 appears가 알맞다.

14 have 뒤에는 heard about it이 생략된 것이다.

15 나는 오늘 Minho와 함께 Smart App Contest에 대해 이야기 하였다. 그는 거기에 참가할 것이라고 이야기하였다. 나는 a Pic Gardener App에 대한 그의 아이디어가 매우 인상 깊었다. 그 것은 내가 식물 사진을 찍을 때 어떻게 식물을 관리해야 하는지 알려주는 앱이었다. 나는 이것이 유용할 것이라고 생각했다. 나는 그가 대회에서 잘할 것이라 믿는다.

16 Jin에 의하여 그림이 그려진 것이므로 ②번이 옳다.

17 ② disappear는 자동사로 수동태가 될 수 없다. was를 삭제한다.

18 의문문이므로 anything을 쓰는 것이 좋으며 -thing으로 끝나는 부정대명사는 '형용사+to부정사' 어순으로 수식을 받는다.

19 본동사가 과거이며 Lamon의 딸이 주어로 쓰이므로 3인칭 과 거동사를 써서 수동태를 만든다.

20 ③ '함께 갈 친구'이므로 전치사 with와 함께 써야 한다.

21 ④ happen은 자동사이므로 수동태로 쓰일 수 없다.

22 ①번은 목적격보어가 원형부정사인 5형식 동사의 수동태이므로 to clean으로 고쳐야 하며, ②번은 친구들에 의해 강아지라고 불리는 것이므로 수동태인 was called, ③번은 방에 불들이 꺼 졌는지를 물어보는 수동태 의문문이므로 주어 the lights에 맞 추어 Were, ⑤번은 바이올린이 연주되는 것이므로 수동태를 쓰 는 것이 옳다.

23 to부정사의 형용사 용법을 활용하여 빈칸을 채울 수 있다.

24 ④ discuss는 타동사이므로 전치사 없이 목적어를 취한다. 따 라서 전치사 about을 삭제하는 것이 옳다.

25 목적어가 복수명사인 my sisters이므로 수동태 be동사를 복수 동사로 쓴다. relieved: 안도한 take care of: ~을 돌보다

26 pick은 '(꽃)을 꺾다', '(과일)을 따다', '~을 고르다'는 의미이다. '~을 줍다'라는 의미로 사용될 때에는 pick up으로 표현한다.

27 ⓐ amazing ⓑ lower ⓒ let ⓓ wrap이 들어가는 것이 옳다.

28 Rapunzel은 그녀의 머리카락으로 사람을 들어 올리는 능력이 있다.

29 하나의 머리에 평균적으로 120,000개의 머리카락이 있다고 하였다. 코끼리 한 마리의 무게는 6톤이다. (0.1x120,000/2) ①, ②, ⑤번은 글을 읽고 답할 수 없다.

30 주어진 문장의 That이 지칭하는 것은 50mv이다. 따라서 ⑤번 에 들어가는 것이 가장 적절하다.

31 ⓐ는 형용사로 쓰인 to부정사로 electricity를 수식하고 있다.

⑤번은 부사로 사용된 to부정사로 '~하기 위하여'라는 의미로 해석된다.

32 마지막 문장을 수동태로 만든 것이다. 주어 자리가 비어 있으므 로 본래 문장의 목적어를 빈칸에 써준다.

단원별 예상문제　　p.150~153

01 (1) take away　(2) turn on　(3) take care of　(4) light up　　02 experiment　　03 (1) turn into　(2) wrap, around　(3) a couple of　　04 ⑤
05 (C) – (E) – (B) – (D) – (A)　　06 have you heard about the Chat Robot?
07 application 08 ⑤　　09 She made a potato clock yesterday.　　10 It can work because potatoes can produce electricity.　　11 ④
12 ③　　13 ④　　14 ③　　15 Did he show the picture to you? / Was the picture shown to you by him?　　16 Practice is the only way to master English.　　17 ⑤　　18 ⑤
19 ③　　20 ⑤　　21 They scare children.
22 ④　　23 Lifting up a house with thousands of balloons　24 the weight of the balloons, the strings

01 take away: ~을 가져가다, turn on: ~을 켜다, take care of: ~을 돌보다, light up: ~을 밝히다, 점등하다

02 무슨 일이 일어나는지 연구해서 새로운 과학적 지식을 얻기 위 해 행해지는 과학적 검사

03 turn into: ~이 되다, wrap A around B: A를 B에 감싸다, a couple of: 한 쌍의, 둘의

04 lift: (동) 들어 올리다, (명) 승강기

05 (C) 무슨 쇼를 보고 있는지 질문 - (E) 대답 및 경험 질문 - (B) 대답 및 구체적인 설명 요구 - (D) 프로그램에 대한 구체적 설 명 - (A) 흥미 표현

07 특정한 일을 하기 위해 고안된 프로그램을 가리키는 말은 application(응용 프로그램)이다.

08 Tom의 엄마가 밖에 비에 놀란다는 설명은 대화의 내용과 일치 하지 않는다.

09 Mina는 어제 감자 시계를 만들었다.

10 Mina의 시계는 감자가 전기를 만들어 내기 때문에 작동할 수 있다.

11 전치사 at의 목적어 자리이므로 동명사로 만들고, '의지할 친구' 이므로 to부정사로 a friend를 수식하게 만드는 것이 옳다.

12 ⓑ disappear는 자동사이므로 수동태로 쓸 수 없다. ⓓ 누군가 와 결혼한 상태임을 표현할 때에는 'be married to'라고 쓰는 것이 옳다.

13 -thing으로 끝나는 부정대명사의 수식은 '형용사+to부정사' 어 순이므로 ④번이 옳다.

14 ③ 능동태의 시제가 과거이므로 were canceled로 쓰는 것이 옳다.

16 practice: 연습 master: ~에 숙달[통달]하다

17 (A) let down: ~을 아래로 내리다 (B) the ability를 수식하는 to부정사 (C) 부정어를 포함하고 있으므로 Unless는 쓸 수 없다.

18 밑줄 친 ⓐ는 '목적'을 나타내는 부사로 사용된 to부정사이다. ① hope의 목적어로 쓰인 명사적 용법 ② 목적격 보어로 사용된 명사적 용법의 to부정사 ③ 진주어 로 사용된 명사적 용법의 to부정사 ④ a chair를 수식하는 형용사적 용법의 to부정사 ⑤ '~하기 위해서'라는 의미의 목적을 나타내는 부사적 용법의 to부정사.

19 make는 produce를 대신하여 쓰일 수 있다. 따라서 밑줄 친 ⓐ를 수동태로 전환한 ③번이 같은 의미의 문장이다.

20 자동차 경적소리가 만들어 내는 소리의 양이 50mv라는 의미이므로 수동태가 아닌 능동태를 쓰는 것이 옳다.

21 괴물들은 에너지를 얻기 위하여 아이들을 겁준다고 하였다.

22 집 한 채를 들어 올리기 위해서는 약 3,570,000개의 풍선이 필요하다고 하였다.

23 that은 풍선으로 집을 들어 올리는 것을 의미한다.

24 집을 들어올릴 계획을 할 때, 집 무게뿐만 아니라 풍선의 무게와 실의 무게 역시 고려해야 한다고 하였다.

하는 것이 자연스럽다.

05 3, 4, 5형식으로 쓰일 수 있는 동사 make를 수동태로 만드는 문제이다. 첫 번째 문장은 3형식 동사로 쓰인 make이고, 두 번째 문장은 4형식 동사로 쓰인 make이다. 이때 사람을 주어로 하는 수동태는 쓸 수 없으므로 직접목적어를 주어로 한 수동태를 만들어 간접목적어에 for를 붙인다. 마지막 문장은 목적어가 목적격 보어의 주체가 되는 5형식으로 목적어인 us를 수동태 주어로 만들고, 목적격보어의 형태는 그대로 유지한다.

06 swim in a pool이므로 전치사 in을 쓰는 것이 옳다.

07 수동태의 주어가 복수명사인 the oranges이므로 복수동사 were를 써서 수동태를 만드는 것에 유의한다.

08 '결정할 시간'이므로 time to decide를 쓸 수 있다.

09 질문: 글에 따르면, 사람들이 탑에 들어가기 위해서 무엇이 내려져야 하나요?

10 사람이 머리카락에 의해 떠받쳐 질 수 있는지를 묻는 문장이다. 밑줄 친 ⓐ에서 hold up의 목적어가 주어로 쓰이고 있으므로 수동태를 답으로 쓰면 된다.

11 해석: 나는 친구를 내 성으로 들이기 위해서 내 머리를 감을 무언가가 필요해. 나는 그것이 강하고 무겁길 원해. 그런 것 가지고 있니? to부정사의 형용사 용법을 활용하여 문장을 만든다.

12 질문: 애니메이션 영화에서 괴물들은 왜 아이들을 겁주나요?

13 A: 자동차 경적 소리에 의해 전기가 만들어질 수 있다는 걸 아니? B: 정말? 난 몰랐어. 얼마나 많은 전기가 만들어지는 데? A: 겨우 50mv야.

🦉 서술형 실전문제   p.154~155

01 It is special because it can hide your message.

02 She needs a card, baking soda and water.

03 카드를 포도 주스로 칠하면 메시지를 볼 수 있다.

04 I have many things to plan

05 (1) Some mistakes were made by me.
　(2) A pretty doll was made for me by my friend.
　(3) We are always made bored by Jason.

06 swim → swim in

07 were not bought

08 You were given enough time to decide.

09 Her long hair must be lowered.

10 is held up

11 to wrap around, strong, heavy

12 They scare children to get energy from their screams.

13 can be produced

01 "Mystery Card"는 메시지를 숨길 수 있기 때문에 특별하다.

02 "Mystery Card"를 만들기 위해 카드, 베이킹 소다 그리고 물이 필요하다.

04 바빠 보인다며 무슨 일이냐고 묻는 말에 계획할 일이 많다고 답

🐇 창의사고력 서술형 문제   p.156

|모범답안|

01 (A) 3 p.m. every Wednesday in May
　(B) The Youth Community Center
　(C) make your own drone and learn how to control it

02 (1) The safe wasn't unlocked.
　(2) My closet was opened by my friend.
　(3) The sandwich was taken away by somebody.
　(4) I was hit by a flying ball.
　(5) Mom's vase was broken by us.
　(6) The flour is poured into a bowl.

03 (1) I have a book to borrow from you.
　(2) We have no money to spend.
　(3) You don't have a right to speak for them.
　(4) She has the reason to believe that.
　(5) There was no chance to win the race.
　(6) People have the desire to learn English.

01 I can't wait for it. 　02 They can do different kinds of experiments. 　03 ⑤ 　04 They should prepare some water, vinegar, baking soda, and beans. 　05 (A) heard　(B) Make　(C) to control 　06 (A) with　(B) in　(C) for　(D) into 　07 ② 　08 (A) Write a message on the card with it.　(B) Paint over the card with grape juice. 　09 ②, ⑤ 　10 ⑤ 　11 Have you heard about the science fair? 　12 ② 　13 Give the other person a chance to talk. 　14 was laughed at by Jason 　15 ③ 　16 ⑤ 　17 ④ 　18 ④ 　19 ② 　20 Wrap your hair around something strong and heavy 　21 ② 　22 ② 　23 electricity from sound, it is helpful 　24 ④

01 'look forward to ~ing'는 '~을 기대하다'라는 의미로 'can't wait for'와 바꾸어 쓸 수 있다.

02 Hojin과 Katy는 과학 박람회에서 다른 종류의 실험을 할 수 있다.

03 ⑤번을 제외한 나머지는 모두 제안을 나타낸다.

04 Dancing Beans를 만들기 위해 약간의 물, 식초, 베이킹 소다 그리고 콩을 준비해야 한다.

05 (A) 경험을 묻는 현재완료로 hear의 과거분사 heard가 알맞다. (B) 명령문에 해당하므로 Make가 알맞다. (C) 어떻게 이를 조절할 수 있는지를 배우라는 의미를 표현하므로 '의문사+to부정사' 형태인 to control이 알맞다.

06 (A) '~와 함께'를 나타내는 with, (B) '~에 넣다'는 의미가 되어야 하므로 in, (C) '이틀 동안'을 나타내므로 for, (D) turn into: ~가 되다

07 would like to: ~하고 싶다

09 enter는 '참가하다, 들어가다'라는 의미로 사용되었다. share: 공유하다 exit: 나가다; 출구

12 상대방이 한 말에 대해 '나도 그렇다'고 말할 때 'So do I.' 또는 'So am I.'를 사용할 수 있다. 상대방이 사용한 동사가 be동사이므로 'So am I.'로 바꾸어 쓸 수 있다.

13 '말할 기회'이므로 a chance를 to talk가 수식하도록 문장을 만든다.

14 laugh at: ~를 비웃다, 놀리다

15 주어진 문장의 to부정사는 rules를 수식하는 형용사로 사용되었다. ③은 something을 수식하는 형용사로 사용된 to부정사이다. make money 돈을 벌다

16 '먹을 것'이 아무것도 없었다는 의미이다. to eat이 nothing을 수식하도록 만드는 것이 옳은 문장이다.

17 ④ 주어가 복수명사인 The towels이므로 복수 동사를 쓰는 것

이 옳다. 따라서 were이다.

18 밑줄 친 ⓐ에는 '실제의 삶 속에서'라는 의미를 완성하는 전치사 in이 들어간다. ① worry about: ~에 대해 걱정하다 ② wait for: ~을 기다리다 ③ be full of: ~으로 가득 차다 ⑤ be known for: ~으로 유명하다 ④ be interested in: ~에 흥미가 있다

19 ⓑ의 to부정사는 the ability를 수식하는 형용사로 사용되었으므로 ②번이 옳다.

20 강하고 무거운 것에 머리카락을 감아야 목이 아프지 않을 것이라고 하였다.

21 양이 너무 적기 때문에 일상의 활동에 유용하지 않다는 것이므로 이유를 나타내는 because가 옳다.

22 ② 괴물들의 도시는 아이들의 비명소리에 의해 동력을 공급 받는다고 하였다.

23 최신 기술로, 우리는 실제로 소리로부터 전기를 만들 수 있다. 그러나 그 양이 너무 적기 때문에 그것이 우리 일상생활에 도움이 된다고 말하기는 어렵다.

24 밑줄 친 ⓐ는 부사로 쓰인 to부정사로 '~하기 위하여'라고 해석된다. ④번은 형용사로 사용된 to부정사이다.

Your Only Limit Is You

시험대비 실력평가 p.164

01 ③   02 ④   03 ①

04 memorable   05 ③

06 (1) cheer up   (2) sit up   (3) satisfied with

     (4) gas pedal   (5) finish line

01 타자에게 공을 던지는 선수를 나타내는 말은 pitcher(투수)이다. catcher: 포수, coach: 코치, hitter: 타자, outfielder: 외야수

02 lap이 '무릎'이라는 뜻도 있지만 이 문장에서는 '한 바퀴'를 의미한다.

03 주어진 문장에서 count는 '중요하다'라는 의미로 사용되었으며 이와 같은 의미로 쓰인 것은 ①번이다. 나머지는 '(수를) 세다'를 의미한다.

04 주어진 관계는 반의어 관계이다. forgettable: 잊을 만한, memorable: 기억할 만한

05 complete: 완전한; 끝내다

06 gas pedal: 가속 페달, finish line: 결승선, cheer up: 기운을 내다, sit up: 바로 앉다, be satisfied with: ~에 만족하다

서술형 시험대비 p.165

01 uncomfortable

02 (1) official   (2) hit   (3) lap   (4) balance

03 (1) win a[the] race   (2) miss a chance

     (3) were filled with

04 (1) I walked ahead of him.

     (2) I heard that my sister won (the) second place.

     (3) I didn't want to miss the chance to meet the famous singer.

05 (1) Why the long face?

     (2) You'll do better next time.

06 (1) The project should be completed in a week.

     (2) He pressed down hard on the gas pedal.

     (3) I was not satisfied with my pitching.

01 주어진 관계는 반의어 관계이다. comfortable: 편안한, uncomfortable: 불편한

02 official: 심판, hit: 부딪히다, lap: 바퀴, balance: 균형

03 win a race: 경주에 이기다, miss a chance: 기회를 놓치다, be filled with: ~로 가득 차다

Conversation

핵심 Check p.166~167

1 (1) Don't take it too hard

    (2) Don't be so hard on yourself

    (3) Cheer up, You can do it

2 (1) me help you

    (2) Do you need any help

    (3) deep / Don't worry, help you

교과서 대화문 익히기

Check(√) True or False p.168

1 T   2 F   3 F   4 T

교과서 확인학습 p.170~171

Listen & Talk 1 A-1

missed, chances, three, pointer / hard, You'll do better

Listen & Talk 1 A-2

volleyball match / close match, strong enough / you're a great player

Listen & Talk 1 B

won the match / Congratulations / pitching / you're a great pitcher, do better

Listen & Talk 2 A-1

first time / keep my balance / hold / Don't let / Sit up, look straight ahead

Listen & Talk 2 A-1

how to stand on my head / Let me help you, catch you

Listen & Talk 2 B

I'm still not comfortable with it / What problem / lift my leg high enough / Let me, side kick

Communication

worried about / Why are / catch high balls / gave away

/ let me help you / my skills get better / Don't worry

Wrap Up 1

Do you come / once a week / easy for me / how to swim / that'll help me a lot

---

시험대비 기본평가   p.172

01 You'll do better next time.

02 ⑤   03 (A) pitching   (B) pitcher   04 ③

02 ⑤번은 상대방에게 도움을 요청하는 표현이며 이를 제외한 나머지는 모두 상대방에게 도움을 제안하고 있다.

03 pitching: 투구, pitcher: 투수

시험대비 실력평가   p.173~174

01 (I'm) Sorry, but I can't help you now.

02 ⑤   03 ③   04 ⑤

05 It(=The score) was eight to seven.   06 ④

07 (B) – (D) – (C) – (A) – (E)

08 I gave away too many goals.   09 ②

10 He takes a swimming class once a week.

11 She teaches them how to swim.   12 ⑤

02 ⑤번을 제외한 나머지는 모두 격려하는 표현이다.

03 (A)close는 '아슬아슬한, 접전의'를 뜻하며 이와 같이 쓰인 것은 ③번이다. ①, ④번은 '닫다' ②번은 '가까운', ⑤번은 '친한'으로 쓰였다.

04 ⑤ Jack은 경기에 이겼다.

05 The Reds팀은 야구 경기에서 8대 7로 이겼다.

06 (A)는 과거시제이므로 won, (B)는 접전을 가리키는 말이므로 close game이다, (C) 이유를 묻고 있으므로 Why가 적절하다.

07 (B) 처음 자전거를 타보는지 여부 질문 - (D) 대답 및 어려움 설명 - (C) 도움 제공 - (A) 감사 표현 및 부탁 - (E) 안심 시키기 및 자전거 가르쳐주기

08 give away: 내주다

09 Megan은 지난 축구 경기에 대해 걱정하다가 James의 도움으로 자신의 실력이 나아지길 희망하고 있다.

10 Jake는 일주일에 한번 수영 수업을 듣는다.

11 Anna는 학교 동아리에서 아이들에게 수영하는 법을 가르친다.

12 ⑤번을 제외한 나머지는 모두 시무룩한 얼굴을 하고 있는 이유를 언급하고 있다.

서술형 시험대비   p.175

01 Can I give you a hand?

02 (A) stand   (B) Kick   (C) catch

03 stand on her head

04 She can't catch high balls.

05 He is going to kick high balls to her.

06 the taegwondo side kick / lift my leg high enough / the kick pad / my side kick

02 stand on one's head: 물구나무서다, kick: ~을 차다, catch: 잡다

03 Sarah는 물구나무서기를 시도하고 있다.

04 Megan이 가진 문제는 그녀가 높은 공을 잡을 수 없는 것이다.

05 James는 Megan의 축구 기술을 향상시키기 위해 그에게 높은 공을 차 줄 것이다.

06 나는 태권도 옆차기를 연습했을 때 실망스러움을 느꼈다. 내가 열심히 연습했음에도 불구하고 나는 편하게 잘 안 되었다. 특히, 나는 내 다리를 높이 들어올릴 수가 없었다. 그것은 나의 가장 큰 문제였다. 다행히, 나의 코치님이 킥 패드를 들고 나를 도와주었다. 나는 코치님에게 나의 옆차기를 보여주었고 그와 함께 많은 연습을 하였다. 나는 나를 도와준 코치님께 정말로 감사했다.

교과서

Grammar

핵심 Check   p.176~177

1 (1) who   (2) whose camera

2 (1) dancing(또는 dance)   (2) shaving(또는 shave)

   (3) watching(또는 watch)   (4) falling(또는 fall)

   (5) pouring(또는 pour)

시험대비 기본평가   p.178

01 (1) I have a friend who speaks English very well.

   (2) We stayed in a hotel which was located near the beach.

   (3) Do you want to see the pictures which I took?

   (4) Jenny took care of a dog whose tail was hurt.

02 (1) playing(또는 play)   (2) making (또는 make)

   (3) talking(또는 talk)   (4) crossing(또는 cross)

03 (1) Did you eat the cake that she bought for you?

   (2) Is there anything that you want to see?

   (3) Did you hear him cry[crying]?

   (4) Kelly sees a person wave[waving] a white flag.

01 (1) He가 사람이고 주격이므로 주격 관계대명사 who. (2) 선행사가 사물인 a hotel이고, 대명사 It이 주격으로 쓰였으므로 관계대명사 which. (3) them이 목적격으로 쓰인 사물이므로 관계대명사 which. (4) Its가 소유격으로 쓰이고 있고 개를 지칭하므로 관계대명사 whose를 쓴다.

02 (1)~(4) 모두 지각동사의 목적격보어의 형태를 묻는 문제이다. 지각동사의 목적격보어는 원형부정사나 현재분사를 쓴다.

03 (1) '그녀가 너에게 사준 케이크'이므로 관계절이 cake를 수식하도록 문장을 만든다. (2) 의문문이나 부정문에서는 anything을 쓴다. (3) 들은 주체는 you이고 '그가 우는 것'이므로 he를 목적격으로 만들고 cry를 목적격보어로 하여 문장을 만든다. (4) '어떤 사람이 깃발을 흔드는 것'이므로 a person을 목적어로, wave를 목적격보어로 하여 영작한다.

시험대비 실력평가 p.179~181

01 ②, ③, ⑤ 02 ④ 03 ③ 04 I like the boy who wanted to come to the party yesterday. 05 ①, ⑤ 06 ⑤ 07 She heard water running(또는 run). 08 ④ 09 ④ 10 ②, ⑤ 11 We heard a dog barking in the middle of the night. 12 ⑤ 13 I know a girl who[that] really enjoys swimming. 14 ③ 15 who[that], which[that], that 16 build[building] 17 ④ 18 is the month that comes before 19 playing 20 ③ 21 come(또는 coming), paint(ing), call(ing), climb(ing)

01 목적격 관계대명사 whom의 자리이다. 따라서 who가 가능하며 that이 쓰여도 무방하다.

02 watch는 지각동사이므로 목적격보어로 원형부정사나 현재분사를 취한다. want는 to부정사를 목적격보어로 취하는 동사이다.

03 ③번 문장은 'Jane has a sister whose hobby is running.'으로 쓰는 것이 우리말을 바르게 옮긴 문장이다.

04 who를 대신하여 that을 써도 무방하다.

05 목적격보어로 원형부정사를 사용하고 있으므로 빈칸에는 지각동사가 들어가는 것이 옳다.

06 모두 주격 혹은 목적격으로 사용된 관계대명사 who를 쓰지만 ⑤번은 소유격 관계대명사 whose의 자리이다.

07 'hear'는 지각동사이므로 목적격보어로 원형부정사나 분사를 사용하여 작문한다.

08 ①, ③, ⑤번은 지각동사로 fly(ing)를 목적격보어로 쓸 수 있으나, ④번은 'allow+목적어+to 부정사'가 수동태로 전환된 것이므로 to fly가 들어간다. ②는 현재진행형으로 쓰이고 있으며 '그 비행기는 관광객들을 집으로 실어 나르는 중이다'라는 의미로 해석 할 수 있다. ⑤ fly in: 날아 들어오다

09 ④번은 선행사가 사람이므로 who를 쓰는 것이 옳다.

10 'He has blond hair.' 혹은 'His hair is blond.'로 표현할 수 있다.

11 '개가 짖는 것'이므로 지각동사 hear의 구조를 이용하여 hear a dog barking을 기본 토대로 문장을 만들 수 있다.

12 소년이 괴롭힘당하는 것이므로 'being bullied'라고 쓰는 것이 옳다.

13 '수영하는 것을 정말로 즐기는'이 소녀를 수식하고 있으므로, 관계대명사를 이용하여 a girl을 수식하도록 한다. enjoy는 동명사를 목적어로 취하는 동사이다.

14 선행사가 사물인 the house이므로 관계대명사 which를 쓰는 것이 옳다.

15 첫 번째 문장은 사람을 선행사로 받는 주격 관계대명사 who 또는 that이 들어가야 한다. 두 번째 문장은 사물을 선행사로 받는 목적격 관계대명사 which 또는 that이 들어가야 하며, 마지막 문장에는 사람과 동물이 혼합되어 있는 선행사이므로 관계대명사 that을 쓰는 것이 옳다.

16 '나는 새로운 주차장이 그들에 의하여 지어지는 것을 보았다.'라고 하였으므로 '나는 그들이 새로운 주차장을 짓는 것을 보았다.'라고 쓰면 된다.

17 ④번은 명사절을 이끄는 접속사 that이다. 명사절을 이끄는 접속사 that은 완전한 문장을 이끈다. 관계대명사 that은 불완전한 문장을 이끈다.

18 8월은 9월 앞에 오는 달이다.

19 진행형을 만드는 Ving와 지각동사의 목적격보어는 모두 현재분사이며, enjoy의 목적어는 동명사이므로 playing이 공통으로 들어간다.

20 ③번은 주격 관계대명사 which로 생략이 불가능하다. 생략가능한 관계대명사는 목적격 관계대명사이다.

21 지각동사 see, hear, watch는 목적격보어로 원형부정사나 현재분사를 취한다. portrait: 초상화

서술형 시험대비 p.182~183

01 (1) Dan lectured on a topic. / The topic was very boring.
(2) I know the woman. / Her necklace was stolen.
02 You will hear birds sing(ing) in the early morning.
03 that, smile(또는 smiling)
04 A fire fighter is someone who puts out fires. / The woman who was in the hospital is in her home now. / The bus which left an hour ago was the last bus. / A train has a number of cars which are all

connected together. /

Milk is the white liquid which is produced by cows, goats, and some other animals.

05 She felt her heart beat(ing) faster.

06 Is the chair which was made by you comfortable?

07 steal(ing) / stolen

08 (1) I don't like stories which(또는 that) have sad endings.

(2) Jason works for a company which(또는 that) makes cars.

(3) We live in a world which(또는 that) is changing all the time.

(4) There are people who(또는 that) are cheering excitedly.

09 We watched a man try(ing) to get off the train.

10 whose / whom(또는 who, that) / who(또는 that)

11 Did you see the window locked?

12 I want to see your fish swim(ming) in a group.

13 that I can do for you

01 lecture: (대학에서) 강의하다 topic: 주제 (1) Dan은 아주 지루한 주제에 관하여 강의했다.

02 지각동사 hear는 목적어와 목적격보어를 이끈다. '새들이 지저귀는 것'이므로 hear birds sing(ing)을 토대로 작문한다.

03 사람과 사물 모두를 선행사로 받아줄 수 있는 관계대명사는 that이며, 지각동사 see는 목적격보어로 원형부정사나 현재분사를 쓴다.

04 which, who를 대신하여 that을 써도 무방하다. put out: ~을 끄다 a number of: 다수의 produce: ~을 생산하다

05 feel은 원형부정사와 현재분사를 목적격보어로 취하는 지각동사이다.

06 which 뿐만 아니라 that도 가능하다.

07 위 문장은 Tyler가 훔치는 주체이므로 빈칸에 원형부정사나 현재분사를 쓰고, 아래 문장은 목적어로 사물이 나와 있으므로 과거분사를 써서 수동 관계를 표현하는 것이 옳다.

08 (1) 나는 슬픈 결말을 가진 이야기를 좋아하지 않는다. (2) Jason은 차를 만드는 회사에서 일한다. (3) 우리는 항상 변화하는 세상에서 산다. (4) 흥분하여 응원하는 사람 들이 있다.

09 get off: ~에서 내리다 try to: ~하려고 애쓰다

10 첫 번째 문장은 빈칸 뒤에 명사가 있으며, 의미상 '남자의 아들'이므로 소유격 관계대명사가 들어가는 것이 옳다. 두 번째 문장은 선행사가 사람이며 이어 나오는 문장에 목적어가 빠져 있으므로 목적격 관계대명사를 쓰는 것이 옳다. 마지막 문장에는 사람을 선행사로 받아주는 주격 관계대명사가 들어가는 것이 옳다.

11 see는 지각동사로 'see+목적어+목적격보어'의 구조로 쓰이며 목적격보어로는 원형부정사와 분사를 사용한다. 창문이 '잠긴' 것이라고 하였으므로 목적어와 수동 관계를 이룬다고 볼 수 있다.

따라서 lock의 과거분사 형태를 쓴다.

12 want는 to부정사를 목적어로 취하는 동사이며, see는 지각동사이다.

13 that을 대신하여 which를 써도 무방하다.

Reading

교과서

확인문제 p.184

1 T 2 F 3 T 4 T 5 F 6 F 7 F

확인문제 p.185

1 T 2 T 3 F 4 F 5 T 6 T

교과서 확인학습 A p.186~187

01 At, track, there are, who are cheering
02 that are, are waiting
03 waves, flag, starts
04 pushes, down hard, as, completes
05 On, pulls right beside
06 won many races, was coming in
07 chance to finish second
08 be satisfied with, place   09 gets to meet
10 to miss, to meet
11 completes, to go
12 sees, ahead, out of
13 closer and closer
14 hits the back end
15 drive into, presses harder on
16 catch up   17 waving a white flag, means
18 right behind
19 getting closer, from the crowd, getting louder
20 can do it   21 feel, beating hard
22 rush across   23 Who
24 filled with tears, finds out that
25 No need for tears   26 can't believe
27 who is standing, is   28 not the winner
29 a real close race
30 didn't win the race, did   31 that counts
32 Did, do my best   33 After, smiles
34 guess, did

1 At the go-kart race track, there are many people who are cheering excitedly.

2 The karts that are making loud engine noises are waiting.

3 An official waves a green flag and the race starts!

4 Max pushes his foot down hard on the gas pedal as he completes his sixth lap on the track.

5 On the straightaway, Max pulls right beside the race's leader, Simon.

6 Last year, Simon won many races, but Max's best result in a race was coming in fifth place.

7 This time, he has a chance to finish second.

8 But he isn't going to be satisfied with second place today.

9 The winner gets to meet the world famous racer L. J. Richards!

10 He doesn't want to miss the chance to meet his role model.

11 Max completes the tenth lap and now has five more laps to go.

12 Max sees Simon's kart ahead, just out of Max's reach.

13 Max's kart gets closer and closer to Simon's.

14 It almost hits the back end of Simon's kart.

15 They drive into the straightaway and Max presses harder on the gas pedal.

16 "I can catch up," says Max.

17 Max sees the official waving a white flag which means the last lap.

18 Max is right behind Simon.

19 The finish line is getting closer, and the cheering from the crowd is getting louder.

20 "I can do it!" Max says loudly.

21 He can feel his heart beating hard.

22 The karts rush across the finish line.

23 Who is the winner?

24 Max's eyes are filled with tears as he finds out that he came in second.

25 "No need for tears, kid," says a man's voice.

26 Max can't believe his eyes.

27 The man who is standing in front of him is L. J. Richards!

28 "Thank you, but I'm not the winner," says Max.

29 "It was a real close race.

30 Even though you didn't win the race, you did your best.

31 That's the thing that counts!" says L. J. Richards.

32 'Did I do my best?' thinks Max.

33 After a moment, he smiles.

34 "Yeah, I guess I did."

01 ⑤   02 that   03 ④   04 ④

05 ④   06 ③   07 ④   08 ⑤

09 (A) getting closer   (B) getting louder

10 beat[beating]   11 ③   12 who

[that] are, getting closer and closer   13 ⑤

14 ⑤   15 The man who is standing in front of him is L. J. Richards!   16 ③   17 ③

18 I did my best.   19 ②   20 the winner has the chance to meet L. J. Richards.

21 whom(또는 that이나 who), the world famous racer

22 ④   23 ②   24 in front of   25 finish line   26 ⑤

01 (A) many people에 수의 일치를 해야 하므로 there are, (B) 주어가 The karts이므로 are, (C) 동사 자리이므로 waves가 옳다.

02 사물과 사람을 모두 받아주는 관계대명사는 that이다.

03 사람들은 신이 나서 응원하고 있다고 하였다. 따라서 ④번이 가장 적절하다.

04 현재 카트들은 기다리고 있는 중이라고 하였다.

05 2등을 할 기회가 있지만 2등으로 만족하지 않을 것이라는 내용이 이어지는 것이 적절하다.

06 내용상 '때'를 나타내는 의미로 쓰인 as라고 볼 수 있다.

07 Simon이 얼마나 많은 경기를 이겼는지는 글을 읽고 답할 수 없다.

08 각각 ① chance ② beside ③ famous ④ push의 유의어이며, lose는 win의 반의어이다.

09 결승선이 더 가까워질수록 관중의 응원 소리가 더 커진다고 할 수 있다. get+비교급: 더 ~하다

10 his heart와의 관계가 능동이므로 원형부정사나 현재분사로 써서 feel의 목적격보어를 만든다.

11 현재시제로 글을 쓰고 있으므로 hits라고 쓰는 것이 옳다.

12 응원하고 있는 사람들은 Max의 카트가 바로 앞에 있는 카트에 점점 가까워지고 있는 것을 본다.

13 (D)는 부사로 '세계'라는 의미로 쓰였다. ①, ④ 딱딱한 ② (이해하거나 답하기) 힘든, 어려운 ③ (육체적이나 정신적으로) 힘든 ⑤ 세계

14 글에는 승자가 나와 있지 않으므로, Max가 2등으로 들어온다는 것은 글의 내용과 일치하지 않는다.

15 '그 앞에 서 있는 남자는 L. J. Richards이다!'는 문장으로 만들어준다.

16 밑줄 친 ⓐ는 명사절을 이끄는 접속사로 쓰인 that이다. ③번은 관계대명사 that이다.

17 count, matter 모두 '중요하다'는 의미이다.

18 앞서 자문한 'Did I do my best?'에 대한 대답이므로 'I did my best.'라고 쓰면 된다.

19 모두 Max를 지칭하지만, ⓑ는 Simon을 지칭하는 대명사이다.

20 Max가 경기에서 이기기를 원하는 이유는 대회의 승자가 L. J. Richards를 만날 기회를 얻기 때문이다.

21 Max가 존경하는 L. J. Richards는 세계에서 유명한 레이서이다.

22 밑줄 친 (A)는 the chance를 수식하는 형용사구로 쓰인 to부정사이다. ① 목적격보어 ② 목적을 나타내는 부사구 ③ 진주어 ④ 형용사구 ⑤ 동사 hope의 목적어로 각각 쓰였다.

23 문장 ⓐ는 Max의 카트가 Simon의 카트를 바짝 추격하여 바로 뒤에 있다는 의미이다.

24 마지막 바퀴에서 Max는 Simon의 바로 뒤에 있다고 하였으므로, Simon은 Max의 바로 앞에 있다고 할 수 있다.

25 경기가 공식적으로 끝나는 트랙 위의 장소는 '결승선'이다.

26 (B)의 첫 문장에 나오는 he는 Simon을 가리키는 것이므로 Simon을 처음 언급하는 (C)가 (B) 앞에 오는 것이 옳다. 2등에 안주할 수 없는 이유를 설명하는 (A)가 (B)에 이어지는 것이 가장 자연스럽다.

🦉 서술형 시험대비   p.194~195

01 there are many people who are cheering excitedly
02 심판이 초록 깃발을 흔들 때
03 ⓐ won   ⓑ to meet   ⓒ to miss
04 who[that] won many races
05 be satisfied   06 in fifth place
07 He pulls right beside Simon.
08 result
09 Max sees Simon's kart going ahead
10 waving a white flag / It means, the last lap
11 closer, cheering, beating
12 stand(ing) in front of
13 He finished the race in (the) second place.
14 Doing our best is more important than being the best.

01 many people을 선행사로 하여 They가 이끄는 문장을 관계사절로 만든다. They가 주어이므로 주격 관계대명사를 사용한다. who 대신 that을 써도 좋다.

02 'An official waves a green flag and the race starts.'라고 하였다.

---

03 ⓐ: win의 과거형, ⓑ: get to V: ~하게 되다, ⓒ: want의 목적어로 to부정사

04 작년에 많은 경기에서 이긴 Simon은 경주의 선두이다.

05 satisfy는 '만족시키다'는 의미이다. '~에 만족하다'는 be satisfied with이다.

06 작년에, Max가 한 경주에서 5등으로 들어왔을 때 그것이 Max의 가장 좋은 결과였다.

08 결과는 대회의 마지막에 존재하는 상황이다.

09 Max는 Simon의 카트가 앞에 있는 것을 본다는 의미이므로 지각동사의 목적격보어를 적절히 이용하여 'Max는 Simon의 카트가 앞에 가고 있는 것을 본다.'는 문장으로 만든다.

10 흰색 깃발을 흔드는 것은 마지막 바퀴라는 의미이다.

11 내가 결승선에 더 가까워졌을 때, 나는 관중들이 응원하는 소리를 들을 수 있었다. 또한 내 심장이 매우 세게 뛰는 것을 느끼기 시작했다.

12 지각동사 see는 목적격보어로 원형부정사나 현재분사를 취한다. 남자가 Max 앞에 서 있는 것이므로 stand 혹은 standing을 쓴다.

13 그는 경주에서 2등을 차지했다.

14 최선을 다하는 것이 최고가 되는 것보다 더 중요하다.

🦉 영역별 핵심문제   p.197~201

01 ①   02 ⑤   03 ②   04 ②
05 (1) keep up with   (2) do their best / take a chance
    (3) is filled with   06 I'll give you a hand.
07 ④   08 I learned how to stand on my head in PE class.   09 ⑤   10 kick   11 ③
12 I teach children how to swim in the school club.
13 ⑤   14 ⓑ → did   15 He was not satisfied with his serves.   16 ⑤   17 ③
18 ③   19 Did you hear your phone ring(ing)?
20 ④   21 ③   22 is a story which expresses traditional beliefs   23 ③
24 the plane take[taking] off / us fight(ing) / Jinna jump(ing) a rope   25 ④   26 ⑤
27 ④   28 the chance to meet his role model
29 ④   30 He feels his heart beating hard.
31 ④

01 누군가를 위해 지지나 칭찬을 보여주기 위해, 또는 용기를 북돋아 주기 위해 크게 소리 지르는 것을 나타내는 말은 cheer(환호하다)이다.

02 volleyball: 배구, dodge ball: 피구

03 주어진 문장에서 official은 '심판'을 의미하며 이와 같은 의미로 쓰인 것은 ②번이다. 나머지는 모두 '공식적인'을 의미한다.

04 place는 명사로 '순위, 등위' 또는 '장소'를 나타내며 동사로는

'~을 놓다'를 나타낸다.

07 ④ Mina는 'Don't let go'라고 하며 자전거를 잡아주기를 부탁하고 있다.

09 ⑤번은 '포기하지 마'라는 의미이다.

10 당신의 발로 누군가나 또는 무언가를 치는 것을 나타내는 말은 kick(차다)이다.

11 (A) 대화의 흐름상 편하게 잘 안된다는 의미가 되어야 하므로 uncomfortable, (B) 다리를 들어 올릴 수 없다는 의미이므로 lift, (C) 킥 패드를 들어준다는 의미가 적절하므로 hold가 되어야 한다.

13 수영이 여전히 쉽지 않지만 수업이 만족스럽지 않다는 내용은 없다.

14 과거형 Did로 질문하고 있으므로 'Yes, I did.'가 알맞다.

15 Jack은 자신의 서브에 만족하지 않았다.

16 선행사가 사람과 동물이 함께 있을 때에는 관계대명사 that을 쓴다.

17 소년들이 서로에게 소리를 지르는 것이므로 현재분사나 원형부정사를 쓰는 것이 옳다.

18 feel은 지각동사이다. '누군가가 우리를 따라오는 것'이므로 목적어로 someone, 목적격보어로 following us를 써서 문장을 만든다.

19 지각동사 hear는 목적격보어로 원형부정사나 현재분사, 과거분사를 취하며, '전화기가 울리는' 것이므로 수동 관계가 성립하지 않는다. 따라서 원형부정사나 현재분사를 사용하여 문장을 만든다.

20 주어진 문장의 빈칸에는 주격 관계대명사 who나 that이 들어간다. ④번에는 소유격 관계대명사 whose가 들어가지만 ① which[that] ② which[that] ③ who(m)[that] ⑤ that이 들어간다.

21 위 문장은 목적격보어로 현재분사를, 아래 문장은 목적격 보어로 to부정사를 취하고 있으므로 각각 heard, would like를 쓰는 것이 적절하다.

22 신화란 전통적인 믿음을 표현하는 이야기이다.

23 ⓐ 주격 관계대명사가 빠져 있다. people who aren't interested in other people at all로 쓰는 것이 옳다. ⓑ 목적격 관계대명사가 생략되어 있으나 빠져도 무방하다. ⓒ which 는 the tip을 선행사로 받아주는 주격 관계대명사이다. ⓓ 목적격 관계대명사로 두 문장이 이어지고 있으므로 대명사 it을 빼는 것이 옳다. ⓔ 주격 관계대명사 that을 사용하여 앞 문장과 연결되어 있다.

24 see, hear, watch는 모두 지각동사이다. 목적어와 목적격보어의 관계가 모두 능동이므로 현재분사나 원형부정사를 목적격보어로 사용하여 문장을 만든다.

25 페달 위를 밟거나 트랙 위를 달리는 것이므로, '~ 위'를 나타낼 때 쓰이는 전치사 on이 공통으로 들어간다.

26 빈칸 ⓒ에는 전치사 with가 들어간다. ① take care of: ~를

돌보다 ② be different from: ~와 다르다 ③ be interested in: ~에 흥미가 있다 ④ get used to: ~에 익숙해지다 ⑤ be filled with: ~으로 가득 차 있다

27 글의 내용으로 보아 2등으로 시작하는 것이 아니라 끝내는 것을 의미한다. 따라서 finish를 쓰는 것이 옳다.

28 '만날 기회'라고 하였으므로 meet을 to부정사로 만들어 chance 를 수식하도록 한다.

29 '경주에서 이기지 못했을 지라도 최선을 다했으면 됐다'는 의미가 가장 적절하다.

30 질문: 결승선에 가까이 올 때 Max는 무엇을 느끼나요?

31 결과를 본 순간 눈물이 가득 찼다고 하였으므로 ④번은 옳지 않다.

단원별 예상문제
p.202~205

01 ② 　　02 (1) Cheer up (2) out of babies' reach
(3) close match 　　03 ⑤ 　　04 ②
05 ② 　　06 ⑤ 　　07 ③ 　　08 ride a
bike[bicycle] 09 ⑤ 　　10 ⑤ 　　11 ③
12 ④ 　　13 Unfortunately we couldn't go to the
wedding which[that] we were invited to. 14 ③
15 ③ 　　16 We watched a B-boy perform(ing)
on the stage. 17 ① 　　18 ③ 　　19 making
loud engine noises 　　20 Max sees the official
waving a white flag which [that] means the last lap.
21 crowd 　　22 ① 　　23 ②, ⑤ 　　24 winner

01 사람이나 자동차 등이 경주하기 위해 특별한 표면을 가진 땅의 일부를 가리키는 말은 track(경주로)이다.

02 cheer up: 기운 내다, out of one's reach: ~에게 닿지 않는, close match: 접전, 아슬아슬한 경기

03 주어진 문장과 나머지 문장에서 tear는 '눈물'이라는 뜻이지만 ⑤번은 '찢어지다'는 뜻이다.

04 엄마의 위로에 대한 대답으로 '저도 그러길 바라요.'가 적절하다.

05 David는 많은 기회를 놓쳐서 낙담하고 있다.

06 David의 엄마가 자책하고 싶어 했다는 설명은 바르지 않다.

07 주어진 문장은 균형을 잡을 수 없다는 Mina의 말에 이어지는 것이 적절하므로 (C)가 알맞다.

08 Mina는 지금 자전거 타는 법을 배우고 있다.

09 Brain의 문제점에 대해 듣고 도와주겠다고 하는 내용이 이어져야 하므로 (E)가 적절하다.

10 코치가 Brain에게 태권도 옆차기를 보여주었다는 설명은 대화의 내용과 일치하지 않는다.

11 첫 번째 문장은 소년의 꿈이 비행기 조종사가 되는 것이므로 소유격 관계대명사가 들어가는 자리이다. 두 번째 문장의 빈칸은 동사를 이끌고 있으므로 주격 관계대명사 자리이다. sour: (맛이) 신

12 see, watch, hear는 모두 지각동사이다. 목적어와 목적격 보어

의 관계에 따라 목적격보어의 형태가 달라지는데, ④번은 음악이 '연주되는 것'이므로 과거분사 played가 들어가고, 나머지는 모두 목적어와 목적격보어의 관계가 능동이므로 원형부정사나 현재분사가 들어간다. play catch: 캐치 볼하다 stadium: 경기장

13 불행히도 우리는 초대받은 결혼식에 갈 수 없었다.

14 hear와 watch는 모두 지각동사이다. serve: 손님 시중을 들다

15 명사절 접속사 that은 완전한 문장을 이끌고, 관계대명사 that은 주어나 목적어가 빠진 불완전한 문장을 이끈다. ③번 문장에서는 전치사 about의 목적어가 비어 있으므로 관계대명사 that이고, 나머지는 모두 명사절을 이끄는 접속사 that이다.

16 watch는 지각동사이며 B-boy가 공연을 하는 것이므로 목적격보어로 원형부정사나 현재분사를 써서 문장을 만든다.

17 빈칸에는 사람을 선행사로 받아주는 주격 관계대명사 who가 들어간다. ① whose ② which ③ who ④ which ⑤ which가 들어간다. who나 which를 대신하여 that이 쓰일 수 있다.

18 ③ 심판이 흔드는 깃발의 색깔은 초록이라고 하였다.

19 지각동사 hear는 목적어와 목적격보어의 관계가 능동일 경우 원형부정사나 현재분사를 목적격보어로 취할 수 있다.

20 관계대명사 which를 대신하여 that을 써도 무방하다.

21 함께 모여 있는 한 무리의 사람들을 '군중'이라고 한다.

22 ④만 일치하는 문장이다. hold one's breath: 숨죽이다

23 빈칸 ⓐ는 동사를 바로 이끌고 있으므로 주격 관계대명사 자리이다.

24 win: 이기다 winner: 승자

02 사람들이나 팀들이 서로 경쟁하는 스포츠 행사를 가리키는 말은 match(경기)이다

03 John이 자신의 투구가 마음에 들지 않은 이유는 2개의 홈런을 허용해서이다.

04 who, which를 대신하여 that을 써도 무방하다.

05 see는 지각동사이며 꽃이 바람에 흔들려 춤추는 것이므로 현재분사나 원형부정사를 이용하여 문장을 만든다.

06 see는 지각동사이다. 목적어와 목적격보어의 관계가 능동인 경우 원형부정사나 현재분사가 목적격보어로 쓰일 수 있고, 수동 관계에 있는 경우 과거분사를 목적격보어로 사용한다.

07 냉장고 안에 넣어두었던 치즈가 어디 있는지를 묻는 문장으로 쓰면 된다.

08 (1) 선행사가 a custom이므로 관계대명사 that이나 which를 쓰는 것이 옳다. (2) 선행사가 사람이므로 목적격 관계대명사 whom이나 that을 써서 문장을 하나로 만든다. (3) 사람이 선행사이므로 관계대명사 who나 that을 이용한다.

09 지각동사 see는 목적어와 목적격보어의 관계가 능동일 경우 원형부정사나 현재분사를 목적격보어로 취할 수 있다.

10 관계사절 'that are making loud engine noises'를 독립된 문장으로 만들어 주면 된다.

11 우리는 카트들이 트랙 위에서 기다리고 있는 것을 볼 것이다. 심판이 초록 깃발을 흔들면 go-kart 경기는 시작된다.

12 Max는 처음에 2등으로 들어왔지만 경주의 결과에 만족하지 않았다.

13 질문: L. J. Richards에 따르면, Max에게 경주에서 무엇이 중요한가요?

서술형 실전문제 p.206~207

01 It was a close game.

02 match

03 Because he allowed two homeruns.

04 (1) who decides, acts   (2) dolls which have
   (3) whose eyes were

05 You can see flowers dance(또는 dancing) in the wind.

06 make[making] / made

07 Where is the cheese which(또는 that) I put in the refrigerator?

08 (1) that has existed for a long time
   (2) whom you saw driving a car
   (3) who don't feel sorry for other people

09 cheer(ing) excitedly

10 The karts are waiting. They are making loud engine noises.

11 wait(ing), waves a green flag, starts

12 satisfied, even though

13 Doing his best is important.

창의사고력 서술형 문제 p.208

|모범답안|

01 (A) our next soccer match   (B) catching high balls
   (C) a hand   (D) kicked high balls to her

02 (1) who teach math to students
   (2) who build buildings
   (3) that is made from coffee beans
   (4) which operates with an engine
   (5) who invented Hangeul

03 (1) I saw some kids splash(ing) around in water.
   (2) Can you hear someone knock(ing) at the door?
   (3) They watched us looking for the key.
   (4) I was listening to her talking[talk] nonsense.
   (5) He felt the phone vibrating[vibrate] in his bag.
   (6) Did you see the woman talk(ing) to herself?

01 (1) do my best (2) is filled with (3) keep up with
(4) was satisfied with 02 ⑤ 03 ⓐ →
satisfied 04 ①, ③ 05 ⑤ 06 She
learned how to stand on her head in PE class.
07 Tom told Sarah to kick her legs in the air again.
08 don't be so hard on yourself 09 He lost
his game and missed too many chances for a three-
pointer. 10 ⑤ 11 ④ 12 ②, ⑤
13 ⑤ 14 I saw Jason and Helen ride(또는
riding) a bike[bicycle] together. 15 There
are a girl and a goat that are resting on the hill.
16 ① 17 ③ 18 ④
19 meet(ing) my role model 20 are filled with
21 ④ 22 ⑤ 23 come, did his best
24 (B) → (D) → (C) → (A) 25 (B)-(A)-(C)

01 be satisfied with: ~에 만족하다, be filled with: ~로 가득
차다, keep up with: ~을 따라잡다, ~에 뒤떨어지지 않다, do
one's best: 최선을 다하다

02 주어진 문장은 '너무 상심하지 마.'라는 뜻으로 Keine의 걱정에
대해 이어질 말로 적절하므로 (E)가 알맞다.

03 be satisfied with: ~에 만족하다

04 worried는 '걱정스러운'을 나타내며 concerned, anxious와
바꾸어 쓸 수 있다.

06 Sarah는 체육 시간에 물구나무서는 법을 배웠다.

07 Tom은 Sarah에게 공중에다 그녀의 다리를 한 번 더 차라고 말
했다.

09 그가 우울한 이유는 농구 경기에 졌고 3점슛을 위한 많은 기회
를 놓쳤기 때문이다.

10 주어진 표현은 홈런을 허용한 John을 격려하는 표현으로 적절
하므로 (E)가 적절하다.

11 빈칸 뒤로 관사가 없는 명사가 나오므로 소유격 관계대명사가
오는 것이 옳다.

12 '누군가가 내 이름을 부르는 소리'이므로 '내 이름이 불리는 소리'
와 의미가 같다.

13 위 문장은 '남자의 지갑이 도난당했다'는 의미이며, 아래 문장은
'모든 학생들에 의해 존경받는 사람'이라는 의미이다. 따라서 위
에는 소유격 관계대명사를, 아래에는 동사가 이어지고 있으므로
주격 관계대명사를 쓰면 된다.

14 see는 지각동사이다. Jason과 Helen은 자전거를 타는 주체가
되므로 현재분사나 원형부정사를 목적격보어로 사용한다.

15 선행사가 '사람+사물'일 때에는 관계대명사 that을 쓰는 것이 옳다.

16 hardly는 '거의 ~하지 않는'이라는 의미의 부사이다. '세게'라는
의미로 쓸 때에는 hard이며 이때 형용사와 부사의 형태가 같다.

17 ③ Simon이 작년에 얼마나 많은 경주에 이겼는지는 알 수 없다.

18 밑줄 친 (A)는 동명사이다. ④번은 지각동사의 목적격보어로
쓰인 현재분사이다.

19 L. J. Richards는 Max의 롤 모델이라고 하였다. 지각동사
see의 목적어로 Max가 왔으므로 목적격보어로 meet 혹은
meeting을 써서 빈칸을 완성한다.

20 be filled with: ~으로 가득 차다

21 ⓓ에서 사용된 close는 '아슬아슬한'이라는 의미로 사용되었다.

22 L. J. Richards는 최선을 다하는 것이 중요하다고 말하며
Max에게 용기를 주고 있다.

23 coming으로 써도 무방하다.

24 (B) 무엇을 하고 있는지 질문 → (D) 물구나무서기를 하고 있
음을 설명 → (C) 도움 제공 → (A) 감사 표현

25 다섯 바퀴가 남은 상황 → (B) Max의 카트가 Simon의 카트
와 점 점 가까워 짐 → (A) Max의 카트가 Simon의 카트 뒷부
분과 부딪힐 수 있을 정도로 가까워 짐 (첫 문장의 It이 지칭하는
것이 Max의 카트) → (C) 마 침내 마지막 바퀴에서 결승선이
더 가까워짐

교과서 파헤치기

Lesson 1

01 매력적인 02 시야 03 굶다
04 주먹, 보살핌 05 구석, 골목 06 장식하다
07 편리한, 유용한 08 샤워, 소나기 09 두다, 놓다; 장소
10 도움이 되는, 유용한 11 애완동물
12 주의 깊은, 조심하는 13 새장, 우리
14 맞다, 어울리다 15 마카롱 16 사진사
17 쥐다, 잡다 18 반복하다 19 보통
20 방과 후 수업 21 누르다 22 규칙; 지배하다
23 자리, 좌석 24 균형 25 가시, 뾰족한 것
26 논평, 견해, 댓글 27 무서워하는, 겁먹은
28 주로 29 사진술, 사진 찍기 30 평화
31 환상적인, 기막히게 좋은 32 고슴도치
33 닦다 34 맛, 미각, 취향 35 ~을 적다
36 ~을 좋아하다, ~에 관심이 많다 37 ~을 둘러보다
38 직접 39 ~에 관심을 갖다 40 나오다
41 ~을 가져오다 42 ~에 익숙해지다 43 ~을 들어올리다[집다]

01 balance 02 wipe 03 skateboard
04 romance 05 fantastic 06 photography
07 romantic 08 blog 09 actor
10 scared 11 theater 12 comment
13 hedgehog 14 taste 15 tip
16 mainly 17 spike 18 peace
19 point 20 corner 21 artistic
22 talent 23 decorate 24 normally
25 bake 26 helpful 27 careful
28 care 29 press 30 repeat
31 attractive 32 cage 33 pet
34 photographer 35 from beginning to end
36 a few 37 clean up 38 sign up (for)
39 look around 40 get used to 41 be interested in
42 pick up 43 in person

1 hedgehog, 고슴도치 2 talent, 재능, 재주
3 rap, (음악) 랩 4 cage, 새장, 우리 5 theater, 영화관
6 repeat, 반복하다 7 decorate, 장식하다
8 seat, 좌석, 자리 9 bake, 굽다 10 peace, 평화
11 photographer, 사진사 12 raise, 세우다, 올리다
13 tip, 조언, 정보 14 hug, 껴안다 15 dry, 마른, 건조한
16 corner, 구석

Listen & Talk 1 A

1 looking at / reading, comments / usually, blog posts / I'm intereste in reading
2 who, on your SNS / favorite, I'm really intereste in / met, in person / the best day

Listen & Talk 1 B

Which after-school class / going to take, on, about / thinking of, photography, I'm interested in taking pictures / heard that, photographer, cool

Listen & Talk 2 A-1

baked, came, dry / know how to bake bread, making, Put, in / tip, did, learn / a cooking show

Listen & Talk 2 A-2

puzzle / there are, take, to finish / I know how to do it quickly, from, group, with / see

Listen & Talk 2 B

broke / Don't, know how to clean up, with bread, in a magazine / With, How / wipe, picks up / go get

Communication

Welcome to, have, show, Let's meet, special talents / I'm interested in music / going to show us / how to sing high notes, show you easy steps / Sounds

Wrap Up 1

what club, join / going to join, into, about / want to join, interested in plants and flowers / sounds, interesting club

Listen & Talk 1 A

1 Mike: Betty, what are you looking at?
  Betty: I'm reading the comments on my blog.
  Mike: What do you usually write blog posts about?
  Betty: I usually write about books. I'm interested in reading .

2 Jenny: Mike, who is the man on your SNS ?

Mike: Oh, he is my favorite baseball player, John Luke. I'm really interested in baseball.

Jenny: Wow, you met him in person !

Mike: Yeah, that was the best day of my life.

Listen & Talk 1 B

Jake: Hello, Elsa. Which after-school class are you going to take?

Elsa: I'm going to take the drama class on Thursdays. What about you, Jake?

Jake: I'm thinking of taking the Tuesday photography class. I'm interested in taking pictures.

Elsa: Oh, I heard that the teacher is a famous photographer.

Jake: Really? That's really cool!

Listen & Talk 2 A-1

W: I baked this bread, but it came out too dry.

M: Oh, I know how to bake bread without making it dry. Put a glass of water in the oven.

W: That's a great tip. Where did you learn that?

M: I saw it on a cooking show .

Listen & Talk 2 A-2

M: Is that a 1000-piece puzzle?

W: Yeah, but there are so many pieces. It'll take a long time to finish.

M: Oh, I know how to do it quickly. Start from the corners, and then group the pieces with the same colors.

W: I see. Thanks.

Listen & Talk 2 B

Minsu: Oh, no. I broke a dish.

Tina: Don't worry. I know how to clean up the glass pieces with bread. I read the tip in a magazine.

Minsu: With bread? How ?

Tina: You can wipe the area with it. It picks up the small pieces.

Minsu: Great tip! Thanks, Tina. I'll go get some bread in the kitchen.

Communication

M: Welcome to It's Your Stage! We have a great show for you today. Let's meet the people with special talents.

W: Hello. I'm Doremi. I'm interested in music.

M: Great! What are you going to show us today?

W: I know how to sing high notes easily. I can show you easy steps.

M: Sounds interesting!

Wrap Up 1

Aron: Emily, what club are you going to join?

Emily: I'm going to join the music club. I'm into music. What about you, Aron?

Aron: I want to join the gardening club. I'm interested in plants and flowers.

Emily: Oh, that sounds like an interesting club.

본문 TEST Step 1   p.09~10

01 Rap, Out   02 Open, mind, heart

03 around, let's, out   04 to write, own

05 can, anything, everything, be   06 when, on, in

07 write down, use, when

08 are, rules, writing   09 Fantastic Pets

10 Welcome, Having, is

11 going, introduce, pet

12 When, got, scared

13 hold, because, raised

14 placed, case, used   15 able, hold, in

16 best, makes, happy   17 Handy, Tips

18 Welcome back

19 Where, normally, in

20 Here is,   21 find, easy, helpful

22 Point, at, far   23 Close, open   24 with, other

25 does, move   26 when, close   27 mainly use

28 means, on, side

29 way, view, better

30 helpful, choose, seat, too

본문 TEST Step 2   p.11~12

01 Out   02 Open, mind, Open, heart

03 around, let's rap, out

04 want to write, own rap

05 about anything, can be, for a rap

06 when, on, in the shower, in

07 write down my ideas, use them, write

08 are no rules, writing, can start   09 Fantastic Pets

10 Welcome to Fantastic, Having

11 going to introduce, hedgehog

12 When, got, scared

13 couldn't hold, because, raised, spikes

14 placed, in her case, got used to

15 was able to hold

16 my best friend, makes me happy

17 Handy, Tips

18 Welcome back

19 Where, normally sit in

20 Here is,　　　21 find, easy and helpful

22 Point, at, far, from

23 Close one eye, open it

24 with the other eye

25 does, finger move

26 when, close　　27 Then, mainly use, right eye

28 means, should sit on, in the theater

29 That way, enjoy, full view, better

30 This information, helpful, choose a seat, too

---

30 이 정보는 네가 교실에서 자리를 고를 때도 도움이 될 거야.

---

1 랩으로 표현해 봐

2 너의 생각을 열어 봐, 너의 마음을 열어 봐

3 주변을 둘러보고 랩으로 표현해 봐

4 안녕. 난 MC Joy야. 너만의 랩을 쓰고 싶니?

5 세상 모든 것들이 랩의 이야깃거리가 될 수 있기 때문에 넌 어떤 것에 대해서든 랩을 할 수 있어.

6 난 버스에서, 샤워 중에 또는 침대에서 아이디어들을 얻어.

7 내 아이디어들을 적어 두고 내가 랩을 쓸 때 그것들을 활용하지.

8 랩을 쓰는 데에는 어떤 규칙도 없어. 넌 오늘 당장 시작할 수 있어!

9 환상의 애완동물

10 '환상의 애완동물'에 온 걸 환영해! 애완동물을 기른다는 건 멋진 일이야.

11 오늘 난 나의 애완 고슴도치인 Polly를 소개할 거야.

12 내가 Polly를 처음 만났을 때, 그 애는 너무 겁을 먹었어.

13 그 애가 가시를 세워서 난 그 애를 손에 쥘 수가 없었어.

14 그래서 내가 그 애의 우리 안에 내 티셔츠를 두었더니 그 애가 내 냄새에 적응했어.

15 마침내, 난 손으로 그 애를 쥘 수 있게 되었지.

16 이제 Polly는 나의 가장 친한 친구이고 항상 나를 행복하게 해 줘.

17 쓸모 있는 팁

18 '쓸모 있는 팁'에 돌아온 걸 환영 해.

19 넌 보통 영화관에서 어디에 앉니?

20 여기 팁이 하나 있어.

21 넌 이것이 쉽고 유용하다는 걸 알게 될 거야.

22 1단계: 멀리 떨어져 있는 물체를 손가락으로 가리켜 봐.

23 2단계: 한쪽 눈을 감았다가 떠 봐.

24 3단계: 반대쪽 눈으로 반복해 봐.

25 언제 네 손가락이 움직이니?

26 오른쪽 눈을 감았을 때니?

27 그렇다면 너는 주로 오른쪽 눈을 사용하는 거야.

28 그 말은 너는 영화관에서 왼편에 앉아야 한다는 걸 뜻해.

29 그렇게 하면, 너는 스크린의 꽉 찬 화면을 더 잘 즐길 수

---

1 Rap It Out

2 Open your mind, Open your heart

3 Look around and let's rap it out

4 Hey, I'm MC Joy. Do you want to write your own rap?

5 You can rap about anything because everything can be a story for a rap.

6 I get ideas when I'm on the bus, in the shower, or in my bed.

7 I write down my ideas and use them when I write my rap.

8 There are no rules for writing raps. You can start today!

9 Fantastic Pets

10 Welcome to Fantastic Pets! Having a pet is great.

11 Today I'm going to introduce my pet hedgehog, Polly

12 When I first got Polly, she was very scared.

13 I couldn't hold her because she raised her spikes.

14 So, I placed my T-shirt in her case and she got used to my smell.

15 Finally, I was able to hold her in my hands.

16 Now, Polly is my best friend and always makes me happy.

17 Handy Tips

18 Welcome back to Handy Tips .

19 Where do you normally sit in a movie theater?

20 Here is a tip.

21 You will find it easy and helpful.

22 Step 1 Point your finger at something far from you.

23 Step 2 Close one eye and open it.

24 Step 3 Repeat it with the other eye.

25 When does your finger move?

26 Is it when you close your right eye?

27 Then you mainly use your right eye.

28 This means you should sit on the left side in the theater.

29 That way, you can enjoy a full view of the screen better.

30 This information is also helpful when you choose a seat in a classroom, too.

Communication Step B

1. Welcome to, yourself
2. interested in painting
3. are, going to
4. how to, show, steps
5. interesting

Look and Write

2. kept, excited, to
3. found, attractive
4. too
5. enjoyed, in
6. made, romantic

Think and Write

1. Welcome to
2. interested, baking
3. give, helpful tips
4. class, basic, skills
5. Anyone, in, one day
6. free, ready for
7. Sign up

Communication Step B

1. A: Welcome to It's Your Stage! Can you introduce yourself?
2. B: Hello. I'm Bob. I'm interested in painting.
3. A: What are you going to show us today?
4. B: I know how to draw a face quickly. I can show you easy steps.
5. A: Sounds interesting!

Look and Write

1. MOVIE REVIEW – SPY COUPLE
2. Thomas: Great action scenes kept me excited from beginning to end.
3. Kelly: I found the main actor attractive.
4. He is a great actor, too!
5. Ria: I enjoyed the music in the movie.
6. It made everything romantic.

Think and Write

1. Welcome to Cooking Class!
2. Are you interested in baking cookies?
3. I can give you some helpful tips!
4. In this class , you will learn basic cooking skills.
5. Anyone can bake cookies in only one day.
6. This class is free and everything is ready for you.
7. Sign up today!

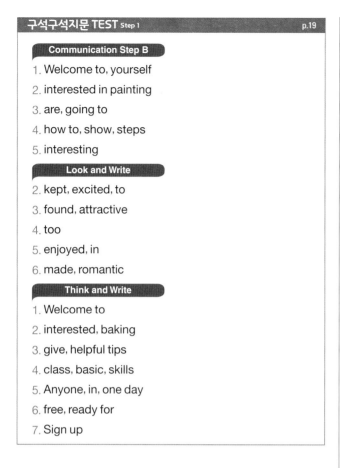

Lesson 2

01 구슬	02 굴뚝	03 싸다, 포장하다
04 훌륭한, 우수한	05 건너다; 십자가	06 모르는[낯선] 사람
07 나타내다, 표현하다		08 장, 박람회
09 준비 운동	10 결혼식, 결혼	11 외국의
12 운 좋은, 행운의	13 괴물, 요괴	14 북, 드럼
15 선물; 현재의, 출석하는		16 가면
17 몽골	18 햇빛	19 재료
20 굴뚝 청소부	21 체계	22 부족
23 전통적인	24 보물	
25 의지하는, 의존하는		26 다음에 나오는
27 전통적인	28 궁전, 왕궁	
29 뛰어나다, 탁월하다		30 다양한, 다른
31 부, 재산	32 공연	33 벽난로, 난로
34 장식이 많은, 화려한		35 확인하다, 살펴보다
36 ～을 상징하다, ～을 나타내다		37 그런데
38 우선, 가장 먼저	39 ～을 끄다	40 ～에 들어가다
41 ～을 치우다	42 ～을 입다, ～을 바르다	
43 ～에 등록하다		

01 treasure	02 decorate	03 band
04 dependent	05 doll	06 different
07 folk music	08 tent	09 excel
10 introduce	11 fancy	12 palace
13 sombrero	14 wealth	15 following
16 fireplace	17 stay	18 rope
19 performance	20 various	21 traditional
22 wedding	23 sunlight	24 chimney
25 stranger	26 express	27 wrap
28 lucky	29 present	30 traditional
31 excellent	32 material	33 monster
34 foreign	35 communicate with	
36 try on	37 for free	38 thanks to
39 look forward to –ing		
40 from country to country		41 first of all
42 check out	43 stand for	

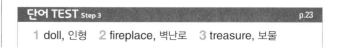

1 doll, 인형   2 fireplace, 벽난로   3 treasure, 보물

4 mask, 가면　5 decorate, 장식하다

6 following, 다음에 나오는　7 folk, 민속의

8 stranger, 모르는[낯선] 사람　9 dependent, 의지하는

10 wrap, 싸다, 포장하다　11 express, 표현하다

12 cross, 건너다　13 lucky, 운이 좋은

14 traditional, 전통적인　15 present, 선물

16 rope, (밧)줄, 끈

대화문 TEST Step 1　p.24~25

Listen and Talk 1 A-1

how is, going / are going to perform / this weekend / sounds like / looking forward to

Listen and Talk 1 A-2

are you going to do / I'm going to go to / last weekend, lots of traditional foods, all over / looking forward to trying

Listen and Talk 1 B

are, doing / signing up / Is, interesting / going to make, African drum, traditional mask / how fun / visiting the museum

Listen and Talk 2 A-1

bought, for, Will / will, enjoys drinking tea / wrap the present / Don't forget to wrap, in red / stands for

Listen and Talk 2 A-2

visit to, Let's meet / see you / don't forget to wear, get into / almost forgot

Listen and Talk 2 B

is crossing, over / a crossing light / didn't know, let's cross the street / come from, right side / forgot about / from country to country, Don't forget to look to the right, you cross

Communication

How, first day / By the way, am I going to stay / going to sleep, tent / I'm looking forward to it / There is, don't forget to put, away / see

---

대화문 TEST Step 2　p.26~27

Listen and Talk 1 A-1

Mike: Elsa, how is your Hula dance class going?

Elsa: Oh, it's great. We are going to perform at the ACB Hall this weekend.

Mike: Wow, that sounds like a big day for you!

Elsa: Yeah, I'm looking forward to the performance.

Listen and Talk 1 A-2

Sora: Chris, what are you going to do this Sunday?

Chris: I'm going to go to the World Food Fair.

Sora: Oh, I was there last weekend. There were lots of traditional foods from all over the world.

Chris:　Great! I'm looking forward to trying them.

Listen and Talk 1 B

Tom: Jane, what are you doing?

Jane: I'm signing up for a program at the African Museum.

Tom: Is there an interesting one?

Jane: Yeah, I'm going to make an African drum and a traditional mask.

Tom: Oh, how fun!

Jane: Yeah, I'm looking forward to visiting the museum.

Listen and Talk 2 A-1

W: I bought this tea for Wang's birthday. Will he like it?

M: Sure, he will. Wang enjoys drinking tea.

W: Great. Then I'll wrap the present.

M: Don't forget to wrap it in red. Red stands for wealth in China.

Listen and Talk 2 A-2

Elsa: Our visit to Gyengbokgung is this Friday. Let's meet at two.

Jake: Okay, I'll see you at the bus stop.

Elsa: Oh, and don't forget to wear a hanbok. we can get into the palace for free in our hanboks .

Jake: Right. I almost forgot.

Listen and Talk 2 B

Amy: Look, Brandon. A horse is crossing the street over there.

Brandon: Yes, there is a crossing light for horses here in London.

Amy: Oh, I didn't know that. That's interesting. Now let's cross the street.

Brandon: Wait! Cars come from the right side in London.

Amy: Right. I forgot about that.

Brandon: Yeah, it's different from country to country. Don't forget to look to the right before you cross in London.

Communication

Sue: How was your first day here in Mongolia?

Jake: It was great. By the way, where am I going to stay tonight?

Sue: You're going to sleep in a ger , a Mongolian tent.

Jake: Oh, I'm looking forward to it.

Sue: You'll like it. There is a fireplace in the ger. So, don't forget to put your things away from the fireplace.

Jake: I see. Thank you.

---

01 I'm Sweepy   02 from, to clean
03 During, help, to keep
04 sweeps bring, luck   05 want, to, at
06 If, see, lucky   07 these are, members
08 folk, always wear
09 to, cool, hot, sunlight
10 want, to look   11 often decorate, with, materials
12 Which, our, best   13 My, a Zulu
14 tribe, South   15 What, think of
16 enjoy making, with
17 each, has, meaning
18 own, to communicate, other
19 to know, the colors / marriage, Yellow, badness, anger
20 send, special, express, beads
21 What message, to make

---

01 I'm   02 from Germany, is to clean chimneys
03 During, help, to keep warm, safe
04 So, think, bring them good luck
05 even want, to be, their weddings
06 If, see me, your lucky day
07 these are, band members
08 play folk music, always wear, big hats
09 In Mexico, wear, to stay cool, hot, strong sunlight
10 want, to look fancy
11 often decorate, with, different materials
12 Which of, like best
13 My name, a Zulu
14 a tribe in South   15 What, think of
16 enjoy making clothes with
17 They are, each color, special meaning
18 When, our own writing system, to communicate
19 to know the meaning of the colors / Good Meaning, Bad Meaning / marriage, death / Yellow, wealth / anger / White, love
20 want to send, special message, express yourself

---

with   21 What message, want to make

---

1 나는 Sweepy야.
2 나는 독일에서 왔고, 내 직업은 굴뚝을 청소하는 거야.
3 겨울에 굴뚝 청소부들은 사람들이 따뜻하고 안전하게 지낼 수 있도록 도와주지.
4 그래서 사람들은 굴뚝 청소부들이 자신들에게 행운을 가져다준다고 생각해.
5 사람들은 심지어 굴뚝 청소부들이 자신의 결혼식에 있기를 바란단다!
6 네가 만일 나를 본다면, 그날은 너의 행운의 날인 거야.
7 내 이름은 José이고, 이 사람들은 마리아치 악단 단원들이야.
8 우리는 민속 음악을 연주하고 항상 솜브레로라는 큰 모자를 쓰지.
9 멕시코에서 사람들은 뜨겁고 강한 햇볕 아래서 시원하게 지내기 위해 이 모자들을 써.
10 우리 마리아치 연주자들은 우리의 솜브레로가 화려하게 보이길 원해.
11 그래서 우리는 종종 여러 가지 재료들을 많이 이용해서 그것들을 장식하지.
12 우리 솜브레로 중 어느 것이 가장 마음에 드니?
13 내 이름은 Ayanda이고 나는 줄루 사람이야.
14 우리는 남아프리카의 부족이지.
15 내 구슬들에 대해 어떻게 생각하니?
16 줄루족 사람들은 구슬로 옷 만드는 것을 즐겨.
17 그것들은 아름답고 각각의 색깔에는 특별한 의미가 있어.
18 우리 자신의 문자 체계가 없었을 때, 우리는 서로 의사소통하기 위해서 구슬들을 이용했어.
19 만약 네가 그 색깔들의 의미를 알고 싶다면, 다음에 나오는 네모를 확인해 봐. / Color, Good Meaning, Bad Meaning / Black, marriage, death / Yellow, wealth, badness / Red, love, anger / White, love
20 만약 네가 누군가에게 특별한 메시지를 보내고 싶다면, 이 구슬들로 네 자신을 표현할 수 있어.
21 너는 어떤 메시지를 만들고 싶니?

---

1 I'm Sweepy.
2 I'm from Germany and my job is to clean chimneys.
3 During winter, chimney sweeps help people to keep warm and safe.
4 So people think chimney sweeps bring them good luck.

5 People even want chimney sweeps to be at their weddings!

6 If you see me, it is your lucky day.

7 My name is José and these are my mariachi band members.

8 We play folk music and always wear our sombreros, or big hats.

9 In Mexico, people wear these hats to stay cool under the hot and strong sunlight.

10 We mariachi players want our sombreros to look fancy.

11 So we often decorate them with a lot of different materials.

12 Which of our sombreros do you like best?

13 My name is Ayanda and I'm a Zulu.

14 We are a tribe in South Africa.

15 What do you think of my beads?

16 Zulu people enjoy making clothes with beads.

17 They are beautiful and each color has a special meaning.

18 When we did not have our own writing system, we used beads to communicate with each other.

19 If you want to know the meaning of the colors, check out the following box. / Color, Good Meaning, Bad Meaning / Black, marriage, death / Yellow, wealth, badness / Red, love, anger / White, love

20 If you want to send someone a special message, you can express yourself with these beads.

21 What message do you want to make?

구석구석지문 TEST Step 1   p.38

Grammar in Real Life

1. going, late, Can, for

2. don't, home

4. be sure

5. get us some ice cream

Think & Write

1. Which, introduce, foregin friends

2. want to introduce

3. can, foregin

4. in, in

5. can, if

6. catch fish with

Wrap Up 3

1. are, going to

---

2. to meet, staying, during

3. from, isn't he

4. looking forward, around

5. Have, with

구석구석지문 TEST Step 2   p.39

Link

1. Mom: Mike, I'm going to be late. Can you make dinner for Sam?

2. Mike: Okay, don't worry. Sam, come home early.

3. Sam: Okay.

4. Mom: Mike and Sam, be sure to do your homework.

5. Sam: I will, Mom. Can you get us some ice cream?

6. Mom: Sure.

Write

1. A: Which festival do you want to introduce to your foregin friends?

2. B: I want to introduce the Haenyeo festival.

3. A: Where and when can your foregin friends enjoy the festival?

4. B: They can enjoy the festival in Jeju in September.

5. A: What can your foreign friends do if they visit the festival?

6. B: They can catch fish with their hands and learn old haenyeo songs.

Culture Project

1. A: What are you going to do this Saturday?

2. B: I'm going to meet my friend, Lashi. He's staying in Korea during the vacation.

3. A: Oh, he's from India, isn't he?

4. B: Yeah, he is. I'm looking forward to showing him around Seoul.

5. A: Great. Have a good time with your friend.

단어 TEST Step 1 — p.40

01 생산하다, 제작하다	02 유용한
03 식초	04 나타나다 05 풍선
06 콩	07 자동차 경적
08 무인 비행기, 무인 항공기	09 전체의
10 실험	11 평균 12 숨기다, 숨다
13 믿을 수 없는	14 불가능한 15 내리다, 낮추다
16 응용 프로그램, 적용	17 능력
18 괴물, 요괴	19 기록하다, 녹음하다
20 보통의, 평범한 21 수집가	
22 겁주다, 겁먹게 하다	23 단 하나의
24 비명, 외침(소리) 25 전기, 전류	26 재미, 놀이, 오락
27 설명하다 28 자물쇠를 열다	29 전체의
30 놓치다, 그리워하다	31 접다
32 활동 33 아픈	34 실
35 둘의, 몇 개의 36 ~을 떠받치다	37 ~라고 하자
38 덧칠하다 39 주입하다, 채워 넣다	
40 ~을 돌보다 41 ~을 제거하다, ~을 치우다	
42 게다가, 더구나 43 ~을 두르다, ~을 감다	

단어 TEST Step 2 — p.41

01 amazingly	02 entire	03 weigh
04 amount	05 balloon	06 electricity
07 average	08 activity	09 fair
10 amusement	11 fold	12 however
13 advice	14 lift	15 miss
16 sore	17 explain	18 possible
19 battery	20 string	21 add
22 pick	23 challenge	24 unlock
25 ring	26 unbelievable	27 appear
28 lower	29 record	30 normal
31 monster	32 ability	33 useful
34 scream	35 take away	36 for example
37 turn off	38 light up	39 pump up
40 pick one's brain		41 turn into
42 in front of	43 take care of	

단어 TEST Step 3 — p.42

1 weigh, 무게를 재다   2 collector, 수집가

3 average, 평균   4 challenge, 도전   5 possible, 가능한

6 scare, 무서워하다   7 add, 더하다   8 experiment, 실험

9 scream, 비명   10 hide, 숨기다   11 drone, 무인 비행기

12 battery, 건전지   13 lift, 들어 올리다

14 lower, 내리다, 낮추다   15 amusement, 재미, 즐거움

16 fair, 박람회

대화문 TEST Step 1 — p.43~44

Listen & Talk 1 A-1

What show watching / watching, Have you heard about it / haven't, about / science to explain / sounds interesting

Listen & Talk 1 A-2

have, heard about / No, I haven't / phone application, can ask / Let me show you, what's, like / going to rain, need / what a great application

Listen & Talk 1 B

Have you heard about, own drone, class, offers, every Wednesday, Make, special drone, how to control it, Don't miss

Listen & Talk 2 A-1

what, made / What do you mean / works with, not with / electricity, interesting

Listen & Talk 2 A-2

what did you do last weekend / made, with / What, mean / put, in vinegar for / turns into / want to, too

Listen & Talk 2 B

let's, science experiment / What do you mean / special, hide your message / How, make / Mix, on the card with / How can you read the card / Paint over, with, and then, appears

Communication

Have you heard about / Yes, I have, going to / going to send, about / What do you mean / take a picutre of, tells, how to take care of it / sounds like, useful

Wrap Up 1

Have, heard about / going to go / too, excited, kinds of experiments / looking forward to

대화문 TEST Step 2 — p.45~46

Listen & Talk 1 A-1

Mike: What show are you watching, Sally?

Sally: I'm watching the Sci-Magic show. It's a new program. Have you heard about it?

Mike: No, I haven't. What's it about?

Sally: The program uses science to explain magic tricks.

Mike: Oh, it sounds interesting.

Listen & Talk 1 A-2

Tom: Mom, have you heard about the Chat Robot?

Mom: No, I haven't. What is it?

Tom: It's a phone application. You can ask any questions and it will answer. Let me show you. "Emily, what's the weather like today?"

Emily: "It's going to rain, so you'll need an umbrella."

Mom: Wow, what a great application!

Listen & Talk 1 B

W: Hello, students. Have you heard about the DIY Drone Class? You can make your own drone in the class. The Youth Community Center offers the class at 3 p.m. every Wednesday in May. Make your special drone and learn how to control it. Don't miss this great chance!

Listen & Talk 2 A-1

Mina: You know what? I made a potato clock yesterday!

Jack: A potato clock? What do you mean?

Mina: My clock works with potatoes, not with batteries. Potatoes can produce electricity.

Jack: That's interesting!

Listen & Talk 2 A-2

Jimmy: Lisa, what did you do last weekend?

Lisa: I made an egg ball with my brother.

Jimmy: An egg ball? What do you mean?

Lisa: We put an egg in vinegar for two days. Then, the egg turns into a ball.

Jimmy: Wow, I want to make one, too!

Listen & Talk 2 B

Minho: Anna, let's make a "Mystery Card" for the science experiment.

Anna: A "Mystery Card?" What do you mean?

Minho: It's a special card. It can hide your message.

Anna: How do you make it?

Minho: Mix baking soda and water. Then, write a message on the card with it.

Anna: How can you read the card?

Minho: Paint over the card with grape juice, and then the message appears.

Communication

Jane: Have you heard about the Smart App Contest?

Minho: Yes, I have. Are you going to enter it?

Jane: Yeah, I'm going to send my idea about a Pic Gardener App.

Minho: A Pic Gardener App? What do you mean?

Jane: When you take a picture of a plant, the app tells you how to take care of it.

Minho: It sounds like a very useful app.

Wrap Up 1

Hojin: Hey, Katy. Have you heard about the science fair?

Katy: Yeah, I'm going to go there.

Hojin: Me, too! I'm excited about doing different kinds of experiments.

Katy: Yeah, I'm also looking forward to it!

본문 TEST Step 1   p.47~48

01 animation, amazing, possible

02 actually, real   03 Let Down

04 must lower, let, in

05 human, hold, person

06 single, average, about

07 All those, couple of

08 With, ability, up

09 wrap, around, heavy

10 doesn't, will, sore   11 Scare for

12 scare, to get, from

13 Amazingly, powered by

14 produce, light up, from

15 be changed into

16 helpful, because, amount, small

17 For example, from, produces

18 only, average, electricity

19 unbelievable, screams, entire

20 Up, Away   21 lifted, flown, thousands

22 Could, actually

23 Let's, weighs about

24 normal, amusement, lift

25 about, to lift up

26 have, about, themselves, strings

27 need, add, few

28 challenge, pumping, all those

본문 TEST Step 2   p.49~50

01 animation, amazing things are possible

02 actually possible, real life   03 Let Down

04 In, must lower, to let people in

05 could, hold up a person

06 Surprisingly, single, hold up average, has about

07 All those hairs, hold up

08 With her hair, the ability to hold up

09 wrap her hair around, strong, heavy

10 doesn't, will get, sore neck   11 Scare for

12 scare children to get, from their screams

13 Amazingly, is powered by

14 could, produce electricity to light up, from

15 be changed into electricity

16 would not, helpful in, because the amount is, small

17 For example, from, car horn, produces

18 of the average, electricity, in our homes

19 an unbelievable amount of screams, light up , entire

20 Up, Up, Away

21 is lifted and flown, thousands of balloons

22 Could, actually work

23 Let's say, weighs about

24 normal, an amusement park, lift about

25 need about, to lift up

26 have to think about, weight, themselves, strings

27 add a few more thousand

28 biggest challenge, pumping up all those

16 그렇지만 그 양이 너무 적기 때문에 그것은 우리의 일상 활동에서는 도움이 되지 않을 것이다.

17 예를 들어, 자동차 경적 소리는 겨우 50밀리볼트를 만들어 낸다.

18 그것은 우리 가정에서 사용하는 일반적인 220볼트 전기의 1/4400밖에 되지 않는다.

19 그래서 도시 전체를 밝히기 위해서는 믿기 어려운 정도로 많은 양의 비명이 필요할 것이다.

20 높이, 높이 그리고 멀리!

21 만화 영화에서 집은 수천 개의 풍선에 의해 들려 올라가고 날아간다.

22 이게 실제로 가능할까?

23 집 한 채의 무게가 5만 킬로그램 정도라고 가정해 보자.

24 놀이공원에 있는 보통의 풍선은 대략 14그램을 들어 올릴 수 있다.

25 그래서 집을 들어 올리기 위해 우리는 약 3,570,000개의 풍선이 필요하다.

26 우리는 또한 풍선 자체와 줄의 무게에 대해서도 생각해야 한다.

27 그렇게 되면, 수천 개의 풍선을 더 추가할 필요가 있다.

28 이제 가장 큰 어려움은 그 모든 풍선에 바람을 넣는 일이다!

본문 TEST Step 3

p.51~52

1 만화 영화에서는 놀라운 일들이 가능하다.

2 하지만 그런 일들이 실생활에서 정말 가능할까?

3 라푼젤, 네 머리카락을 내려!

4 만화 영화에서 라푼젤은 사람들이 탑에 들어오게 하기 위해서 그녀의 긴 머리카락을 내려야 한다.

5 하지만 인간의 머리카락이 정말로 사람을 들어 올릴 수 있을까?

6 놀랍게도 그렇다! 머리카락 한 가닥은 100그램의 무게를 들어 올릴 수 있고 보통 머리에는 12만 개 정도의 머리카락이 있다.

7 그 모든 머리카락은 코끼리 두 마리를 들어 올릴 수 있다!

8 라푼젤에게는 머리카락으로 사람을 들어 올릴 수 있는 능력이 있다.

9 하지만 그녀는 머리카락을 어떤 강하고 무거운 것에 감아야 한다.

10 만약 그렇게 하지 않으면 그녀는 목이 많이 아플 것이다.

11 우리는 에너지를 얻기 위해 겁을 준다

12 만화 영화에서 괴물들은 아이들의 비명에서 에너지를 얻기 위해 아이들을 겁준다.

13 놀랍게도 그들의 도시는 이 소리로 동력을 공급받는다!

14 하지만 정말 소리로부터 도시를 밝히는 전기를 만들 수 있을까?

15 그렇다. 소리는 전기로 바뀔 수 있다.

본문 TEST Step 4~Step 5

p.53~56

1 In animation movies, amazing things are possible.

2 But are they actually possible in real life?

3 Let Down Your Hair, Rapunzel!

4 In the animation, Rapunzel must lower her long hair to let people in her tower.

5 But could human hair really hold up a person?

6 Surprisingly, yes! A single hair can hold up 100g and an average head has about 120,000 hairs.

7 All those hairs could hold up a couple of elephants!

8 With her hair, Rapunzel has the ability to hold up a person.

9 But she should wrap her hair around something strong and heavy.

10 If she doesn't, she will get a very sore neck.

11 We Scare for Energy

12 In the animation, monsters scare children to get energy from their screams.

13 Amazingly, their city is powered by this sound!

14 But could we actually produce electricity to light up a city from sound?

15 Yes, sound can be changed into electricity.

16 But it would not be helpful in our everyday

activities because the amount is too small.

17 For example, the sound from a car horn only produces 50mv.

18 That is only 1/4400 of the average 220v of electricity in our homes.

19 So, we would need an unbelievable amount of screams to light up an entire city.

20 Up, Up and Away!

21 The house is lifted and flown by thousands of balloons in the animation.

22 Could that actually work?

23 Let's say that a house weighs about 50,000kg.

24 A normal balloon at an amusement park can lift about 14g.

25 So we need about 3,570,000 balloons to lift up the house.

26 We also have to think about the weight of the balloons themselves and the strings.

27 Then, we need to add a few more thousand balloons.

28 Now, the biggest challenge is pumping up all those balloons!

구석구석지문 TEST Step 2 p.58

Grammar in Real Life

1. This is Jack's plan for this week.

2. There is a lot of work to do.

3. He needs to go to the library on Monday.

4. He has two books to borrow from the library.

5. Also he has science homework to finish by Thursday.

6. On Friday, he will be in the school talent show.

7. So, he will practice performing the songs at the talents show all this week.

Think & Write

1. Hello, my name is June.

2. Today I'd like to talk about my new wearable technology, SuperEye.

3. It is helpful to take pictures and video-record.

4. It is also useful to show me a map .

5. Try it out and experience a new world!

Wrap Up 3

1. Amy: Have you heard about the special event at the science museum?

2. Brian: No, I haven't. What's the event?

3. Amy: There are science magic shows during the weekend, but only for this month.

4. Brian: Oh, thank you for the information. I'll visit there this weekend.

구석구석지문 TEST Step 1 p.57

Grammar in Real Life

1. plan for

2. a lot of

3. to go, on

4. to borrow

5. science homework, by, foreign

6. On, talent show,

7. practice performing, talents show

Think & Write

1. my name

2. I'd like, talk about, wearable

3. helpful to take

4. show me a map

5. Try it out

Wrap Up 3

1. Have you heard, special, science museum

2. haven't

3. There are, during, only for

4. thank, for, there

단어 TEST Step 1 p.59

01 놀랄 정도의, 굉장한	02 무서운, 심한
03 목소리	04 (경주, 대회 등의) 등위, 장소
05 엔진, 기관	06 막다, 방해하다 07 흥분하여, 기를 쓰고
08 갈채를 보내다, 환호성을 지르다	
09 아슬아슬한 승부, 접전	10 지방의
11 (자동차의) 가속 페달	12 부딪치다
13 (경주에서 트랙의) 한 바퀴, 무릎	
14 시끄러운, (소리가) 큰	
15 (운동 경기의) 심판; 공식의	16 타격
17 매달다, 걸다	18 일직선의, 즉시의 19 3점슛
20 차다, 걷어차다	21 중요하다, (수를) 세다
22 깊은	23 복잡한, 붐비는 24 기억할 만한
25 해산물	26 돌진하다 27 뛰다, 치다, 두드리다
28 완성하다, 달성하다; 완전한	29 결승선
30 군중, 관객	31 투수
32 수리하다, 고정시키다	33 앞에, 앞선
34 누르다, 밀어붙이다	
35 (모험 삼아) 해 보다	
36 자세를 바로 하다, 바로 앉다	37 기회를 놓치다
38 ~에 만족하다 39 기운을 내다	40 ~로 가득 차다
41 최선을 다하다 42 ~에 뒤떨어지지 않다	
43 ~에게 닿지 않는, ~의 힘이 미치지 않는	

단어 TEST Step 2 p.60

01 beat	02 count	03 ahead
04 volleyball	05 track	06 pitching
07 finish line	08 flag	09 seafood
10 deep	11 complete	12 fix
13 crowded	14 memorable	15 kart
16 crowd	17 rush	18 pitcher
19 tear	20 press	21 terrible
22 cheer	23 excitedly	24 voice
25 close match	26 block	27 three-pointer
28 hang	29 punch	30 loud
31 amazing	32 straightaway	33 local
34 place	35 be satisfied with	
36 cheer up	37 do one's best	38 win a race
39 be filled with	40 keep up with	41 miss a chance
42 sit up	43 take a chance	

단어 TEST Step 3 p.61

1 kart, 소형 경주용 자동차 2 count, 중요하다, 가치가 있다
3 complete, 완성하다 4 kick, 차다 5 pitcher, 투수
6 tear, 눈물 7 track, 경주로, 트랙 8 seafood, 해산물
9 voice, 목소리 10 engine, 엔진 11 volleyball, 배구
12 memorable, 기억할 만한 13 cheer, 응원하다, 갈채를
보내다 14 block, 막다, 방해하다 15 crowd, 관객, 관중
16 finish line, 결승선

대화문 TEST Step 1 p.62~63

Listen & Talk 1 A-1
how, basketball game / lost, missed, chances, three,
pointer / don't be so hard, You'll do better, hope so

Listen & Talk 1 A-2
volleyball match / You were great / but, were not
strong enough / you're a great player, do better

Listen & Talk 1 B
heard, won the match, Eight to seven, Congratulations
/ a close game, not happy with, pitching / Why, say /
allowed two homeruns / you're a great pitcher, do
better

Listen & Talk 2 A-1
first time riding / can't keep my balance / Let me help,
hold / Don't let / Sit up, look straight ahead

Listen & Talk 2 A-1
are, doing / how to stand on my head, trying, not easy
/ Let me help you, Kick, catch you / try again

Listen & Talk 2 B
Did, practice / I'm still not comfortable with it / What
problem, having / can't lift my leg high enough / Let
me, hold, Show, side kick

Communication
worried about our / Why are, worried / couldn't catch
high balls / gave away / let me help you, kick high balls
/ my skills get better / Don't worry, do better

Wrap Up 1
Do you come to / take a swimming class, once a week
/ When, start the class / Last month, easy for me / let
me help, how to swim / that'll help me a lot

대화문 TEST Step 2 p.64~65

Listen & Talk 1 A-1
Mom: David, how was your basketball game today?
David: We lost, Mom. I missed too many chances for a

three-pointer.

Mom: Oh, don't be so hard on yourself. You'll do better next time.

David: I hope so.

Listen & Talk 1 A-2

Jack: Did you come and watch my volleyball match yesterday?

Irene: Yeah, I did. That was a great volleyball match. You were great!

Jack: Thanks, but it was a close match. My serves were not strong enough.

Irene: Oh, you're a great player. You'll do better next time.

Listen & Talk 1 B

Emily: I heard your baseball team, the Reds, won the match. Eight to seven, right? Congratulations, John!

John: Thanks. It was a close game. I'm not happy with my pitching.

Emily: Why do you say that?

John: I allowed two homeruns.

Emily: Oh, you're a great pitcher. You'll do better next time.

Listen & Talk 2 A-1

Mike: Is it your first time riding a bike, Mina?

Mina: Yes, it is. I just can't keep my balance.

Mike: Let me help you. I'll hold your bike.

Mina: Thanks, Mike. Don't let go, okay?

Mike: Don't worry. Sit up and look straight ahead.

Listen & Talk 2 A-1

Tom: What are you doing, Sarah?

Sarah: I learned how to stand on my head in PE class. So I'm trying it now but it's not easy.

Tom: Let me help you. Kick your legs in the air again. I'll catch you.

Sarah: Oh, thanks. I'll try again.

Listen & Talk 2 B

Coach: Hey, Brian. Did you practice the *taegwondo* side kick?

Brian: Yes, Coach. But I'm still not comfortable with it.

Coach: What problem are you having?

Brian: Well, I can't lift my leg high enough.

Coach: I see. Let me help you. I'll hold this kick pad for you. Show me your side kick.

Communication

Megan: I'm worried about our next soccer match, James.

James: Why are you worried, Megan?

Megan: Well, I couldn't catch high balls in the last soccer match. I gave away too many goals.

James: I see. Here, let me help you. I'll kick high balls to you.

Megan: Oh, that'll really help. I hope my skills get better.

James: Don't worry. You'll do better next time.

Wrap Up 1

Anna: Hi, Jake. Do you come to the pool often?

Jake: Oh, hi, Anna. I take a swimming class here once a week.

Anna: When did you start the class?

Jake: Last month. But swimming is still not easy for me.

Anna: Oh, let me help you. I teach children how to swim in the school club.

Jake: Oh, that'll help me a lot. Thanks.

본문 TEST Step 1   p.66~67

01 At, there, who, cheering
02 that, making, are, waiting
03 waves, flag, starts
04 pushes, down as, completes
05 On, pulls, beside
06 won, result, coming, place
07 chance, finish second
08 going, satisfied, place
09 gets, meet, famous
10 miss, chance, role
11 completes, tenth, laps
12 ahead, out, reach   13 gets, closer
14 almost hits, end
15 drive into, presses harder   16 catch up
17 official waving, means
18 right behind   19 getting, cheering, crowd, louder
20 can do, loudly 21 feel, beating hard
22 rush across, finish   23 Who, winner
24 filled with, out
25 need, tears, voice   26 can't believe
27 standing, front, is
28 but, not, winner   29 real close race
30 Even, win, best   31 that counts
32 Did, best   33 After, smiles 34 guess, did

01 At, track, there are, who are cheering excitedly

02 that are making loud, are waiting

03 official waves, flag, starts

04 pushes, down hard, as, completes, sixth lap

05 On the straightaway, pulls right beside

06 won many races, was coming in fifth place

07 chance to finish second

08 be satisfied with second place   09 gets to meet

10 to miss, to meet his role model

11 completes the tenth lap, to go

12 sees, ahead, out of

13 gets closer and closer

14 hits the back end

15 drive into, presses harder on the gas pedal

16 can catch up

17 waving a white flag, means the last lap

18 right behind

19 getting closer, cheering from the crowd, getting louder

20 can do it, says loudly

21 can feel, beating hard

22 rush across the finish line   23 Who, winner

24 filled with tears, finds out that, in second

25 No need for tears

26 can't believe his eyes

27 who is standing in front of, is   28 not the winner

29 a real close race

30 Even though, didn't win the race, did

31 that counts   32 Did, do my best, thinks

33 After a moment, smiles   34 guess, did

10 그는 그의 역할 모델을 만날 수 있는 기회를 놓치길 원하지 않는다.

11 Max는 10바퀴를 다 돌고 이제 5바퀴를 더 돌아야 한다.

12 Max는 앞에 바로 닿을 듯한 거리에 있는 Simon의 카트를 본다.

13 Max의 카트는 Simon의 카트에 점점 더 가까워진다.

14 Max의 카트는 Simon의 카트의 뒷부분에 거의 닿을 것 같다.

15 그들은 직선 구간을 운전해가고, Max는 가속 페달을 더 세게 밟는다.

16 "나는 따라잡을 수 있어." Max가 말한다.

17 Max는 심판이 마지막 바퀴라는 것을 알려주는 흰색 깃발을 흔드는 것을 본다.

18 Max는 Simon 바로 뒤에 있다.

19 결승점이 점점 가까워지고, 관중으로부터 들리는 환호성이 점점 커진다.

20 "나는 할 수 있어!" Max는 큰 소리로 말한다.

21 그는 그의 심장이 세게 뛰는 것을 느낄 수 있다.

22 카트들이 돌진해 결승점을 지난다.

23 누가 승자인가?

24 Max는 자신이 2등으로 들어왔다는 것을 알았을 때, 눈에 눈물이 가득 찬다.

25 "울 필요 없단다, 얘야." 어떤 남자의 목소리가 말한다.

26 Max는 그의 눈을 믿을 수 없다.

27 그 앞에 서 있는 남자는 L. J. Richards이다!

28 "고마워요, 하지만 저는 일등이 아니에요." Max가 말한다.

29 "정말 아슬아슬한 경기였어.

30 네가 비록 경기를 이기지 못했지만, 너는 최선을 다했어.

31 중요한 것은 바로 그거란다!" L. J. Richards가 말한다.

32 '나는 최선을 다했을까?' Max는 생각한다.

33 잠시 후에, 그는 미소를 짓는다.

34 "네, 저는 최선을 다한 것 같아요."

1 고카트 경기 트랙에 신이 나서 응원하고 있는 많은 사람들이 있다.

2 시끄러운 엔진 소음을 내고 있는 카트들이 기다리고 있다.

3 심판이 초록 깃발을 흔들고, 경기가 시작된다!

4 Max는 트랙을 여섯 바퀴 돌았을 때, 발로 가속 페달을 힘껏 누른다.

5 직선 구간에서 Max는 경기에서 선두를 달리고 있는 Simon의 바로 옆까지 다가간다.

6 작년에 Simon은 경기에서 여러 번 이겼지만 Max의 최고 경기 성적은 5등으로 들어온 것이었다.

7 이번에 그는 2등으로 끝낼 수 있는 기회를 잡았다.

8 그러나 그는 오늘 2등으로 만족하지 않을 것이다.

9 우승자는 세계적으로 유명한 경주 선수인 L. J. Richards를 만나게 된다!

1 At the go-kart race track, there are many people who are cheering excitedly.

2 The karts that are making loud engine noises are waiting.

3 An official waves a green flag and the race starts!

4 Max pushes his foot down hard on the gas pedal as he completes his sixth lap on the track.

5 On the straightaway, Max pulls right beside the race's leader, Simon.

6 Last year, Simon won many races, but Max's best result in a race was coming in fifth place.

7 This time, he has a chance to finish second.

8 But he isn't going to be satisfied with second

place today.

9 The winner gets to meet the world famous racer L. J. Richards!

10 He doesn't want to miss the chance to meet his role model.

11 Max completes the tenth lap and now has five more laps to go.

12 Max sees Simon's kart ahead, just out of Max's reach.

13 Max's kart gets closer and closer to Simon's.

14 It almost hits the back end of Simon's kart.

15 They drive into the straightaway and Max presses harder on the gas pedal.

16 "I can catch up," says Max.

17 Max sees the official waving a white flag which means the last lap.

18 Max is right behind Simon.

19 The finish line is getting closer, and the cheering from the crowd is getting louder.

20 "I can do it!" Max says loudly.

21 He can feel his heart beating hard.

22 The karts rush across the finish line.

23 Who is the winner?

24 Max's eyes are filled with tears as he finds out that he came in second.

25 "No need for tears, kid," says a man's voice.

26 Max can't believe his eyes.

27 The man who is standing in front of him is L. J. Richards!

28 "Thank you, but I'm not the winner," says Max.

29 "It was a real close race.

30 Even though you didn't win the race, you did your best.

31 That's the thing that counts!" says L. J. Richards.

32 'Did I do my best?' thinks Max.

33 After a moment, he smiles.

34 "Yeah, I guess I did."

구석구석지문 TEST Step 1   p.76

Listen & Talk C

1. why the long face

2. couldn't block, other player

3. Don't worry, do better

Grammar in Real Life

1. cook who cooks delicious

2. always goes, which, fresh

3. is always crowded with, who

4. want you to try, most popular

Think & Write

1. between, and, was held, on

2. won, by a score

3. memorable players

4. One of, was

5. made a basket, the end of

6. great match

7. are looking forward

구석구석지문 TEST Step 2   p.77

Listen & Talk C

1. Amy: Michael, why the long face?

2. Michael: I couldn't block the other player.

3. Amy: Don't worry, Michael. You'll do better next time.

Grammar in Real Life

1. Ms. Green is a good cook who cooks delicious Italian food.

2. She always goes to the local store which has many fresh vegetables.

3. Her restaurant is always crowded with people who like to eat her food.

4. I want you to try her seafood pizza which is the most popular.

Think & Write

1. A basketball match between Class 1 and Class 2 was held at school on Friday.

2. Class 1 won the game by a score.

3. There are some memorable players.

4. One of them was Sarah.

5. She was the player who made a basket one second before the end of the game.

6. It was a great match.

7. We are looking forward to the next match.

MEMO

MEMO

1학기 전과정

적중 100 plus

영어 기출 문제집

정답 및 해설

비상 | 김진완

적중 **100** + 특별부록

Plan B

우리학교
최신기출

비상 · 김진완 교과서를 배우는

학교 시험문제 분석 · 모음 · 해설집

전국단위 학교 시험문제 수집 및 분석
출제 빈도가 높은 문제 위주로 선별
문제 풀이에 필요한 상세한 해설

중2-1
영어

비상 · 김진완

◎ 선택형 문항의 답안은 컴퓨터용 수정 싸인펜을
　사용하여 OMR 답안지에 바르게 표기하시오.
◎ 서술형 문제는 답을 답안지에 반드시 검정
　볼펜으로 쓰시오.
◎ 총 33문항 100점 만점입니다. 문항별 배점
　은 각 문항에 표시되어 있습니다.

[대전 ○○중]

1. 빈칸에 들어갈 말로 가장 적절한 것은?　　(2점)

• Do you want to keep your shirts _____?
• Baking Soda can make your shoes _____?

① old　　　　　② safe
③ lost　　　　　④ clean
⑤ happy

[대전 ○○중]

2. 짝지어진 단어의 관계가 나머지와 <u>다른</u> 것은?　(2점)

① luck - lucky　　② enter - entry
③ noise - noisy　　④ health - healthy
⑤ wealth - wealthy

[관악구 ○○중]

3. 다음 밑줄 친 부분의 쓰임이 옳은 것은?　　(3점)

① I am <u>interesting</u> in taking pictures.
② I met the president <u>in person</u>!
③ I have no <u>artist</u> talent, but I enjoy drawing.
④ I'm <u>luck</u> to meet such a kind person like you.
⑤ I am afraid my idea is <u>differ</u> from you.

[광진구 ○○중]

4. 다음 빈칸에 가장 알맞은 것은?　　(2점)

• I finally got used _____ up early in the morning.

① wake　　　　　② waking
③ to wake　　　　④ to waking
⑤ waked

[송파구 ○○중]

5. 다음 짝지어진 대화 중 <u>어색한</u> 것은?　　(3점)

① A: We need to make a house.
　 B: I know how to make a house with trees. I'll show you.
② A: Are you interested in baseball?
　 B: Yes. My hobby is to play baseball.
③ A: Mom, I'm going out to ride my skateboard.
　 B: Okay. Don't forget to wear your helmet.
④ A: I baked this bread, but it came out too dry.
　 B: I ate some bread last night.
⑤ A: What are you going to do this Sunday?
　 B: I'm going to visit my grandparents.

[경기 ○○중]

6. 다음 대화의 빈칸에 들어갈 말로 가장 적절한 것은?
　　(3점)

Jake: Hello, Elsa. Which after-school class are you going to take?
Elsa: I'm going to take the drama class on Thursdays. What about you, Jake?
Jake: I'm thinking of taking the photography class. I'm interested in _____.
Elsa: Oh, I heard that the teacher is a famous photographer.
Jake: Really? That's really cool!

① playing drums
② sending photos
③ taking pictures
④ drawing pictures
⑤ studying drama

7. <보기>의 (A)~(E)가 자연스러운 대화가 되도록 알맞은 순서대로 배열한 것은? (3점)

<보기>

(A) Don't worry. I know how to clean up the glass pieces with bread. I read the tip in a magazine.

(B) With bread? How?

(C) You can wipe the area with it. It picks up the small pieces.

(D) Oh, no. I broke a dish.

(E) Great tip! Thanks. I'll go get some bread in the kitchen.

① (A) - (C) - (B) - (D) - (E)

② (A) - (B) - (D) - (E) - (C)

③ (A) - (E) - (D) - (B) - (C)

④ (D) - (A) - (B) - (C) - (E)

⑤ (D) - (B) - (C) - (E) - (A)

8. 다음 대화의 빈칸에 알맞은 것은? (3점)

A: I baked this bread, but it came out too dry.

B: Oh, I know _____.
Put a glass of water in the oven.

A: That's a great tip. Where did you learn that?

B: I saw it on a cooking show.

① how to use the oven

② how to bake some cookies

③ how to put a glass of water

④ how to enjoy a cooking show

⑤ how to bake bread without making it dry

9. 다음 대화의 빈칸에 알맞은 것은? (4점)

A: Is that a 1000-piece puzzle?

B: Yeah, but there are so many pieces. It'll take a long time to finish.

A: Oh, I know _____. Start from the corners, and then group the pieces with the same colors.

① when to finish it

② what to buy for it

③ where tho move it

④ how to do it quickly

⑤ how to solve it safely

10. 다음 글의 내용을 바르게 설명하고 있는 것은? (4점)

When does your finger move? Is it when you close your right eye? Then you mainly use your right eye. This means you should sit on the left side in the theater. That way, you can enjoy a full view of the screen better. This information is also helpful when you choose a seat in a classroom, too.

① 눈 건강에 유익한 정보를 제공하고 있다.

② 우리는 보통 양쪽 눈을 동일하게 사용한다.

③ 영화 스크린을 잘 보기 위해서는 중간쯤에 앉는 것이 유리하다.

④ 오른쪽 눈을 주로 사용하는 사람은 영화관에서 오른쪽에 앉는 것이 유리하다.

⑤ 왼쪽 눈을 주로 사용하는 사람은 교실에서 오른쪽에 앉는 것이 유리하다.

11. 다음 중 어법상 올바른 문장을 모두 고르면? (4점)

① You made him anger.

② I found the book difficulty.

③ Try to keep your shoes clean.

④ Are you good at taking pictures?

⑤ She is looking forward to go to the movies.

12. 다음 대화에서 어법상 어색한 것은? (3점)

M: ⓐBetty, what are you looking?
W: ⓑI'm reading the comments on my blog.
M: ⓒWhat do you usually write blog posts about?
W: ⓓI usually write about books.
  ⓔI'm interested in reading.

① ⓐ ② ⓑ ③ ⓒ ④ ⓓ ⑤ ⓔ

13. 다음 (A)~(E) 중 밑줄 친 부분의 역할이 같은 것 끼리 묶인 것은? (3점)

(A) My hobby is riding a bike in the park.
(B) I want to visit many places. Traveling makes me happy.
(C) Reading a book is not Bart's hobby.
(D) Thank you for cleaning my room.
(E) Avoid forgetting important events by setting the alarm.

① (A), (B) ② (A), (D)
③ (B), (C) ④ (B), (D)
⑤ (C), (D)

[14~15] 다음 글을 읽고, 물음에 답하시오.

Welcome to *Fantastic Pets*! ⓐHave a pet is great. Today I'm going to ⓑintroducing my pet hedgehog, Polly. (A) When I first ⓒget Polly, she was very ⓓscared. (B) So, I placed my T-shirt in her cage and she got used to my smell. (C) Finally, I was able to hold her in my hands. (D) Now, Polly is my best friend and always makes me ⓔhappily. (E)

14. 위 글에서 아래 주어진 문장이 들어가기에 가장 알맞은 곳은? (4점)

I couldn't hold her because she raised her spikes.

① (A) ② (B) ③ (C)
④ (D) ⑤ (E)

15. 위 글의 밑줄 친 ⓐ~ⓔ 중에서 어법에 맞는 것은? (2점)

① ⓐ ② ⓑ ③ ⓒ ④ ⓓ ⑤ ⓔ

16. 다음 글의 밑줄 친 ⓐ~ⓔ 중 흐름상 어울리지 않는 문장은? (3점)

ⓐ Are you interested in baking? ⓑ I can teach you how to make some delicious bread. ⓒ I know how to bake bread without making it dry. ⓓ I also know how to draw a face quickly. ⓔ I can teach you some helpful tips!

① ⓐ ② ⓑ ③ ⓒ ④ ⓓ ⑤ ⓔ

17. 다음 일일 강좌 홍보문을 읽고 답할 수 <u>없는</u> 질문은?

(3점)

> **Welcome to Justin's Ride with Style!**
> Are you interested in riding a skateboard? I can give you some helpful tips! In this class, you will learn to balance on the skateboard. Anyone can ride a skateboard in only one day. This class is free and everything is ready for you. Sign up today.

① What's the name of the class?

② What is the class about?

③ What will you learn?

④ How much money do you need to take the class?

⑤ Where can you sign up for the class?

[18~20] 다음 글을 읽고, 물음에 답하시오.

> **Welcome to *Fantastic Pets*!**
> ⓐ<u>To have</u> a pet is great. (A) Today I am going to introduce my pet hedgehog, Polly. (B) ⓑ<u>If</u> I first got Polly, she was very ⓒ<u>scary</u>. (C) I couldn't hold her because she raised her spikes. (D) Finally, I was able to ⓓ<u>holding</u> her in my hands. (E) Now, Polly is my best friend and always makes me ⓔ<u>happily</u>.

18. 밑줄 친 ⓐ~ⓔ 중 표현이 옳은 것은? (2점)

① ⓐ   ② ⓑ   ③ ⓒ   ④ ⓓ   ⑤ ⓔ

19. 위 글의 (A) ~ (E) 중 다음 문장이 들어갈 위치로 가장 알맞은 것은? (3점)

> So, I placed my T-shirt in her cage and she got used to my smell.

① (A)   ② (B)   ③ (C)

④ (D)   ⑤ (E)

20. 위 글에서 다음 영영풀이에 해당되는 단어를 찾아 쓰시오. (3점)

> to lift or move something to a higher level

→ _____

[21~22] 다음 글을 읽고, 물음에 답하시오.

> Hey, I'm MC Joy. Do you want to write your own rap? You can rap about anything because everything can be a story for a rap. I get ideas _____ I'm on the bus, in the shower, or in my bed. I write down my ideas and use them when I write my rap. There are no rules for writing raps. You can start today!

21. 위 글의 빈칸에 가장 알맞은 단어는? (3점)

① when   ② which   ③ who

④ what   ⑤ why

22. 위 글의 주제로 가장 알맞은 것은? (4점)

① The types of raps

② Joy's favorite rap

③ The history of rap

④ The most popular rap

⑤ The way to write your own rap

[23~24] 다음 글을 읽고, 물음에 답하시오.

Welcome back to *Handy Tips*. Where do you ⓐnormally sit in a movie theater? Here is a tip. You will find it easy and helpful.
Step 1: Point your finger at something far from you.
Step 2: Close one eye and open it.
Step 3: Repeat ⓑit with the other eye.
When does your finger move? Is it ⓒwhen you close your right eye? Then you mainly use your right eye. ⓓThis means you should sit on the left side in the theater. That way, you can enjoy a full view of the screen ⓔbetter. This information is also helpful when you choose a seat in a classroom, too.

23. 밑줄 친 ⓐ~ⓔ에 대한 설명으로 옳은 것은?   (4점)
① ⓐ는 'always'와 의미가 같다.
② ⓑ는 'close one eye'를 의미한다.
③ ⓒ는 'When do you have dinner?'의 밑줄 친 부분과 쓰임이 같다.
④ ⓓ는 'You mainly use your right eye.'를 가리킨다.
⑤ ⓔ는 'good'의 비교급 의미로 사용되었다.

24. Which one is true about the above passage?   (4점)
① If your finger moves when you close your left eye, you mainly use your right eye.
② When you mainly use your left eye, seats on the left side are the best choice.
③ If your finger moves when you close your right eye, seats on the right side are the best choice.
④ This tip is helpful only when you choose a seat in the movie theater.
⑤ When you mainly use your right eye, you'd better choose your seat on the left side in the theater.

[25~27] 다음 글을 읽고, 물음에 답하시오.

Welcome to *Fantastic Pets*! Having a pet is great. Today I'm going to introduce my pet hedgehog, Polly. When I first got Polly, she was very scared. I couldn't hold her because she raised her spikes. So, I placed my T-shirt in her cage and she ⓐ_____(~에 익숙해졌다) my smell. (A)_____, I was able to hold her in my hands. Now, Polly is my best friend and always makes me happy.
(I = Sam)

25. 위 글을 읽고 답할 수 있는 질문은?   (3점)
① How often did Polly raise her spikes?
② Where did Sam place Polly's cage?
③ How did Sam feel about Polly when he first got Polly?
④ Why did Sam place his T-shirt in Polly's cage?
⑤ What does Polly like to do in her cage?

26. 위 글의 빈칸 (A)에 알맞은 말은?   (2점)
① Mainly   ② Accidentally
③ Shortly   ④ Fortunately
⑤ Finally

27. 위 글의 ⓐ의 빈칸을 괄호의 우리말 의미에 맞게 세 단어로 채워 문장을 완성하시오.   (3점)
→ So, I placed my T-shirt in her cage and she _____ _____ _____ my smell.

[28~31] 다음 글을 읽고, 물음에 답하시오.

> Handy Tips
>
> Welcome back ⓐto *Handy Tips*. Where do you normally sit in a movie theater? (A) Here is a tip. (B)
> Step1: Point your finger at ⓑfar something from you.
> Step2: Close one eye and open it.
> Step3: Repeat it with ⓒthe other eye.
> (C) When does your finger move? (D) Is it when you close your right eye? Then you mainly use your right eye. (E) This means you should sit on the left side in the theater. That way, you can enjoy a full view of the screen better. This information ⓓis also helpful when you choose a ⓔseat in a classroom, too.

28. 위 글의 (A)~(E) 중 아래 문장이 들어갈 알맞은 곳은? (3점)

> You will find it easy and helpful.

① (A) ② (B) ③ (C)
④ (D) ⑤ (E)

29. 위 글을 읽고 대답할 수 <u>없는</u> 질문은? (3점)

① Is this tip useful for you?
② What is the first step in the tip?
③ What is the best tip to send this information better?
④ When you use this tip, what can you enjoy better in the theater?
⑤ If you mainly use your right eye, does your finger move when you close your right eye?

30. 위 글의 밑줄 친 ⓐ~ⓔ 중 <u>잘못된</u> 곳을 찾아, 그 기호를 쓰고 바르게 고치시오. (2점)

→ _____

31. 위 글을 읽고 질문에 대답을 완성하시오. (4점)

> Q: When you mainly use your right eye, on which side should you sit in the theater?
> A: I should _____ in the theater.

→ _____

[32~33] 다음 글을 읽고, 물음에 답하시오.

> Welcome to *Fantastic Pets*! ⓐHave a pet is great. Today I'm going to ⓑintroducing my pet hedgehog, Polly. When I first got Polly, she was very ⓒscared. I couldn't hold her because she raised her spikes. So, I ⓓplace my T-shirt in her cage and she got used to my smell. _____㉠_____, I was able to hold her in my hands. Now, Polly is my best friend and always makes me ⓔhappily.

32. 위 글의 밑줄 친 ⓐ~ⓔ 중 어법상 쓰임이 적절한 것은? (3점)

① ⓐ ② ⓑ ③ ⓒ ④ ⓓ ⑤ ⓔ

33. 위 글의 빈칸 ㉠에 들어갈 말로 가장 알맞은 것은? (3점)

① Finally ② However
③ For example ④ By the way
⑤ From now on

반		점수	
이름			

문항수 : 선택형(31문항) 서술형(2문항)   20 . . .

◎ 선택형 문항의 답안은 컴퓨터용 수정 싸인펜을 사용하여 OMR 답안지에 바르게 표기하시오.
◎ 서술형 문제는 답을 답안지에 반드시 검정 볼펜으로 쓰시오.
◎ 총 33문항 100점 만점입니다. 문항별 배점은 각 문항에 표시되어 있습니다.

[광주 ㅇㅇ중]

1. 다음 영영 뜻풀이에 해당하는 단어로 가장 알맞은 것은?   (3점)

> _____ : physically strong and not likely to become weak

① wealth   ② healthy   ③ material
④ death   ⑤ talent

[구로구 ㅇㅇ중]

2. 다음 빈칸에 가장 알맞은 단어를 고르시오.   (2점)

> • Try to keep a _____ between work and play.

① balance   ② change   ③ skill
④ fair   ⑤ tune

[강남구 ㅇㅇ중]

3. Which of the following is NOT an adjective? (3점)
① wonderful   ② artistic
③ mouthful   ④ majestic
⑤ unhelpful

[중랑구 ㅇㅇ중]

4. 다음 빈칸에 들어갈 표현으로 알맞은 것은?   (2점)

> • I'm afraid that my idea is _____ from yours.

① different   ② same
③ dependent   ④ difficult
⑤ excellent

[중랑구 ㅇㅇ중]

5. 대화를 읽고 답할 수 없는 질문을 고르면?   (3점)

> (W: Woman, M: Man)
> M: Oh, no. I broke a dish.
> W: Don't worry. I know how to clean up the class pieces with bread. I read the tip in a magazine.
> M: With bread? How?
> W: You can wipe the area with it. It picks up the small pieces.
> M: Great tip! Thanks, Tina. I'll go get some bread in the kitchen.

① 어떤 일이 일어났는가?
② 여자는 어떤 신문을 읽었는가?
③ 여자는 남자에게 어떤 조언을 하였는가?
④ 빵으로 어떻게 유리를 치우는가?
⑤ 빵은 어디에 있는가?

[서초구 ㅇㅇ중]

6. Which of the following is NOT in the same usage as in the underlined part in this example?
     (4점)

> ex) My favorite activity is <u>rapping</u> to hip-hop beats.

① The cars are <u>moving</u> very fast on the highway.
② <u>Recycling</u> cans is very important.
③ The girl kept <u>laughing</u> all day long.
④ You should start <u>going</u> so that you can be on time.
⑤ Her problem is <u>spending</u> too much money.

7. Which of the following has a different relation between words? (3점)

① peace : peaceful
② romance : romantic
③ fantasy : fantastic
④ excel : excellent
⑤ noise : noisy

8. Which cannot be an answer to the question below? (2점)

• What are you interested in?

① I'm interested in watching movies.
② I'm into reading comics these days.
③ I like baking cookies for fun.
④ I enjoy learning new dance moves lately.
⑤ I know how to speak in five different languages.

9. 다음 대화를 읽고 (가)~(다)에 들어갈 말을 바르게 연결한 것은? (4점)

M: Emily, what club are you going to join?
W: I'm going to join the music club. I'm (가)_____ music. What (나)_____ you, Aron?
M: I want to join the gardening club. I'm interested in plants and flowers.
W: Oh, that sounds (다)_____ an interesting club.

	(가)	(나)	(다)
①	into	about	like
②	to	on	with
③	of	with	on
④	into	way	like
⑤	to	on	with

10. 다음 밑줄 친 부분의 쓰임이 어법상 나머지와 다른 것은? (2점)

I enjoy ①playing sports.
My hobby is ②playing basketball.
I'm good at ③playing soccer, too.
My friends are interested in ④watching basketball games.
So, I'm ⑤going to meet my friends and watch TV together tomorrow.

① ② ③ ④ ⑤

11. Which is grammatically incorrect? (3점)

① I decided traveling to China next month.
② I love to play soccer.
③ I hope to go to America next week.
④ Taking pictures is something I'm good at.
⑤ To study is very important.

12. Which of the following is correct? (3점)

① A: What do you usually write blog posts about?
   B: I'm reading the comments on my blog.
② A: Who is the man on your SNS?
   B: Wow, you met him in person!
③ A: I'm thinking of taking the photography class.
   B: Oh, I liked to draw pictures.
④ A: I baked this bread, but it came out too dry.
   B: Put a glass of water in the oven next time.
⑤ A: Oh, no. I broke the cup.
   B: Don't worry. I saw it on TV last night.

[13~14] 다음 대화를 읽고, 물음에 답하시오.

A: Oh, no. I broke a dish.
B: Don't worry. I know how to clean up the glass pieces with bread. I read the tip in a magazine.
A: With bread? How?
B: You can wipe the area with it. It picks up the small pieces.
A: Great tip! Thanks. I'll go get some bread in the kitchen.

13. 위 대화를 읽고 이어지는 Q&A에 알맞은 단어를 대화에서 찾아 쓰시오. **(4점)**

Q: How do I (A)_____ up the glass (B)_____ easily?
A: (C)_____ the area with (D)_____.

(A) _____ (B) _____
(C) _____ (D) _____

14. 위 대화의 내용과 일치하는 것은? **(3점)**
① 빵은 부엌에 있다.
② 요령은 신문에 나와 있다.
③ A와 B는 해결 방법을 알고 있다.
④ 접시에 빵의 작은 조각들이 있다.
⑤ 빵으로 접시 닦는 방법을 알고 있다.

[15~16] 다음 대화를 읽고, 물음에 답하시오.

M: Hello, Elsa. Which after-school class are you going to take?
W: I'm going to take the drama class on Thursdays. What about you, Jake?
M: I'm thinking of taking the Tuesday photography class. _____
W: Oh, I heard that the teacher is a famous photographer.
M: Really? That's really cool!

15. 위 대화의 빈칸에 가장 적절한 것은? **(3점)**
① I'm interested in baking.
② I'm interested in reading.
③ I'm interested in volleyball.
④ I'm interested in taking pictures.
⑤ I'm interested in movies.

16. 위 대화의 내용과 일치하는 것은? **(3점)**
① The drama class is on Tuesdays.
② The photography class is on Thursdays.
③ They are talking about a special photographer.
④ Elsa is thinking of taking the photography class.
⑤ A famous photographer teaches the Tuesday photography class.

17. Put the sentences ⓐ~ⓔ in the correct order. **(4점)**

Handy Tips
Welcome back to *Handy Tips*. Where do you normally sit in a movie theater? Here is a tip. You will find it easy and helpful.
ⓐ When you close your right eye, does your finger move?
ⓑ Then you mainly use your right eye more than your left one.
ⓒ Point your finger at something far from you.
ⓓ This means you should sit on the left side in the theater.
ⓔ Close one eye and open it. Repeat it with the other eye.

① ⓐ-ⓑ-ⓒ-ⓔ-ⓓ   ② ⓐ-ⓒ-ⓑ-ⓓ-ⓔ
③ ⓑ-ⓒ-ⓓ-ⓔ-ⓐ   ④ ⓒ-ⓓ-ⓔ-ⓐ-ⓑ
⑤ ⓒ-ⓔ-ⓐ-ⓑ-ⓓ

18. 대화를 읽고 두 사람의 방과 후 신청서에서 옳지 않은 것을 고르면? (3점)

M: Hello, Elsa. Which after-school class are you going to take?

W: I'm going to take the drama class on Thursdays. What about you, Jake?

M: I'm thinking of taking the Tuesday photography class. I'm interested in taking pictures.

W: Oh, I heard that the teacher is a famous photographer.

M: Really? That's really cool!

After-school class	
name	Elsa
Class	① 드라마반
Day of week	② 목요일

After-school class	
name	③ Jake
Class	④ 독서반
Day of week	⑤ 화요일

19. 다음 글의 내용과 일치하는 것은? (3점)

Hey, I'm MC Joy of the program called *Rap It Out*. Do you want to write your own rap? You can rap about anything because everything can be a story for a rap. I get ideas when I'm on the bus, in the shower, or in my bed. I write down my ideas and use them when I write my rap. There are no rules for writing raps. You can start today!

① *Rap It Out* is the title of MC Joy's program.

② Special things can be a story for a rap.

③ People can start writing raps after taking a rest.

④ MC Joy gets ideas from others' raps.

⑤ There are some rules for writing raps.

20. 다음 정원이의 일기를 읽고 어법상 어색한 것을 고르면? (3점)

April 30th, Tuesday

① When Mom left home, she asked me to do these three things.

② You should keep your room clean.
③ Don't the door leave open.
④ If your sister comes back from school, keep her warm and give her something to drink.

⑤ Mom wants me to be a good boy, but I find it difficult.

①　　　②　　　③　　　④　　　⑤

[21~22] 다음 글을 읽고, 물음에 답하시오.

Hey, I'm MC Joy. Do you want to write your ①owned rap? You can rap about anything because ②nothings can be a story for a rap. I get ideas ③if I'm on the bus, in the shower, or in my bed. I write down my ideas and use them ④when I write my rap. (A)랩을 쓰는 데에는 어떤 규칙들도 없다. You can ⑤be start today!

21. 위 글의 (A)를 바르게 영작한 것은? (3점)

① There is no rules for write raps.

② There are no rules for write raps.

③ There is no rules for writing raps.

④ There are no rules for writing raps.

⑤ There is not rules for writing raps.

22. 위 글의 밑줄 친 부분들 중에서 어법상 또는 흐름상 올바르게 사용된 것은? (4점)

① owned　　　② nothing　　　③ if

④ when　　　　⑤ be

[23~26] 다음 글을 읽고, 물음에 답하시오.

Welcome back to ⓐ*Handy Tips*. Where do you ⓑnormally sit in a movie theater? (A) Here is a tip. (가)[it / easy and useful / you / will / find].
Step 1: Point your finger at something far from you.
Step 2: Close one eye and open it.
Step 3: ⓒRepeat it with the other eye.
When does your finger move? (B) Is it when you close your right eye? (C) Then you mainly use your right eye. (D) This means you should sit on the left side in the theater. (E) This ⓓinformation is also useful when you ⓔchoose a seat in a classroom, too.

23. 위 글의 흐름상 아래 문장이 들어갈 자리로 가장 알맞은 곳은? (4점)

That way, you can enjoy a full view of the screen better.

① (A) ② (B) ③ (C)
④ (D) ⑤ (E)

24. 위 글의 밑줄 친 ⓐ~ⓔ의 의미로 적절하지 않은 것은? (2점)

① ⓐ 쓸모 있는 ② ⓑ 규칙적으로
③ ⓒ 반복하다 ④ ⓓ 정보
⑤ ⓔ 선택하다

25. 위 글의 내용상 (가)에 적절한 문장으로 주어진 단어를 올바르게 배열한 것은? (3점)

① You will find it easy and useful.
② You will find easy and useful it.
③ You find easy and useful it will.
④ It will easy and useful you find.
⑤ It will find you easy and useful.

26. 위 글의 내용과 일치하지 않는 것은? (3점)

① 위 글은 일상생활에 사용할 수 있는 정보를 주는 글이다.
② tip의 첫 번째 단계는 가까이에 있는 물체를 손가락으로 가리키는 것이다.
③ 오른쪽 눈을 감았다가 떴을 때 사물을 가리키고 있던 손가락이 움직이면 주로 사용하는 눈은 오른쪽이다.
④ 오른쪽 눈을 주로 사용하는 사람은 극장에서 왼쪽에 앉아야 한다.
⑤ 위 tip은 교실에서도 유용하게 사용할 수 있다.

[27~28] 다음 글을 읽고, 물음에 답하시오.

Hey, I'm MC Joy. Do you want to write your own rap? You can rap about anything because everything can be a story for a rap. I get ideas when I'm on the bus, in the shower, or in my bed. I write down my ideas and use them when I write my rap. There are no rules for writing raps. You can start today!

27. 다음 (1)~(3) 문장이 위 글의 내용과 일치하면 T, 일치하지 않으면 F를 골라 순서대로 바르게 배열한 것은? (3점)

(1) MC Joy uses a bus, takes a shower, and goes to bed to get her ideas. (T / F)
(2) When MC Joy gets her ideas, she writes them down to write her own rap. (T / F)
(3) Everything can be a story for a rap, so we can rap about anything. (T / F)

① T-T-T ② F-F-T
③ F-T-T ④ F-T-F
⑤ T-F-T

28. 위 글에서 말하려고 하는 것은? (3점)

① 나만의 rap을 쓰는 요령
② 듣기 좋은 rap 고르기
③ rap을 노래하는 알맞은 장소
④ 유명한 rapper가 되기 위한 조건
⑤ rap을 위한 아이디어 공유하기

30. 위 글의 밑줄 친 ⓐ*Handy* 대신 쓸 수 있는 단어로 알맞은 것은? (2점)

① useful   ② careful
③ peaceful   ④ colorful
⑤ powerful

31. 위 글을 읽고 답할 수 <u>없는</u> 질문으로 가장 알맞은 것은? (3점)

① How many times should you use this tip?
② What is the first step in the tip?
③ When you use this tip, what can you enjoy better in the theater?
④ If you mainly use your right eye, when does your finger move?
⑤ When you mainly use your right eye, on which side should you sit in the theater?

[광주 ○○중]

[29~33] 다음 글을 읽고, 물음에 답하시오.

Welcome back to ⓐ*Handy Tips.* Where do you normally sit in a movie theater? Here (A)[is / are] a tip. You will find it easy and helpful.
Step 1: Point your finger at (B)[something far / far something] from you.
Step 2: Close one eye and open it.
Step 3: Repeat it with the other eye.
When does your finger move? Is it when you close your right eye? Then you mainly use your right eye. ⓑThis means you should sit on the left side in the theater. That way, you can enjoy a full view of the screen ⓒ better. This information is also helpful when you choose a (C)[sit / seat] in a classroom, too.

32. 위 글의 밑줄 친 ⓒbetter와 같은 품사로 쓰인 문장으로 가장 알맞은 것은? (3점)

① He is reading a <u>better</u> story.
② She looks <u>better</u> than yesterday.
③ You will feel <u>better</u> soon.
④ I try to do the work <u>better</u>.
⑤ I need more money to buy <u>better</u> food.

29. 위 글의 괄호 (A), (B), (C)에 들어갈 말로 가장 알맞은 것은? (3점)

	(A)	(B)	(C)
①	is	something far	seat
②	is	something far	sit
③	is	far something	seat
④	are	far something	seat
⑤	are	something far	sit

33. 위 글의 밑줄 친 ⓑThis가 의미하는 내용을 우리말로 서술하시오. (4점)

→ _____

◎ 선택형 문항의 답안은 컴퓨터용 수정 싸인펜을 사용하여 OMR 답안지에 바르게 표기하시오.
◎ 서술형 문제는 답을 답안지에 반드시 검정 볼펜으로 쓰시오.
◎ 총 27문항) 100점 만점입니다. 문항별 배점은 각 문항에 표시되어 있습니다.

[영등포구 ○○중]

1. 다음에서 밑줄 친 부분의 의미가 바른 것은?   (3점)

① You met him in person. (인간적으로)

② Stay tuned for my story. (채널 고정)

③ Red stands for wealth in China. (견디다)

④ We can get into the palace for free in our *hanboks*. (자유롭게)

⑤ This gallery is known for its excellent collection of art. (~에게 알려져 있다)

[경기 ○○중]

2. 다음 밑줄 친 stands for 대신 적절한 것은?   (2점)

W: I bought this tea for Wang's birthday. Will he like it?
M: Sure, he will. Wang enjoys drinking tea.
W: Great. Then I'll wrap the present.
M: It would be nice to wrap it in red. Red stands for wealth in China.

① is located   ② lines up   ③ rises
④ means   ⑤ wraps

[마포구 ○○중]

3. 다음 중 짝지어진 대화가 어색한 것은?   (3점)

① A: I was going to visit Victoria Peak in Hong Kong.
   B: Don't forget to take pictures there.

② A: Jane, what are you doing?
   B: I'm signing up for a program at the African Museum.

③ A: I bought this tea for Wang's birthday. Will he like it?
   B: Sure, I think so.

④ A: Don't forget to wear your helmet.
   B: Don't worry, I won't.

⑤ A: Are you going to go to the Italian Food Center this weekend?
   B: Yeah, I can't wait to try many kinds of foods.

[영등포구 ○○중]

4. 다음 대화의 내용과 일치하지 않는 것은?   (4점)

A: Look, Brandon. A horse is crossing the street over there.
B: Yes, there is a crossing light for horses here in London.
A: Oh, I didn't know that. That's interesting. Now let's cross the street.
B: Wait. Cars come from the right side in London.
A: Right, I forgot about that.
B: Yeah, it's different from country to country. Don't forget to look to the right before you cross in London.

① 말 한 마리가 길을 건너고 있다.
② 런던에는 말을 위한 신호등이 있다.
③ B는 A보다 런던에 대해 잘 알고 있다.
④ 런던에서는 자동차들이 오른쪽에서 온다.
⑤ 모든 나라에서는 길을 건너기 전 오른쪽을 봐야 한다.

[마포구 ○○중]

5. 다음 주어진 단어들을 모두 사용하여 대화의 빈칸을 채우시오. 필요시 변형이나 추가할 것.   (5점)

look / traditional / games / play

A: I'm going to go to the History Museum of Vietnam.
B: Wow, sounds interesting!
A: Yeah, I'm _____. I can't wait for it.

- 13 -

6. 다음 글의 목적으로 가장 적절한 것은? (4점)

¡Hola! Im a Mexican doll. My name is José and these are my mariachi band members. We play folk music and always wear our sombreros, or big hats. In Mexico, people wear these hats to stay cool under the hot and strong sunlight. We mariachi players want our sombreros to look fancy. So we often decorate them with a lot of different materials. Which of our sombreros do you like best?

① 인형 제작 강의에 신청하려고

② 멕시코 인형 만드는 방법을 배우려고

③ 인형을 안전하게 가지고 노는 요령을 알려주려고

④ 멕시코 여행을 위해 다양한 장소를 문의하려고

⑤ 인형의 특징을 묘사하여 멕시코의 독특한 문화를 소개하려고

7. 다음 남자의 마지막 말에 대한 여자의 응답으로 가장 적절한 것은? (M: 남자, W: 여자) (4점)

M: Jane, what are you doing?
W: I'm signing up for a program at the African Museum.
M: Is there an interesting one?
W: Yeah, I'm going to make an African drum and a traditional mask.
M: Oh, how fun!
W: _____

① Let's just go see that movie.

② You should stop surfing the Internet.

③ No, I don't have to stay up all night.

④ You look hungry. Would you like something to eat?

⑤ Yeah, I'm looking forward to visiting the museum.

8. 다음 중 대화의 빈칸에 들어갈 말로 가장 알맞은 것은? (3점)

A: Chris, what are you going to do this Sunday?
B: I'm going to go to the Italian food restaurant.
A: Wow, sounds great!
B: Yeah, _____.

① don't forget to eat pizza

② you can learn to make pizza

③ I'm interested in making pizza

④ I know how to make pizza

⑤ I'm looking forward to eating pizza

9. 다음 대화의 내용과 일치하지 않는 것은? (4점)

W: Look, Brandon. A horse is crossing the street over there.
M: Yes, there is a crossing light for horses here in London.
W: Oh, I didn't know that. That's interesting. Now let's cross the street.
M: Wait! Cars come from the right side in London.
W: Right, I forgot about that.
M: Yeah, it's different from country to country. Don't forget to look to the right before you cross in London.

① 위의 두 사람은 현재 런던에 있다.

② 런던에는 말을 위한 교통 신호등이 있다.

③ 런던에서는 우회전만 가능하다.

④ 교통 체계는 나라마다 다르다.

⑤ 런던에서는 길을 건널 때 오른쪽을 확인해야 한다.

10. 다음 빈칸에 적절하지 <u>않은</u> 것은? (4점)

> M: Jane, what are you doing?
> W: I'm signing up for a program at the African Museum.
> M: Is there an interesting one?
> W: Yeah, I'm going to make an African drum and a traditional mask.
> M: Oh, how fun!
> W: Yeah, _____

① I hope I can visit the museum.

② I'm eager to visit the museum.

③ I'm unable to visit the museum.

④ I can't wait to visit the museum.

⑤ I'm looking forward to visiting the museum.

11. 다음 빈칸에 적절하지 <u>않은</u> 것은? (3점)

> M: Hey, what are you going to do this Sunday?
> W: Hello. I'm going to go to the World Food Fair.
> M: Oh! I was there last weekend. There were lots of traditional foods from all over the world.
> W: Great! _____

① I can wait to try them.

② I'm expecting to try them.

③ I hope to try lots of foods there.

④ I'm looking forward to trying them.

⑤ I want to have lots of foods there.

12. 다음 대화 중 가장 자연스러운 것은? (4점)

① A: Elsa, how is your Hula dance class going?
　 B: My hobby is dancing Hula.

② A: Will he like his birthday present?
　 B: Sure, he likes wrapping up a present.

③ A: Chris, what are you going to do this Sunday?
　 B: That sounds great!

④ A: What are you going to show us today?
　 B: This show is very exciting.

⑤ A: I'm going to visit the World Food Fair.
　 B: Oh, Really? I was there last weekend.

[13~14] 다음 대화를 읽고, 물음에 답하시오.

> Guide: How was your first day here in Mongolia?
> Thor: It was great. By the way, where am I going to stay tonight?
> Guide: You're going to sleep in a *ger*, a Mongolian tent.
> Thor: Oh, _____
> Guide: You'll like it. There is a fireplace in the *ger*. So, you should remember to put your things away from the fireplace.
> Thor: I see. Thank you.

13. 위 대화의 빈칸에 들어갈 말로 가장 적절한 것은? (4점)

① I will forgive you.

② don't forget anything.

③ I'm looking forward to it.

④ I have to be careful not to sleep.

⑤ it will be fun to do some exciting activities.

14. 위 대화의 내용과 일치하지 <u>않는</u> 것은? (3점)

① Thor는 몽고에 머무르고 있다.

② Thor는 오늘밤 *ger*에 머무를 예정이다.

③ *ger*는 몽고식 텐트이다.

④ *ger*는 밤에 많이 추울 것이다.

⑤ 화덕 주변에 물건을 치워야 한다.

[15~16] 다음 대화를 읽고 물음에 답하시오.

> W: Look! A horse is (A)[crossing / crossed] the street over there.
> M: Yes, there is a crossing light for horses here in London.
> W: Oh, I didn't know that. That's interesting. Now let's (B)[cross / to cross] the street.
> M: Wait! Cars come from the right side in London.
> W: Right, I forgot about that.
> M: Yeah, it's different from country to country. Don't forget (C)[looking / to look] to the right before you cross in London.

15. 위 대화의 주제로 가장 적절한 것은? (4점)

① how to ride a horse in London
② why horses need a crossing light
③ differences in crossing the street in London
④ learning how to drive a car in other countries
⑤ things you have to do after crossing the street

16. 위 대화의 (A), (B), (C) 각각 어법에 맞는 표현으로 가장 적절한 것은? (4점)

	(A)	(B)	(C)
①	crossing	cross	looking
②	crossing	cross	to look
③	crossing	to cross	to look
④	crossed	to cross	looking
⑤	crossed	cross	to look

[17~19] 다음 글을 읽고 물음에 답하시오.

> Sawbona! My name is Ayanda and I'm a Zulu. We are a tribe in South Africa. What do you think of my beads? Zulu people enjoy making clothes with beads.

(A) They are beautiful and each color has a(n) _____ meaning. When we did not have our own writing system, we used beads to communicate with each other. If you want to know the meaning of the colors, check out the following box.

(B) If you want to send someone a(n) _____ message, you can express yourself with these beads. What message do you want to make?

(C)

Color	Good Meaning	Bad Meaning
Black	marriage	death
Yellow	wealth	badness
Red	love	anger
White	love	-

17. 위의 주어진 글 다음에 이어질 글의 순서로 가장 적절한 것은? (4점)

① (A) - (B) - (C) ② (A) - (C) - (B)
③ (B) - (A) - (C) ④ (B) - (C) - (A)
⑤ (C) - (B) - (A)

18. 위 글의 빈칸에 공통으로 들어갈 말로 가장 적절한 것은? (3점)

① scary   ② entire   ③ special
④ sweet   ⑤ average

19. 위 글의 내용과 일치하지 <u>않는</u> 것은? (4점)

① Zulu is a tribe in South Africa.
② Zulu people enjoy making clothes with beads.
③ Zulu people used beads to communicate with each other.
④ White color beads have good and bad meanings.
⑤ If you use these beads, you can express yourself.

[20~21] 다음 대화를 읽고 물음에 답하시오.

Mom: Mike, I'm going to be late. Can you make dinner for Sam?

Mike: OK, don't worry. Sam, come home early.

Sam: OK.

Mom: Mike and Sam, be sure to do your homework.

Sam: I will. Can you get us some ice cream?

Mom: I want to know if there's ice cream in the refrigerator first.

Mike: OK. I will check it out right now. No, it's empty now.

Mom: Don't lie to me. I bought ice cream the day before yesterday.

Mike: I ate ice cream yesterday already.

Mom: Oh... come on... guys. You have to care your body and health. Too much ice cream will make you fat. This is last time to buy you ice cream. OK?

Mike: OK, mom.

Sam: Oh... brother, you are bad. You finished ice cream alone! Don't do that next time!

Mike: Sorry, man.

20. 위 대화의 내용과 일치하지 <u>않는</u> 것은? (3점)

① 엄마는 집에 늦게 돌아올 예정이다.

② Sam과 Mike는 숙제가 있다.

③ 지금 냉장고에는 아이스크림이 없다.

④ 아이스크림을 너무 많이 먹으면 살이 찔 수 있다.

⑤ Sam은 어제 아이스크림을 먹었다.

21. 위 대화를 보고, 주어진 단어를 활용해 우리말에 맞게 영작하시오. (5점)

(1) Mike는 Sam에게 집에 일찍 오라고 말했다. (tell)

→ Mike _____.

(2) Sam은 Mike에게 아이스크림을 함께 먹자고 요청했다. (ice cream / ask / eat / together)

→ Sam _____.

[22~24] 다음 글을 읽고 물음에 답하시오.

Sawbona! My name is Ayanda and I'm a Zulu. We are a tribe in South Africa. What do you think of my beads? Zulu people enjoy making clothes with beads. They are beautiful and each color (A)[have / has] a special meaning. When we did not have our own writing system, we used beads to communicate with each other. (B)[As / If] you want to know the meaning of the colors, check out the following box.

Color	Good Meaning	Bad Meaning
Black	marriage	death
Yellow	wealth	badness
Red	love	anger
White	love	-

If you want to (D)<u>send someone a special message</u>, you can express yourself with these beads. (C)[How / What] message do you want to make?

22. 위 글의 (A)~(C)에서 어법이나 문맥상 알맞은 말이 바르게 짝지어진 것은? (4점)

	(A)	(B)	(C)
①	have	If	How
②	have	As	What
③	has	As	How
④	has	As	What
⑤	has	If	What

23. 위 글의 내용과 일치하지 <u>않는</u> 것은? (4점)

① Ayanda is from South Africa.

② Zulu people communicated with each other by using beads.

③ There was a time when Zulu people had no writing system.

④ The bad meaning of red-colored beads is death.

⑤ You can express love with red or white color.

24. 위 글의 밑줄 친 (D)send someone a special message를 아래 <보기>와 같이 변형할 때, 빈칸에 들어갈 말로 가장 적절한 것은? (3점)

<보기>
• send a special message _____ someone

① to   ② of   ③ for
④ at   ⑤ on

[대구 ○○중]

[25~27] 다음 글을 읽고, 물음에 답하시오.

(A) Sawbona!
My name is Ayanda and I'm a Zulu. We are a tribe in South Africa. What do you think of my beads? (B) Zulu people enjoy making clothes with beads. They are beautiful and each color has a special meaning. When we did not have our own writing system, we used beads to communicate with each other. (C)

Color	Good Meaning	Bad Meaning
Black	marriage	death
Yellow	wealth	badness
Red	love	anger
White	love	-

If you want to send someone a special message, you can express yourself with these beads. (D)
What message do you want to make? (E)

25. 위 글에서 다음 문장이 들어갈 위치로 가장 적절한 곳은? (4점)

If you want to know the meaning of the colors, check out the following box.

① (A)   ② (B)   ③ (C)
④ (D)   ⑤ (E)

26. 위 글을 읽고, 다음 대화의 내용과 일치하도록 (A) 와 (B)의 빈칸에 각각 들어갈 단어로 가장 적절한 것을 고르면? (4점)

Jiho: Suzy, What are you doing?
Suzy: I am making a special bracelet for my sister. Tomorrow is her wedding day.
Jiho: Congratulations!
Suzy: Thanks. Do you remember the story of the Zulu, a tribe in South Africa?
Jiho: Of course. ⓐ그들은 서로 소통하기 위해 구슬들을 사용했어.
Suzy: Yes. After I learned the story, I decided to make a bracelet with beads to send my sister a special message.
Jiho: That's a good idea! But you should remember that there are (A)_____ meanings for each color of bead.
Suzy: Right. Each bead can have both a good meaning and a bad meaning at the same time.
Jiho: What message do you want to send?
Suzy: A love message without a bad meaning.
Jiho: I see, then why don't you use a (B)_____ colored bead? It only has good meaning of love.
Suzy: Oh! I like it. Thank you. Jiho.

         (A)   (B)
① same   black
② different   white
③ different   red
④ same   white
⑤ opposite   yellow

27. 위 대화의 밑줄 친 ⓐ의 우리말에 맞게 다음 주어진 단어들을 알맞게 배열하시오. (4점)

each other / used / communicate / they / to / beads / with

→ _____

2학년 영어 1학기 중간고사(2과) 2회

문항수 : 선택형(28문항) 서술형(2문항)   20 . . .

반 이름

점수

◎ 선택형 문항의 답안은 컴퓨터용 수정 싸인펜을 사용하여 OMR 답안지에 바르게 표기하시오.
◎ 서술형 문제는 답을 답안지에 반드시 검정 볼펜으로 쓰시오.
◎ 총 30문항 100점 만점입니다. 문항별 배점은 각 문항에 표시되어 있습니다.

[마포구 ○○중]

1. 다음 각 단어의 뜻풀이가 바르게 되도록 빈칸에 알맞은 말을 순서대로 나열한 것은? (3점)

- raise: to lift something to a _____ position
- repeat: to tell people something _____ once
- hedgehog: a small brown animal with sharp _____ covering its back

① safe   only   fur
② different   only   spikes
③ different   more than   fur
④ higher   less than   spikes
⑤ higher   more than   spikes

[영등포구 ○○중]

2. 다음 중 밑줄 친 부분이 어색한 것은? (3점)

① You must be <u>careful</u> with the knife.
② Suddenly the pyramids came into <u>view.</u>
③ My parents don't eat meat, not <u>even</u> eggs.
④ I'm learning English to <u>express</u> with foreigners.
⑤ Unfortunately there is an exception to every <u>rule</u>.

[영등포구 ○○중]

3. 다음 중 단어의 관계가 나머지와 <u>다른</u> 것은? (2점)

① useful : handy
② different : similar
③ usually : normally
④ fantastic : excellent
⑤ folk music : traditional music

[대구 ○○중]

4. 다음 중 우리말을 영어로 바르게 옮기지 <u>못한</u> 것은? (2점)

① 내일 비가 올지 안 올지 모르겠어.
   → I don't know if it will rain tomorrow.
② 한복 입을 것을 잊지 마.
   → Don't forget to wear a *hanbok*.
③ 많은 학생들은 학교생활에 만족감을 느꼈다.
   → Many students satisfied with life in school.
④ 중요한 날인 것 같네요!
   → It sounds like a big day!
⑤ 나의 아빠는 내가 친구들과 함께 캠핑 갈 것을 요청하셨다.
   → My dad asked me to go camping with my friends.

[양천구 ○○중]

5. 다음 대화의 흐름상 빈칸에 들어갈 표현을 〈보기〉의 단어들을 모두 사용하여 완성할 때 네 번째 오는 단어는? (3점)

A: Jane, what are you doing?
B: I'm signing up for a program at the African Museum.
A: Is there an interesting one?
B: Yeah, I'm going to make an African drum and a traditional mask.
A: Oh, how fun!
B: _____ _____ _____ _____ _____ the museum.

〈보기〉
forward / I'm / to / looking / visiting

① to   ② I'm   ③ forward
④ looking   ⑤ visiting

- 19 -

6. 다음 글의 내용과 일치하지 <u>않는</u> 것은? (4점)

My name is José and these are my mariachi band members. We play folk music and always wear our sombreros, or big hats. In Mexico, people wear these hats to stay cool under the hot and strong sunlight. We mariachi players want our sombreros to look fancy. So we often decorate them with a lot of different materials. Which of our sombreros do you like best?

① José is one of the mariachi band members.

② The mariachi band plays Mexican folk music.

③ Big hats help people to stay cool under the hot sunlight.

④ The mariachi band players like to wear original sombreros.

⑤ There are many kinds of materials to decorate sombreros.

[7~8] 다음 대화를 읽고 물음에 답하시오.

Betty: Hi, Mike. What are you going to do during the vacation?

Mike: Hey, I'm going to take a trip to Sweden. What about you?

Betty: I'm also planning to travel to Mongolia. Where are you going to stay there?

Mike: I'm going to sleep in an ice hotel.

Betty: Really? I heard the room is cold at night. So, _____

Mike: I see. Thank you. How about you?

Betty: I'm going to sleep in a *ger*. There is a fireplace in the *ger*. I need to put my things away from the fireplace.

Mike: Oh, you know well.

7. 위 대화의 내용과 일치하는 것은? (3점)

① 스웨덴에는 게르라는 숙소가 있다.

② Mike는 얼음 호텔에서 머물 것이다.

③ Mike는 머물 곳에 대해 잘 알고 있다.

④ Betty와 Mike는 함께 여행을 갈 예정이다.

⑤ Mike는 Betty에게 다른 나라의 숙소에 머무를 때 유의해야 할 점을 알려주고 있다.

8. 위 대화의 빈칸에 들어가기에 <u>어색한</u> 표현은? (3점)

① be sure to wear a hat.

② you should wear a hat.

③ you are wearing a hat.

④ remember to wear a hat.

⑤ why don't you wear a hat?

[9~10] 다음 글을 읽고 물음에 답하시오.

Guten Tag! I'm Sweepy. I'm from Germany and my job is to clean chimneys. During winter, chimney sweeps help people to keep warm and safe. (A)_____, people think chimney sweeps bring them happiness. People even want chimney sweeps to be at their weddings! If you see me, it is your (B)luck day.

9. 위 글의 빈칸 (A)에 들어갈 말로 가장 적절한 것은?

(4점)

① So   ② In short   ③ But

④ Besides   ⑤ For example

10. 위 글의 밑줄 친 (B)를 알맞은 형으로 고치시오.

(3점)

(B)_____

[11~12] 다음 글을 읽고 물음에 답하시오.

Dolls around the World
Guten Tag! We're Sweepy. ⓐWe are from Germany and our job is to clean chimneys. During winter, chimney sweeps help people to keep warm and safe. So people think ⓑthey bring ⓒthem good luck. People even want ⓓthem to be at their weddings! If you see ⓔus, it is your lucky day.

11. 위 글과 관련되어 다음 대화의 빈칸에 가장 적절한 것은? (3점)

A: Why do people think chimney sweeps bring them good luck?
B: Because chimney sweeps _____.

① always work diligently
② want to live in Germany
③ build the chimneys
④ like going to weddings with people
⑤ help people to keep warm during winter

12. 위 글의 밑줄 친 ⓐ~ⓔ 중 가리키는 대상이 다른 하나는? (4점)
① ⓐ　　② ⓑ　　③ ⓒ　　④ ⓓ　　⑤ ⓔ

[13~14] 다음 글을 읽고 물음에 답하시오.

Guten Tag! I'm Sweepy. (A) I'm from Germany and my job is to clean chimneys. (B) During winter, chimney sweeps help people _____ warm and safe. (C) People even want chimney sweeps to be at their weddings! (D) If you see me, it is your lucky day. (E)

13. 위 글의 흐름상 아래 문장이 들어갈 자리로 가장 알맞은 곳은? (4점)

So people think chimney sweeps bring them good luck.

① (A)　　　　② (B)　　　　③ (C)
④ (D)　　　　⑤ (E)

14. 위 글의 빈칸에 들어갈 말로 올바른 것은? (2점)
① keep　　　② keeps　　　③ kept
④ keeping　　⑤ to keeping

[15~16] 다음 글을 읽고 물음에 답하시오.

¡Hola! My name is José and ⓐthese are my mariachi band members. We play folk music and ⓑalways wear our sombreros, or big hats. In Mexico, people ⓒwear these hats to stay cool under the hot and strong sunlight. We mariachi players ⓓwant to our sombreros to look fancy. So we often ⓔdecorate them with a lot of different materials. Which of our sombreros do you like best?

15. 위 글의 José에 대한 설명으로 옳은 것은? (4점)
① 민속 음악을 연주한다.
② 작은 모자를 쓰고 있다.
③ 악기를 다양한 물건으로 장식한다.
④ 호세가 살고 있는 지역에는 바람이 강하다.
⑤ 솜브레로는 단지 장식의 목적으로 착용한다.

16. 위 글의 밑줄 친 ⓐ~ⓔ 중 어법상 바르지 않은 것은? (3점)
① ⓐ　　② ⓑ　　③ ⓒ　　④ ⓓ　　⑤ ⓔ

[17~18] 다음 글을 읽고 물음에 답하시오.

My name is José and these are my mariachi band members. We play folk music and always wear our sombreros, (A)[or / and] big hats. In Mexico, people wear these hats (B)[in order to / to get used to] stay cool under the hot and strong sunlight. We mariachi players want our sombreros (C)[to look / looking] fancy. So we often decorate them with a lot of different materials. Which of our sombreros do you like best?

17. 위 글을 읽고 답할 수 <u>없는</u> 질문은? (단, they는 the mariachi band members이다.) (4점)

① What do they do?

② Why do people wear sombreros in Mexico?

③ What do they wear all the time?

④ What are their instruments made of?

⑤ Why do they decorate their sombreros?

18. 위 글의 (A)~(C)에 어법상 적절한 것은? (4점)

	(A)	(B)	(C)
①	or	in order to	to look
②	or	to get used to	looking
③	or	in order to	looking
④	and	to get used to	to look
⑤	and	to get used to	looking

[19~20] 다음 글을 읽고 물음에 답하시오.

Guten Tag! I'm Sweepy. I'm from Germany and my job is to clean chimneys. During winter, chimney sweeps help people to keep warm and safe. So people think chimney sweeps bring them good luck. People even want chimney sweeps to be at their weddings! If you see me, it is your lucky day.

¡Hola! My name is José and these are my mariachi band members. (A) We play folk music and always wear our sombreros, or big hats. (B) In Mexico, people wear these hats to stay cool under the hot and strong sunlight. (C) We mariachi players want our sombreros to look fancy. (D) Which of our sombreros do you like best? (E)

19. 위 글의 (A)~(E) 중 주어진 문장이 들어가기에 알맞은 곳은? (3점)

So we often decorate them with a lot of different materials.

① (A) ② (B) ③ (C)

④ (D) ⑤ (E)

20. 위 글을 읽고 다음의 질문에 바르게 답한 것끼리 〈보기〉에서 골라 짝지은 것은? (4점)

Q: Why do people want chimney sweeps to be at their weddings?

A: It's because (A)_____.

Q: Why do Mexican people wear big hats?

A: It's because (B)_____.

〈보기〉

ⓐ they need to be warm and safe

ⓑ they want to be fancy with their hats

ⓒ people believe that they bring good luck

ⓓ they can stay cool under the hot sunlight with them

	(A)	(B)
①	ⓐ	-	ⓑ
②	ⓐ	-	ⓒ
③	ⓑ	-	ⓒ
④	ⓒ	-	ⓑ
⑤	ⓒ	-	ⓓ

[21~22] 다음 글을 읽고 물음에 답하시오,

Sawbona! My name is Ayanda and I'm a Zulu. We are a tribe in South Africa. What do you think of my beads? Zulu people enjoy (A)[to make / making] clothes with beads. They are beautiful and each color (B)[have / has] a special meaning. When we did not have our own writing system, we used beads (C)[communicating / to communicate] with each other. If you want to know the meaning of the colors, check out the following box.

Color	Good Meaning	Bad Meaning
Black	marriage	death
Yellow	wealth	badness
Red	love	anger
White	love	—

If you want to send someone a special message, you can express yourself with these beads. What message do you want to make?

21. 위 글의 (A)~(C)에서 어법상 적절한 표현으로 짝 지어진 것은? (3점)

	(A)	(B)	(C)
①	to make	has	communicating
②	to make	have	to communicate
③	making	have	to communicate
④	making	has	to communicate
⑤	making	has	communicating

22. 위 글의 내용과 일치하지 <u>않는</u> 것은? (4점)

① Zulu is a tribe in South Africa.
② White beads have only one meaning.
③ Zulu people make clothes with beads.
④ Good meaning of yellow and red beads is the same.
⑤ Zulu communicated with each other by using beads.

[23~25] 다음 글을 읽고, 물음에 답하시오.

¡Hola! My name is José and these are my mariachi band members. We play folk music and always wear our sombreros, (A)or big hats. In Mexico, people wear these hats to stay cool under the hot and strong sunlight. We mariachi players want our sombreros (B)_____ fancy. So we often decorate them with a lot of different materials. (C)_____ of our sombreros do you like best?

23. 위 글의 밑줄 친 (A)or를 우리말로 옮기시오. (4점)

→ _____

24. 빈칸 (B), (C)에 들어갈 가장 적절한 것은? (4점)

	(B)	(C)
①	look	What
②	to look	What
③	to look	Which
④	looking	Which
⑤	looking	How

25. 위 글의 내용과 일치하지 <u>않는</u> 것은? (3점)

① 주인공의 이름은 호세이다.
② 마리아치 악단 단원은 민속 음악을 연주한다.
③ 솜브레로는 큰 모자를 말한다.
④ 마리아치 연주자들은 솜브레로가 화려하게 보이기를 원한다.
⑤ 솜브레로는 한 종류의 재료로 장식한다.

[26~28] 다음 글을 읽고 물음에 답하시오.

My name is Ayanda and I'm a Zulu. We are a tribe in South Africa. Zulu people enjoy making clothes with beads. They are beautiful and each color has a special meaning. When we didn't have our own writing system, we used beads to communicate with each other. ⓐIf you want to know the meaning of the colors, check out the following box.

Color	Good Meaning	Bad Meaning
Black	marriage	death
Yellow	wealth	badness
Red	love	anger
White	love	-

26. 위 글의 내용을 토대로 다음과 같이 대화할 때, 빈칸 (A), (B)에 가장 적절한 것은?   (3점)

M: Hey, you have something special in your hand. What are they?
W: Oh, they are beads and each color has a different (A)_____.
M: Really? My sister just got a job and I want to give a special present for her.
W: Then, how about (B)_____ beads? People believe that (B)_____ beads make them rich.
M: Wow, that's cool!

	(A)	(B)
①	meaning	yellow
②	meaning	black
③	clothes	yellow
④	clothes	white
⑤	system	black

27. 위 글의 내용을 읽고 알 수 있는 것은?   (4점)
① 줄루는 남아프리카의 부족 이름이다.
② 빨간색 구슬의 나쁜 의미는 죽음이다.
③ 줄루족 사람들은 구슬로 인형을 만든다.
④ 검정색 구슬은 결혼이나 분노를 의미한다.
⑤ 구슬을 이용해서 새로운 문자 체계를 개발했다.

28. 위 글의 밑줄 친 ⓐIf의 쓰임과 다른 것은?   (3점)
① You'll find the house if you arrive.
② I'll get healthier if I don't eat fast food.
③ I don't know if she lives close to school
④ You may sleep in class if you eat too much.
⑤ Close the window if it rains in the afternoon.

[29~30] 다음 글을 읽고 물음에 답하시오.

Guten Tag! I'm Sweepy. (A) I'm from Germany and my job is to clean chimneys. (B) During winter, chimney sweeps help people to keep warm and safe. (C) People even want chimney sweeps to be at their weddings! (D) If you see me, it is your lucky day. (E)

29. 위 글의 (A)~(E) 중 다음 문장이 들어갈 가장 알맞은 곳은?   (3점)

So people think chimney sweeps bring them good luck.

① (A) ② (B) ③ (C) ④ (D) ⑤ (E)

30. 위 글을 바탕으로 다음 빈칸에 들어갈 말로 가장 옳은 것은?   (4점)

Q: Why people want chimney sweeps to be at their weddings?
A: It's because _____.

① the chimneys are dirty
② they have weddings during winter
③ they want to keep warm and safe
④ they feel lucky if chimney sweeps are there
⑤ they want chimney sweeps to clean their chimneys

2학년 영어 1학기 기말고사(3과) 1회

문항수 : 선택형(28문항) 서술형(1문항)

반 이름		점수
20 . . .		

◎ 선택형 문항의 답안은 컴퓨터용 수정 싸인펜을
  사용하여 OMR 답안지에 바르게 표기하시오.
◎ 서술형 문제는 답을 답안지에 반드시 검정
  볼펜으로 쓰시오.
◎ 총 29문항 100점 만점입니다. 문항별 배점
  은 각 문항에 표시되어 있습니다.

[인천 ○○중]

1. 빈칸에 공통으로 들어갈 가장 알맞은 것은? (3점)

> A: I want to get the shoes _____.
> B: _____? What do you mean?

① BFF　　　② YOLO　　　③ Q&A
④ ASAP　　　⑤ AKA

[송파구 ○○중]

2. 다음 중 형태의 변화가 나머지와 다른 것은? (2점)
① able - ability
② active - activity
③ creative - creativity
④ possible - possibility
⑤ usual - usually

[광진구 ○○중]

3. 다음 대화의 괄호 (A), (B), (C) 안에서 문맥상 올바른 것은? (3점)

> M: Lisa, what did you do last weekend?
> W: I (A)[make / made] an egg ball with my brother.
> M: An egg ball? Can you explain what it is?
> W: We put an egg in vinegar (B)[for / of] two days. Then, the egg turns into a ball.
> M: Wow, I want to (C)[make / making] one, too!

　　　(A)　　　(B)　　　(C)
① make　　　of　　　making
② make　　　for　　　make
③ made　　　for　　　making
④ made　　　for　　　make
⑤ made　　　of　　　making

[구로구 ○○중]

4. 다음 빈칸에 들어갈 적절한 단어가 아닌 것은? (4점)

> • The boxes _____ 50kg.
> • The job was a big _____.
> • The _____ of light affects the growth of a plant.
> • The _____ town was destroyed.

① weigh　　　② entire
③ average　　　④ challenge
⑤ amount

[송파구 ○○중]

5. 다음 빈칸에 들어갈 적절한 단어가 아닌 것은? (4점)

> • Hearts normally _____ fast when we exercise.
> • It takes a few weeks to _____ the homework.
> • The water began to _____ into the hole.
> • His foods always _____ the customers.

① beat　　　② complete
③ flow　　　④ press
⑤ satisfy

[금천구 ○○중]

6. 아래 영어 의미와 this가 가리키는 단어는? (4점)

> • a form of energy that can be carried by wires and is used for heating and lighting, and to provide power for machine
> • Power plants make this.

① string　　　② average
③ amusement　　　④ experiment
⑤ electricity

7. 다음 Jack의 주간 일정표를 보고, 문장을 완성하시오. 각 문항을 두 단어로 완성할 것. (5점)

	Mon.	Tue.	Wed.	Thur.	Fri.
Do a lot of Work!	Library: Return two books		finish English homework		perform the play at the talent show ♪♪

This is Jack's plan for this week. There is a lot of work (1)_____. He needs to go to the library on Monday. He has two books (2)_____ to the library. Also, he has English homework (3)_____ by Wednesday. On Friday, he will be in the school talent show. So, he will practice the play (4)_____ all this week.

(1) _____ (2) _____
(3) _____ (4) _____

8. 다음 대화의 순서를 바르게 나열한 것은? (3점)

What show are you watching, Sally?

(A) No, I haven't. What's it about?
(B) It's a new program. The program uses science to explain magic tricks.
(C) I'm watching the Sci-Magic show. Have you heard about it?
(D) Oh, it sounds interesting.

① (B) - (D) - (A) - (C)
② (B) - (D) - (C) - (A)
③ (C) - (A) - (B) - (D)
④ (C) - (A) - (D) - (B)
⑤ (C) - (D) - (B) - (A)

9. 다음 빈칸에 들어갈 가장 적절한 표현은? (3점)

A: What did you do last weekend?
B: I made an egg ball with my brother.
A: An egg ball? _____
B: We put an egg in vinegar for two days. Then, the egg turns into a ball.

① You know what?
② What do you mean?
③ Have you heard about it?
④ Are you going to make it?
⑤ How is your egg ball going?

10. (A)와 (B)에 들어갈 단어가 올바른 것은? (4점)

• There is a strong ____(A)____ of rain this afternoon.
• What did you ____(B)____ say at the meeting? Tell me more about it.

	(A)	(B)
①	possibility	amazingly
②	possibility	actually
③	ability	surprisingly
④	ability	actually
⑤	activity	surprisingly

11. 빈칸에 들어갈 적절한 단어가 아닌 것은? (4점)

<Science Experiment Project>
Making a "_____ Card"
How It Works
1. _____ baking soda and water.
2. _____ a message on the card with it.
3. _____ over the card with grape juice.
4. _____, the message appears.

① Mystery ② Mix ③ Write
④ Lift ⑤ Then

12. 다음 주어진 말 다음에 이어질 대화의 순서가 올바른 것은? (3점)

> Lisa, what did you do last weekend?
> (A) Wow, I want to make one, too!
> (B) An egg ball? What do you mean?
> (C) I made an egg ball with my brother.
> (D) We put an egg in vinegar for two days. Then, the egg turns into a ball.

① (A) - (D) - (B) - (C)
② (B) - (C) - (D) - (A)
③ (C) - (B) - (D) - (A)
④ (D) - (B) - (C) - (A)
⑤ (D) - (B) - (A) - (C)

13. 주어진 말에 이어질 순서로 바른 것은? (4점)

> Have you heard about the Smart App Contest?
> (A) A Song Sherlock App? What do you mean?
> (B) Yes, I have.
> (C) When you sing some part of a song, the app tells you its title.
> (D) I'm going to send my idea about a Song Sherlock App.

① (A) - (B) - (C) - (D)
② (A) - (B) - (D) - (C)
③ (A) - (D) - (C) - (B)
④ (B) - (D) - (A) - (C)
⑤ (B) - (D) - (C) - (A)

[14~16] 다음 글을 읽고 물음에 답하시오.

> In the animation, Rapunzel must ⓐlow her long hair to let people in her tower. (A) But could human hair really hold up a person? (B) A single hair can hold up 100g and an average head has about 120,000 hairs. (C) All those hairs could hold up a couple of elephants! (D) With her hair, Rapunzel has the ability ⓑhold up a person. (E) But she should wrap her hair around something strong and heavy. If she doesn't, she will get a very sore neck.

14. 위 글의 (A)~(E) 중 주어진 문장이 들어갈 가장 적절한 곳은? (3점)

> Surprisingly, yes!

① (A)   ② (B)   ③ (C)
④ (D)   ⑤ (E)

15. 위 글의 밑줄 친 ⓐ, ⓑ를 어법에 맞는 형태로 바르게 연결한 것은? (4점)

① low – hold   ② low – to hold
③ lower – hold   ④ lower – to hold
⑤ lowers – holds

16. 위 글을 읽고 답할 수 <u>없는</u> 것은? (3점)

① Could human hair hold up a person?
② How many hairs does an average head have?
③ How many grams can a single human hair hold up?
④ What does Rapunzel have to do to let people in her tower?
⑤ What should Rapunzel do before she climbs up a high building?

[17~18] 다음 글을 읽고 물음에 답하시오.

We Scare for Energy

In the animation, monsters scare children to get energy from their screams. @Amazingly, their city are powered by this sound! But could we actually produce electricity which can light up a city from sound? ⓑYes, sound can is changed into electricity. But it would not be helpful in our everyday activities because the amount is too small. For example, the sound from a car horn only produces 50mv. That is only 1/4400 of the average 220v of electricity in our homes. ⓒSo, we would need an unbelievable amount of screams to light up an entire city.

Up, Up and Away!

ⓓThe house is lifted and flow by thousands of balloons in the animation. Could that actually work?
Let's say that a house weighs about 50,000kg. A normal balloon at an amusement park can lift about 14g. So we need about 3,570,000 balloons to lift up the house. We also have to think about the weight of the balloons themselves and the strings. Then, we need to add a few more thousand balloons. ⓔ Now, the biggest challenge is to pumping up all those balloons!

17. 위 글의 밑줄 친 @~ⓔ 중 어법상 옳은 것을 고르면? (3점)

① @ ② ⓑ ③ ⓒ ④ ⓓ ⑤ ⓔ

18. 위 글을 읽고 내용과 일치하는 것에는 T, 일치하지 <u>않는</u> 것에는 F를 바르게 표시한 것은? (4점)

		T	F
①	Monsters can get energy by scaring children.		∨
②	The sound from a car horn produces 1/4400 of the average 220v of electricity in our homes.	∨	
③	We can light up an entire city with a small amount of screams.	∨	
④	The weight of a normal balloon is about 14g.	∨	
⑤	We need more than 3,570,000 balloons to lift up a 50,000kg house.		∨

[19~20] 다음 글을 읽고 물음에 답하시오.

We can change sound into electricity. But it would not be helpful in our everyday activities because the amount is too small. For example, the sound from a car horn only produces 50 mv. That is only 1/4400 of the average 220v of electricity in our homes. So, we would need an unbelievable amount of screams <u>to light</u> up an entire city.

19. 위 글의 밑줄 친 'to light'와 쓰임이 같은 것은? (3점)

① Her wish is <u>to be</u> with you.
② They want <u>to live</u> in Rome someday.
③ I went to Seoul <u>to visit</u> my grandmother.
④ Superman has the power <u>to move</u> the subway.
⑤ It is hard for me <u>to decide</u> which book to read.

20. 위 글을 한 문장으로 요약할 때 빈칸에 들어갈 말로 가장 적절한 것은? (3점)

Sound can be changed into (A)_____, but the amount is too (B)_____.

	(A)	(B)
①	light	small
②	horn	big
③	scream	small
④	activity	big
⑤	electricity	small

[21~22] 다음 글을 읽고 물음에 답하시오.

The house is lifted and flown by thousands of balloons in the animation. Could that actually <u>work</u>? (A) Let's say that a house <u>weighs</u> about 50,000kg. (B) A normal balloon at an amusement park can lift about 14g. (C) So we need about 3,570,000 balloons to <u>lift</u> up the house. (D) Then, we need to <u>add</u> a few more thousand balloons. (E) Now, the biggest <u>challenge</u> is pumping up all those balloons!

21. 위 글의 (A)~(E) 중 주어진 문장이 들어가기에 가장 적절한 곳은? (4점)

We also have to think about the weight of the balloons themselves and the strings.

① (A) ② (B) ③ (C) ④ (D) ⑤ (E)

22. 위 글에 나오는 단어의 뜻을 바르게 해석한 것은? (3점)

① work: 작품
② weigh: 무게가 ~이다
③ lift: 줄
④ add: 보통의
⑤ challenge: 기회

[23~25] 다음 글을 읽고 물음에 답하시오.

In the animation, monsters scare children to get energy from their screams. Amazingly, their city (A)(power) by this sound! But could we actually produce electricity to light up a city from sound?
Yes, sound can be changed into electricity. But it would not be helpful in our everyday activities because the amount is too small. For example, the sound from a car horn only produces 50mv. That is only 1/4400 of the average 220v of electricity in our homes. So, we would need an unbelievable amount of screams to light up an entire city.

23. 위 글의 주제로 가장 적절한 것은? (3점)

① Energy from water
② Energy from sound
③ Our everyday activities
④ Sound from a car horn
⑤ The origin of electricity

24. 위 글의 괄호 안의 동사 (A)power의 알맞은 형태는? (3점)

① can power   ② is powered
③ is powering   ④ would power
⑤ were powered

25. 위 글의 내용과 일치하는 것은? (4점)

① 만화 영화에서 괴물들은 아이들의 웃음으로부터 에너지를 얻기 위해 아이들을 겁준다.
② 소리는 전기로 바뀔 수 없다.
③ 어린아이들의 비명에서 나오는 소리의 양은 많아서 실제로 우리의 일상 활동에 도움이 된다.
④ 자동차 경적으로부터 생산되는 전기의 양은 가정에서 사용하는 220v 전기의 4400분의 1밖에 되지 않는다.
⑤ 전체 도시를 밝히기 위해 우리는 적은 양의 비명이 필요하다.

[26~29] 다음 글을 읽고 물음에 답하시오.

Possible or Impossible
In animation movies, amazing things are possible. But are they actually possible in real life?

Let Down Your Hair, Rapunzel!
In the animation, Rapunzel must lower her long hair to let people in her tower. But could human hair really hold up a person? @<u>Surprisingly</u>, yes! A single hair can hold up 100g and an average head has about 120,000 hairs. All those hairs could hold up

a couple of elephants! With her hair, Rapunzel has the ability to hold up a person. But she should wrap her hair around something strong and heavy. If she doesn't, she will get a very sore neck.

We Scare for Energy
In the animation, monsters scare children to get energy from their screams. ⓑAmazingly, (A)their city is powered by this sound! But could we actually produce electricity to light up a city from sound?
Yes, sound can be changed into electricity. But it would not be helpful in our everyday activities because the amount is too small. ⓒFor example, the sound from a car horn only produces 50mv. That is only 1/4400 of the average 220v of electricity in our homes. ⓓBut, we would need an unbelievable amount of screams to light up an entire city.

Up, Up and Away!
(B)The house is lifted and flown by thousands of balloons in the animation. Could that actually work?
ⓔLet's say that a house weighs about 50,000kg. A normal balloon at an amusement park can lift about 14g. So we need about 3,570,000 balloons to lift up the house. We also have to think about the weight of the balloons themselves and the strings. Then, we need to add a few more thousand balloons. Now, the biggest challenge is pumping up all those balloons!

26. 위 글의 내용과 일치하는 것은? (4점)
① 머리카락 한 가닥은 14g의 무게를 들어올릴 수 있다.
② 우리의 머리카락은 코끼리 두 마리를 들어올릴 수 있다.
③ 보통 사람의 머리에는 120만개 정도의 머리카락이 있다.
④ 라푼젤은 자신이 탑에 들어가기 위해 머리카락을 내려야 한다.
⑤ 라푼젤은 머리카락으로 타인의 목을 감싸서 들어올릴 수 있다.

27. 위 글의 내용과 일치하는 대화는? (4점)
① Q: What does Rapunzel have to do to let people in her tower?
  A: She has to make her hair strong.
② Q: How is the city powered?
  A: It is powered by light.
③ Q: Why do monsters scare children?
  A: They scare children to get screams from energy.
④ Q: How many grams can a normal balloon at an amusement park lift?
  A: It can lift about 100g.
⑤ Q: What is the most difficult thing to lift up a house with balloons?
  A: Pumping up all the balloons is the hardest thing.

28. 위 글의 ⓐ~ⓔ 중, 흐름상 어색한 것은? (3점)
① ⓐ ② ⓑ ③ ⓒ ④ ⓓ ⑤ ⓔ

29. 위 글 (A), (B)를 능동태로 옳게 바꾼 것은? (3점)
① (A) this sound power their city
  (B) Thousands of balloons lift and fly the house
② (A) this sound power their city
  (B) Thousands of balloons lifts and flies the house
③ (A) this sound powers their city
  (B) Thousands of balloons lift and fly the house
④ (A) this sound powers their city
  (B) Thousands of balloons lifts and flies the house
⑤ (A) this sound powered their city
  (B) Thousands of balloons lifted and flew the house

◎ 선택형 문항의 답안은 컴퓨터용 수정 싸인펜을
사용하여 OMR 답안지에 바르게 표기하시오.
◎ 서술형 문제는 답을 답안지에 반드시 검정
볼펜으로 쓰시오.
◎ 총 29문항 100점 만점입니다. 문항별 배점
은 각 문항에 표시되어 있습니다.

[경북 ○○중]

1. 다음 글의 목적으로 가장 적절한 것은?   (3점)

Hello, students. Have you heard about the DIY Drone Class? You can make your own drone in the class. The Youth Community Center offers the class at 3 p.m. every Wednesday in May. Make your special drone and learn how to control it! Don't miss this great chance!

① 무인기 잡지를 홍보하려고
② 무인기 구매를 권유하려고
③ 무인기 경품을 홍보하려고
④ 무인기 강좌를 홍보하려고
⑤ 무인기 배송 지연에 대해 사과하려고

[금천구 ○○중]

2. 다음 대화가 자연스럽도록 (A)~(D)를 순서대로 배열한 것은?   (4점)

M: Have you heard about the Smart App Contest?
(A) Yeah, I'm going to send my idea about a Pic Gardener App.
(B) Yes, I have. Are you going to enter it?
(C) When you take a picture of a plant, the app tells you how to take care of it.
(D) Really? What do you mean by that?
W: It sounds like a very useful app.

① (A) - (D) - (B) - (C)
② (A) - (B) - (C) - (D)
③ (B) - (A) - (D) - (C)
④ (B) - (D) - (A) - (C)
⑤ (C) - (A) - (D) - (B)

[송파구 ○○중]

3. 다음 (A)~(E) 중 아래 주어진 문장이 들어갈 위치로 가장 적절한 것은?   (3점)

Have you heard about the DIY Drone Class?

(A) Hello, students. (B) You can make your own drone in the class. (C) The Youth Community Center offers the class at 3 p.m. every Wednesday in May. (D) Make your special drone and learn how to control it. (E) Don't miss this great chance!

① (A)   ② (B)   ③ (C)   ④ (D)   ⑤ (E)

[부산 ○○중]

4. 다음 짝지어진 두 문장에서 밑줄 친 단어의 의미가 같은 것은?   (4점)

① It costs about $100.
   These are books about animals.
② What kind of movie do you like?
   It was really kind of you to help me.
③ It was a close match.
   The doors open and close automatically.
④ I don't want to miss the chance.
   The sale prices were too good to miss.
⑤ I'll be with you in a second.
   Korean team scored a second goal just after half-time.

5. 다음 짝지어진 두 사람의 대화가 <u>어색한</u> 것은? (3점)

① A: Have you heard about the Sci-Magic show?

   B: No, I haven't.

② A: My results are bad today.

   B: That's okay. You'll do better next time.

③ A: What are "Dancing Beans"?

   B: They are beans that move in the water like they're dancing.

④ A: Can I pick your brain about my science-homework, Mina?

   B: Pick my brain? What do you mean?

⑤ A: 24/7? What do you mean?

   B: It means "24 days a week, 7 hours a day."

6. 다음 대화의 빈칸 ⓐ~ⓓ에 들어갈 말이 <u>다른</u> 하나는? (3점)

> M: (ⓐ) about making a "Mystery Card" for the science project?
>
> W: A "Mystery Card?" (ⓑ) do you mean?
>
> M: It's a special card. It can hide your message.
>
> W: Sounds interesting! (ⓒ) do you make it?
>
> M: Mix baking soda and water. Then, write a message on the card with it.
>
> W: (ⓓ) can you read the card?
>
> M: Paint over the card with grape juice, and then the message appears.

① ⓐ   ② ⓑ   ③ ⓒ

④ ⓓ   ⑤ 없음

7. 다음 빈칸 ⓐ와 ⓑ에 들어갈 말이 차례대로 알맞게 짝지어진 것은? (3점)

> **Up, Up and Away!**
> The house is ⓐ_____ and flown by thousands of balloons in the animation. Could that actually work?
> Let's say that a house weighs about 50,000kg. A normal balloon at a(n) ⓑ_____ park can lift about 14g. So we need about 3,570,000 balloons to lift up the house.

① lifted – amusement

② lifted – magic trick

③ lifting – amusement

④ lifting - magic trick

⑤ been lifted - magic trick

8. 다음 문장의 빈칸에 가장 알맞은 것은? (2점)

> Do you know the way _____ your anger?

① calm down   ② calms down

③ to calm down   ④ calming down

⑤ to calming down

9. 다음 밑줄 친 부분 중 어법상 <u>어색한</u> 것은? (3점)

① There is a lot of work <u>to do.</u>

② I need a bench <u>to sit.</u>

③ An elephant <u>was lifted up by</u> balloons.

④ What did you <u>actually say at</u> the meeting?

⑤ There is a strong <u>possibility of rain</u> tomorrow.

10. 다음 글의 ①~⑤ 중에서 흐름상 아래 문장이 들어가기에 적절한 곳은? (4점)

> All those hairs could hold up a couple of elephants!

> Could human hair really hold up a person? (①) Surprisingly, yes! (②) A single hair can hold up 100g and an average head has about 120,000 hairs. (③) With her hair, Rapunzel has the ability to hold up a person. (④) But she should wrap her hair around something strong and heavy. (⑤) If she doesn't, she will get a very sore neck.

11. 아래의 밑줄 친 부분과 쓰임이 <u>다른</u> 것은? (3점)

> This time, he has a chance <u>to finish</u> the work.

① I have too many things <u>to do</u> today.

② He has two books <u>to borrow</u> from the library.

③ She will practice the songs <u>to perform</u> at the talent show.

④ Don't forget <u>to put</u> an egg in vinegar for two days.

⑤ He has no house <u>to live</u> in.

12. 다음 안내방송을 듣고 답할 수 <u>없는</u> 것은? (4점)

> Hello, students. Have you heard about the DIY Drone Class? You can make your own drone in the class. The Youth Community Center offers the class at 3 p.m. every Wednesday in May. Make your special drone and learn how to control it. Don't miss this great chance!

① Who offers the class?

② What is the title of the class?

③ When do the students have the class?

④ How long does it take to finish the class?

⑤ What can the students make in the class?

[13~14] 다음 글을 읽고 물음에 답하시오.

> A lot of students do not like science. Then why do students ⓐ<u>dislike</u> science? Maybe they think science is difficult. But science is actually easy. Look around you. Science is everywhere!
>
> What do you do when you have sweat stains on your clothes? All you have to do is squeeze lemon juice and water onto the stain or use baking soda before washing. Like this, where there is a chemical change, there is chemistry.
>
> Is there a way to remove dust ⓑ<u>without</u> washing the blanket? As you may know, shaking the dust off the blanket is the best way. If you shake the blanket, the blanket moves back and forth while dust tries to ⓒ<u>move</u>. This is possible because of inertia.
>
> If you want to distinguish good and bad rice, put the rice in salt water and mix it with your hand. When you do this, the bad rice will float. This is possible because of the ⓓ<u>difference</u> in the concentration of salt water.
>
> When the ping pong ball gets crushed, just prepare hot water and a cup. Place the ball in the cup, pour the ⓔ<u>boiling</u> water over it, and the heat will make the ball pop back into a round shape. This is possible through heat expansion.

13. 위 글을 읽고 답할 수 있는 질문은? (4점)

① What is inside the bad rice?

② What makes the ping pong ball get crushed?

③ How can you get rid of dust from the blanket?

④ Where can you get lemon to remove sweat stains?

⑤ How much salt do you need when you pick out bad rice?

14. 위 글의 밑줄 친 ⓐ~ⓔ 중 글의 흐름상 <u>어색한</u> 것은? (4점)

① ⓐ   ② ⓑ   ③ ⓒ   ④ ⓓ   ⑤ ⓔ

[15~17] 다음 글을 읽고 물음에 답하시오.

Rapunzel must ⓐ<u>lower</u> her long hair to let people in her tower. But could human hair really hold up a person? (A)<u>Amaze</u>, yes! A single hair can hold up 100g and an ⓑ<u>average</u> head has about 120,000 hairs. All those hairs could ⓒ<u>hold up</u> a couple of elephants! With her hair, Rapunzel has the ability (B)<u>to hold up</u> a person. But she should ⓓ<u>wrap</u> her hair around something strong and heavy. If she doesn't, she will get a very ⓔ<u>sore</u> neck.

15. 위 글의 밑줄 친 (A)를 알맞은 형으로 고치시오.

(3점)

(A)_____

16. 위 글의 밑줄 친 ⓐ~ⓔ 중 문맥상 의미가 가장 적절하게 연결된 것은? (3점)

① ⓐ lower – 낮은
② ⓑ average – 평균의
③ ⓒ hold up – 기다리다
④ ⓓ wrap – 마치다
⑤ ⓔ sore – 신맛의

17. 위 글의 밑줄 친 (B)와 쓰임이 같은 것은? (3점)

① The program uses science <u>to explain</u> magic tricks.
② You'll learn <u>to control</u> your drone.
③ I'm going <u>to send</u> my idea about the App.
④ The alarm clock lights up when it's time <u>to get</u> up.
⑤ I'm looking forward <u>to climbing</u> up the tower.

[18~19] 다음 글을 읽고 물음에 답하시오.

In animation movies, amazing things are possible. But are they actually (A)[possible / possibility] in real life?
In the animation, Rapunzel must lower her long hair to let people in her tower. But could human hair really hold up a person? (B)[Surprisingly / Surprising], yes! A single hair can hold up 100g and an average head has about 120,000 hairs. All those hairs could hold up a couple of elephants! With her hair, Rapunzel has the (C)[able / ability] to hold up a person. But she should wrap her hair around something strong and heavy. If she doesn't, she will get a very sore neck.

18. 위 글의 (A), (B), (C) 각각에 들어갈 말로 가장 적절한 것은? (4점)

	(A)	(B)	(C)
①	possible	Surprising	able
②	possibility	Surprising	ability
③	possible	Surprisingly	able
④	possibility	Surprisingly	ability
⑤	possible	Surprisingly	ability

19. 위 글의 내용과 일치하지 <u>않는</u> 것은? (4점)

① 만화영화에서 라푼젤은 사람들이 탑에 들어오게 하기 위해서 그녀의 긴 머리카락을 내려주어야 한다.
② 머리카락 한 가닥은 100그램의 무게를 들어 올릴 수 있다.
③ 한 사람의 모든 머리카락은 코끼리 두 마리를 들어 올릴 수 없다.
④ 라푼젤은 사람을 들어 올릴 수 있는 능력을 가지고 있다.
⑤ 라푼젤이 사람을 들어 올리기 위해서는 강하고 무거운 어떤 것에 그녀의 머리를 감아야 한다.

[20~22] 다음 글을 읽고 물음에 답하시오.

Monsters scare children (A)to get energy from their screams. Surprisingly, their city ⓐpowered by this sound! But could we actually produce electricity ⓑto light up a city from sound? Yes, sound can ⓒbe turned into electricity. But it would not be helpful in our everyday activities because the amount is too small. _____, the sound from a car horn only ⓓproduces 50 mv. That is only 1/4400 of the average 220 v of electricity in our homes. So, an unbelievable amount of screams would ⓔbe needed to light up an entire city.

20. 위 글의 빈칸에 가장 적절한 것은? (3점)

① However　　　② For example

③ So　　　　　　④ Actually

⑤ Enough

21. 위 글의 밑줄 친 ⓐ~ⓔ 중 쓰임이 <u>어색한</u> 것은?

(4점)

① ⓐ　　② ⓑ　　③ ⓒ　　④ ⓓ　　⑤ ⓔ

22. 위 글의 밑줄 친 (A)to get과 쓰임이 같은 것은?

(3점)

① Australia is a good place <u>to visit</u> all year round.

② He can't miss the chance <u>to meet</u> her.

③ What message do you want <u>to send</u>?

④ Zulu people like <u>to make</u> clothes with beads.

⑤ My dad turned off the TV <u>to go</u> to bed.

[23~24] 다음 글을 읽고 물음에 답하시오.

Let Down Your Hair, Rapunzel!

In the animation, Rapunzel must (A)[lower / lift] her long hair to let people in her tower. But could human hair really hold up a person?

Surprisingly, yes! A single hair can hold up 100g and an average head has about 120,000 hairs. All those hairs could hold up a couple of elephants! With her hair, Rapunzel has the (B)[ability / challenge] to hold up a person. But she should wrap her hair around something strong and heavy. If she doesn't, she will get a very (C)[sore / soft] neck.

23. 위 글의 괄호 (A), (B), (C) 안에 들어갈 말이 바르게 묶인 것은? (4점)

	(A)	(B)	(C)
①	lower	ability	sore
②	lower	challenge	sore
③	lower	ability	soft
④	lift	ability	soft
⑤	lift	challenge	soft

24. 다음 문장들 중 위 글을 읽고 알 수 있는 사실로 가장 알맞은 것은? (3점)

① Rapunzel often lets people in her tower.

② Rapunzel doesn't want to leave her tower.

③ A single human hair usually weighs 100g.

④ Rapunzel is going to hold up elephants with her hair.

⑤ To hold up a person with human hair is not impossible.

[25~27] 다음 글을 읽고 물음에 답하시오.

We Scare for Energy

In the animation, monsters scare children ⓐ to get energy from their screams. Amazingly, their city is powered by this sound!

(A)

Yes, sound can be changed into electricity. But it would not be helpful in our everyday activities because the amount is too small.

(B)

So, we would need an unbelievable amount of screams to light up an entire city.

(C)

But could we actually produce electricity to light up a city from sound?

(D)

For example, the sound from a car horn only produces 50mv. That is only 1/4400 of the average 220v of electricity in our homes.

---

25. (A)~(D)를 글의 흐름에 맞게 배열하면? (4점)

① (A) - (B) - (C) - (D)

② (A) - (B) - (D) - (C)

③ (B) - (A) - (D) - (C)

④ (B) - (C) - (A) - (D)

⑤ (C) - (A) - (D) - (B)

26. 위 글의 밑줄 친 ⓐ와 쓰임이 <u>다른</u> 것은? (3점)

① I went to the airport <u>to see</u> him.

② I went shopping <u>to buy</u> a new bag.

③ Monica studied hard <u>to pass</u> the test.

④ She has so many things <u>to do</u> today.

⑤ He shouted a lot <u>to scare</u> the children.

27. 위 글의 내용을 <u>잘못</u> 이해한 사람은? (4점)

① 정수: 소리는 전기로 바뀔 수 있어.

② 보라: 자동차 경적 소리는 50밀리볼트를 만들어 내.

③ 준서: 소리로 만든 전기는 실제로는 일상생활에 도움이 되지 않을 거야.

④ 민희: 자동차 경적 소리로 만들어 내는 전기는 220볼트의 1/440이야.

⑤ 찬희: 도시를 밝히려면 믿기 어려울 정도의 많은 양의 비명이 필요해.

[28~29] 다음 글을 읽고 물음에 답하시오.

The house is lifted and ⓐ<u>flies</u> by thousands of balloons in the animation. Could that actually work?

Let's say that a house weighs about 50,000 kg. A normal balloon at an amusement park can lift about 14g. So we need about 3,570,000 balloons ⓑ<u>to lift up</u> the house. We also have to think about the weight of the balloons ⓒ<u>themselves</u> and the strings. Then, we need to add ⓓ<u>a few</u> more thousand balloons. Now, the biggest challenge is ⓔ<u>pumping up</u> all those balloons!

---

28. 위 글의 밑줄 친 ⓐ~ⓔ 중, 어법상 <u>어색한</u> 것은? (4점)

① ⓐ   ② ⓑ   ③ ⓒ   ④ ⓓ   ⑤ ⓔ

29. 다음 각 질문 중에서 위 글을 읽고 답할 수 <u>없는</u> 것을 고르시오. (4점)

① What lifts up the house in the animation?

② Is it possible to lift up a house with balloons in the animation?

③ About how many grams can a normal balloon at an amusement park lift?

④ How much does a balloon cost?

⑤ What would be the biggest challenge in lifting up a house with balloons?

◎ 선택형 문항의 답안은 컴퓨터용 수정 싸인펜을 사용하여 OMR 답안지에 바르게 표기하시오.
◎ 서술형 문제는 답을 답안지에 반드시 검정 볼펜으로 쓰시오.
◎ 총 25문항 100점 만점입니다. 문항별 배점은 각 문항에 표시되어 있습니다.

[광주 ○○중]

1. 다음의 영영사전 뜻풀이로 가장 적절한 것을 고르시오. (4점)

• a large sculpture of a person or an animal, made of stone or metal

① cartoon
② blender
③ statue
④ figure
⑤ item

[영등포구 ○○중]

2. 다음 짝지어진 두 단어의 관계가 나머지와 <u>다른</u> 하나는? (3점)

① actual – actually
② amazing – amazingly
③ possible – possibly
④ love – lovely
⑤ surprising – surprisingly

[대전 ○○중]

3. 다음 빈칸에 들어갈 말로 <u>어색한</u> 것은? (3점)

• Jonghyun watched _____.

① the duck swimming
② Dohun to play volleyball
③ his mom reading the cookbook
④ Sol and Han clean the classroom
⑤ his brother inline skating in the park

[대전 ○○중]

4. 다음 글의 내용으로 알 수 <u>없는</u> 것은? (4점)

A soccer match between ABC school and Mount school was held at the school field on June 24th. ABC school won the game by 3 to 1. There were some memorable players. One of them was Sangmin. Sangmin was the player who scored the most points. It was a great match. We are looking forward to the next match.

① 경기 결과
② 경기의 종류
③ 경기가 열린 날짜
④ 경기가 열린 장소
⑤ 경기에 참여한 선수들의 명단

[영등포구 ○○중]

5. 다음 대화를 읽고 관계대명사를 활용하여 주어진 문장을 완성하시오. (5점)

Ann: Who is your girl friend?
John: My girl friend is over there.
Ann: There are so many people.
John: She wears a T-shirt. It has pink color with stripes.
Ann: I like the T-shirt. By the way, many girls wear it. Hmm, anything else about your girl friend?
John: She has a long straight hair.
Ann: Oh, I got it. She is Jenny!

(1) Ann likes the T-shirt _____.
(2) Jenny is John's girl friend, _____.

6. 다음 말에 이어질 대화를 순서대로 바르게 배열한 것은? (3점)

Is it your first time riding a bike, Mina?

(A) Thanks, Mike. Don't let go, okay?
(B) Yes, it is. I just can't keep my balance.
(C) Don't worry. Sit up and look straight ahead.
(D) Let me help you. I'll hold your bike.

① (A) - (B) - (C) - (D)
② (B) - (A) - (C) - (D)
③ (B) - (D) - (A) - (C)
④ (C) - (A) - (B) - (D)
⑤ (C) - (D) - (A) - (B)

8. 다음 글의 흐름으로 보아, 주어진 문장이 들어가기에 가장 적절한 곳을 고르시오. (4점)

Last year, Simon won many races, but Max's best result in a race was coming in fifth place.

On the straightaway, Max pulls right beside the race's leader, Simon. (A) This time, he has a chance to finish second. (B) But he isn't going to be satisfied with second place today. (C) The winner gets to meet the world famous racer L. J. Richards! (D) He doesn't want to miss the chance to meet his role model. (E)

① (A)　② (B)　③ (C)　④ (D)　⑤ (E)

7. 주어진 글 다음에 이어질 글의 순서로 가장 적절한 것을 고르시오. (4점)

Max's eyes are filled with tears as he finds out that he came in second.

[보기]
(A) "It was a real close race. Even though you didn't win the race, you did your best. That's the thing that counts!" says L. J. Richards.
(B) "No need for tears, kid," says a man's voice. Max can't believe his eyes. The man who is standing in front of him is L. J. Richards! "Thank you, but I'm not the winner," says Max.
(C) 'Did I do my best?' thinks Max. After a moment, he smiles. "Yeah, I guess I did."

① (A) - (B) - (C)　② (B) - (A) - (C)
③ (B) - (C) - (A)　④ (C) - (B) - (A)
⑤ (C) - (A) - (B)

9. 다음 글에 나타난 분위기로 가장 알맞은 것을 고르시오. (4점)

Max sees the official waving a white flag which means the last lap. Max is right behind Simon. The finish line is getting closer, and the cheering from the crowd is getting louder.
"I can do it!" Max says loudly. He can feel his heart beating hard. The karts rush across the finish line. Who is the winner?

① boring　② calm
③ exciting　④ peaceful
⑤ dangerous

[10~12] 다음 글을 읽고 물음에 답하시오.

Max's eyes ⓐare filled with tears as he finds out (A)that he came in second. "No need for tears, kid," says a man's voice. Max can't believe his eyes. The man ⓑwho is standing in front of him is L. J. Richards! "Thank you, but I'm not the winner," says Max. "It was a real close race. ⓒEven though you didn't win the race, you did your best. That's the thing that ⓓcounts!" says L. J. Richards. 'Did I do my best?' thinks Max. ⓔAfter a moment, he smiles. "Yeah, I guess (B)I did."

10. 위 글의 ⓐ~ⓔ를 바꿔 쓸 때, 다음 중 가장 <u>어색</u>한 것은? (4점)

① ⓐ are filled with　　→ are full of

② ⓑ who　　→ that

③ ⓒ Even though　　→ As though

④ ⓓ counts　　→ matters

⑤ ⓔ After a moment　　→ After a while

11. 위 글의 밑줄 친 (A)that과 쓰임이 같은 것을 고르면? (4점)

① You look very smart in <u>that</u> suit.

② He thinks <u>that</u> his son is a genius.

③ Could you possibly open <u>that</u> window?

④ They live in a house <u>that</u> has a garden.

⑤ I know a girl <u>that</u> plays the piano well.

12. 위 글의 밑줄 친 (B)<u>I did</u>가 구체적으로 의미하는 것은? (4점)

① 최선을 다해 플레이했다.

② 경기에서 이기지 못했다.

③ 경기에서 결국 승리했다.

④ 평소 연습이 부족했다.

⑤ 누구보다 열심히 연습했다.

[13~14] 다음 글을 읽고 물음에 답하시오.

ⓐMax completes the tenth lap and now has five more laps going. ⓑMax sees Simon's kart ahead, just out of Max's reach. Max's kart gets closer and closer to Simon's. It almost hits the back end of Simon's kart. ⓒThey drive to the straightaway and Max presses harder in the gas pedal.

"I can catch up," says Max.

Max (A)(the, waving, a, last, official, white, means, sees, that, the, flag, lap). Max is right behind Simon. ⓓThe finish line is getting closer, but the cheering from the crowd is getting louder.

"I can do it!" Max says loudly. ⓔHe can feel his heart beat hard. The karts rush cross the finish line. Who is the winner?

13. 위 글의 밑줄 친 ⓐ~ⓔ 중 어법상 옳은 문장들로 짝지어진 것은? (4점)

① ⓐ, ⓑ　　② ⓐ, ⓓ　　③ ⓑ, ⓔ

④ ⓒ, ⓓ　　⑤ ⓒ, ⓔ

14. 위 글의 (A)의 괄호에 주어진 단어들을 글의 흐름에 알맞게 배열할 때, 6번째로 오는 단어는 무엇인가? (4점)

① flag　　② white　　③ means

④ waving　　⑤ official

[15~16] 다음 글을 읽고 물음에 답하시오.

"No need for tears, kid," says a man's voice. Max can't believe his eyes. L. J. Richards is standing in front of him! "Thank you, but I'm not the winner," says Max. "It was a real close race. (A)_____ you didn't win the race, you did your best. That's very important!" says L. J. Richards. 'Did I do my best?' thinks Max. (B)_____, he smiles, "Yeah, I guess I did."

15. 위 글의 (A)와 (B)에 들어갈 말로 알맞게 짝지어 진 것은? (4점)

	(A)	(B)
①	Because	However
②	Because	Therefore
③	For example	At first
④	Even though	After a moment
⑤	Even though	A long time ago

16. 위 글을 읽고 다음 질문에 대한 답을 할 때 알맞은 것은? (4점)

• What does L. J Richards think is important in a race?

① He thinks doing one's best is important.
② He thinks entering a big race is important.
③ He thinks winning the first place is important.
④ He thinks we must be the champion in a race.
⑤ He thinks happiness has something to do with grades.

[17~18] 다음 글을 읽고 물음에 답하시오.

Tara eased out a long breath and threw the ball. The umpire called, "Ball four!" She saw her coach call for time and start walking toward the ⓐmound.
Tara's team had a 2-1 lead, but she gave up a triple and a walk to the past two batters. There were no outs in the bottom of the last inning. "I think we need to sit you down," Coach said. "I'm OK, Coach. I'll get these next three batters out," said Tara.
Coach and Bryan, the catcher, left the mound. (A)The batter, Micah, was leading the league in homeruns. (B)Tara could smell French fries cooking at the ⓑrefreshment stand. (C)She used to eat it without any sauce. (D)She couldn't wait to celebrate this win with a ⓒheap of them.
(E)However, the count was full. Three balls and two strikes. She took a deep breath and threw.
The pitch was low and outside, but Micah took a swing and missed. Micah was out. Tara and the runner from third rushed toward home plate. Bryan tossed the ball and Tara tagged the sliding runner. The umpire shouted, "Out!" Tara fired the ball to Jordan at second base. Jordan tagged the runner for out number three. "ⓓTriple play!" Bryan yelled. He and his teammates ran toward the mound. Game over. As Tara walked off the field, Bryan said, "Why did Micah swing at that wild pitch? It wasn't near the strike zone." Tara laughed. "Maybe he couldn't wait to get some ⓔFrench fries." "I know I can't," Bryan said. "Let's go."

17. 위 글에서 전체 흐름과 관계 없는 문장은? (4점)
① (A) ② (B) ③ (C) ④ (D) ⑤ (E)

18. 위 ⓐ~ⓔ의 사전적 정의가 잘못된 것은? (4점)

① ⓐ: a large rounded amount of earth which a pitcher stands on to throw a ball to a catcher
② ⓑ: the stand where snacks or drinks served as a light meal
③ ⓒ: a large number of something laid on top of each other
④ ⓓ: an action of getting two outs in a single play in baseball
⑤ ⓔ: long and thin pieces of potato fried in oil

[19~21] 다음 글을 읽고 물음에 답하시오.

Seconds from Winning

At the go-kart race track, (A)there are many people who are cheering excitedly. (B)The karts that are making loud engine noises are waiting. An official waves a green flag and the race starts!

Max pushes his foot down hard on the gas pedal as he completes his sixth lap on the track. On the straightaway, Max pulls right beside the race's leader, Simon. Last year, Simon won many races, but Max's best result in a race was coming in fifth place. This time, he has a chance to finish second. But he isn't going to be satisfied with second place today. The winner gets to meet the world famous racer L. J. Richards! He doesn't want to miss the chance to meet his role model.

Max completes the tenth lap and now has five more laps to go. Max sees Simon's kart ahead, just out of Max's reach. Max's kart gets closer and closer to Simon's. It almost hits the back end of Simon's kart. They drive into the straightaway and Max presses harder on the gas pedal.

"I can catch up," says Max.

(C)Max sees the official waving a white flag which means the last lap. Max is right behind Simon. The finish line is getting closer, and the cheering from the crowd is getting louder. "I can do it!" Max says loudly. He can feel his heart beating hard. The karts rush across the finish line. Who is the winner?

Max's eyes are filled with tears as he finds out that he came in second.

"No need for tears, kid," says a man's voice. Max can't believe his eyes. (D)The man who is standing in front of him is L. J. Richards!

"Thank you, but I'm not the winner," says Max.

"It was a real close race. Even though you didn't win the race, you did your best. (E)That's the thing that counts!" says L. J. Richards.

'Did I do my best?' thinks Max. After a moment, he smiles. "Yeah, I guess I did."

19. 위 글의 밑줄 친 (A)~(E)가 두 문장이 합쳐진 것이라고 볼 때, 원래의 각 문장들로 적절하게 나눈 것은?
(4점)

① (A) there are many cheering people. Who are cheering excitedly.

② (B) The karts are making. The karts are waiting loud engine noises.

③ (C) Max sees the official waving a white flag. The official waves the white flag for the last lap.

④ (D) The man is L. J. Richards. He is standing in front of him.

⑤ (E) That's the thing. Which thing counts.

20. 위 글의 내용과 일치하는 대화만을 <보기>에서 있는 대로 고른 것은?
(5점)

<보기>

(F) Q: What did Max do when he completed his sixth lap on the track?
A: He pulled his kart right beside the track.

(G) Q: Why did Max want to win the race?
A: Because he wanted to have a chance to meet his role model, L. J. Richards.

(H) Q: When Max had five more laps to go, what happened?
A: Max's kart got closer to Simon's and hit it.

(I) Q: Why did Max press harder on the gas pedal when Simon and he drove into the straightaway?
A: He wanted to catch up with Simon.

(J) Q: Why did L. J. Richards come to see Max?
A: Because Max won the race.

① (F), (J)　　② (G), (I)　　③ (H), (I)

④ (G), (H), (I)　　⑤ (F), (H), (I), (J)

21. 위 글을 다음과 같이 요약할 때, 빈칸에 들어갈
    알맞은 것은?   (4점)

Max tries hard to win the kart race and meet
his role model. He comes (A)_____ to
winning the race, but he is always behind
Simon. He ends up coming in second
(B)_____, but he actually meets his role
model. Max learns a valuable lesson that
(C)_____ isn't everything in a race; doing
the best is the most important thing.

	(A)	(B)	(C)
①	first	prize	victory
②	close	place	losing
③	close	place	winning
④	second	place	losing
⑤	second	prize	winning

22. 위 글을 읽고 질문에 답하시오.   (5점)

Q: How many laps do racers complete in
   this race?
A: _____ _____ _____ _____
   in the race. (주어는 대명사로, 숫자는 영어로
   쓸 것.)

정답: _____

23. 위 글에서 ⓐ~ⓔ의 밑줄 친 부분의 의미가 옳은
    것은?   (4점)

① just out of Max's reach: Max의 도착 지점에
② almost hits the back end: 뒤쪽의 끝선을 거의
   넘다
③ drive into the straightaway: 똑바로 앞으로 빠
   져들다
④ catch up with Simon: Simon을 따라잡다
⑤ getting closer: 곧 닫혀져 가고 있다

[영등포구 ○○중]

[22~25] 다음 글을 읽고 물음에 답하시오.

Max completes the tenth (A)laps and now
has five more laps to go. Max sees Simon's
kart ahead, ⓐjust out of Max's reach. Max's
kart gets closer and closer to Simon's. It ⓑ
almost hits the back end of Simon's kart.
They ⓒdrive into the straightaway and Max
presses harder on the gas pedal.
"I can ⓓcatch up with Simon," says Max.
Max sees the official waving a white flag
which (B)mean the last lap. Max is right
behind Simon. The finish line is ⓔgetting
closer, and the cheering from the crowd is
getting louder.
"I can do it!" Max says (C)loudly. He can
feel his heart (D)to beat hard. The karts rush
across the finish line. Who is the winner?
Max's eyes (E)filled with tears as he finds
out that he came in second.

24. 위 글의 내용으로 답할 수 없는 질문은?   (4점)

① Who is the winner?
② Why does Max want to win this race?
③ What does waving a white flag mean?
④ How does Max feel when he gets near the
   finish line?
⑤ When Max pushes harder on the gas pedal,
   what does Max say?

25. 위 글의 (A)~(E) 중 옳은 것은?   (4점)

① (A) laps   ② (B) mean
③ (C) loudly   ④ (D) to beat
⑤ (E) filled

◎ 선택형 문항의 답안은 컴퓨터용 수정 싸인펜을 사용하여 OMR 답안지에 바르게 표기하시오.
◎ 서술형 문제는 답을 답안지에 반드시 검정 볼펜으로 쓰시오.
◎ 총 27문항 100점 만점입니다. 문항별 배점은 각 문항에 표시되어 있습니다.

[동대문구 ○○중]

1. 다음 중 밑줄 친 단어의 쓰임이 올바르지 <u>않은</u> 것을 고르시오. (3점)

① There is a strong <u>possibility</u> of rain tomorrow.
② I want to have the <u>ability</u> to speak English well.
③ She was an <u>amazingly</u> good cook.
④ <u>Surprisingly</u>, many doctors don't tell you that.
⑤ Although he is nearly 80, he is still very <u>activity</u>.

[양천구 ○○중]

2. 다음 중에서 각 대화의 흐름이 가장 자연스러운 것은? (3점)

① A: I can't wash this car alone. It's too big.
   B: Can I give you a hand?
   A: Sorry, but I can't help you now.
② A: Is it your first time riding a bike?
   B: Yes, it is. I just can't keep my balance.
   A: Let me help you. I'll hold your bike.
③ A: Michael, why the long face?
   B: I could keep up with the other runners today.
   A: Don't worry. You'll do better next time.
④ A: What problem are you having?
   B: I couldn't hit the curve balls.
   A: I'll give you some help. I'll hold a kick pad for you.
⑤ A: I heard your baseball team won the match.
   B: It was a close game. I'm happy with my pitching.
   A: Why do you say that?
   B: I allowed two homeruns.

[동대문구 ○○중]

3. 다음 중 어법상 올바른 문장을 <u>모두</u> 찾아낸 것을 고르시오. (4점)

㉠ Did you hear someone play the piano last night?
㉡ He avoided to meet the reporters.
㉢ She told me clean the room.
㉣ Where was the key found?
㉤ They will be amazed if they will hear the truth.

① ㉡, ㉢   ② ㉠, ㉢, ㉣
③ ㉢, ㉤   ④ ㉡, ㉣, ㉤
⑤ ㉠, ㉣

[영등포구 ○○중]

4. 다음 대화문의 각 문장들을 옳은 순서대로 나열한 것을 고르면? (3점)

(A) Oh, thanks. I'll try again.
(B) I learned how to stand on my head in PE class. So I'm trying it now but it's not easy.
(C) What are you doing, Sarah?
(D) Let me help you. Kick your legs in the air again. I'll catch you.

① (A) – (B) – (C) – (D)
② (B) – (C) – (D) – (A)
③ (C) – (B) – (D) – (A)
④ (C) – (D) – (B) – (A)
⑤ (D) – (C) – (B) – (A)

[5~11] 다음 글을 읽고 물음에 답하시오.

At the go-kart race track, there are many people who are cheering excitedly. ⓐThe karts are waiting. The karts are making loud engine noises. An official waves a green flag and the race starts!

Max pushes his foot down hard on the gas pedal as he completes his sixth lap (A)_____ the track. On the straightaway, Max pulls right beside the race's leader, Simon. Last year, Simon won many races, but Max's best result in a race was coming (B)_____ fifth place. This time, he has a chance to finish second. But he isn't going to be satisfied (C)_____ second place today. The winner gets to meet the world famous racer L. J. Richards! He doesn't want to miss the chance to meet his role model.

Max completes the tenth lap and now has five more laps to go. Max sees Simon's kart ahead, just out of Max's reach. Max's kart gets closer and closer (D)_____ Simon's. It almost hits the back end of Simon's kart. They drive (E)_____ the straightaway and Max presses harder on the gas pedal.

"I can catch up," says Max.

Max sees the official waving a white flag which means the last lap. Max is right behind Simon. The finish line is getting closer, and the cheering from the crowd is getting louder. "I can do it!" Max says loudly. He can feel his heart beating hard. The karts rush across the finish line. Who is the winner?

5. 위 글의 밑줄 친 (A)~(E)에 들어갈 알맞은 낱말들로 짝지어진 것은? (3점)

	(A)	(B)	(C)	(D)	(E)
①	in	to	by	with	into
②	in	to	with	with	through
③	on	to	with	to	in
④	on	in	with	to	into
⑤	on	in	by	win	into

6. 위 글의 go-kart race에 관한 내용으로 알맞지 않은 것은? (4점)

① Many people are cheering at the race track.
② A green flag is the starting sign.
③ The racers press the gas pedal to drive faster.
④ The racers must complete 15 laps.
⑤ An official shows a white flag to get the racers to speed up on the final lap.

7. 위 글의 내용을 바르게 이해한 것은? (4점)

① Max's best result in a race last year was second place.
② Max kept pressing hard on the gas pedal throughout the race.
③ Max has a special reason to wish to be the winner in this race.
④ Max almost hit the right side of the Simon's kart.
⑤ Max wants to be the world famous racer like his role model.

8. 위 글의 밑줄 친 ⓐ의 두 문장을 한 문장으로 바르게 연결한 것은? (3점)

① The karts which is waiting the karts are making loud engine noises.
② When the karts are making loud engine noises, racers are waiting.
③ The karts which are making loud engine noises are waiting.
④ The karts which are waiting makes loud engine noises.
⑤ The karts which is waiting makes loud engine noises.

9. 위 글을 읽고 답할 수 없는 것은?　(4점)

① What are many people doing at the race track?

② How many straightaways are there in the race?

③ Who is L. J. Richards?

④ Why does an official wave a white flag during the race?

⑤ Who is the race's leader now?

10. 위 글에서 질문에 대한 답의 내용을 찾아 문장으로 쓰시오.　(5점)

Q: Who is the official?

→ The man _____ a flag is the official. (진행형을 쓸 것, that 불가)

답: _____

11. 위 글의 내용에 따라 아래 질문에, 주어진 낱말을 바르게 배열하여 답하시오.　(5점)

Q: Who will be the winner of the race?

→ The racer _____ will be the winner of the race.
(reaches, first, who, the finish line)

답: _____

12. 다음 대화의 빈칸에 들어갈 말로 가장 어색한 것은?　(3점)

A: _____
B: Don't worry, James. There's always a next time.

① My serves were not strong enough.

② I couldn't block the other player in rugby.

③ I did well in the match. My punches were fantastic.

④ My results were very terrible today.

⑤ I missed too many chances for a three-pointer in the basketball game.

13. 다음 중 아래 대화문의 빈칸에 들어갈 말로 필요하지 않은 것은?　(4점)

A: I'm sorry, Judy. I missed too many dance _____.
B: That's okay. You were just _____.
A: I made so many _____ at the dance performance.
B: It wasn't that bad. You'll do _____ next time.

① mistakes　　② moves

③ chances　　④ nervous

⑤ better

[14∼17] 다음 글을 읽고 물음에 답하시오.

(A)

Max sees the official waving a white flag ⓐ<u>that</u> means the last lap. Max is right behind Simon. The finish line is getting closer, and the cheering from the crowd is getting louder. "I can do it!" Max says loudly. He can feel his heart beating hard. The karts rush across the finish line. Who is the winner?

(B)

"It was a real close race. Even though you didn't win the race, you did your best. ⓑ<u>That's</u> the thing ⓒ<u>that</u> counts!" says L. J. Richards.

'Did I do my best?' thinks Max. After a moment, he smiles. "Yeah, I guess I did."

(C)

Max completes the tenth lap and now has five more laps to go. Max sees Simon's kart ahead, just out of Max's reach. Max's kart gets closer and closer to Simon's. It almost hits the back end of Simon's kart. They drive into the straightaway and Max presses harder on the gas pedal. "I can catch up," says Max.

(D)

Max's eyes are filled with tears as he finds out ⓓ<u>that</u> he came in second.

"No need for tears, kid," says a man's voice. Max can't believe his eyes. The man ⓔ<u>that</u> is standing in front of him is L. J. Richards! "Thank you, but I'm not the winner," says Max.

---

14. 위 글의 (A)∼(D)의 순서로 알맞은 것은? (4점)

① (A) - (C) - (B) - (D)
② (C) - (A) - (D) - (B)
③ (C) - (B) - (A) - (D)
④ (D) - (A) - (C) - (B)
⑤ (D) - (C) - (A) - (B)

15. 위 글의 ⓐ∼ⓔ 중 어법상 쓰임이 관계대명사가 아닌 것은? (정답 2개) (4점)

① ⓐ   ② ⓑ   ③ ⓒ   ④ ⓓ   ⑤ ⓔ

16. 위 글을 통해 얻을 수 있는 교훈으로 가장 가까운 것은? (3점)

① Practice makes perfect.
② Slow and steady wins the race.
③ Working hard is the mother of good luck.
④ A broken hand works, but not a broken heart.
⑤ Learn from the past, live in the present, create the future.

17. 다음은 어떤 독자가 이야기의 주인공 Max에게 쓴 편지이다. 위 글의 내용과 가장 관련이 적은 것은? (3점)

안녕, Max!

고카트 경기를 치르느라 고생 많았어. ⓐ<u>열다섯 바퀴나 돌아야 한다니 굉장히 어려운 경기일 것 같아.</u> ⓑ<u>점점 Simon의 카트에 가까워져서 거의 칠 것 같았을 때 나도 모르게 긴장이 되어 손에 땀을 쥐었어.</u> ⓒ<u>그리고 심판이 하얀 깃발을 흔들었을 때 이제 마지막 바퀴라는 생각에 빨리 역전하기를 기도했어.</u> ⓓ<u>하지만 큰 차이로 2등을 하는 바람에 네가 우는 모습을 보았을 때, 나도 마음이 아팠어.</u> ⓔ<u>그래도 너의 롤 모델인 L. J. Richards를 만났고, 그가 너에게 격려의 말을 해 주어서 다행이야.</u> (하략)

---

① ⓐ   ② ⓑ   ③ ⓒ   ④ ⓓ   ⑤ ⓔ

[18~20] 다음 글을 읽고 물음에 답하시오.

Max completes the tenth lap and now has five more laps to go. Max sees Simon's kart ahead, just out of Max's reach. Max's kart gets closer to Simon's. It (A)[almost / rarely] hits the back end of Simon's kart. They drive into the straightaway and Max presses harder on the gas pedal.

"I can catch up," says Max.

Max sees the official ⓐ[waving / to wave] a white flag ⓑ[which / who] means the last lap. Max is (B)[right / far] behind Simon. The finish line is getting closer, and the cheering from the crowd ⓒ[is / are] getting louder.

"I can do it!" Max says loudly. He can feel his heart beating (C)[weak / hard]. The karts rush across the finish line. Who is the winner?

18. 위 글 (A), (B), (C)에서 문맥상 가장 적절한 어휘를 고르면?　(4점)

	(A)	(B)	(C)
①	almost	right	weak
②	almost	right	hard
③	almost	far	weak
④	rarely	right	weak
⑤	rarely	far	hard

19. 위 글의 괄호 ⓐ~ⓒ 안에서 어법상 적절한 것을 고르면?　(3점)

	ⓐ	ⓑ	ⓒ
①	waving	which	is
②	waving	who	are
③	to wave	which	is
④	to wave	which	are
⑤	to wave	who	is

20. 위 글의 밑줄 친 "I can do it!"에서 it이 의미하는 바를 한글로 쓰시오.　(5점)

<조건>
• '그것'이라는 해석을 쓰는 것이 아님.
• it이 지칭하는 바, 그 내용을 쓸 것.

답: _____

[21~23] 다음 글을 읽고 물음에 답하시오.

Max's eyes are filled with tears as he finds out that he came in second.

"No need for tears, kid," says a man's voice. ⓐMax can't believe his eyes. (A) The man who is standing in front of him is L. J. Richards! (B) "Thank you, but I'm not the winner," says Max.

"It was a real close race. (C) That's the thing that counts!" says L. J. Richards.

(D) 'Did I do my best?' thinks Max. (E) After a moment, he smiles. "Yeah, I guess I did."

21. 위 글에서 Max의 심경 변화로 옳은 것은?　(4점)

① disappointed → satisfied
② interested → bored
③ happy → embarrassed
④ excited → surprised
⑤ sad → ashamed

22. 위 글의 흐름으로 보아, 아래 주어진 문장이 들어가기에 가장 적절한 곳은?　(3점)

Even though you didn't win the race, you did your best.

① (A)　② (B)　③ (C)　④ (D)　⑤ (E)

23. 위 글의 밑줄 친 ⓐ의 이유를 우리말로 쓰시오. (5점)

답: _____

[24~25] 다음 글을 읽고 물음에 답하시오.

ⓐ_____ the go-kart race track, there are many people who are cheering excitedly. (A) The karts that are making loud engine noises are waiting. (B) Max pushes his foot down hard ⓑ_____ the gas pedal as he completes his sixth lap on the track. (C) On the straightaway, Max pulls right beside the race's leader, Simon. (D) Last year, Simon won many races, but Max's best result in a race was coming in fifth place. (E) This time, he has a chance to finish second. But he isn't going to be satisfied ⓒ_____ second place today. The winner gets to meet the world famous racer L. J. Richards! He doesn't want to miss the chance to meet his role model.

24. 위 글의 흐름상 다음 문장이 들어갈 가장 알맞은 곳은?　(4점)

An official waves a green flag and the race starts!

① (A)　② (B)　③ (C)　④ (D)　⑤ (E)

25. 위 글의 빈칸 ⓐ~ⓒ에 들어갈 것으로 가장 적절한 것은?　(3점)

	ⓐ	ⓑ	ⓒ
①	At	on	with
②	At	of	of
③	On	of	to
④	On	at	with
⑤	In	at	of

[26~27] 다음 글을 읽고 물음에 답하시오.

Max completes the tenth lap and now has five more laps to go. Max sees Simon's kart ahead, just out of Max's reach. ⓐMax's kart gets close and close to Simon's. It almost hits the back end of Simon's kart. They drive into the straightaway.

"I can catch up," says Max.

ⓑMax sees the official waving a white flag which means the last lap. Max is right behind Simon. The finish line is getting closer, and the cheering from the crowd is getting louder.

"I can do it!" Max says loudly. ⓒHe can feel his heart beating hardly. The karts rush across the finish line. Who is the winner?

Max's eyes are filled with tears as he finds out that he came in second.

"No need for tears, kid," says a man's voice. Max can't believe his eyes. ⓓThe man which is standing in front of him is L. J. Richards!

"Thank you, but I'm not the winner," says Max.

"It was a real close race. ⓔEven though you don't win the race, you did your best. That's the thing that counts!" says L. J. Richards.

'Did I do my best?' thinks Max. After a moment, he smiles. "Yeah, I guess I did."

26. 위 글의 ⓐ~ⓔ 중 어법상 올바른 문장은?　(4점)

① ⓐ　② ⓑ　③ ⓒ　④ ⓓ　⑤ ⓔ

27. 위 글을 읽고 대답할 수 없는 것은?　(3점)

① What does the white flag mean?
② Why did Max cry?
③ Who is the winner of the race?
④ Did Simon do his best?
⑤ How many laps do racers have to complete in the race?

정답 및 해설

Lesson 1 (중간)

01 ④	**02** ②	**03** ②	**04** ④	**05** ④	**06** ③	**07** ④
08 ⑤	**09** ④	**10** ⑤	**11** ③, ④		**12** ①	**13** ③
14 ②	**15** ④	**16** ④	**17** ⑤	**18** ①	**19** ④	
20 raise		**21** ①	**22** ⑤	**23** ④	**24** ⑤	**25** ④
26 ⑤	**27** got used to	**28** ②	**29** ③			
30 ⓑ, something far		**31** sit on the left side				
32 ③	**33** ①					

01 셔츠나 신발을 깨끗하게 유지하다/만들다

02 ②는 '동사-명사'의 관계이다. 나머지는 '명사-형용사'이다.

03 ① interesting → interested ③ artist → artistic ④ luck → lucky ⑤ differ → different

04 get used to V-ing: ~에 익숙해지다

05 빵을 구웠는데, 너무 뻑뻑하다고 하자, 어젯밤 빵을 먹었다고 말하는 대화는 어색하다.

06 방과 후 수업으로 사진 수업을 수강하려고 한다는 대화이므로, 사진 촬영에 관심이 있다는 것이 적절하다.

07 (D) 그릇을 깼다는 말에 (A) 걱정하지 말라며 빵으로 유리 조각 치우는 법을 안다고 하자 (B) 빵으로 어떻게 하느냐고 묻고 (C) 빵으로 치우면 작은 조각들을 치울 수 있다고 답하고 (E) 고맙다고 말하는 순서이다.

08 빵이 뻑뻑하게 구워지는 문제를 얘기하자, 마르지 않게 만들면서 빵을 굽는 법을 안다는 대화가 적절하다.

09 복잡한 퍼즐을 완성하는 데 오래 걸릴 것 같다고 말하자, 빨리 할 수 있는 요령을 설명하는 대화이다. ⑤는 safely 때문에 답이 될 수 없음에 유의한다.

10 주로 사용하는 눈을 찾아서, 그 눈의 반대편 쪽 좌석에 앉으면, 꽉 찬 화면을 더 잘 즐길 수 있다는 내용이다.

11 be good at V-ing: ~를 잘하다, look forward to V-ing: ~하기를 고대하다
① anger → angry ② difficulty → difficult
⑤ go → going

12 내용상 무엇을 보고 있느냐는 질문이다. "What are you looking at?"과 같이 전치사 at이 필요하다.

13 모두 동명사들로서 (B), (C)는 주어 역할이다. (A)는 보어, (D)는 전치사의 목적어, (E)는 타동사의 목적어로 사

용되었다.

14 Polly가 나를 무서워해서 가시털을 세웠다는 내용에 이어지는 글이다. 주어진 문장 뒤에 그 해결을 위해 내 티셔츠를 Polly의 우리에 넣어주는 내용이 이어지므로 (B)가 적절하다.

15 ① Have → Having ② introducing → introduce ③ get → got ⑤ happily → happy

16 전체 내용이 빵 굽기와 관련되는데, ④만 얼굴 그림을 빨리 그리는 법에 대한 내용이므로 글의 흐름상 어울리지 않는다.

17 강좌의 이름, 주제, 내용, 비용 등을 알 수 있지만, 어디에서 등록하는지는 나와 있지 않다.

18 Having/To have 둘 다 주어가 가능하다.
② If → When ③ scary → scared
④ holding → hold ⑤ happily → happy

19 냄새에 익숙해져서 Polly를 만질 수 있게 되었다는 내용이므로, (D)가 적절한 위치이다.

20 raise: 들어올리다, 세우다

21 내용상 버스를 타거나, 샤워 중, 침대에 있을 때(when) 등, 언제든 아이디어를 얻는다는 것이므로 ①이 적절하다.

22 '당신만의 랩을 쓰는 유용한 조언'이 주제이다.

23 ⓐ의 normally는 usually, mostly와 의미가 같다. ⓑ의 it은 'Close one eye and open it.'을 가리킨다. ⓒ의 when은 (the time)이 생략되어 명사절 역할이며, When do you ~의 when은 의문부사이다. ⓔ의 better는 well의 비교급으로 쓰였다.

24 주로 사용하는 눈이 오른쪽이라면, 영화관에서 왼쪽 좌석을 선택하는 것이 좋다는 ⑤가 적절하다.

25 Sam이 Polly의 우리에 자신의 티셔츠를 놓은 것은 Polly가 Sam에게 익숙하지 않아, 두려워했기 때문이며 위 글을 읽고 답할 수 있다. 나머지는 본문을 읽고 답할 수 없는 질문이다.

26 Sam의 노력으로 마침내, Polly를 안을 수 있게 되었으므로, 정답은 ⑤ Finally이다. Eventually, In the end로 바꿔 쓸 수 있다.

27 get used to ~: ~에 익숙해지다

28 적절한 조언을 주겠다고 한 내용 뒤에, 그 조언이 쉽고 유용한 것을 알 수 있을 것이라고 하는 것이 자연스럽다.

29 이 정보를 더욱 잘 보낼 수 있는 가장 좋은 조언에 대한 내용은 본문에 나와 있지 않다.

30 -thing, -body, -one 등으로 끝나는 부정대명사는 something important처럼 수식어가 뒤에서 꾸며준다.

31 주로 사용하는 눈과 반대편 좌석에 앉는 것이 좋다.

32 ① Have → Having ② introducing → introduce
④ place → placed ⑤ happily → happy

33 나를 무서워하는 애완 고슴도치 Polly의 우리에, 티셔츠를 놓아두고, 냄새에 익숙하게 했다는 내용 뒤에, 마침내 Polly를 손에 안을 수 있게 되었다는 내용이므로, Finally가 적절하다.

Lesson 1 (중간)

```
01 ②  02 ①  03 ③  04 ①  05 ②  06 ①  07 ④
08 ⑤  09 ①  10 ⑤  11 ①  12 ④
13 (A) pick (B) pieces (C) Wipe (D) bread
14 ①  15 ④  16 ⑤  17 ⑤  18 ④  19 ①  20 ③
21 ④  22 ④  23 ⑤  24 ②  25 ①  26 ②  27 ③
28 ①  29 ①  30 ①  31 ①  32 ④
33 당신이 주로 사용하는 눈이 오른쪽 눈이라는 것
```

01 healthy: 건강한, 신체적으로 강하고, 약해지지 않을 듯한

02 일과 놀이의 균형(balance)을 유지하라.

03 mouthful은 명사로서 '한 입, 한 입 가득'의 의미이다.

04 전치사 from과 함께 쓰면서, '다르다'는 뜻의 ①이 적절하다.

05 여자는 잡지에서 조언을 얻었다. 신문과는 관련이 없다.

06 보기의 rapping은 동명사이다. ①의 moving은 현재분사로서 진행형으로 사용되었다. 나머지는 모두 동명사이다.

07 ④는 '동사 : 형용사'이고, 나머지는 모두 '명사 : 형용사'이다.

08 관심사에 대한 질문에. ①~④는 흥미/선호인 반면, ⑤는 '다섯 개 언어를 말하는 방법을 안다'는 내용으로, 질문에 대한 답변과 가장 거리가 멀다.

09 be into A: A를 좋아하다, What about you? 너는 어때?, sound like A: A처럼 들리다

10 ⑤는 현재분사이다. 나머지는 모두 동명사로 사용되었다.

11 decide는 to부정사를 목적어로 취한다.

12 ④ 빵을 구웠는데, 너무 뻑뻑하다고 하자 다음에는 물 한 잔을 오븐에 넣으라는 대화가 가장 자연스럽다.

13 (B) 유리 조각들(pieces)을 떨어뜨린 주변에 (D) 빵(bread)으로 (C) 문지르면(Wipe), (A) 집어올린다(pick)는 내용의 대화이다.

14 부엌에 가서 빵을 가져오겠다고 했으므로, ①이 정답이다.

15 사진 수업을 수강할 생각이므로, 사진 촬영에 흥미가 있다.

16 사진 수업은 화요일이고, 유명한 사진작가가 강의하기로

되어 있으므로, ⑤가 가장 적절하다.

17 ⓒ 너에게서 떨어진 것을 가리켜라.
ⓔ 한쪽 눈씩 감았다 떴다를 반복하라.
ⓐ 오른쪽 눈을 감을 때, 손가락이 움직이는가?
ⓑ 그러면 주로 오른쪽 눈을 쓰는 것이다.
ⓓ 이것은 당신이 영화관에서 왼쪽에 앉아야 하는 것을 의미한다.

18 Jake는 독서반이 아니라, 사진반이다.

19 *Rap It Out*은 MC Joy의 프로그램 제목이다.

20 Don't the door leave open.에서 leave와 the door의 어순이 바뀌었다. Don't leave the door open이 적절하다.

21 There are +복수, for(전치사)+writing(동명사)에 유의한다.

22 각각 ① own ② everything ③ when ⑤ be 삭제

23 영화관의 좌석에 앉는 방법 뒤가 적절하다.

24 normally 보통, 대개

25 5형식 문장 구조를 활용하여, 적절히 배열한다.

26 가까이에 있는 물체가 아니라, 멀리 떨어진 물체이다.

27 (1) MC Joy가 아이디어를 얻기 위해 버스를 타거나, 샤워를 하는 것은 아니다. (F) (2), (3)은 본문 내용과 일치한다.

28 이 글은 나만의 랩을 쓰는 유용한 조언에 관한 내용이다.

29 (A) 주어가 a tip이므로 동사는 is
(B) -thing으로 끝나는 대명사는 뒤에서 수식
(C) a 뒤에는 명사로 쓰일 수 있는 seat이 적절하다.

30 handy 유용한, 쓸모 있는 = useful, helpful

31 이 조언을 몇 차례나 사용해야 하는지와 같은 질문에 답할 수 있는 내용은 본문에 나와 있지 않다. 기본적으로 일상생활 어디에서나 사용 가능한 조언이다.

32 위 글의 밑줄 친 ⓒ의 better는 부사 well의 비교급이다.
④ I try to do the work better.에서도 부사로 쓰였으며, 나머지는 모두 형용사 good의 비교급으로 사용되었다.

33 오른쪽 눈을 주로 쓰는 것은 영화관에서 왼쪽 좌석에 앉아야 하는 것을 의미한다는 내용이므로, This는 앞 문장의 내용을 가리킨다.

Lesson 2 (중간) 1회

```
01 ②  02 ④  03 ①  04 ⑤
05 looking forward to playing traditional games
06 ⑤  07 ⑤  08 ⑤  09 ③  10 ③  11 ①  12 ⑤
13 ③  14 ④  15 ③  16 ②  17 ②  18 ③  19 ④
20 ⑤
21 (1) told Sam to come home early
   (2) asked Mike to eat ice cream together
22 ⑤  23 ④  24 ①  25 ③  26 ②
27 They used beads to communicate with each other.
```

01 ① 직접 ③ 나타내다 ④ 공짜로 ⑤ ~로 알려져 있다 '~에게'의 의미가 되려면, 'be known to'를 쓴다.

02 '나타내다', '상징하다', '의미하다' 모두 비슷한 뜻이다.

03 'was going to ~'는 과거의 계획을 나타낸다. 그런데, 사진 찍는 것을 잊지 말라고 하는 것은 어색한 대화이다.

04 길을 건너기 전에 오른쪽을 보는 것은 런던에서이다.

05 '전통 놀이를 해보고 싶다'는 뜻이 된다.

06 멕시코의 마리아치 연주자들과 솜브레로 등을 소개하고 있다.

07 대화 내용상 박물관 방문에 대한 기대감을 표현한다.

08 주말 계획에 대해 답변해 준 뒤, 이탈리아 레스토랑에서 ⑤ 피자를 먹을 것이 몹시 기대된다는 내용이다.

09 런던에서는 길을 건널 때 오른쪽을 확인해야 하지만, 런던에서 우회전만 가능하다는 것은 내용과 일치하지 않는다.

10 박물관 방문에 대한 기대감을 표현하는 부분인데, unable to visit은 박물관에 갈 수 없다는 엉뚱한 내용이 된다.

11 기대감을 표현할 때는 can't wait to V를 쓴다. can wait는 기다릴 수 있다는 뜻이 되어, 문맥상 어색하다.

12 ⑤ 음식 박람회에 가겠다고 하니까 지난주에 갔었다는 대화가 가장 자연스럽다. 나머지는 모두 어색하다.

13 몽고 텐트에서 자게 될 것에 대한 기대감을 표현한다.

14 ger가 춥다는 내용은 위 대화에 나오지 않았으므로 내용과 일치하지 않는다.

15 위 대화는 런던의 도로 교통에 대한 안내와 차이점이다.

16 (A) 길을 건너(crossing) (B) let's 동사원형(cross) (C) 'Don't forget to ~' ~할 것을 잊지 마.

17 (A) 구슬 색에 의미가 있다는 소개 뒤에 (C) 표가 나오고 (B) 어떤 메시지를 보내고 싶은지 물어보는 순서이다.

18 특별한 의미, 특별한 메시지, 빈칸 모두 special이 적절하다.

19 도표를 보면, 흰 색 구슬만이 나쁜 의미가 없다. 그러므로 ④ 행운과 불행의 의미를 모두 갖는다는 것은 틀리다.

20 어제 아이스크림을 먹은 것은 Sam이 아닌 Mike이다.

21 'tell/ask+목적어+to부정사' 구조의 문장이다.

22 (A) 'each+명사'는 단수 취급한다. (B) 조건의 부사절이다. (C) What+명사: '무슨 ~'

23 붉은 색 구슬의 안 좋은 의미는 '분노'이지, '죽음'이 아니다. 그러므로 ④가 내용과 일치하지 않는다.

24 4형식 동사 send는 3형식으로 전환해서 부사구를 만들 때, 간접목적어 앞에 전치사 to를 쓴다.

25 '색의 의미를 설명하는 도표' 앞에 오는 것이 적절하므로, (C)가 가장 알맞은 자리가 된다.

26 구슬은 색깔별로 각각 다른(different) 의미를 지니고 있으며, 오직 '사랑'이라는 좋은 의미만을 가진 색은 white이다.

27 to부정사의 부사적 용법 중 '목적'을 이해하는 문제이다. 주어진 단어를 적절히 배열한다.

Lesson 2 (중간) 2회

```
01 ⑤  02 ④  03 ②  04 ③  05 ①  06 ④  07 ②
08 ③  09 ①  10 lucky       11 ⑤  12 ③  13 ③
14 ①  15 ①  16 ④  17 ④  18 ①  19 ④  20 ⑤
21 ④  22 ④  23 즉  24 ③  25 ⑤  26 ①  27 ①
28 ③  29 ③  30 ④
```

01 raise: 어떤 것을 더 높이 들다, repeat: 사람들에게 1번 이상 말하다, hedgehog: (고슴도치) 날카로운 가시털이 등을 덮고 있는 작은 갈색 동물

02 ④ express(표현하다) → communicate(의사소통하다)이 적절하다.

03 모두 유의어(비슷한 말)의 관계인데, ②만 반의어 관계이다.

04 satisfy는 '만족시키다'라는 뜻이므로 만족감을 느끼려면 수동태로 표현해야 한다. satisfied를 were satisfied로 고치는 것이 적절하다.

05 I'm looking forward to visiting (the museum)이므로, 네 번째에 해당하는 단어는 전치사 to이다.

06 마리아치 연주자들이 자신의 솜브레로를 근사하게 보이도록 장식한다고 했는데, ④는 원래의 솜브레로를 쓰는 것을 좋아한다고 했으므로, 내용과 일치하지 않는다.

07 Mike는 Sweden의 얼음 호텔에서, Betty는 Mongolia의 ger에서 머물 예정이다. 내용과 일치하는 것은 ②이다.

08 스웨덴의 얼음 호텔방이 밤에 추우니까 모자를 쓰라는 권유의 표현이다. ③은 '모자를 쓰고 있다'는 뜻이 되어 어색

하다.

09 굴뚝 청소부가 사람들에게 도움을 주는 내용 뒤에 사람들이 그들이 행운을 가져온다고 여기게 되는 내용이 이어지는 것이므로, 빈칸 (A)에는 인과 관계의 So가 적절하다.

10 luck의 형용사형은 lucky이다.

11 굴뚝 청소부가 행운을 가져오는 이유는 ⑤이다.

12 모두 굴뚝 청소부들을 뜻하는데 ⓒ만 people을 가리킨다.

13 굴뚝 청소부가 행운을 가져오는 이유 뒤인 (C)가 적절하다.

14 'help+목적어+(to) V' 형태이다. keep 또는 to keep이 알맞다.

15 José는 민속 음악을 연주하는 마리아치 밴드 멤버이므로, ①번이 내용과 일치한다.

16 ④ want to our sombreros → want our sombreros가 적절하다. 동사 want는 목적어 sombreros 뒤에 to부정사를 쓴다.

17 마리아치 멤버들이 사용하는 악기가 무엇으로 만들어졌는지는 본문에 나와 있지 않으므로 ④는 답할 수 없는 질문이다.

18 (A) 솜브레로, 즉(or) 커다란 모자 (B) 햇빛 아래에서 시원하게 지내기 위해서(in order to) (C) 'want+목적어' 뒤에 to부정사를 쓴다.

19 우리가 솜브레로를 장식하는 내용이므로, 그 이유가 되는 문장 뒤에 와야 한다.

20 Q: 왜 굴뚝 청소부가 결혼식에 오기를 원하는가? (A) 그들이 행운을 가져온다고 믿어서. Q: 왜 멕시코인들은 큰 모자를 쓰는가? (B) 모자를 쓰면 뜨거운 햇빛 아래에서 시원하니까.

21 (A) enjoy는 동명사를 목적어로 취한다. (B) 'each+명사'는 단수 취급한다. (C) '~하기 위해' to부정사의 부사적 용법(목적)

22 노란색과 붉은 구슬의 좋은 의미가 같은 것이 아니라, 붉은색과 흰색이 같으므로, ④는 일치하지 않는다.

23 or에는 「즉, 다시 말하면」의 뜻이 있다.

24 (B) 'want+목적어+to부정사'의 5형식이다. (C) '우리 솜브레로들 중 어느 것'을 물어볼 때는 '선택의문사 Which'를 쓴다.

25 솜브레로는 많은 다른 재료들로 장식한다.

26 구슬의 색은 다른 (A)의미가 있고, (B)노란색은 부를 뜻한다.

27 본문의 내용과 일치하는 것은 ①번뿐이다.

28 ⓐ의 if는 부사절을 이끄는 접속사이다. ③번 문장만 know의 목적어가 되는 명사절을 이끄는 접속사로 사용되었다.

29 So는 원인 뒤에 결과를 이끄는 접속사이다. (C)가 알맞다.

30 굴뚝 청소부는 행운을 가져온다고 생각하고, 행운을 부르는 것은 '운 좋은(lucky)'이라는 뜻이므로 ④번이 적절하다.

Lesson 3 (기말)

> **01** ④ **02** ⑤ **03** ④ **04** ③ **05** ④ **06** ⑤
> **07** (1) to do (2) to return (3) to finish (4) to perform
> **08** ③ **09** ② **10** ② **11** ④ **12** ③ **13** ④ **14** ②
> **15** ④ **16** ⑤ **17** ③ **18** ② **19** ③ **20** ⑤ **21** ④
> **22** ② **23** ② **24** ② **25** ④ **26** ② **27** ⑤ **28** ④
> **29** ③

01 ASAP: As soon as possible 가능한 빨리

02 ①~④는 '형용사-명사'인데, ⑤ '형용사-부사'의 관계이다.

03 (A) 과거시제이므로 made가 적절하다.
(B) 기간은 for로 나타낸다.
(C) want 뒤에는 to부정사를 쓴다.

04 순서대로 weigh, challenge, amount, entire가 들어가야 한다. 그러므로, ③ average는 빈칸에 들어갈 수 없다.

05 순서대로 beat, complete, flow, satisfy가 들어가야 한다. 그러므로, ④ press는 빈칸에 들어갈 수 없다.

06 영영 뜻풀이와 문장 속의 this는 모두 '전기'를 가리킨다.

07 표에 나온 동사와 to부정사의 '형용사적 용법'을 활용한다.

08 '무슨 쇼를 보고 있니?'라는 물음에, [(C) Sci-Magic 쇼. 들어봤어? - (A) 아니, 뭔데? - (B) 새 프로그램인데, 마술 비밀을 과학으로 설명해 줘. - (D) 오, 흥미로운 걸.]의 순서이다.

09 egg ball이 무엇인지 반문하며, 물어보는 표현이 적절하다.

10 오후에 비가 올 (A) 가능성, (B) 실제로 무슨 말을 했나?

11 위에서부터 순서대로 Mystery, Mix, Write, Paint, Then 등이 들어가야 한다. ④ Lift는 해당하지 않는다.

12 '지난 주말에 뭐 했니?'라는 질문에 (C)'달걀 공을 만들었다.'는 대답이 이어지고, (B) '달걀 공이 무슨 말이니?'라는 질문에 (D) 달걀 공을 만드는 방법에 관한 설명이 이어지고, (A)'나도 하나 만들고 싶다.'는 순서가 적절하다.

13 '스마트앱 대회에 대해 들어봤니?'라는 질문에 [(B) 응. - (D) Song Sherlock 앱 아이디어를 보낼 거야. - (A) 그게 뭔데? - (C) 노래 일부를 부르면, 제목을 알려주는 거야.]의 순서가 적절하다.

14 (A)의 질문 뒤에 들어가야 하므로 (B)가 적절하다.

15 ⓐ 동사이므로 lower, ⓑ ability를 후치 수식하는 to부정사

16 위 글을 읽고 ⑤ '라푼젤이 고층건물을 오르기 전에 무엇을 해야 하는지'에 대한 질문에 답은 할 수 없다.

17 ① are → is ② is → be ④ flow → flown ⑤ to pumping→ to pump 또는 pumping

18 ② 자동차 경적 소리가 일반 가정에서 사용하는 평균 220v의 1/4400의 전기를 생산한다는 것은 맞는 문장이다.

19 '부사적 용법(목적)'으로 사용된 to는 ③이다.

20 소리는 (A) 전기로 전환될 수 있지만, 그 양이 너무 (B) 적다.

21 '풍선 자체의 무게 뿐 아니라, 줄의 무게도 고려해야 한다.'는 내용 뒤에, 그러므로 풍선 수를 더할 필요가 있다는 내용이 오기 때문에, (D)가 적절한 자리이다.

22 ① work(동사) '효과가 있다, 작용하다' ③ lift(동사) '들어올리다' ④ add(동사) '더하다' ⑤ challenge(명사) '어려움'

23 이 글은 '소리를 에너지로 전환 가능한가'에 대한 내용이다.

24 수동태 문장이다. 도시가 이 소리에 의해 에너지 공급을 받는다는 내용이 되어야 하므로, 'be+powered+by' 형태이다.

25 경적 소리로 만들어지는 전기는 50mv이고, 일반 가정의 220v의 1/4400에 불과한 매우 소량이다.

26 사람의 머리카락 12만개는 대략 코끼리 두 마리를 들 수 있다.

27 풍선으로 집을 들어올리는 가장 큰 어려움은 바람 넣기이다.

28 ⓓ But → So 또는 Therefore와 같은 인과 관계가 필요하다.

29 주어에 맞게 동사의 수일치에 유의한다.

Lesson 3 (기말) ②회

01 ④	02 ③	03 ②	04 ④	05 ⑤	06 ②	07 ①
08 ③	09 ②	10 ③	11 ④	12 ④	13 ③	14 ③
15 Amazingly	16 ②	17 ④	18 ⑤	19 ③	20 ②
21 ①	22 ⑤	23 ①	24 ⑤	25 ⑤	26 ④	27 ④
28 ①	29 ④

01 이 글은 무인기 제작 및 조종 강좌를 홍보하고 있다.

02 '스마트앱 대회 들어봤니?'라는 질문에 [(B) 들어봤어, 너는 참가할 거야? - (A) 응. Pic Gardener 앱 아이디어를 보낼 거야. - (D) 정말? 그게 뭔데? - (C) 식물 사진을 찍으면 돌보는 법을 말해주는 거야.]의 순서가 적절하다.

03 홍보글이므로, 학생들에게 인사말을 하고난 직후에 강좌에 대해 들어 본 적 있는지 묻는 (B)의 자리가 가장 적절하다.

04 ④의 miss는 두 문장 모두 '놓치다'의 뜻으로 쓰였다. '그리워하다'의 뜻도 기억해야 한다. 다른 단어들은 순서대로, ① about: 대략, ~에 관해 ② kind: 종류, 친절한 ③ close: 아슬아슬한, 닫히다 ⑤ second: 초(금방), 두 번째 등의 뜻이다.

05 ⑤ 24 days a week, 7 hours a day → 24 hours a day, 7 days a week으로 고치는 것이 적절하다.

06 ⓑ에는 What이 들어가야 한다. ⓐ, ⓒ, ⓓ는 모두 How가 들어가는 것이 적절하다. 단, ⓐ는 What, How 둘 다 가능함.

07 ⓐ 수동태이므로 과거분사 lifted, ⓑ 놀이공원은 amusement park이다.

08 to부정사의 '형용사적' 용법으로 '~하는 방법'을 표현한다.

09 to sit → to sit on

10 All those hairs가 가리키는 것은 ③ 앞의 12만개의 머리카락이다. 그러므로 ③에 들어가는 것이 가장 적절하다.

11 to부정사가 명사 뒤에서 명사를 수식하는 '형용사적' 용법들이 나왔는데, ④만 forget의 목적어인 '명사적' 용법이다.

12 본문만으로는 수업이 끝나는 데 얼마나 걸리는 알 수 없다.

13 ① 나쁜 쌀에 무엇이 들었는지, ② 탁구공을 구긴 것이 무엇인지, ④ 레몬은 어디서 구하는지, ⑤ 나쁜 쌀을 구분할 때, 소금은 얼마나 필요한지는 대답할 수 없다.

14 글의 흐름상 담요를 털면, 담요가 앞뒤로 움직이는 동안, 먼지는 가만히 있으려고 하는 관성의 원리에 대한 언급이므로, ③ move를 stay로 바꾸는 것이 적절하다.

15 문장 수식 부사가 와야 하므로 Amazingly가 적절하다.

16 ① 낮추다 ③ 들어올리다 ④ 감싸다 ⑤ 뻐근한, 아픈

17 (B)와 같이 to부정사의 '형용사적' 용법으로, 앞의 명사를 수식하는 것은 ④이다.

18 각각 (A) 형용사, (B) 부사, (C) 명사가 들어가야 한다. possible, surprisingly, ability 등이 적절하다.

19 ③ 없다 → 있다

20 '소리를 전기 에너지로 바꿔도 그 양이 너무 적다'는 구체적인 사례가 뒤에 이어지므로, ② For example이 적절하다.

21 ① powered → is powered가 되어야 한다.

22 (A)는 to부정사의 '부사적 용법(목적)'으로 쓰였다. 같은 용법으로 사용된 것은 ⑤ '자러 가기 위해서'이다.

23 각각 (A) '낮추다' (B) '능력' (C) '아픈'의 뜻을 가진 단어들이 필요하다. lower, ability, sore가 적절하다.

24 '사람의 머리카락으로 사람을 들어 올리는 것은 불가능하지 않다.'가 되어, 본문의 내용과 일치한다.

25 '놀랍게도 도시가 소리에 의해 에너지를 얻는다'라는 문장 뒤에 [(C) 실제로, 소리로 도시를 밝힐 수 있을까? (A) 물론, 다만 그 양이 너무 적다. (D) 예를 들어, 경적 소리를 전기로 바꾸면 가정용 220v의 1/4400 정도이다. (B) 그래서, 도시 전체를 밝히려면 믿을 수 없이 엄청난 양의 소리가 필요할 것이다.]의 순서가 적절하다.

26 ⓐ는 to부정사의 '부사적 용법(목적)'으로 'V하기 위해서'라는 뜻이다. ④의 to부정사만 '형용사적' 용법으로 사용되었다.

27 1/440이 아니라, 1/4400이다.

28 ① flies → flown

29 위 글로는 '풍선 하나가 (비용이) 얼마나 하는지'는 답할 수 없다.

Lesson 4 (기말)

```
01 ③   02 ④   03 ②   04 ⑤
05 (1) which[that] has pink color with stripes
   (2) who has a long straight hair
06 ③   07 ②   08 ①   09 ③   10 ③   11 ②   12 ①
13 ③   14 ②   15 ④   16 ①   17 ③   18 ④   19 ④
20 ②   21 ③   22 They complete fifteen laps
23 ④   24 ②   25 ③
```

01 영영 뜻풀이를 해석하면, 사람이나 동물의 커다란 조각으로서 금속이나 돌로 만들어진 것이므로, ③ 조각상이 적절하다. ① 만화 ② 믹서기 ④ 형태, 인물 ⑤ 항목, 품목

02 모두 형용사와 형용사 뒤에 −ly를 붙인 부사들의 짝인데, ④만 명사+형용사의 짝이다.

03 watch가 지각동사이므로, 목적어 Dohun 뒤에 to부정사가 오는 ②는 빈칸에 들어가기에 부적절하다.

04 이 글은 두 학교의 축구 시합과 결과, 인상적인 선수에 관한 글이다. ⑤ '참여 선수들의 명단'은 알 수 없다.

05 주격 관계대명사는 who, which, that인데 선행사 girl friend는 계속적 용법이므로 who를 쓴다. that은 쓸 수 없다.

06 Mina, 이번이 첫 자전거 라이딩이니? [(B) 응. 균형을 못 잡겠어. (D) 도와줄게. 잡아줄게. (A) 고마워, 놓지 마, 응? (C) 걱정 마. 똑바로 앉아서 정면을 봐!]의 순이다.

07 2등인 것을 알고 슬퍼함 [(B) Richards의 격려 (A) 비록 우승은 못했지만 최선을 다했으니 됐어. (C) 네!]의 순이다.

08 '작년에 Simon이 여러 차례 우승을 했지만, Max의 최고 결과는 5위였다'는 문장은 '이번만큼은 2위로 들어올 기회'라는 문장 앞에 오는 것이 가장 적절하다.

09 심판의 마지막 바퀴를 알리는 신호와, 치열한 경기 장면으로 보아 '흥미진진한(exciting)'이 분위기로 가장 적절하다.

10 ③ Even though는 '비록 ~할지라도'의 뜻을 가진 '양보'의 접속사이지만, As though는 '마치 ~인 것처럼'의 뜻이다.

11 (A)와 ②의 that은 접속사이다. 각각 ①, ③: 지시형용사, ④, ⑤: 관계대명사이다.

12 (B)는 구체적으로 'I did my best.'를 뜻한다.

13 ⓐ going → to go
ⓒ drive to → drive into, harder in → harder on
ⓓ but → and

14 주어진 단어들을 알맞게 배열하면, Max 'sees the official waving a white flag that means the last lap.'이다. 여섯 번째 오는 단어는 'white'가 된다.

15 (A) '비록' 승리는 못했어도, (B) '잠시 후', 그는 미소짓는다.

16 이 글의 주제는 '최선을 다하는 것'의 가치이다.

17 승리 후 감자튀김을 먹고 싶지만 ③ '소스 없이 먹곤 했었다'는 전체 글의 흐름과 관계 없는 문장이다.

18 Triple play는 아웃카운트 3개를 얻는 것을 말한다. ④는 Double play를 뜻하는 말이다.

19 관계대명사는 '접속사+대명사'의 역할이므로, 연결된 문장을 각각 나눌 때, 선행사에 유의하고, 관계대명사는 없앤다.

20 내용과 일치하는 대화들은 (G), (I) 2개이다.

21 (A) come close to V-ing: 거의 V할 뻔하다 (B) come in second place: 2등으로 들어오다 (C) 승리보다 중요한 것은 최선을 다하는 것

22 열 바퀴 후에 다섯 바퀴 남았다고 했으므로, 총 15바퀴이다.

23 catch up with: '~를 따라잡다'라는 뜻이다.

24 교과서 전체 지문에는 나와 있지만, 위 글에는 Max가 왜 1위를 하고 싶은지 쓰여 있지 않음에 유의한다.

25 ① → lap ② → means ④ → beat(ing)
⑤ → are filled

08 ③ 09 ② 10 who is waving

11 who reaches the finish line first 12 ③ 13 ③

14 ② 15 ②, ④ 16 ③ 17 ④ 18 ② 19 ①

20 Simon을 따라잡고, 우승을 차지하는 것 21 ①

22 ③ 23 자신의 롤 모델이 자신을 만나러 왔기 때문에

24 ② 25 ① 26 ② 27 ④

---

01 '비록 거의 80세임에도, 그는 여전히 매우 활동적이다.'라는 문장이므로, ⑤ activity → active가 적절하다.

02 '② A: 자전거 처음 타니? B: 응. 균형을 못잡겠어. A: 도와줄게, 내가 자전거를 잡아줄 거야.'가 대화의 흐름상 가장 자연스럽다.

03 ⓛ avoid는 동명사를 목적어로 취하므로, to meet→ meeting, ⓒ 'tell+목적어+to부정사' 형태이다. clean → to clean ⓜ 조건문 If절에는 will을 쓰지 않는다. will hear→ hear

04 [(C) Sarah야, 뭐 해? (B) 체육시간에 물구나무서기를 배웠는데, 잘 안 되네. (D) 도와줄게. 발을 다시 차봐, 잡아줄게. (A) 고마워.]의 순이다.

05 (B) '몇 위로 들어오다'는 'come in 기수+th place'이며, (C) 'be satisfied with(~에 만족하다)' 등에 유의한다.

06 심판이 흰 기를 드는 것은 마지막 바퀴를 알리는 것이지 ⑤ '가속'하라고 하는 것은 아니다.

07 Max는 1등이 되어서, 자신의 롤 모델을 만나고 싶어한다.

08 karts를 받는 관계대명사 which와 복수동사 are가 적절하게 쓰인 것을 찾는다.

09 경주에 얼마나 많은 직선주로가 있는지는 위 글을 읽고 대답할 수 없는 질문이다.

10 선행사가 사람, that은 쓸 수 없으므로, who is waving.

11 글의 내용상 finish line을 먼저 통과하는 주자가 우승자가 된다. 관계대명사 who를 The racer 바로 뒤에 쓰고, 알맞게 어순대로 배열한다.

12 왜 우울한지 물어본 후에, 걱정하지 말라고 위로하는 것을 보면, 속상하거나 안 좋은 일이 빈칸에 들어가야 한다. 그런데 ③은 '시합을 잘했고, 펀치가 좋았다.'이므로 부적절하다.

13 위 대화문의 빈칸에는 순서대로 moves(동작들), nervous(긴장한), mistakes(실수들), better(더 낫게)가 된다. ③ chances(기회, 가능성)는 빈칸에 필요하지 않다.

14 [(C) 10바퀴째 돌고, 5바퀴 남고 가속 (A) 마지막 바퀴째, 결승선을 통과 후 눈물, 롤 모델이 다가와 위로 (B) 깨달음을 얻고 만족을 느낌]의 순이다.

15 ⓐ, ⓒ, ⓔ 관계대명사 ⓑ 지시대명사, ⓓ 접속사

16 이 글의 주제는 '최선을 다하는 것'이다. 주어진 보기들 중에서는 ③ '근면은 행운의 어머니'가 '최선'과 가장 관련이 깊다고 볼 수 있다.

17 It was a real close race.라는 문장으로 보아, 아슬아슬한 간발의 차이로 2위가 되었음을 알 수 있다. 큰 차이로 2등을 한 것도 아니고, 그것이 Max가 운 이유도 아니다.

18 (A) '거의' 부딪힐 뻔하다 (B) '바로' 뒤 (C) '힘차게' 뛰는

19 ⓐ 지각동사가 있다. ⓑ 선행사가 사물이며 ⓒ 주어가 단수이다.

20 Max는 자신의 롤 모델을 만나기 위해 우승을 갈망하고, 눈앞에 우승이 거의 다가왔다는 사실을 염두에 둔다.

21 2등을 하게 되어 슬프고 실망했지만 위로에 만족을 느꼈다.

22 '최선을 다했다'는 말이므로 '그것이 가장 중요하다' 앞에 와야 한다.

23 롤 모델인 Richards를 만나는 것이 1등을 하고 싶었던 가장 큰 이유였기 때문에, Max는 자신의 눈을 믿을 수가 없었다.

24 '심판이 깃발을 흔들고 경주가 시작된다'는 문장은, '굉음을 내며 대기 중인 카트들'과 '트랙에서 달리고 있는' 장면 사이에 들어가야 한다. 그러므로 (B)에 들어가는 것이 가장 적절하다.

25 ① At the go-kart race track
② push one's foot down hard on the gas pedal
③ be satisfied with 등의 표현에 유의한다.

26 ⓐ close and close → closer and closer
ⓒ hardly → hard
ⓓ which → who[that]
ⓔ don't → didn't

27 위 글로는 Simon이 최선을 다했는지를 분명히 답할 수 없다.

MEMO